CLEMENTE · ANATOMY

ANATOMY
A Regional Atlas of the Human Body

Carmine D. Clemente, Ph.D.

Professor of Anatomy and Director of the Brain Research Institute
University of California at Los Angeles School of Medicine;
Professor of Surgery (Anatomy)
Charles R. Drew Postgraduate Medical School
Los Angeles, California

Third Edition

Urban & Schwarzenberg · Baltimore–Munich 1987

The pictures on the end leaves of the present volume show reproductions of the work of "Andreas Vesalii de corporis humani fabrica libri septem", which appeared in Basel in 1542. Andreas Vesalius (* Brussels 1514, † 1564) urged and practiced the dissection of human bodies and may be considered to be the founder of Modern Anatomy.

Editor's address:

Carmine D. Clemente, Ph. D., Professor of Anatomy and Director, Brain Research Institute UCLA School of Medicine, Los Angeles, California 90024 USA

Publisher's addresses:

Urban & Schwarzenberg, Inc.
7 East Redwood Street
Baltimore, Maryland 21202
USA

Urban & Schwarzenberg
Pettenkoferstraße 18
D-8000 München 2
Germany

The illustrations of this atlas were originally published in
    Sobotta, Atlas der Anatomie des Menschen, edited by H. Ferner and J. Staubesand,
    Urban & Schwarzenberg,
with the exception of figures 16, 18, 38, 39, 178, 183, 315, 334, 337, 365, 384, 405, 407, 506, 517, 584, 595, 596, 607, 611, 616, 617, 742, 749, 752, 780, 782, 792, 804 (from Benninghoff/Goerttler, Lehrbuch der Anatomie des Menschen, edited by H. Ferner and J. Staubesand, Urban & Schwarzenberg); 6, 36, 73, 96, 97, 113, 133, 150, 200, 271, 298, 304, 311, 342, 400, 401, 457 (from Lothar Wicke, Atlas of Radiologic Anatomy, 3rd. Ed., Urban & Schwarzenberg); 13, 14, 34, 63, 64, 120, 132, 136, 170, 176, 188, 208, 209, 212, 214, 219, 220, 226, 227, 230, 239, 240, 243–246, 253, 257, 258, 296, 299, 300, 320, 331, 332, 388, 393, 399, 444, 446, 448, 459, 486–491, 515, 516, 521, 574, 587, 588, 592, 593, 615, 634, 635, 640, 642, 654–657, 678, 686, 712–721, 723–725, 733, 735, 737, 739, 740, 746, 747, 779, 787, 789, 793, 801 (from Eduard Pernkopf, Atlas of Topographical and Applied Human Anatomy, 2nd Ed., edited by H. Ferner, Urban & Schwarzenberg).
Figures 17, 119, 232, 502, 504 were drawn for this atlas by Jill Penkhus.

The first edition of this atlas was published in 1975 by Urban & Schwarzenberg (ISBN 3-541-07141-9) and copublished in North America by Lea & Febiger, Philadelphia (ISBN 0-8121-0496-X).

Library of Congress Cataloging-in-Publication Data

Clemente, Carmine D.
    Anatomy, a regional atlas of the human body.

    Includes index.
    1. Anatomy, Surgical and topographical--Atlases.
I. Title. [DNLM: 1. Anatomy, Regional--atlases.
QS 17 C626a]
QM531.C57 1986   611'.0022'2   85-11157
ISBN 0-8067-0323-7

Printed in Germany by Kastner & Callwey, Fotosatz, Offsetdruck, München.

ISBN 0-8067-0323-7 Baltimore

ISBN 3-541-70323-7 Munich

PREFACE TO THE THIRD EDITION

Once again my primary objective in the preparation of this edition has been to facilitate the task of the learning of anatomy by students in the medical, dental and other health professions. Because of the popularity and acceptance of the two previous editions, it has been possible in this edition to expand the coverage of certain regions of the body that were treated more thinly in the 1975 and 1981 editions. I extend my appreciation to the publisher for allowing me this freedom. It is sometimes said that if a book used in the teaching of a major professional field ever achieves a third edition, there is a possibility that it has finally reached maturity. I hope that this is the case with this atlas. There are many changes in this book and a large number of these were suggested by students and by my professional colleagues. I have the good fortune of being able to teach anatomy to first-year medical students at UCLA as well as to surgical residents at the Martin Luther King, Jr. Memorial Hospital here in Los Angeles. This consistent exposure to students who are studying human anatomy for the first time and others who are reviewing anatomy during their residency training period helps to keep me informed of student needs and how certain body regions could be more completely or more clearly demonstrated in the atlas.

There are 96 new figures included in this edition while six figures from the 2nd edition have been eliminated. This net increase of 90 figures represents a 13% enlargement of the atlas over the previous edition. Of the new figures, a total of 34 (35%) were added to the sections on the thorax, abdomen and pelvis, 37 (39%) were added to the limbs and 25 (26%) were added to the sections on neck and head. More specifically, for the thorax some of the figures added depict the bony thoracic cage, the position of the heart within the chest, the coronary arteries, the sympathetic trunks and the fetal heart. Four new cross sections at various levels of the abdomen along with additional figures on the anterior abdominal wall, the female inguinal region, lymphatics of the stomach, the appendix and its blood supply, the posterior abdominal wall, and the female perineum have been included. In the sections on the upper and lower extremities there is an additional coverage of the shoulder and elbow joints and especially the knee joint. Other figures illustrating the surface anatomy and cutaneous innervation of the limbs, as well as arteriograms and other X-rays have also been included. The section on neck and head has been enhanced by 10 new figures on the eye, 6 on the oral cavity, and 4 on the ear. Five other figures on the neck and dura mater have also been added.

As in previous editions the figures in this atlas are derived principally from the Johannes Sobotta collection and from the Eduard Pernkopf collection. The latter were initially published in Professor Pernkopf's multivolume classic textbook *Topographische Anatomie des Menschen* and then were later incorporated in atlas format. Additionally, a number of other figures have come from the Benninghoff-Goerttler textbooks and nearly all of the radiographs have come from the *Atlas of Radiologic Anatomy* (3rd Edition) by Dr. Lothar Wicke of Vienna. I wish to extend my sincere thanks to Professors Helmut Ferner of Vienna and Jochen Staubesand of Freiburg, who edit the German editions of the Sobotta and Pernkopf atlases and the Benninghoff-Goerttler books, and to Dr. Wicke for use of his elegant radiographs.

One of the more significant features of this edition is the fact that over 225 of the figures used in this book are precise repaintings of the older illustrations used in former editions. Further, a number of other figures which were black and white illustrations in previous editions now are presented in full color. This new art is, for the most part, brighter and more vivid in color than the old, and my many thanks go to the several artists who produced these new works because their creations strictly adhered to the older illustrations and resulted in meticulously perfect reproductions. These were necessary for the continued publications of the atlas, and I wish to thank the publisher for the significant expenditure involved.

I wish to thank the many students who have written to me for their kind comments and for offering suggestions of how this atlas might be improved. I both encourage and welcome users of this edition to do the same. My appreciation also goes to Dr. Caroline Belz Caloyeras who, with dedication, edited and typed the manuscript for this edition and helped prepare the index. At Urban & Schwarzenberg I wish to thank Mr. Michael Urban and Wulf J. Dietrich in Munich and Mr. Braxton Mitchell and Norman W. Och in Baltimore for their continuing support in this effort to create an atlas that best meets the needs of students. Finally and most importantly, I want to thank my wife, Julie, for her patience and for her compassionate and generous spirit in support of my writing efforts.

CARMINE D. CLEMENTE

Los Angeles, California, December, 1986

FROM THE PREFACE TO THE FIRST EDITION

Twenty-five years ago, while a student at the University of Pennsylvania, I marvelled at the clarity, completeness, and boldness of the anatomical illustrations of the original German editions of Professor Johannes Sobotta's Atlas and their excellent three-volume, English counterparts, the recent editions of which were authored by the late Professor Frank H. J. Figge. It is a matter of record that before Worl War II these atlases were the most popular ones consulted by American medical students. In the United States, with the advent of other anatomical atlases, the shortening of courses of anatomy in the medical schools, and the increase in publishing cost, the excellent but larger editions of the Sobotta atlases have become virtually unknown to a full generation of students. During the past twenty years of teaching Gross Anatomy at the University of California at Los Angeles I have found only a handful of students who are familiar with the beautiful and still unexcelled Sobotta illustration.

This volume introduces several departures from the former Sobotta atlases. It is the first English edition that presents the Sobotta plates in a regional sequence – the pectoral region and upper extremity, the thorax, the abdomen, the pelvis and perineum, the lower extremity, the back, vertebral column and spinal cord, and finally the neck and head. This sequence is consistent with that followed in many courses presented in the United States and Canada and one which should be useful to students in other countries.

Several illustrations never before published are presented in this Atlas. These have been drawn by Jill Penkhus, who for a number of years has been the resident medical artist in the Anatomy Department at the UCLA School of Medicine.

Many have contributed to bringing this Atlas to fruition. I wish to thank Dr. David S. Maxwell, Professor and Vice Chairman for Gross Anatomy and my colleague at UCLA, for his encouragement and suggestions. I also with to express my appreciation to Caroline Belz and Louise Campbell, who spent many hours proofreading and typing the original text. I especially wish to thank Mary Mansor for constructing the index – a most laborious task. I am grateful to Barbara Robins for her assistance in typing some of the early parts of the manuscript, and above all, to her sister Julie, who is my wife and who makes all of my efforts worthwhile through her encouragement and devotion.

Los Angeles, California, January 1975

Carmine D. Clemente

FROM THE PREFACE TO THE SECOND EDITION

Seldom does a professor experience more gratification than when students at home and throughout the world express kind words regarding a teaching resource which he had offered tentatively and, initially, with some trepidation. After publication of the first edition of this altlas, I received nearly two hundred letters from medical and dental students, students of kinesiology, physical therapy and nursing as well as residents in the surgical specialties. Not one failed to comment in some manner on the beauty of the reproduced Sobotta figures (for which the publishers should be commended), and most letters made excellent suggestions of items to be included in future editions, while others uncovered typographical errors or mistaken facts. I am most grateful because this feedback information allowed me to alter labels and correct misspellings in time for the subsequent reprintings of the first edition and to add important transition figures in this edition.

The wide distribution and adoption of this atlas has allowed an opportunity for its revision. I have observed the use of the first edition in the classroom and in the gross anatomy laboratory setting for over five years, and this has given me further direction in assembling this revision. The addition of 130 figures and the elimination of only 10 published in the first edition represents an increase of 120 figures, or slightly over 20 percent. These have not been distributed equally among the seven parts of the atlas. Nearly one-third of the new figures were added to the section on neck and head, another one-third to the sections on thorax and abdomen, and the remaining one-third to the extremities, the pelvis and the back.

Some special emphasis has been placed in this edition on the inclusion of figures illustrating radiographic views of different regions, lymphatic drainage, the anatomy of the newborn, more material on the oral cavity, as well as additional cross sections of the limbs.

I am most grateful to Dr. Caroline Belz who contributed superb editorial assistance in the preparation of the text for this edition and to Mrs. Joyce Fried who spent many hours helping to revise the index. From Urban & Schwarzenberg, I wish to thank Mr. Michael Urban, Dr. Richard Degkwitz and Mr. Klaus Gullath in Munich and Mr. Braxton Mitchell in Baltimore for their conceptual suggestions and for the practical solution of innumerable problems. And, as always, to my wife, Julie, I owe a continuing debt of gratitude for her selflessness and for her true understanding of the academic way of life.

Los Angeles, California, January 1981

Carmine D. Clemente

CONTENTS

PART   I   PECTORAL REGION AND UPPER EXTREMITY

    A. Body Regions and Dermatomes   FIGS.   1– 2
    B. Mammary Gland and a typical spinal nerve   FIGS.   3– 10
    C. Anterior thoracic region and pectoral muscles   FIGS. 11– 16
    D. Axilla: Muscles and vessels; the brachial plexus   FIGS. 17– 20
    E. Shoulder Region: Muscles, vessels, nerves and bones   FIGS. 21– 28
    F. Shoulder joint   FIGS. 29– 36
    G. Upper extremity: Surface anatomy, superficial nerves and vessels
        and the deep fascia   FIGS. 37– 48
    H. Brachial region: Anterior and posterior   FIGS. 49– 60
    I. Upper extremity and cross sections of the brachium   FIGS. 61– 64
    J. Antebrachial region   FIGS. 65– 79
    K. Bones of the forearm, the elbow joint and cross sections of the antebrachium   FIGS. 80–101
    L. Dorsum of the hand   FIGS. 102–105
    M. Palmar aspect of the hand   FIGS. 106–117
    N. Skeleton of the wrist and hand; cross sections of the hand and fingers   FIGS. 118–128
    O. Joints of the wrist and fingers   FIGS. 129–135

PART   II   THE THORAX

    A. Thoracic cage: Clavicle, sternum, ribs and intercostal structures   FIGS. 136–151
    B. Pleura, bronchial tree and lungs   FIGS. 152–169
    C. Position of the heart and its valves in the thoracic cavity   FIGS. 170–174
    D. Newborn heart; fetal and adult circulations   FIGS. 175–183
    E. Mediastinum viewed from the right and left sides   FIGS. 184–185
    F. Middle mediastinum: Pericardium and heart   FIGS. 186–213
    G. Median sagittal and frontal sections of the thorax   FIGS. 214–215
    H. Posterior mediastinum: Organs, vessels, nerves, thoracic duct and diaphragm   FIGS. 216–230

PART   III   THE ABDOMEN

    A. Anterior abdominal wall inguinal region: Muscles, vessels and nerves   FIGS. 231–254
    B. Anterior abdominal wall and visceria of the newborn child   FIGS. 255–256
    C. Abdominal cavity. Organ relations and peritoneum   FIGS. 257–264
    D. Abdominal cavity: Celiac axis, stomach and spleen   FIGS. 265–278
    E. Abdominal cavity: Liver, biliary system and gall bladder   FIGS. 279–284
    F. Abdominal cavity: Duodenum and pancreas   FIGS. 285–293
    G. Abdominal cavity: Mesenteric vessels, nerves, lymphatics;
        the small and large intestine, rectum   FIGS. 294–316
    H. Posterior abdominal wall: Kidney, ilopsoas region, lumbar plexus,
        lumbar sympathetic trunk, lumbar lymphatic channels and lumbar vessels   FIGS. 317–342

PART   IV   THE PERINEUM AND PELVIS

    A. Male perineum: Muscles, vessels and nerves; penis   FIGS. 343–352
    B. Male pelvis: Bladder, seminal vesicle, prostate; muscles and vessels;
        urethra, male urogenital diaphragm   FIGS. 353–366
    C. Female perineum: External genitalia; female urogenital diaphragm;
        muscles, vessels and nerves   FIGS. 367–371
    D. Female pelvis: Muscles, uterus, ovary, blood vessels and lymphatics   FIGS. 372–387
    E. Osteology and ligaments of the pelvis   FIGS. 388–398
    F. Fetus *in utero;* X-ray of pelvis   FIGS. 399–401

Contents continued

PART V THE LOWER EXTREMITY

A. Vessels, dermatomes and superficial nerves; surface anatomy and lymph nodes   FIGS. 402–415
B. Anterior thigh: Muscles, vessels and nerves   FIGS. 416–423
C. Gluteal region and posterior thigh   FIGS. 424–430
D. Femur and hip joint   FIGS. 431–439
E. Knee: Popliteal fossa and knee joint   FIGS. 440–459
F. Leg: Superficial nerves and vessels; anterior and lateral compartments   FIGS. 460–467
G. Dorsum of the foot   FIGS. 468–471
H. Leg: Posterior compartment; tibia and fibula   FIGS. 472–485
I. Cross sections of thigh and leg   FIGS. 486–491
J. Plantar aspect of the foot; bones of the foot   FIGS. 492–505
K. Tendons at the ankle; joints of the foot   FIGS. 506–514
L. Cross sections of the foot   FIGS. 515–516

PART VI THE BACK, VERTEBRAL COLUMN AND SPINAL CORD

A. Cutaneous nerves, dermatomes, regions of the back   FIGS. 517–521
B. Muscles of the back: Superficial, intermediate and deep   FIGS. 522–526
C. Posterior neck and suboccipital region   FIGS. 527–529
D. Atlas, axis, cervical joints, cervical vertebrae   FIGS. 530–543
E. Vertebral column, thoracic vertebrae and costovertebral joints   FIGS. 544–554
F. Lumbar vertebrae, sacrum and coccyx   FIGS. 555–562
G. Spinal cord, spinal roots, blood supply   FIGS. 563–573

PART VII THE NECK AND HEAD

A. Surface anatomy of the neck and the platysma muscle; vessels and nerves of the anterior and posterior triangles of the neck   FIGS. 514–582
B. The strap muscles, the great blood vessels and lymphatic channels of the neck; the thyroid gland   FIGS. 583–593
C. Prevertebral region: Muscles and vertebral artery   FIGS. 594–596
D. Submandibular region: Suprahyoid muscles and submandibular gland   FIGS. 597–600
E. Anterior skull, anterior face and muscles of facial expression   FIGS. 601–605
F. Lateral face, parotid gland, muscles of mastication, the lateral skull and the temporomandibular joint   FIGS. 606–617
G. Blood vessels, nerves and lymphatics of the head, including the superficial and deep face and the infratemporal fossa   FIGS. 618–625
H. Calvaria, diploic veins, dura mater and meningeal vessels   FIGS. 626–636
I. Dural sinuses, cranial cavity, inferior surface of the brain, internal carotid artery, base of the skull   FIGS. 637–647
J. The orbit and eye: Muscles, vessels, nerves and eyeball   FIGS. 648–681
K. External nose, nasal cavity, nasal sinuses and nasopharynx   FIGS. 682–695
L. Mandible, maxilla and teeth   FIGS. 696–721
M. Oral cavity, palate, tongue and oropharynx   FIGS. 722–747
N. The pharyngeal constrictor muscles; pharyngeal vessels and nerves; laryngopharynx   FIGS. 748–755
O. The larynx, laryngeal cartilages, muscles and vessels   FIGS. 756–772
P. The external, middle and internal ear; temporal bone and facial canal; the cochlea and semicircular canals   FIGS. 773–805

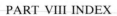

PART VIII INDEX   Pages 417–439

PART I: PECTORAL REGION AND UPPER EXTREMITY

Fig. 1: The Regions of the Body: Anterior View

Every surface area and region of the body has been identified by a specific name in order to describe more precisely the location of anatomical structures. Note that regions are named after underlying or adjacent bones (sternal, parietal, frontal, temporal, infraclavicular, femoral) while other regions are named for underlying muscles (sternocleidomastoid, deltoid, pectoral). Still other regions are named after specialized anatomical structures (umbilical, oral, nasal).

Fig. 2: Dermatomes of the Anterior Trunk

A dermatome is an area of skin whose cutaneous innervation is supplied by a single dorsal root of a spinal nerve. Although there is some overlap between dermatomes, they are of value in determining interruption in function of the spinal cord and its roots.

NOTE: the nipple is generally supplied by the 4th or 5th thoracic nerve and the region around the umbilicus receives sensory innervation from the 9th and 10th thoracic nerves.

Figs. 1, 2   I

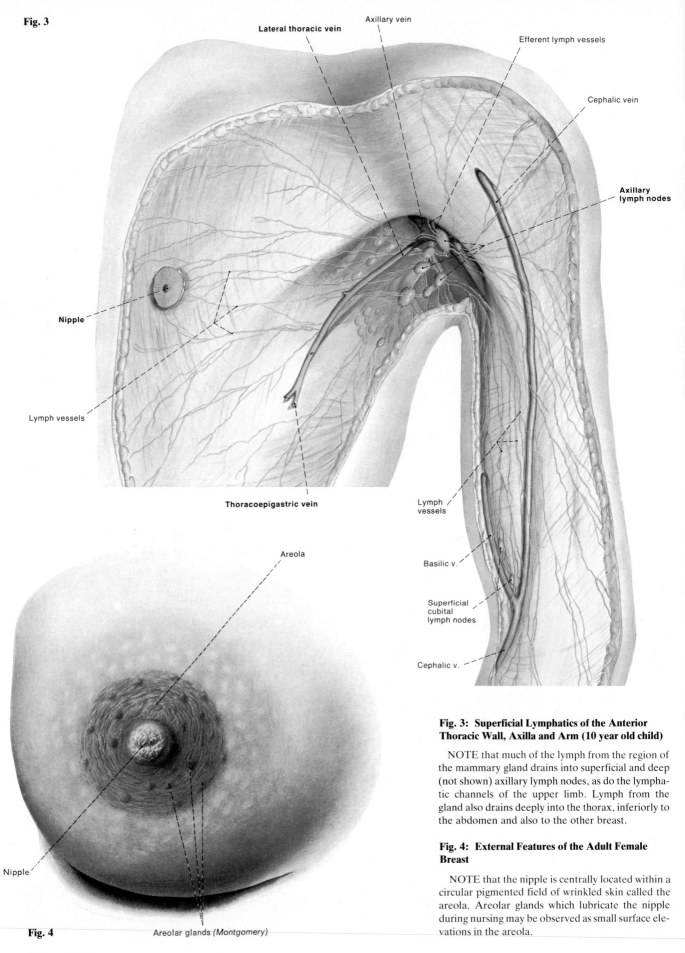

Fig. 3

Lateral thoracic vein

Axillary vein

Efferent lymph vessels

Cephalic vein

Axillary lymph nodes

Nipple

Lymph vessels

Thoracoepigastric vein

Lymph vessels

Basilic v.

Superficial cubital lymph nodes

Cephalic v.

Areola

Fig. 4

Nipple

Areolar glands *(Montgomery)*

Fig. 3: Superficial Lymphatics of the Anterior Thoracic Wall, Axilla and Arm (10 year old child)

NOTE that much of the lymph from the region of the mammary gland drains into superficial and deep (not shown) axillary lymph nodes, as do the lymphatic channels of the upper limb. Lymph from the gland also drains deeply into the thorax, inferiorly to the abdomen and also to the other breast.

Fig. 4: External Features of the Adult Female Breast

NOTE that the nipple is centrally located within a circular pigmented field of wrinkled skin called the areola. Areolar glands which lubricate the nipple during nursing may be observed as small surface elevations in the areola.

Figs. 3, 4

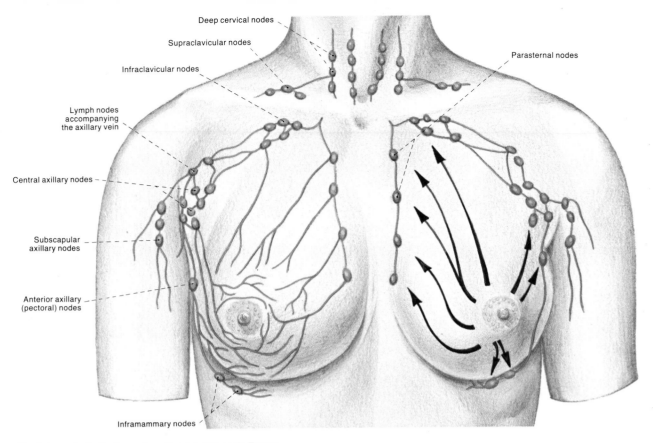

Fig. 5: Lymphatic Drainage from the Adult Female Breast

NOTE: 1) the extremely numerous lymph vessels of the breast originate in the connective tissue and laciferous ducts of the organ and communicate with the subareolar plexus deep to and around the nipple.

2) nearly three-quarters of the lymph from the breast passes laterally and superiorly to pectoral, subscapular, central axillary and infraclavicular nodes, as well as to nodes that course along the axillary vein. Most of the remaining lymph passes medially to parasternal nodes that course with the internal thoracic vessels. Lymph may also drain inferiorly along the anterior thoracic wall and communicate with upper abdominal nodes; some lymph may also drain to the opposite breast.

Fig. 6: Lymphangiogram of the Pectoral and Axillary Lymph Nodes

(From: Wicke, L., *Atlas of Radiologic Anatomy*, 3rd Edition, Urban & Schwarzenberg, Baltimore, 1982).

Figs. 5, 6   I

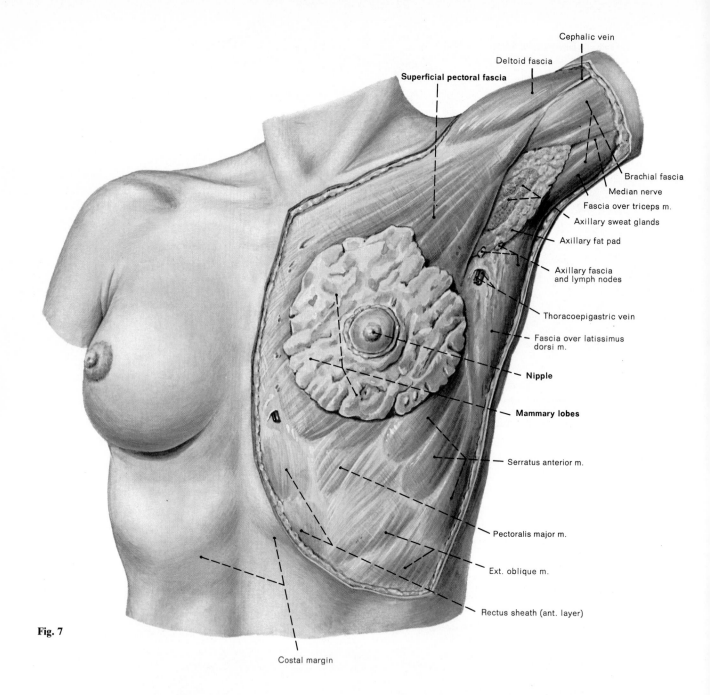

Cephalic vein

Deltoid fascia

Superficial pectoral fascia

Brachial fascia

Median nerve

Fascia over triceps m.

Axillary sweat glands

Axillary fat pad

Axillary fascia
and lymph nodes

Thoracoepigastric vein

Fascia over latissimus
dorsi m.

Nipple

Mammary lobes

Serratus anterior m.

Pectoralis major m.

Ext. oblique m.

Rectus sheath (ant. layer)

Fig. 7

Costal margin

Fig. 7: Anterior Pectoral Dissection (Adult Female)
   NOTE: 1) the lobular nature of the mammary gland extending toward the axilla and its location anterior to the pectoralis major muscle.
   2) the superficial axillary lymph and sudoriferous (sweat) glands.

Fig. 8: Sagittal Section through Mammary Gland of Gravid Female
   NOTE: 1) the radial arrangement of the lobes of glandular tissue. These lobes are comprised of smaller lobules and are separated from one another by fat and the supporting connective tissue.
   2) the lactiferous duct system. Each of the 15 to 20 lobes has its own duct which opens by means of a small orifice onto the nipple.
   3) that the mammary gland is separated from the pectoralis major muscle by the pectoral fascia and that connective tissue strands (suspensory ligaments of Cooper) within the gland extend toward this fascia.

Fig. 9: Right Mammary Gland: Dissection of the Nipple
   A circular piece of skin has been removed in this dissection. With the incised margin of the skin around the nipple retracted, the lactiferous ducts can be observed perforating onto the surface and arranged circumferentially around the nipple.

Fig. 10: Two Typical Spinal Nerves: Their Origin, Branches and Connections to the Sympathetic Trunk
   NOTE: 1) each spinal nerve attaches to the spinal cord by two roots: an afferent or sensory dorsal root and an efferent or motor ventral root. Each dorsal root contains a spinal ganglion comprised of afferent neuron cell bodies.
   2) the two spinal roots join to form the spinal nerve, which in turn divides into a dorsal ramus coursing posteriorly and a ventral ramus coursing anteriorly. During their course, these rami divide further to innervate the body segment with both sensory and motor fibers.
   3) the spinal nerve communicates with the sympathetic trunk carrying preganglionic sympathetic fibers to the trunk (white ramus) and post-ganglionic fibers from the trunk (gray ramus).

Fig. 7

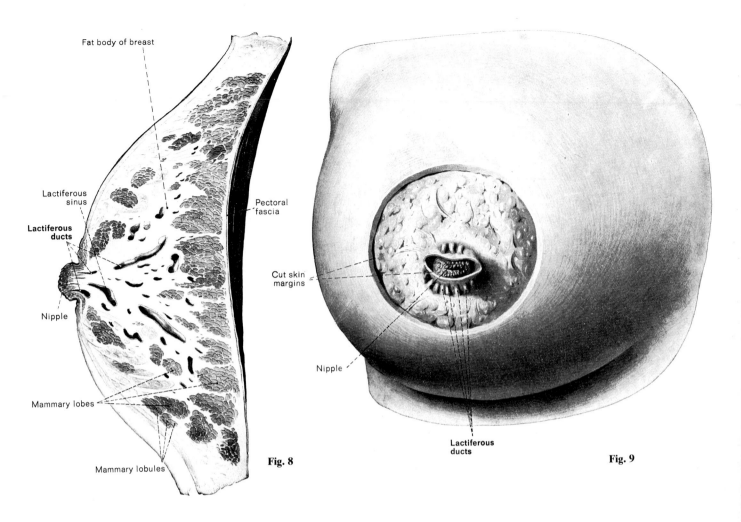

Fat body of breast

Lactiferous sinus

Lactiferous ducts

Nipple

Mammary lobes

Mammary lobules

Pectoral fascia

Fig. 8

Cut skin margins

Nipple

Lactiferous ducts

Fig. 9

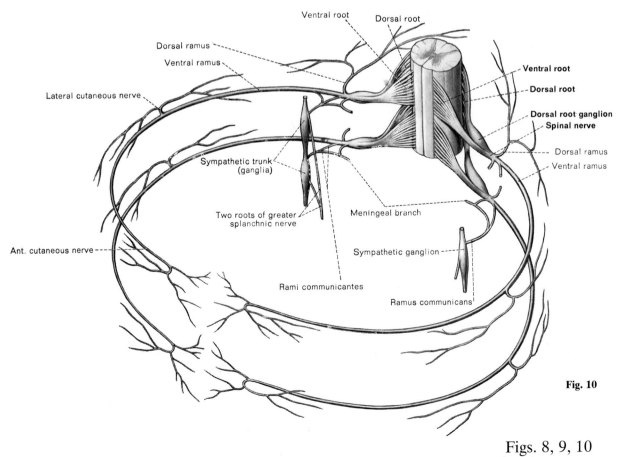

Ventral root

Dorsal root

Dorsal ramus

Ventral ramus

Lateral cutaneous nerve

Sympathetic trunk (ganglia)

Two roots of greater splanchnic nerve

Meningeal branch

Ant. cutaneous nerve

Rami communicantes

Sympathetic ganglion

Ramus communicans

Ventral root

Dorsal root

Dorsal root ganglion

Spinal nerve

Dorsal ramus

Ventral ramus

Fig. 10

Figs. 8, 9, 10   **I**

Supraclavicular nn.
(C 3, C 4)
superficial
cervical aa. vv.

Cephalic vein

Intercostobrachial
nerve (T 2)
external mammary a.v.
(from lat. thoracic)

Sternal
lymph node
internal
thoracic a.v.

Cephalic vein

Ant. cutaneous nn.
(T 1 – T 4)

Lat. thoracic a.
Thoracoepigastric v.

IX

Sup. epigastric a.v.

Lat.
cutaneous nn.
(T 3, T 4)

T 3

T 4

T 5

T 6

VIII

External
oblique muscle

VII

Lateral cutaneous nerves
(branches of intercostal
nerves T 5 – T 12)

T 7

VIII

T 8

VIII

T 9
T 10

IX

← T 5

IX

Ant. cutaneous nerves
(branches of inter-
costal nerves
T 5 – T 12)

T 11

IX

IX

T 12

IX

← T 12

X

Paraumbilical veins

X

XI

Medial umbilical
ligament

XI

Pyramidalis muscle

XI

XII

Iliohypogastric nerve

Superficial iliac
circumflex a.v.

XII

Superficial
circumflex iliac a.v.

Inf. epigastric a.v.

Ilioinguinal nerve
Genitofemoral nerve
Superficial epigastric a.v.

Rectus
abdominis muscle

External pudendal a.v.

Ant. femoral
cutaneous n.

Great saphenous vein

Fig. 11: Superficial Vessels and Nerves of the Ventral Trunk: Pectoral Region and Anterior Abdominal Wall

OBSERVE: 1) the cutaneous innervation of the anterior trunk which is derived from a) the supraclavicular nerves (C$_3$, C$_4$);
b) the intercostal nerves (anterior cutaneous T 1 – T 12; lateral cutaneous T 2 – T 12); c) iliohypogastric and ilioinguinal nerves (L 1).

2) the thoracoepigastric venous anastomosis between the thoracoepigastric and lateral thoracic veins superiorly and the superficial circumflex iliac and superficial epigastric veins inferiorly.

3) the mammary gland: its innervation (T2–T6) and its blood supply (branches of internal thoracic artery, lateral thoracic artery). Additionally, the mammary gland may receive small branches from the intercostal arteries which may enter the deep surface of the gland.

4) the nipple at the level of T 4 and the umbilicus at the level of T 10.

Fig. 11

Platysma muscle (cut)

Deltopectoral triangle

Cephalic vein

Deltoid muscle

Sternocleidomastoid muscle

Pectoralis major muscle — Deltoid muscle

Brachial fascia

Axillary fascia

Deltopectoral triangle

Pectoralis major muscle

Serratus anterior muscle

Costoxiphoid ligaments

Linea alba

External oblique muscle

IV

V

VI

Serratus anterior muscle

Latissimus dorsi muscle

Pectoralis major muscle
(abdominal portion)

External oblique muscle

Umbilicus

Ant. sup. iliac spine

Superficial fascia

External oblique
aponeurosis

Spermatic cord

Fundiform ligament of penis

Rectus sheath (ant. layer)

Ant. sup. iliac spine

Intercrural fibers

Medial crus of superficial
inguinal ring

Cremaster muscle

Reflected ligament

Suspensory ligament of penis

Body of penis

Fig. 12: The Superficial Thoracic and Abdominal Muscle

   OBSERVE that the pectoralis major arises from the medial half of the clavicle, the costal margin of the sternum, the 2nd to 6th ribs and the upper part of the aponeurosis of the external oblique. Also note the deltopectoral triangle and the course of the cephalic vein as it empties into the axillary vein.

Fig. 12   I

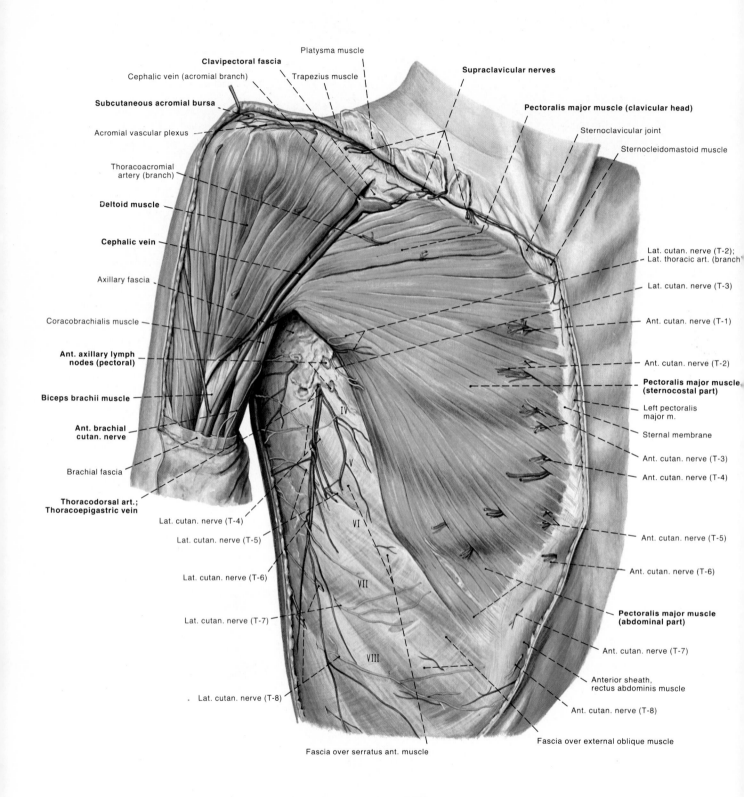

Fig. 13: The Pectoralis Major and Deltoid Muscles, Anterior View

NOTE: 1) segmentally arranged lateral and anterior cutaneous nerves which branch from the intercostal nerves. These penetrate through the intercostal spaces approximately in the mid-axillary line (lateral cutaneous nerves) and, more anteriorly, along the lateral border of the sternum through the substance of the pectoralis major muscle (anterior cutaneous nerves).

2) the 4th to the 8th ribs are numbered sequentially with Roman numerals.

3) the thoracoepigastric vein and the thoracodorsal artery piercing the deep fascia and coursing along the mid-axillary line.

Fig. 13

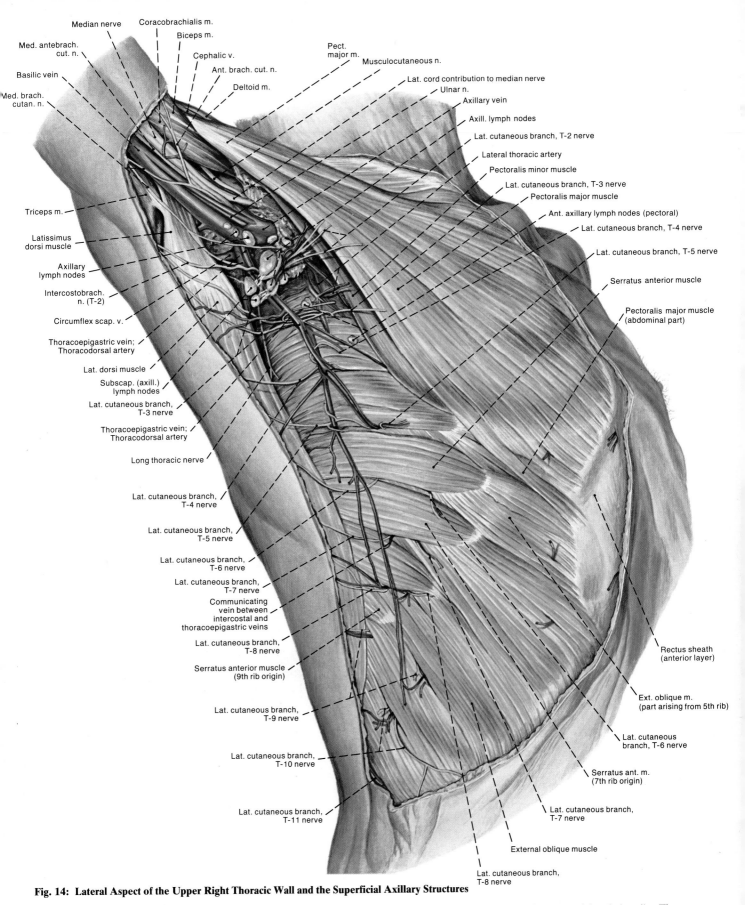

Median nerve
Med. antebrach. cut. n.
Coracobrachialis m.
Biceps m.
Cephalic v.
Ant. brach. cut. n.
Deltoid m.
Pect. major m.
Musculocutaneous n.
Lat. cord contribution to median nerve
Ulnar n.
Axillary vein
Axill. lymph nodes
Lat. cutaneous branch, T-2 nerve
Lateral thoracic artery
Pectoralis minor muscle
Lat. cutaneous branch, T-3 nerve
Pectoralis major muscle
Ant. axillary lymph nodes (pectoral)
Lat. cutaneous branch, T-4 nerve
Lat. cutaneous branch, T-5 nerve
Serratus anterior muscle
Pectoralis major muscle (abdominal part)

Basilic vein
Med. brach. cutan. n.
Triceps m.
Latissimus dorsi muscle
Axillary lymph nodes
Intercostobrach. n. (T-2)
Circumflex scap. v.
Thoracoepigastric vein; Thoracodorsal artery
Lat. dorsi muscle
Subscap. (axill.) lymph nodes
Lat. cutaneous branch, T-3 nerve
Thoracoepigastric vein; Thoracodorsal artery
Long thoracic nerve
Lat. cutaneous branch, T-4 nerve
Lat. cutaneous branch, T-5 nerve
Lat. cutaneous branch, T-6 nerve
Lat. cutaneous branch, T-7 nerve
Communicating vein between intercostal and thoracoepigastric veins
Lat. cutaneous branch, T-8 nerve
Serratus anterior muscle (9th rib origin)
Lat. cutaneous branch, T-9 nerve
Lat. cutaneous branch, T-10 nerve
Lat. cutaneous branch, T-11 nerve

Rectus sheath (anterior layer)
Ext. oblique m. (part arising from 5th rib)
Lat. cutaneous branch, T-6 nerve
Serratus ant. m. (7th rib origin)
Lat. cutaneous branch, T-7 nerve
External oblique muscle
Lat. cutaneous branch, T-8 nerve

Fig. 14: Lateral Aspect of the Upper Right Thoracic Wall and the Superficial Axillary Structures

NOTE: 1) the serratus anterior is a fleshy sheet of muscle that arises as separate muscular digitations from the upper eight of nine ribs. The lower four of these slips interdigitate with bundles of the external oblique muscle which also arise from the ribs.

2) the partially exposed superficial vessels and certain peripheral nerves from the brachial plexus. These become visible after the axillary space is entered by removing the skin of the armpit and the subjacent axillary fascia. The axillary sheath surrounding the axillary artery and the cords of the brachial plexus are still intact.

3) the intermediate and central axillary lymph nodes within the axillary space, as well as a few of the pectoral nodes that lie along the inferolateral border of the pectoralis major and the lateral surface of the serratus anterior.

Fig. 14   I

Fig. 15: The Deltopectoral Triangle (Right)

With the clavicular head of the pectoralis major muscle severed,
    OBSERVE: 1) the internal investing layer of fascia deep to the pectoralis major;
2) the clavipectoral fascia which lies between the pectoralis major and the thoracic wall;
3) the course of the cephalic vein as it pierces the clavipectoral fascia to join the axillary vein.

**Fig. 16: The Pectoralis Minor, Serratus Anterior
and Latissimus Dorsi Muscles, Lateral View (Right)**

    NOTE that the pectoralis major muscle has been
reflected, thereby revealing: 1) the underlying pectoralis minor muscle, which arises on the coracoid
process and inserts on the 2nd to the 6th ribs;

    2) the serratus anterior muscle attaching to the
ribs and forming the medial wall of the axilla;

    3) the latissimus dorsi muscle helping to form
the posterior axillary fold and inserting into the
humerus.

Figs. 15, 16

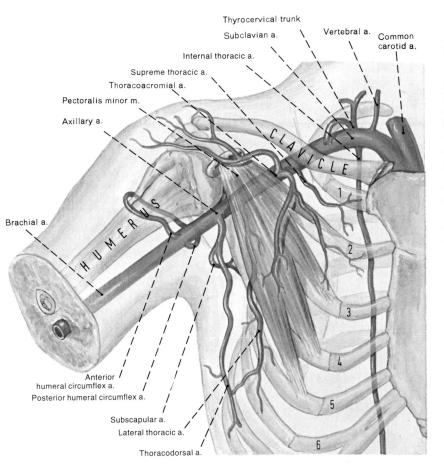

Thyrocervical trunk
Subclavian a.
Internal thoracic a.
Supreme thoracic a.
Thoracoacromial a.
Pectoralis minor m.
Axillary a.
Vertebral a.
Common carotid a.
CLAVICLE
HUMERUS
Brachial a.
Anterior humeral circumflex a.
Posterior humeral circumflex a.
Subscapular a.
Lateral thoracic a.
Thoracodorsal a.

Fig. 17: The Branches of the Axillary Artery

NOTE: 1) as the subclavian artery passes beneath the clavicle, it becomes the axillary artery. The axillary artery becomes the brachial artery in the upper arm (at the level of the tendon of the teres major muscle). In the axilla the pectoralis minor muscle crosses anterior to the axillary artery, thereby, for descriptive purposes, dividing the vessel into three parts.

2) from the 1st part of the axillary artery (medial to the pectoralis minor and lateral to the clavicle) branches one vessel, the supreme thoracic artery. From the 2nd part (beneath the muscle) branch two vessels, the thoracoacromial artery and the lateral thoracic. From the 3rd part of the axillary (lateral to the pectoralis minor muscle) are derived three branches, the subscapular artery and the anterior and posterior humeral circumflex arteries.

3) that the subscapular artery is the largest branch from the axillary artery. It descends from the main trunk and, 4 to 5 cm from its origin, it usually divides into the thoracodorsal and circumflex scapular arteries (shown but not labelled). The thoracodorsal artery descends along the lateral aspect of the thorax to supply the latissimus dorsi muscle and other structures. The circumflex scapular artery traverses the triangular space and courses around the lateral border of the scapula to enter the infraspinatus fossa.

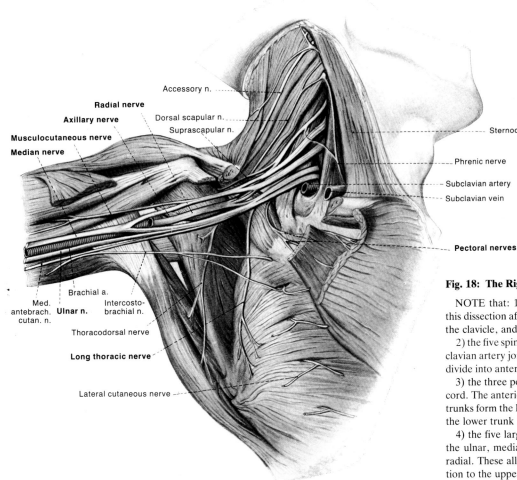

Accessory n.
Radial nerve
Axillary nerve
Dorsal scapular n.
Suprascapular n.
Musculocutaneous nerve
Median nerve
Sternocleidomastoid muscle
Phrenic nerve
Subclavian artery
Subclavian vein
Pectoral nerves
Med. antebrach. cutan. n.
Brachial a.
Ulnar n.
Intercosto-brachial n.
Thoracodorsal nerve
Long thoracic nerve
Lateral cutaneous nerve

Fig. 18: The Right Brachial Plexus

NOTE that: 1) the brachial plexus is exposed in this dissection after removal of the pectoral muscles, the clavicle, and the axillary vessels;

2) the five spinal roots immediately above the subclavian artery join to form three trunks, which then divide into anterior and posterior divisions;

3) the three posterior divisions form the posterior cord. The anterior divisions of the upper and middle trunks form the lateral cord. The anterior division of the lower trunk forms the medial cord;

4) the five large terminal nerves of the plexus are the ulnar, median, musculocutaneous, axillary and radial. These all supply motor and sensory innervation to the upper limb.

Figs. 17, 18   **I**

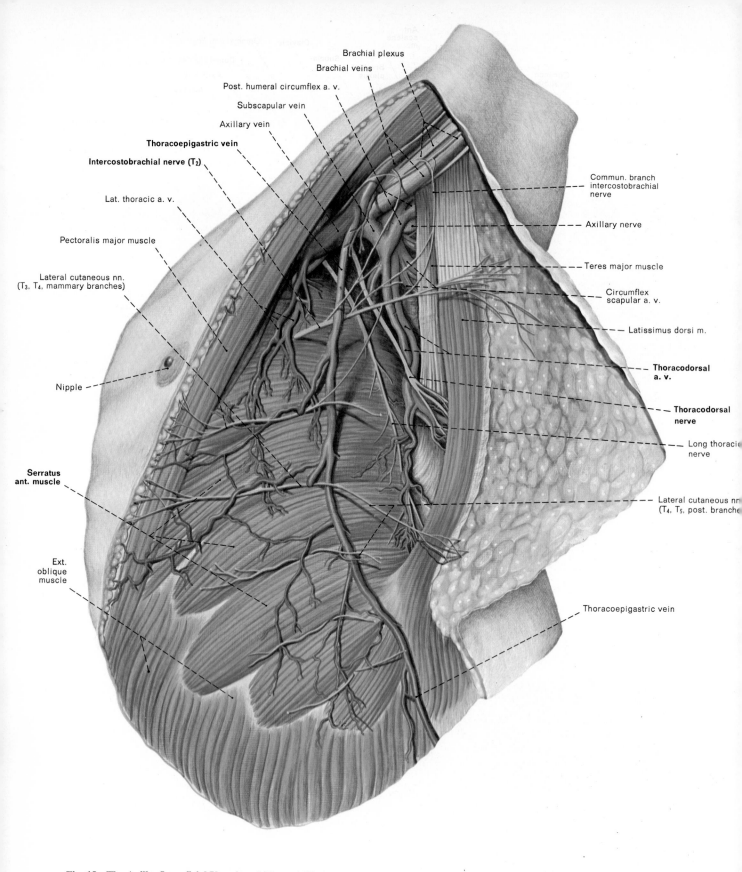

Brachial plexus

Brachial veins

Post. humeral circumflex a. v.

Subscapular vein

Axillary vein

Thoracoepigastric vein

Intercostobrachial nerve (T₂)

Lat. thoracic a. v.

Pectoralis major muscle

**Lateral cutaneous nn.
(T₃, T₄, mammary branches)**

Nipple

**Serratus
ant. muscle**

**Ext.
oblique
muscle**

**Commun. branch
intercostobrachial
nerve**

Axillary nerve

Teres major muscle

**Circumflex
scapular a. v.**

Latissimus dorsi m.

**Thoracodorsal
a. v.**

**Thoracodorsal
nerve**

**Long thoracic
nerve**

**Lateral cutaneous nn.
(T₄, T₅, post. branches**

Thoracoepigastric vein

Fig. 19: The Axilla: Superficial Vessels and Nerves left)

OBSERVE: 1) that the boundaries of the axilla are, a) anteriorly, the pectoralis major muscle; b) posteriorly, the subscapularis, teres major and latissimus dorsi muscles; c) medially, the serratus anterior muscle covering the ribs, and; d) laterally, the bicipital groove of the humerus.

2) that the inferior portion of the serratus anterior muscle arises from the lower ribs as fleshy interdigitations with the external oblique muscle.

3) the serratus anterior is innervated by the long thoracic nerve (C 5, 6, 7) and the latissimus dorsi is innervated by the thoracodorsal nerve (C 5, 6, 7).

4) the axillary vein lies medial to the axillary artery and the cords of the brachial plexus.

5) the descending course of the thoracoepigastric vein and the lateral thoracic artery and vein.

Fig. 19

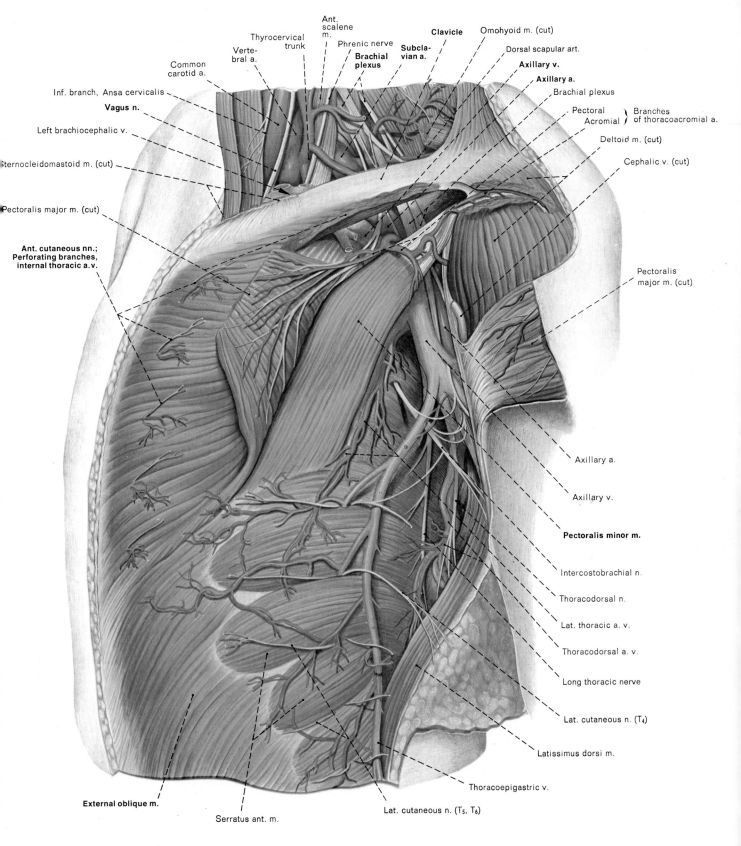

Inf. branch, Ansa cervicalis
Vagus n.
Left brachiocephalic v.
Sternocleidomastoid m. (cut)
Pectoralis major m. (cut)
**Ant. cutaneous nn.;
Perforating branches,
internal thoracic a. v.**

Common
carotid a.
Verte-
bral a.
Thyrocervical
trunk
Ant.
scalene
m.
Phrenic nerve
**Brachial
plexus**
Clavicle
Omohyoid m. (cut)
**Subcla-
vian a.**
Dorsal scapular art.
Axillary v.
Axillary a.
Brachial plexus
Pectoral
Acromial
} Branches
of thoracoacromial a.
Deltoid m. (cut)
Cephalic v. (cut)

Pectoralis
major m. (cut)

Axillary a.
Axillary v.
Pectoralis minor m.
Intercostobrachial n.
Thoracodorsal n.
Lat. thoracic a. v.
Thoracodorsal a. v.
Long thoracic nerve
Lat. cutaneous n. (T₄)
Latissimus dorsi m.
Thoracoepigastric v.
Lat. cutaneous n. (T₅, T₆)

External oblique m.
Serratus ant. m.

Fig. 20: The Axilla (left): Deep Vessels and Nerves

OBSERVE: 1) that the subclavian artery becomes the axillary artery as it passes beneath the clavicle;

2) that the pectoralis minor muscle is helpful in describing the underlying axillary artery in its course through the axilla, since the three parts of the axillary artery are medial, beneath and lateral to the pectoralis minor;

3) that the axillary vein courses medial to the axillary artery and it receives tributaries not only from the upper extremity but from the thorax as well;

4) that the axillary artery is surrounded by the three cords of the brachial plexus;

5) that the thoracoacromial artery divides into pectoral, acromial, deltoid and small clavicular branches (the latter are not shown in the figure);

6) that the intercostobrachial (T₂) nerve pierces the thoracic cage through the 2nd intercostal space in its course toward the axilla and arm.

Fig. 20   I

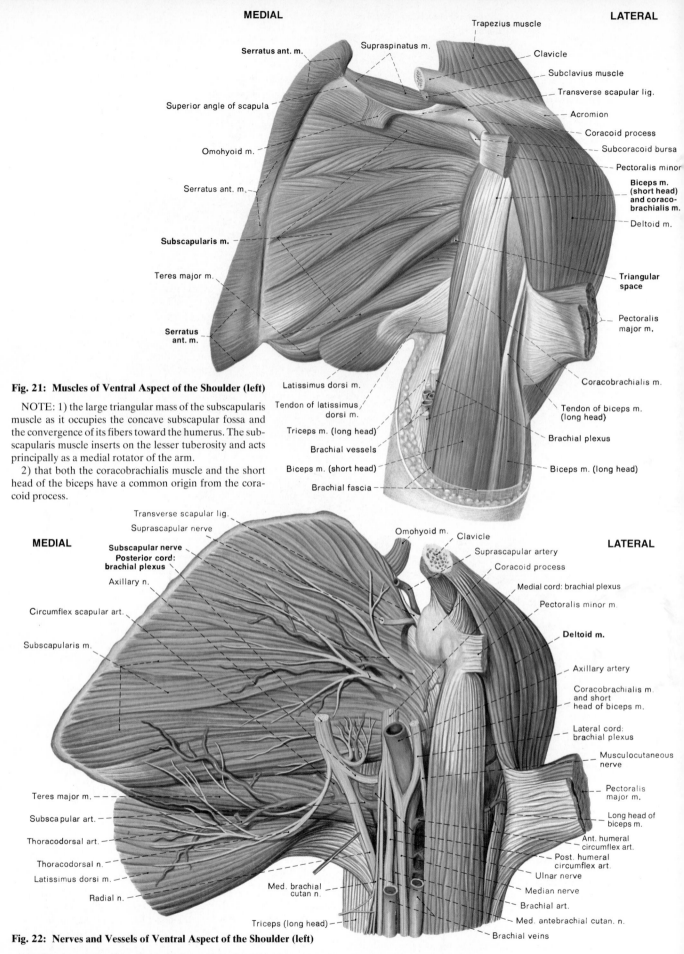

MEDIAL **LATERAL**

Serratus ant. m.
Supraspinatus m.
Trapezius muscle
Clavicle
Subclavius muscle
Transverse scapular lig.
Acromion
Coracoid process
Subcoracoid bursa
Pectoralis minor
Superior angle of scapula
Biceps m. (short head) and coraco-brachialis m.
Deltoid m.
Omohyoid m.
Serratus ant. m.
Subscapularis m.
Teres major m.
Triangular space
Pectoralis major m.
Serratus ant. m.
Coracobrachialis m.
Latissimus dorsi m.
Tendon of latissimus dorsi m.
Triceps m. (long head)
Brachial vessels
Biceps m. (short head)
Brachial fascia
Tendon of biceps m. (long head)
Brachial plexus
Biceps m. (long head)

Fig. 21: Muscles of Ventral Aspect of the Shoulder (left)

NOTE: 1) the large triangular mass of the subscapularis muscle as it occupies the concave subscapular fossa and the convergence of its fibers toward the humerus. The subscapularis muscle inserts on the lesser tuberosity and acts principally as a medial rotator of the arm.

2) that both the coracobrachialis muscle and the short head of the biceps have a common origin from the coracoid process.

Transverse scapular lig.
Suprascapular nerve
Omohyoid m.
Clavicle
MEDIAL **LATERAL**
Subscapular nerve Posterior cord: brachial plexus
Axillary n.
Suprascapular artery
Coracoid process
Medial cord: brachial plexus
Pectoralis minor m.
Circumflex scapular art.
Deltoid m.
Subscapularis m.
Axillary artery
Coracobrachialis m. and short head of biceps m.
Lateral cord: brachial plexus
Musculocutaneous nerve
Pectoralis major m.
Teres major m.
Subscapular art.
Long head of biceps m.
Thoracodorsal art.
Ant. humeral circumflex art.
Thoracodorsal n.
Post. humeral circumflex art.
Latissimus dorsi m.
Ulnar nerve
Radial n.
Median nerve
Med. brachial cutan n.
Brachial art.
Med. antebrachial cutan. n.
Triceps (long head)
Brachial veins

Fig. 22: Nerves and Vessels of Ventral Aspect of the Shoulder (left)

NOTE: the relationship of the medial, lateral and posterior cords of the brachial plexus to the axillary artery. The posterior cord has been pulled medially from behind the plexus in this dissection.

Figs. 21, 22

LATERAL

MEDIAL

Spine of scapula   Acromion
Deltoid m.
Trapezius m.
Levator scapulae m.
Subdeltoid bursa
Teres minor m.
Supraspinatus m.
Surgical neck of humerus
Tendon of biceps, Long head
Rhomboideus minor m.
Quadrangular space
Tendon of pect. major m.
Infraspinatus m.
Deltoid m.
Biceps m.
Rhomboideus major m.
Triangular space
Triceps m., Long head
Teres major m.
rachialis m.
Triceps m., Lat. head

Fig. 23: Dorsal Scapular Muscles (left)

NOTE: 1) that the long head of the triceps intersects a space between the teres minor and teres major thereby forming a more laterally located quadrangular space and a more medial triangular space;

2) through the quadrangular space pass the post. humeral circumflex artery and the axillary nerve, while the circumflex scapular branch of the subscapular artery passes through the triangular space (see Fig. 24);

3) since the lateral border of the quadrangular space is the surgical neck of the humerus, the axillary nerve and post. humeral circumflex art. are in danger if the bone is fractured at this site.

LATERAL

MEDIAL

Supraspinatus m.
Suprascapular art.
Sup. transverse scapular lig.
Suprascapular n.
Clavicle
Acromial branch
Deltoid m.
Supraspinatus m.
Spine of the scapula
f. transverse scapular lig.
Infraspinatus m.
omial arterial network
Teres minor m.
Infraspinatus m.
Circumflex scapular art.
Joint capsule
Teres major m.
Nerve to teres minor
Deltoid m.
Triceps m. (long head)
Axillary nerve
Lat. brachial cutaneous n. (axillary branch)
Post. humeral circumflex art.

Fig. 24: Nerves and Vessels of Dorsal Scapular Region (left)

NOTE: 1) that the sup. transverse scapular lig. bridges across the scapular notch and the suprascapular nerve passes beneath the ligament while the suprascapular artery usually passes above it;

2) that the axillary nerve supplies four structures: the deltoid muscle, the teres minor muscle, the capsule of the shoulder joint and the skin over the shoulder joint;

3) that the axillary nerve and post. humeral circumflex artery achieve the dorsal aspect of the shoulder through the quadrangular space, while the circumflex scapular artery reaches the infraspinatus fossa through the triangular space.

Figs. 23, 24   **I**

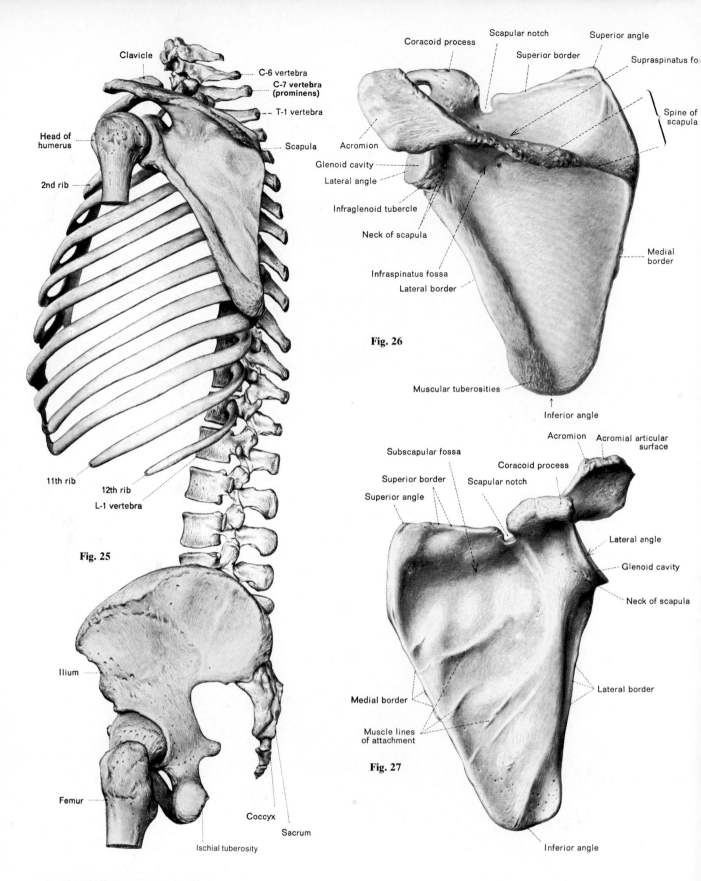

Fig. 25 (labels): Clavicle · C-6 vertebra · C-7 vertebra (prominens) · T-1 vertebra · Head of humerus · Scapula · 2nd rib · 11th rib · 12th rib · L-1 vertebra · Ilium · Femur · Ischial tuberosity · Coccyx · Sacrum

Fig. 26 (labels): Coracoid process · Scapular notch · Superior border · Superior angle · Supraspinatus fo[ssa] · Spine of scapula · Acromion · Glenoid cavity · Lateral angle · Infraglenoid tubercle · Neck of scapula · Infraspinatus fossa · Lateral border · Medial border · Muscular tuberosities · Inferior angle

Fig. 27 (labels): Subscapular fossa · Acromion · Acromial articular surface · Superior border · Coracoid process · Scapular notch · Superior angle · Lateral angle · Glenoid cavity · Neck of scapula · Medial border · Lateral border · Muscle lines of attachment · Inferior angle

Fig. 25: Skeleton of Trunk with Scapula and Pelvis
NOTE that the flat triangular shaped scapula articulates with the head of the humerus and the clavicle. It is also attached to the rib cage by muscles.

Fig. 26: The Left Scapula (Dorsal Surface)
NOTE that the socket for the head of the humerus is formed by the glenoid cavity and is further enlarged by the coracoid and acromial processes along with their related ligaments. The spine of the scapula separates the dorsal surface into supraspinatus and infraspinatus fossae.

Fig. 27: The Left Scapula (Ventral Surface)
NOTE that much of the ventral surface is a concave fossa within which lies the subscapularis muscle.

Figs. 25, 26, 27

Fig. 28: The Left Scapula, Lateral View

NOTE: 1) the supraglenoid and infraglenoid tubercles from which arise the long heads of the biceps and triceps muscles, respectively;

2) the anteriorly projecting coracoid process to which are attached the pectoralis minor, short head of the biceps, and the coracobrachialis muscles.

Fig. 29: The Left Glenoid Cavity and Scapuloclavicular Joint (Lateral View)

NOTE: 1) exposure of the glenoid cavity was achieved by removal of the articular capsule at the glenoid labrum;

2) the attachment of the tendon of the long head of the biceps muscle at the supraglenoid tubercle and that of the long head of the triceps at the infraglenoid tubercle have been left intact;

3) the shallowness of the glenoid cavity is slightly deepened (4 to 6 mm.) by the glenoid labrum;

4) the protection afforded to the shoulder joint superiorly by the acromion, coracoid process and clavicle and their ligamentous attachments and by the tendon of the long head of the biceps.

Fig. 30: Frontal Section through Right Shoulder Joint

NOTE: 1) that the tendon of the long head of the biceps arises from the supraglenoid tuberosity and is at once enclosed by a reflection of the synovial sheath. Thus, although the tendon passes through the joint, it is not contained within the synovial cavity of the joint;

2) the capsule of the joint is composed of a dense fibrous outer layer and a thin synovial inner layer. It is this thin inner layer which reflects itself around the biceps tendon in its course through the joint;

3) a bursa is a sac lined with a synovial-like membrane containing a small amount of fluid. Bursae are found at sites subjected to friction and normally do not communicate with the joint capsule. In the shoulder, separate bursae are found between the capsule and the subscapularis, infraspinatus and deltoid tendons as well as other muscles, and between the capsule and the coracoid and acromial processes (subacromial bursa).

Figs. 28, 29, 30   **I**

Fig. 31: Left Shoulder Joint and Acromioclavicular Joint (Anterior View)

NOTE: 1) that the clavicle is attached by ligaments to both the acromion (acromioclavicular lig) and the coracoid process (coracoclavicular lig.) of the scapula. The acromion and coracoid process are themselves connected by the coracoacromial ligament;

2) neither the acromion nor the clavicle articulates directly with the humerus, whereas the coracoid process and the glenoid labrum afford attachment of the scapula to the humerus;

3) the acromion, coracoid process and clavicle assist in the protection of the shoulder joint from above. Thus, the joint is weakest inferiorly and anteriorly, the directions in which most dislocations occur;

4) the glenohumeral ligaments are thickened bands which tend to strenghten somewhat the capsule of the joint anteriorly;

5) the position of the long tendon of the biceps traversing the articular cavity to its point of attachment on the supraglenoid tubercle.

Clavicle
Conoid lig.
Trapezoid lig.
Coracoclavicular lig.
Sup. transverse scapular lig.
Acromioclavicular lig.
Coracoacromial lig.
Coracoid process
Acromion
Opening into subacromial bursa
Coracohumeral lig.
Subscapularis m.
Synovial sheath of biceps tendon
Triceps m. (long head)
Glenohumeral ligaments
Biceps m. (long head)
Humerus

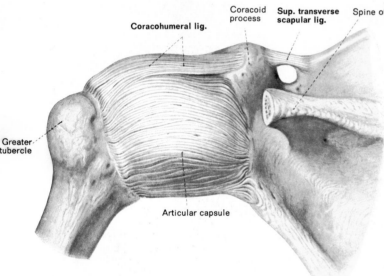

Coracohumeral lig.
Coracoid process
Sup. transverse scapular lig.
Spine of scapula
Greater tubercle
Articular capsule

Fig. 32: Capsule of Left Shoulder Joint (Posterior View)

NOTE: 1) the articular capsule completely surrounds the joint, being attached beyond the glenoid cavity on the scapula above and to the anatomical neck of the humerus below;

2) the superior part of the capsule is further strengthened by the coracohumeral ligament.

Fig. 33: Left Shoulder Joint (Posterior View)

NOTE: 1) the shoulder joint is a freely moving ball and socket joint. The capsule of the joint is not drawn tightly between the humeral head and scapula but attached loosely over these bony structures;

2) the tendons of the supraspinatus, infraspinatus and teres minor blend superiorly and posteriorly with the capsule of the joint. These muscles along with the subscapularis anteriorly form a muscular encasement lending some support in the maintenance of the head of the humerus in its socket;

3) the close relationship of the long head of the triceps to the capsule of joint. When the arm is abducted the triceps is drawn even closer to the capsule to help prevent dislocation.

Acromial extremity of clavicle
Acromioclavicular lig.
Acromion
Spine of scapula
Coracoacromial lig.
Supraspinatus m.
Articular capsule
Triceps m. (long head)
* Infraspinatus m.
** Teres minor m.
Body of humerus

Figs. 31, 32, 33

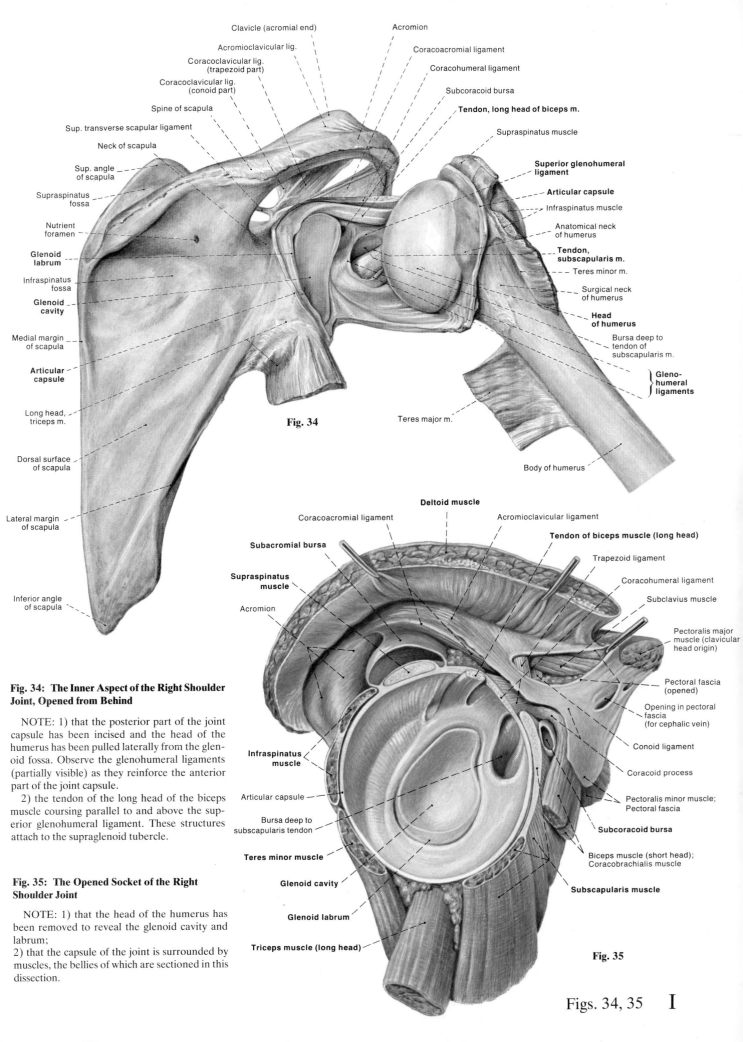

Clavicle (acromial end)
Acromioclavicular lig.
Coracoclavicular lig. (trapezoid part)
Coracoclavicular lig. (conoid part)
Spine of scapula
Sup. transverse scapular ligament
Neck of scapula
Sup. angle of scapula
Supraspinatus fossa
Nutrient foramen
Glenoid labrum
Infraspinatus fossa
Glenoid cavity
Medial margin of scapula
Articular capsule
Long head, triceps m.
Dorsal surface of scapula
Lateral margin of scapula
Inferior angle of scapula

Acromion
Coracoacromial ligament
Coracohumeral ligament
Subcoracoid bursa
Tendon, long head of biceps m.
Supraspinatus muscle
Superior glenohumeral ligament
Articular capsule
Infraspinatus muscle
Anatomical neck of humerus
Tendon, subscapularis m.
Teres minor m.
Surgical neck of humerus
Head of humerus
Bursa deep to tendon of subscapularis m.
Gleno-humeral ligaments
Teres major m.
Body of humerus

Fig. 34

Fig. 34: The Inner Aspect of the Right Shoulder Joint, Opened from Behind

NOTE: 1) that the posterior part of the joint capsule has been incised and the head of the humerus has been pulled laterally from the glenoid fossa. Observe the glenohumeral ligaments (partially visible) as they reinforce the anterior part of the joint capsule.

2) the tendon of the long head of the biceps muscle coursing parallel to and above the superior glenohumeral ligament. These structures attach to the supraglenoid tubercle.

Fig. 35: The Opened Socket of the Right Shoulder Joint

NOTE: 1) that the head of the humerus has been removed to reveal the glenoid cavity and labrum;
2) that the capsule of the joint is surrounded by muscles, the bellies of which are sectioned in this dissection.

Coracoacromial ligament
Deltoid muscle
Acromioclavicular ligament
Tendon of biceps muscle (long head)
Subacromial bursa
Trapezoid ligament
Coracohumeral ligament
Supraspinatus muscle
Subclavius muscle
Acromion
Pectoralis major muscle (clavicular head origin)
Pectoral fascia (opened)
Opening in pectoral fascia (for cephalic vein)
Conoid ligament
Infraspinatus muscle
Coracoid process
Articular capsule
Pectoralis minor muscle; Pectoral fascia
Bursa deep to subscapularis tendon
Subcoracoid bursa
Teres minor muscle
Biceps muscle (short head); Coracobrachialis muscle
Glenoid cavity
Subscapularis muscle
Glenoid labrum
Triceps muscle (long head)

Fig. 35

Figs. 34, 35   I

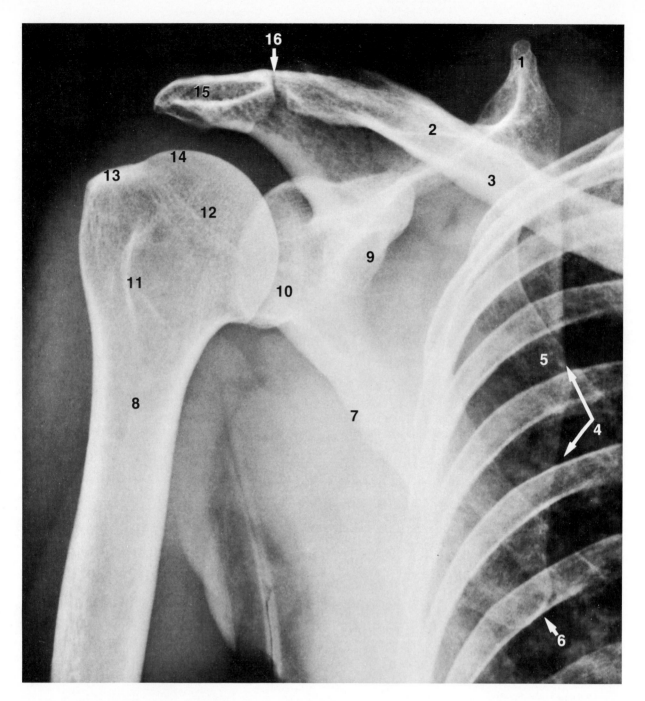

Fig. 36: Radiograph of the Right Shoulder Region

1. Superior angle of scapula
2. Spine of scapula
3. Clavicle
4. Medial margin of scapula
5. Second rib
6. Inferior angle of scapula
7. Lateral margin of scapula
8. Surgical neck of humerus
9. Coracoid process
10. Glenoid cavity
11. Lesser tubercle
12. Anatomical neck of humerus
13. Greater tubercle
14. Head of humerus
15. Acromion
16. Acromioclavicular joint

NOTE: 1) the clavicle, scapula and humerus are importantly involved in the radiographic anatomy of the shoulder region. The acromioclavicular joint is a planar joint formed by the apposition of the lateral end of the clavicle and the medial border of the acromion.

2) the glenohumeral joint, more commonly called the shoulder joint, is remarkably loose and provides a free range of movement. Observe the wide separation between the humeral head and glenoid cavity, and that only a small part of the humeral head is in contact with the cavity at any time.

3) that inferior *dislocations* of the head of the humerus are common because of minimal protection to this part of the joint. A *shoulder separation* results from the dislocation of the acromion beneath the lateral end of the clavicle, usually because of a strong blow to the lateral aspect of the joint.

4) the smooth surface of the head of the humerus and that it is almost hemispherical in shape. Covered with hyalin cartilage, the humeral head is slightly constricted at the anatomical neck, which forms a circumferential line separating the articular part superomedially from the greater and lesser tubercles inferolaterally.

5) that below the tubercles, the humerus shows another constriction that is called the surgical neck. Fractures of the humerus frequently occur at this site. (From Wicke, L. *Atlas of Radiologic Anatomy*, 3rd Edition, Urban & Schwarzenberg, Baltimore, 1982).

Fig. 36

Fig. 37: Surface Anatomy of the Right Upper Extremity, Anterior Aspect

NOTE: 1) the vertically oriented medial bicipital furrow along the medial aspect of the arm (or brachium). The basilic vein and medial antebrachial cutaneous nerve course just beneath the skin along this furrow, while slightly deeper are found the brachial artery and veins and the median and ulnar nerves.

2) the cubital fossa located in front of the elbow joint between the contours made by the bellies of the flexor and extensor muscles in the upper forearm.

3) the location of the styloid processes of the ulna and radius at the wrist. By palpation determine that the radial styloid process extends about 1 cm lower than that of the ulna.

Fig. 38: The Distribution of Cutaneous Nerves, Anterior Aspect of the Right Upper Extremity

Fig. 39: The Distribution of Cutaneous Nerves, Posterior Aspect of the Right Upper Extremity

Figs. 37, 38, 39   I

MEDIAL · LATERAL

Post. supraclavi-
cular n. (C 3, 4)

MEDIAL · LATERAL

Basilic vein

Med. brachial
cutan. n. (C 8, TI, 2)

Med. antebrachial
cutan. n. (C 8, TI)

Cephalic vein

Lat. antebrachial
cutan. n.
(C 5, 6, 7)

Med. antebrachial
cutan. n. (C 8, TI)
ulnar branch

Median
cubital vein

Med. antebrachial
cutan. n. (C 8, TI)
anterior branch

Intercosto-
brachial n. (T 2)

Branches
of med. brachial
cutan. n.
(C 8, TI, 2)

Cephalic vein

Basilic vein

Median ante-
brachial vein

Med. antebrachial
cutan. n. (C 8, TI)

Lat. antebrachial
cutan. nn. (C 5, 6, 7)

Cephalic vein

Basilic vein

Ulnar
branch

Med. ante-
brachial
cutan. n.
(C 8-TI)

Ant.
branch

Lat. antebrachial
cutan. n. (C 5, 6, 7)

Median cubital vein

Post. antebrachial
cutan. n. (C 5, 6, 7, 8)

Palmar branch
of ulnar n.

Radial nerve
(superficial branch)

Radial artery

Palmar branch
of median n.

Median ante-
brachial vein

Basilic vein

Fig. 40: Arm; Superficial Veins and Cutaneous Nerves of Left Upper Limb (Anterior Surface)

NOTE: 1) the basilic vein ascends on the medial (ulnar) aspect of the arm, pierces the deep fascia and at the lower border of the teres major joins the brachial vein to form the axillary vein. The cephalic vein ascends laterally in the arm in its course toward the axillary vein.

2) the principal sensory nerves of the anterior arm are the medial and lateral brachial cutaneous nerves and the intercostobrachial nerve.

Fig. 41: Forearm; Superficial Veins and Cutaneous Nerves of Left Upper Limb (Anterior Surface)

NOTE: 1) the median cubital vein, interconnecting the cephalic and the basilic veins in the cubital fossa.

2) the main sensory nerves of the anterior forearm are the medial antebrachial cutaneous nerve (derived from the medial cord of the brachial plexus) and the lateral antebrachial cutaneous nerve, which is the continuation of the musculocutaneous nerve.

Figs. 40, 41

Thoracoacromial a. v. acromial cutan. network

Post. supraclavi-
cular nn. (C 3, 4)

...an branch
of axillary
...ve (C 5, 6)

Post. brach.
cutan. n. (C 5–8)

Cephalic vein

Post. antebrach.
cutan. n. (C 5–8)

Med. brach.
cutan. n. (C 8, TI, 2)

Olecranon
process

LATERAL

MEDIAL

LATERAL

MEDIAL

Superficial branches
post. humeral circum. a. v.

Lat. brachial
cutan. n. (C 5, 6)
from axillary n.

Post brach.
cutan. n.
(C 5 – 8, radial)

Cephalic vein

Post. antebrachial
...tan. n. (C 5–8, radial)

Communicating
branch between
lat. brach.
and post.
antebrachial nn.

Med. brachial
cutan. n. (C 8, TI, 2)

Radial n.,
Superficial branch

Basilic vein

Lat. epicondyle
of humerus

Cephalic vein

Post. antebrachial
cutan. n. (C 5–8)

Olecranon
process

Ulnar nerve,
cutan. branch
to dorsal hand

Fig. 42: Arm; Superficial Veins and Cutaneous Nerves of Left Upper Limb (Posterior Surface)

NOTE: 1) that the posterior surface of the arm receives cutaneous innervation from branches of the radial (posterior brachial cutaneous n.) and axillary (lateral brachial cutaneous n.) nerves, both of which are derived from the posterior cord of the brachial plexus.

2) the posterior antebrachial cutaneous nerve (from the radial n.) perforates the lateral head of the triceps about five centimeters above the elbow. It pierces the superficial fascia on the posterolateral surface of the arm, but sends cutaneous branches to the dorsal surface of the forearm, as well as a communicating branch to cutaneous rami of the axillary nerve.

Fig. 43: Forearm; Superficial Veins and Cutaneous Nerves of the Left Upper Limb (Posterior Surface)

NOTE: 1) branches of the radial nerve (posterior antebrachial cutaneous and superficial radial) contribute the principal cutaneous innervation to the posterior aspect of the forearm.

2) at the wrist the dorsal branch of the ulnar nerve passes backward onto the dorsal surface of the wrist and hand.

3) the basilic (ulnar side, medial) and cephalic (radial side, lateral) veins commence on the dorsum of the hand and wrist and ascend in the forearm.

Figs. 42, 43   I

Fig. 44: Variations in the Venous Pattern of the Upper Extremity

NOTE that the superficial veins of the upper extremity are quite variable and yet are of significance clinically. The median cubital vein in the cubital fossa is especially used for the withdrawal of blood and for procedures necessitating the injection of fluids into the vascular system. In this regard, care must be taken not to injure the median nerve nor puncture the brachial artery, which both lie deep to the median cubital vein and the subjacent bicipital aponeurosis on which the vein rests.

Fig. 45: Dermatomes of the Upper Limb

NOTE: the dermatomes of the upper limb are supplied by the 5th cervical to the 1st thoracic segments of the spinal cord. The boundary between the 5th cervical and the 1st thoracic dermatomes ventrally is called the ventral axial line of the upper limb. The 4th cervical dermatome lies in the neck. Commencing with the 5th cervical dermatome and proceeding radially around the upper limb, the dermatomes can be followed sequentially to the 1st thoracic and thus, the ventral axial line.

Fig. 46: Valves Visible in an Opened Segment of Vein

NOTE: 1) venous valves are formed by semilunar folds of the tunica intima strengthened by connective tissue containing a thick network of elastic fibers.

2) arrows on in left (pointing to the right) indicate the normal direction of blood flow, i.e. toward the heart, in which case the valves open easily. Arrows on the right (pointing to the left) indicate the reversed direction of blood flow, whereby regurgitated blood quickly becomes trapped in the expanded sinus, causing the valves to close and thus to interrupt the backflow. Incompetent valves result in the formation of varicosed veins.

Figs. 44, 45, 46

Fig. 47: The Deep Fascia Overlying the Brachial and Antebrachial Muscles of the Left Upper Extremity, Anterior View

NOTE: 1) the medial bicipital furrow that separates the flexor from the extensor compartments of the arm, and the hiatuses in the deep fascia through which course the basilic vein and the lateral antebrachial cutaneous nerve.

2) the bicipital aponeurosis. This is an extension medially from the tendon of insertion of the biceps brachii muscle that courses over the brachial artery to fuse with the deep fascia of the forearm.

Fig. 48: The Deep Fascia Overlying the Brachial and Antebrachial Muscles of the Left Upper Extremity, Posterior View

NOTE: 1) the subcutaneous olecranon bursa that lubricates the postero-lateral aspect of the olecranon between the sites of attachment of the triceps and anconeus muscles.

2) the hiatus in the lateral intermuscular septum through which the posterior antebrachial cutaneous nerve penetrates the deep fascia to reach the superficial fascia and skin of the posterior forearm.

Figs. 47, 48   **I**

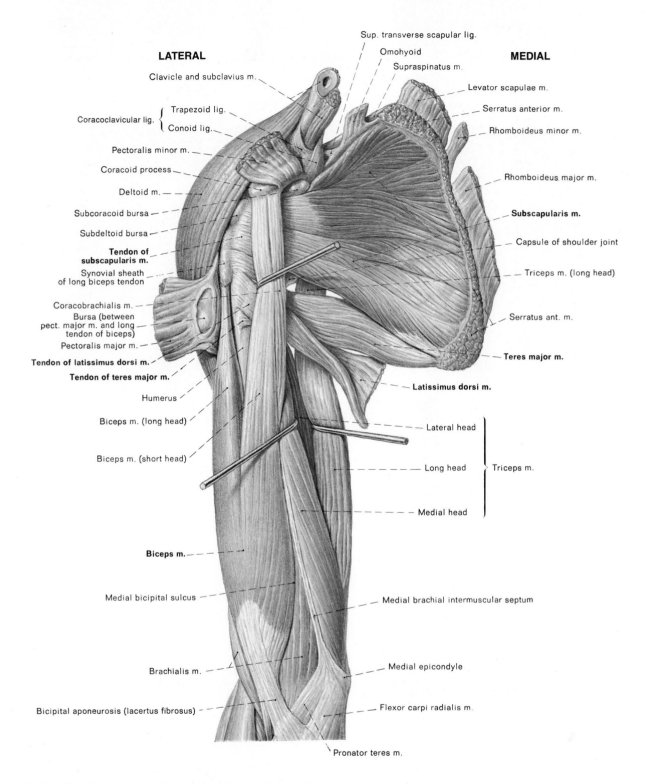

LATERAL

MEDIAL

Sup. transverse scapular lig.

Omohyoid

Supraspinatus m.

Clavicle and subclavius m.

Levator scapulae m.

Serratus anterior m.

Trapezoid lig.

Coracoclavicular lig. {

Conoid lig.

Rhomboideus minor m.

Pectoralis minor m.

Coracoid process

Rhomboideus major m.

Deltoid m.

Subcoracoid bursa

Subscapularis m.

Subdeltoid bursa

Capsule of shoulder joint

Tendon of subscapularis m.

Triceps m. (long head)

Synovial sheath of long biceps tendon

Coracobrachialis m.

Bursa (between pect. major m. and long tendon of biceps)

Serratus ant. m.

Pectoralis major m.

Tendon of latissimus dorsi m.

Teres major m.

Tendon of teres major m.

Latissimus dorsi m.

Humerus

Biceps m. (long head)

Lateral head

Biceps m. (short head)

Long head

Triceps m.

Medial head

Biceps m.

Medial bicipital sulcus

Medial brachial intermuscular septum

Brachialis m.

Medial epicondyle

Bicipital aponeurosis (lacertus fibrosus)

Flexor carpi radialis m.

Pronator teres m.

Fig. 49: Muscles of the Right Shoulder and Arm (Anterior View)

NOTE: 1) the insertion of the subscapularis muscle on the lesser tubercle of the humerus. Distal to this, from medial to lateral, insert the teres major, latissimus dorsi and pectoralis major muscles.

2) attaching to the coracoid process are the pectoralis minor m., coracobrachialis m. and the short head of the biceps m.

3) the insertion of the pectoralis major m. and the long tendon of the biceps muscle are frequently separated by a bursa.

4) in the arm, the flexor compartment (biceps, coracobrachialis and brachialis) is separated from the extensor compartment (triceps) by an intermuscular septum of deep fascia.

Fig. 49

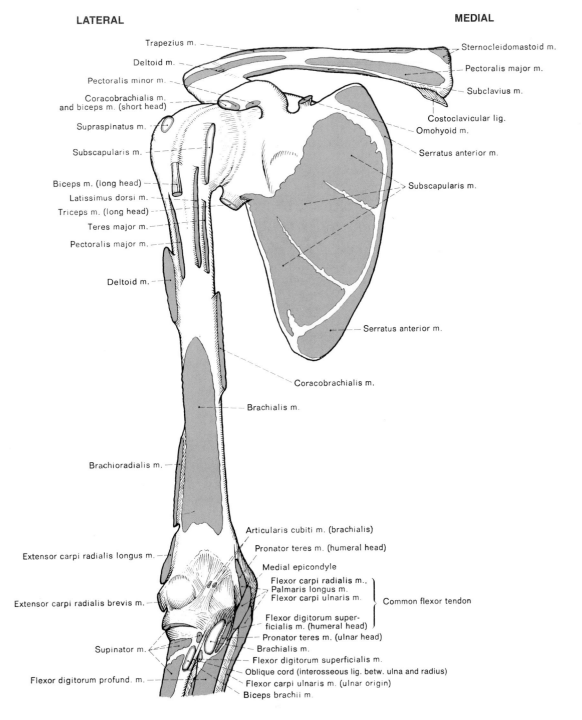

LATERAL   MEDIAL

Trapezius m.
Deltoid m.
Pectoralis minor m.
Coracobrachialis m.
and biceps m. (short head)
Supraspinatus m.
Subscapularis m.
Biceps m. (long head)
Latissimus dorsi m.
Triceps m. (long head)
Teres major m.
Pectoralis major m.
Deltoid m.
Brachialis m.
Brachioradialis m.
Extensor carpi radialis longus m.
Extensor carpi radialis brevis m.
Supinator m.
Flexor digitorum profund. m.

Sternocleidomastoid m.
Pectoralis major m.
Subclavius m.
Costoclavicular lig.
Omohyoid m.
Serratus anterior m.
Subscapularis m.
Serratus anterior m.
Coracobrachialis m.
Articularis cubiti m. (brachialis)
Pronator teres m. (humeral head)
Medial epicondyle
Flexor carpi radialis m.,
Palmaris longus m.
Flexor carpi ulnaris m.
Flexor digitorum super-
ficialis m. (humeral head)
Pronator teres m. (ulnar head)
Brachialis m.
Flexor digitorum superficialis m.
Oblique cord (interosseous lig. betw. ulna and radius)
Flexor carpi ulnaris m. (ulnar origin)
Biceps brachii m.

Common flexor tendon

Fig. 50: Anterior View of Bones of the Upper Limb (Including Proximal End of Radius and Ulna) Showing Attachments of Muscles

NOTE: 1) the broad *origin* of the subscapularis in the subscapular fossa of the scapula and its *insertion* on the lesser tubercle of the humerus proximal to the insertions of the latissimus dorsi and teres major muscles. The subscapularis is an adductor and medial rotator of the arm.

2) the brachialis muscle *arises* from the distal three-fifths of the anterior surface of the humerus and *inserts* on the coronoid process of the ulna. This muscle is the strongest flexor of the forearm.

3) the short head of the biceps m. *arises* with the coracobrachialis m. from the coracoid process, while the long head *arises* from the supraglenoid tubercle of the scapula.

4) the coracobrachialis *inserts* onto the shaft of the humerus near its middle, while the biceps inserts onto the tuberosity of the radius and onto the deep fascia of the forearm by way of the bicipital aponeurosis.

5) the coracobrachialis flexes and adducts the arm at the shoulder joint, while the biceps flexes and supinates the forearm, with the long head assisting in flexion of the arm at the shoulder joint.

Fig. 50   **I**

Omohyoid m.
Serratus anterior m.
Superior angle of scapula
Levator scapulae m.
Supraspinatus m.
Rhomboideus minor m.
Spine of scapula
Trapezius m. tendon
Infraspinatus m.
Rhomboideus major m.
Teres major m.
Triceps m. (long head)
Latissimus dorsi m.
Triceps m. (lateral head)
Triceps m. (medial head)
Tendon of triceps m.
Medial epicondyle
Olecranon process
Anconeus m.
Flexor carpi ulnaris m.
Posterior border of ulna

MEDIAL

Clavicle
Costoclavicular lig.
Subclavius m.
Trapezius m.
Acromion
Deltoid m.
Subdeltoid bursa
Supraspinatus m. tendon
Teres minor m.
Articular capsule of shoulder joint
Quadrangular space
Body of humerus
Deltoid m.
Triangular space
Brachial artery
Median nerve
Ulnar nerve
Triceps m. (lateral head)
Triceps m. (medial head)
Radial nerve
Brachialis m.
Lat. brachial intermuscular septum
Brachioradialis m.
Ext. carpi radialis longus m.
Lateral epicondyle
Antebrachial fascia
Ext. carpi radialis brevis m.
Ext. digitorum (communis) m.
Ext. carpi ulnaris m.

LATERAL

Fig. 51: Muscles of the Shoulder and Deep Arm (Posterior View)

NOTE: 1) that with the deltoid muscle and the lateral head of the triceps muscle severed, the course of the radial nerve in the upper arm is revealed.

2) the sequential insertions of the supraspinatus, infraspinatus and teres minor muscles on the greater tubercle of the humerus.

3) the boundaries of the quadrangular and triangular spaces.

Fig. 51

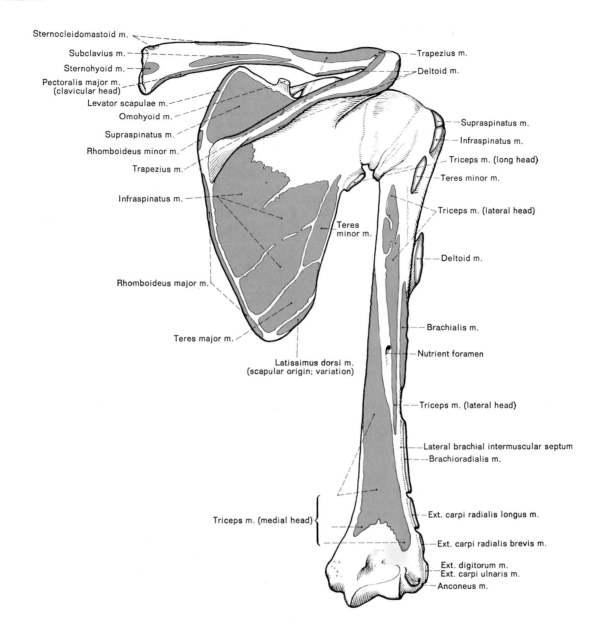

Sternocleidomastoid m.

Subclavius m.

Sternohyoid m.

Pectoralis major m.
(clavicular head)

Levator scapulae m.

Omohyoid m.

Supraspinatus m.

Rhomboideus minor m.

Trapezius m.

Infraspinatus m.

Rhomboideus major m.

Teres major m.

Latissimus dorsi m.
(scapular origin; variation)

Triceps m. (medial head)

Teres
minor m.

Trapezius m.

Deltoid m.

Supraspinatus m.

Infraspinatus m.

Triceps m. (long head)

Teres minor m.

Triceps m. (lateral head)

Deltoid m.

Brachialis m.

Nutrient foramen

Triceps m. (lateral head)

Lateral brachial intermuscular septum

Brachioradialis m.

Ext. carpi radialis longus m.

Ext. carpi radialis brevis m.

Ext. digitorum m.
Ext. carpi ulnaris m.

Anconeus m.

Fig. 52: Posterior View of the Clavicle, Scapula and Humerus Showing Muscle Attachments

NOTE: 1) that dorsally the vertebral border of the scapula is attached to the trunk by the levator scapulae and the rhomboideus major and minor muscles, whereas on the ventral scapular surface (see Fig. 50) the serratus anterior attaches along the vertebral border.

2) the supraspinatus muscle arising from the medial two-thirds of the supraspinatus fossa.

3) the origins of the teres major and teres minor muscles along the axillary border of the scapula, and the broad origin of the infraspinatus muscle from the infraspinatus fossa.

4) that onto the spine of the scapula and extending to the lateral third of the clavicle are attached the trapezius and deltoid muscles.

5) most of the posterior surface of the humerus affords origin to the medial and lateral heads of the triceps muscle, while the long head arises from the infraglenoid tubercle of the scapula.

6) the alignment of the tendinous insertions of the supraspinatus, infraspinatus, and teres minor muscles which, along with the tendon of the subscapularis (see Figs. 49 and 50), from the so-called "rotator cuff" of the shoulder joint. This musculotendinous cuff significantly strengthens the joint, but is also the site of inflammatory reactions resulting in pain brought on by trauma or aging.

Fig. 52   I

Figs. 53, 54

Fig. 53: Superficial View of Muscles on the Anterior Aspect of the Left Arm

NOTE: that the biceps muscle extends across both the shoulder and elbow joints, but that the coracobrachialis muscle extends only across the shoulder joint.

Fig. 54: Vessels and Nerves of the Anterior Arm (left)

NOTE: 1) the median nerve crosses the brachial artery anteriorly from lateral to medial just above the cubital fossa.

2) neither the ulnar nor median nerve gives off branches in the arm.

3) the origin of the median nerve from both the medial and lateral cords of the brachial plexus. Observe that also arising from the medial cord are the medial brachial and medial antebrachial cutaneous nerves, the former coursing to the brachium (or arm) and arising more proximally from the medial cord than the latter, which courses to the antebrachium (or forearm).

Fig. 55: Deep View of Muscles on the Anterior Aspect of the Left Arm

NOTE: In this dissection both the long head and short head of the biceps brachii muscle have been severed and reflected in order to reveal the underlying brachialis muscle. The coracobrachialis muscle has been left intact.

Fig. 56: The Nerves and Arteries of the Anterior Arm (left)

NOTE: 1) the short head of the biceps muscle has been pulled aside to reveal the musculocutaneous nerve which supplies the coracobrachialis, biceps and brachialis muscles. This nerve continues into the forearm as the lateral antebrachial cutaneous nerve.

2) the superficial course of the brachial artery in the arm. Its branches include the profunda brachii artery and the superior and inferior ulnar collateral arteries in addition to its muscular branches.

Figs. 55, 56   I

Clavicle

Supraspinatus m.

Trape-
zius m.

Infra-
spinatus
fascia

Deltoid
muscle

Teres
major

**Deltoid
muscle**

Lat. brachial
cutan. n.
(axillary)

Deltoid
branch,
Profunda
brachii ar

Pectoralis
major m.

Teres
major m.

Triceps m
(long hea

Radial nerve

Latissimus
dorsi m.

Post. brachial
cutan. n.
(radial)

Profunda
brach. art.

Biceps m.

**Triceps m.
(long head)**

Brachial art.

Brachialis m.

Triceps m.
(lat. head)

**Triceps m.
(lat. head)**

Biceps m.

Lat. inter-
muscular septum

Lat. inter-
muscular septum

Brachialis m.

Brachioradialis m.

**Triceps m.
(med. head)**

**Post. antebrach.
cutan. n.**

Radial
collateral art.

Ext. carpi
radialis
longus m.

Tendon,
Triceps m.

Triceps m.
(med. head)

Inf. ulnar
collater. art.

Lat. antebrach.
cutan. n.

Olecranon

Lat. epicondyle

Ulnar nerve

Lateral
epicondyle

Antebrachial
fascia

Anconeus m.

Cubital
anastomos

Olecranon

Ext. carpi
radialis brevis m.

Ext. carpi
radialis mm.

Fig. 57: The Muscles of the Arm (Lateral View)

NOTE: 1) the deltoid muscle acting as a whole abducts the arm. The clavicular portion flexes and medially rotates the arm, while the scapular portion extends and laterally rotates the arm.

2) the lateral intermuscular septum separates the anterior muscular compartment from the posterior muscular compartment.

Fig. 58: Nerves and Arteries of the Left Posterior Arm (Superficial Branches)

NOTE: 1) the origin of the profunda brachii artery from the brachial artery and its relationship to the radial nerve. The long head of the triceps has been pulled medially.

2) the relationship of the ulnar nerve to the olecranon process and the vascular anastomosis around the elbow.

3) the site of attachment of the deltoid muscle on the humerus, and the relationship of this attachment to the uppermost fibers of the brachialis muscle, the lateral intermuscular septum, and the lateral head of the triceps muscle (see also Fig. 50).

Figs. 57, 58

Fig. 59: labels:
Deltoid m. — Infraspinatus m. — Subdeltoid bursa — Tendon, triceps m. (long head) — Teres minor m. — Teres minor m. — Surgical neck, humerus — Quadrangular space — Tendon, biceps m. (long head) — Teres major m. — Tendon, pect. maj. m. — Triceps m. (long head) — Deltoid m. — Triceps m. (lat. head) — Radial groove — Biceps m. — Triceps m. (med. head) — Brachialis m. — Lat. intermuscular septum — Brachioradialis m. — Tendon, Triceps m. — Ext. carpi radialis longus m. — Olecranon — Ext. carpi radialis brevis m. — Anconeus m. — Superficial extensor muscles — Antebrachial fascia

Fig. 60 labels:
Capsule of shoulder joint — Axillary n. — Teres minor m. — Deltoid m. — Quadrangular space — Teres major m. — Post. humeral circumflex art. — Post. brachial cutan. n. — Deltoid branch, profunda art. — Brachial artery — Triceps m. (long head) — Radial n. — Profunda brachii art. — Triceps m. (lat. head) — Biceps m. — Middle collateral art. — Radial collateral art. (Anterior branch) — Brachialis m. — Post. antebrach. cutan. n. — Triceps m. (med. head) — Radial collateral art. (Post. branch) — Lat. antebrach. cutan. n. — Inf. ulnar collateral art. — Lat. epicondyle — Cubital anastomosis — Ulnar nerve — Ext. carpi radialis muscles — Ulnar recurrent art. — Anconeus m.

Fig. 59: Deep Muscles of the Arm and Shoulder (Postero-lateral View)

NOTE: in this dissection much of the deltoid and teres minor muscles was removed, and the lateral head of the triceps muscle was transected and reflected. Observe the radial groove between the medial and lateral heads of the triceps.

Fig. 60: The Deep Nerves and Arteries of the Posterior Arm

NOTE: 1) the course of the axillary nerve and posterior humeral circumflex artery through the quadrangular space to achieve the deltoid muscle and dorsal shoulder region.

2) the course of the radial nerve and profunda brachii artery along the musculospiral groove to the posterior brachial region. The groove lies along the body of the humerus between the origins of the lateral and medial heads of the triceps muscle.

3) the common insertion of the triceps muscle onto the olecranon process of the ulna.

Figs. 59, 60   I

Splenius capitis m.
Trapezius m.
Omohyoid m.
Levator scapulae m.
Scalene mm. (ant., med., post.)
Sternohyoid m.
Acromion
Sternocleidomastoid m.
Spine of scapula
Clavicle
Deltoid m.
Trapezius m.
Pectoralis major m.
Infraspinatus fascia
Serratus ant. m.
Post. humeral circumflex a.
Teres minor m.
Ant. humeral circumflex a.
Teres major m.
Pect. maj. m. (abd. part)
Deep brachial a.
Triceps m. (long head)
Ext. oblique m.
Triceps m. (lat. head)
Hiatus, post. brachial n.
Costal margin
Lat. dorsi m.
Rectus sheath
Hiatus, lat. antebrach. cutan. n.
Triceps m.
Biceps m.
Lat. intermuscular septum
Brachialis m.
Triceps m. (med. head)
Pronator teres m.
Olecranon
Lateral epicondyle
Anconeus m.
Extensor carpi radialis long m.
Ext. digitorum m.
Brachioradialis m.
Extensor carpi radialis brevis m.
Radius
Flexor carpi radialis m.
Flexor pollicis longus m.
Tendon, extensor digitorum m.
Abductor pollicis long. m.
Ext. pollicis brevis m.
Extensor retinaculum
Tendon, ext. pollicis longus m.
Tendon, abd. pollicis longus m.
Tendon, ext. pollicis brevis m.
Adductor pollicis m.
Dorsal interosseous mm.

Axillary a.
Sup. ulnar collateral a.
Middle collateral a.
Brachial a.
Radial collateral a.
Inf. ulnar collateral a.
Anastomosis at elbow joint
Radial a.
Ulnar recurrent a.
Radial recurrent a.
Recurrent inteross. a.
Ulnar a.
Common interosseous a.
Post. interosseous a.
Ant. interosseous a.
Median a.
Radial a.
Dorsal carpal br. (ulnar a.)
Palmar carpal br. (radial a.)
Palmar carpal br. (ulnar a.)
Superficial palmar br. (radial a.)
Deep palmar arch
Superficial palmar arch

Fig. 61: Muscles of the Thorax and Right Upper Extremity, Lateral View

Fig. 62: Arteries of the Upper Extremity (Schematic Representation)

Figs. 61, 62

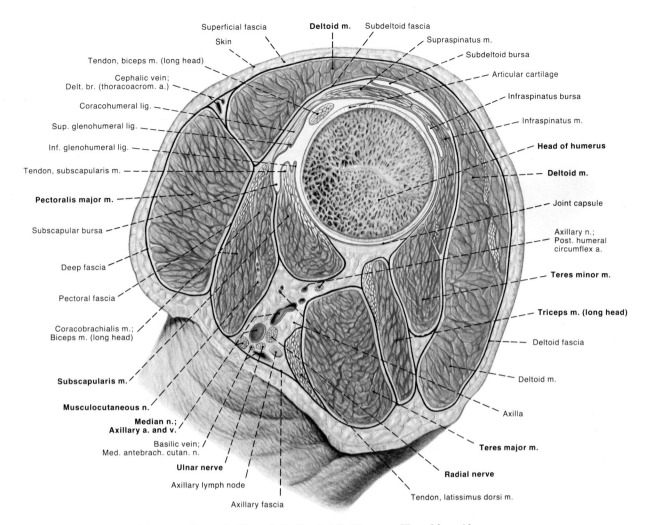

Fig. 63: Cross Section of the Right Upper Extremity Through the Head of the Humerus, Viewed from Above

Superficial fascia
Skin
Deltoid m.
Subdeltoid fascia
Supraspinatus m.
Subdeltoid bursa
Articular cartilage
Infraspinatus bursa
Infraspinatus m.
Head of humerus
Deltoid m.
Joint capsule
Axillary n.;
Post. humeral circumflex a.
Teres minor m.
Triceps m. (long head)
Deltoid fascia
Deltoid m.
Axilla
Teres major m.
Radial nerve
Tendon, latissimus dorsi m.

Tendon, biceps m. (long head)
Cephalic vein;
Delt. br. (thoracoacrom. a.)
Coracohumeral lig.
Sup. glenohumeral lig.
Inf. glenohumeral lig.
Tendon, subscapularis m.
Pectoralis major m.
Subscapular bursa
Deep fascia
Pectoral fascia
Coracobrachialis m.;
Biceps m. (long head)
Subscapularis m.
Musculocutaneous n.
Median n.;
Axillary a. and v.
Basilic vein;
Med. antebrach. cutan. n.
Ulnar nerve
Axillary lymph node
Axillary fascia

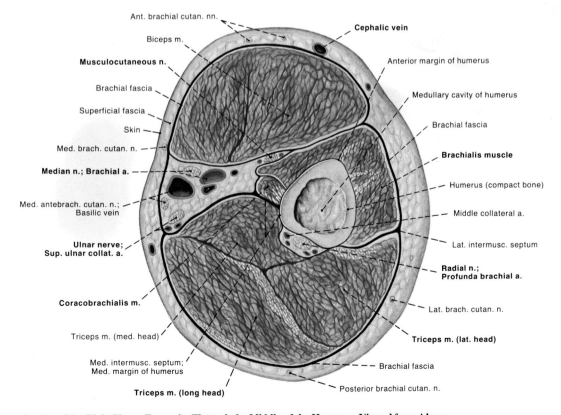

Fig. 64: Cross Section of the Right Upper Extremity Through the Middle of the Humerus, Viewed from Above

Ant. brachial cutan. nn.
Biceps m.
Musculocutaneous n.
Brachial fascia
Superficial fascia
Skin
Med. brach. cutan. n.
Median n.; Brachial a.
Med. antebrach. cutan. n.;
Basilic vein
Ulnar nerve;
Sup. ulnar collat. a.
Coracobrachialis m.
Triceps m. (med. head)
Med. intermusc. septum;
Med. margin of humerus
Triceps m. (long head)

Cephalic vein
Anterior margin of humerus
Medullary cavity of humerus
Brachial fascia
Brachialis muscle
Humerus (compact bone)
Middle collateral a.
Lat. intermusc. septum
Radial n.;
Profunda brachial a.
Lat. brach. cutan. n.
Triceps m. (lat. head)
Brachial fascia
Posterior brachial cutan. n.

Figs. 63, 64   I

Triceps m. (med. head)

Med. intermuscular septum

Bicipital aponeurosis

Medial epicondyle

Antebrachial fascia

Superficial ant. forearm muscles

Flexor carpi ulnaris m.

Palmaris longus m.

Flex. carpi radialis m.

Flex. digitorum superficialis m.

Tendon, Flex. carpi ulnaris m.

Tendon, palmaris longus m.

Tendon, Flex. carpi radialis m.

Biceps m.

Brachialis m.

Tendon, Biceps m.

Brachioradialis m.

Ext. carpi radialis longus m.

Ext. carpi radialis brevis m.

Flex. digitorum superficialis m.

Abd. pollicis longus m.

Tendon, Brachioradialis m.

Flex. pollicis longus m.

Tendon, Abd. pollicis longus m.

Pronator quadratus m.

Extensor retinaculum

Triceps m. (med. head)

Med. intermuscular septum

Med. epicondyle

Flex. carpi ulnaris m.

Palmaris longus m.

Humeroulnar head, Flex. digit. superf. m.

Flex. carpi radialis m.

Flex. digitorum superficialis m.

Tendon, Flex. carpi ulnaris m.

Tendon, Palmaris longus m.

Tendon, Flex. carpi radialis m.

Brachialis m.

Tendon, Brachialis m.

Brachioradialis m.

Supinator m.

Bicipitoradial bursa

Tendon, Biceps m.

Ext. carpi radialis longus m.

Pronator teres m.

Radial head, Flex. digitorum superficialis m.

Abd. pollicis longus m.

Flex. pollicis longus m.

Pronator quadratus m.

Tendon, Ext. pollicis brevis m.

Tendon, Brachioradialis m.

Fig. 65: The Left Anterior Forearm Muscles, Superficial Group

NOTE: 1) that the brachioradialis m. is studied with the posterior forearm muscles instead of the anterior muscles.

2) that the anterior forearm muscles arise from the medial epicondyle of the humerus and include the pronator teres (not labelled), flexor carpi radialis, palmaris longus and flexor carpi ulnaris. Beneath these is the flexor digitorum superficialis.

Fig. 66: The Flexor Digitorum Superficialis Muscle and Related Muscles (left)

NOTE: 1) the palmaris longus, flexor carpi radialis and tendon of the biceps have been cut to reveal the flexor digitorum superficialis and pronator teres.

2) the triangular cubital fossa is bounded medially by the superficial flexors and laterally by the extensors. Its floor is the brachialis muscle.

Figs. 65, 66

Fig. 67: Nerves and Arteries, Anterior Aspect of the Left Forearm (Superficial View)

Labels for Fig. 67 (left):
Ulnar nerve · Sup. ulnar collateral art. · Median nerve · Inf. ulnar collateral art. · Medial intermuscular septum · Medial epicondyle · Brachialis m. · Median nerve · Ulnar artery · Bicipital aponeurosis · Pronator teres muscle · Flexor carpi radialis muscle · Palmaris longus m. · Flexor carpi ulnaris muscle · Flexor digitorum superficialis muscle · Ulnar nerve · Ulnar artery · Palmar branch, Ulnar nerve · Dorsal branch, Ulnar nerve · Ulnar nerve · Dorsal carpal br., Ulnar artery

Biceps m. · Brachial art. · Radial nerve · Brachio-radialis m. · Rad. collateral art. · Bicipital aponeurosis · Deep branch, Radial nerve · Tendon, Biceps m. · Radial a. · Superfic br., Radial nerve · Deep br., Radial nerve · Radial recurrent a. · Supinator m. · Tendon, Brachioradialis m. · Radial artery · Median nerve · Palmar branch, Median nerve · Superficial palmar br., Radial artery

Labels for Fig. 68 (right):
Brachial art. · Median n. · Med. epicondyle · Brachialis m. · Pronator teres, (Ulnar head) · Ulnar recurrent art. · Pronator teres, (Humeral head) · Median n. · Flex. carpi radialis m. · Radial head, Flex. digit. superficialis m. · Ulnar art. · Ulnar n. · Tendon, Flex. carpi ulnaris m. · Dorsal br., Ulnar n. · Dorsal carpal br., Ulnar art.

Biceps m. · Radial nerve · Deep Radial n. · Ulnar art. · Radial art. · Radial recurrent art. · Superf. branch, Radial n. · Supinator m. · Brachioradialis muscle · Common interosseus art. · Pronator teres m. · Flex. pollicis long. m. · Radial art. · Superf. br., Radial n. · Tendon, Brachioradialis m. · Palmar br., median n. · Radial art. · Tendon, Flex. carpi radialis m. · Tendon, Palmaris longus m. · Superf. palmar br., Radial art.

Fig. 68: Nerves and Arteries, Anterior Aspect of Left Forearm

Fig. 67: Nerves and Arteries, Anterior Aspect of the Left Forearm (Superficial View)

NOTE: 1) the bicipital aponeurosis has been reflected to reveal the underlying median nerve, brachial artery, and tendon of insertion of the biceps brachii muscle.

2) the brachioradialis muscle has been pulled laterally (toward the radial side) in order to expose the course of the radial artery and the division of the radial nerve into its superficial and deep branches.

3) that the radial artery, as it descends in the forearm, courses anterior to the tendon of the biceps brachii muscle, the supinator muscle, the tendon of insertion of the pronator teres, and the belly of the flexor pollicis longus (the latter not labelled in this figure, but see Fig. 68).

Fig. 68: Nerves and Arteries, Anterior Aspect of Left Forearm

NOTE: 1) the pronator teres and flexor carpi radialis muscles are reflected just below the cubital fossa to reveal the origins of the ulnar and radial arteries.

2) at the wrist, the flexor carpi ulnaris muscle is severed to expose the ulnar nerve and artery.

3) that the median nerve lies deep to the flexor digitorum superficialis throughout much of its course in the forearm, but just above the wrist it usually becomes visible between the tendons, with the flexor pollicis longus and flexor carpi radialis on its radial side and the tendons of the palmaris longus and flexor digitorum superficialis on its ulnar side.

Figs. 67, 68   **I**

Fig. 69: The Left Anterior Forearm Muscles, Deep Group

NOTE: 1) the superficial anterior forearm muscles have been removed to reveal the three muscles of the deep group. These include the flexor digitorum profundus, the flexor pollicis longus and the pronator quadratus.

2) the pronator quadratus is a small quadrangular muscle situated at the distal end of the forearm beneath the tendons of the flexor digitorum profundus and flexor pollicis longus. It is only partially shown in this dissection and can better be seen in Fig. 114.

3) the tendons of the flexor digitorum profundus to the ring and little fingers and the middle and index fingers appear to be fused at the wrist, as if they were two structures rather than four.

Fig. 70: Nerves and Arteries of Left Anterior Forearm (Deep Dissection)

NOTE the division of the brachial artery into the radial and ulnar. The common interosseous artery branches from the ulnar artery and divides immediately into anterior and posterior interosseous arteries. Observe the courses of the median and ulnar nerves.

Figs. 69, 70

Fig. 71: **Nerves and Arteries at the Elbow (Medial View)**

NOTE: the ulnar nerve enters the forearm directly behind the medial epicondyle.

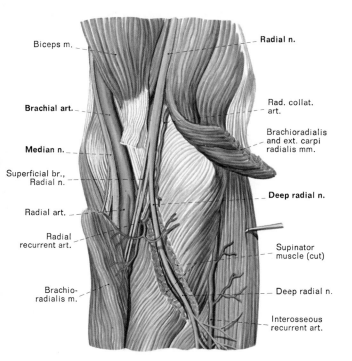

Fig. 72: **Nerves and Arteries at the Elbow (Lateral View)**

NOTE: the deep radial nerve passes into the forearm in front of the lateral part of the elbow joint. It then courses dorsally through the supinator muscle to supply the posterior forearm muscles.

Fig. 73: **A Brachial Arteriogram Showing the Origins of the Vessels that Supply the Elbow and Forearm**

1. Profunda brachii artery
2. Brachial artery
3. Superior ulnar collateral artery
4. Radial collateral artery
5. Inferior ulnar collateral artery
6. Radial recurrent artery
7. Radial artery
8. Ulnar artery
9. Ulnar recurrent artery
10. Recurrent interosseous artery
11. Common interosseous artery
12. Posterior interosseous artery
13. Anterior interosseous artery

Brachialis m.

Brachio-
radialis m.

Ext. carpi
radialis
longus m.

Lat. epi-
condyle

Antebrachial
fascia

Ext. carpi
radialis
brevis m.

Antebrachial
fascia

Ext. digi-
torum m.

Abductor
pollicis
long. m.

Ext. pollicis
brevis m.

Tendons,
Ext. carpi
radialis long.
and brev. mm.

Lat. inter-
muscular septum

Triceps m.
(med. head)

Triceps m.
(med. head)

Tendon,
Triceps m.

Olecranon

Anconeus m.

Flex. carpi
ulnaris m.

Ext. carpi
ulnaris m.

Ext. digiti
minimi m.

Tendon, Ext.
carpi ulnaris m.

Ulna, Distal
extremity

Ext. digitorum m.

Extensor
retinaculum

Biceps m.

Brachialis m.

Brachio-
radialis m.

Ext. carpi
rad. long. m.

Lat. epi-
condyle

Ext. carpi
rad. brev. m.

Tendon, Brachio-
radialis m.

Tendon,
Ext. carpi
rad. long m.

Tendon,
Ext. carpi rad.
brev. m.

Abd. pollicis
long. m.

Ext. pollicis
brevis m.

Tendon, Abd. pol-
licis long m

Tendon, Ext. pol-
licis brev. m.

Tendons, Ext. carpi rad.
long. and brev. mm.

Radius

Triceps m.

Triceps m.
(lat. head)

Lat. inter-
muscular septum

Triceps m.
(med. head)

Tendon,
Triceps m.

Olecranon

Anconeus m.

Flex. carpi
ulnaris m.

Ext. digitorum m

Ext. digiti
minimi m.

Ext. carpi
ulnaris m.

Ext. pollicis
long. m.

Extensor
retinaculum

Fig. 74: Posterior Muscles of the Left Forearm, Superficial Group

NOTE that most of the superficial extensor muscles arise from the lateral epicondyle of the humerus. These are the extensor carpi radialis brevis, the extensor digitorum, the extensor digiti minimi and the extensor carpi ulnaris. The brachioradialis and extensor carpi radialis longus arise from the supracondylar ridge.

Fig. 75: Posterior Muscles (Superficial) of the Left Forearm, Lateral View

NOTE: 1) the superficial location of the brachioradialis muscle.

2) three muscles of the thumb: extensor pollicis longus, extensor pollicis brevis and abductor pollicis longus.

3) the closely investing extensor retinaculum under which the extensor tendons pass into the dorsum of the hand.

Figs. 74, 75

Fig. 76: Nerves and Arteries of the Left Posterior Forearm

NOTE: 1) the extensor digiti minimi and extensor digitorum have been separated from the extensor carpi ulnaris to expose the deep radial nerve and posterior interosseous artery coursing inferiorly in the posterior forearm.

2) the anastomoses at the elbow and wrist.

Fig. 77: The Thumb Muscles of the Left Posterior Forearm

NOTE: 1) that the three thumb muscles (abductor pollicis longus and extensors pollicis brevis and longus) are exposed when the extensor digitorum and extensor digiti minimi muscles are partially removed. Observe also the extensor indicis muscle coursing to the index finger.

2) the tendon compartments formed by the extensor retinaculum at the wrist.

Figs. 76, 77   I

Fig. 78: Nerves and Arteries of the Left Posterior Forearm (Deep Dissection)

NOTE: 1) the extensor digitorum muscle is separated from the extensor carpi radialis brevis and pulled medially to reveal the posterior interosseous artery and deep radial nerve.

2) the emergence of the deep radial nerve to the posterior forearm through the supinator muscle.

3) the posterior interosseous nerve is a continuation inferiorly of the deep radial nerve and may be seen coursing deep to the extensor pollicis longus muscle. This muscle has been cut at the wrist in this dissection.

Fig. 79: The Left Posterior Forearm Muscles, Deep Group

NOTE: 1) all of the superficial posterior forearm muscles have been removed except the anconeus. The five deep muscles are the supinator, abductor pollicis longus, extensors pollicis brevis and longus and extensor indicis.

2) the supinator is a broad muscle, arising from the lateral epicondyle of the humerus and from the ridge of the ulna. It courses obliquely to insert around the upper third of the radius.

Figs. 78, 79

Fig. 80: Bones of the Right Forearm Showing Attachments of Muscles (Anterior View)

Labels (Fig. 80, left):
- Brachioradialis m.
- Brachialis m.
- Ext. carpi radialis long. m.
- Articularis cubiti m. (brachialis)
- Pronator teres m. (humeral head)
- Ext. carpi radialis brev. m.
- Common flexor tendon
- Flex. digit. superficialis m.
- Pronator teres m. (ulnar head)
- Brachialis m.
- Flex. digit. superficialis m.
- Oblique cord
- Biceps m.
- Supinator m.
- Flex. carpi ulnaris m. (aponeurotic ulnar origin)
- Flex. digit. superficialis m. (radial head)
- Pronator teres m.
- Interosseous membrane
- Flex. digit. profundus m.
- Flex. pollicis long. m.
- Pronator quadratus m.
- Brachioradialis m.
- Pronator quadratus m.

Fig. 81: Bones of the Right Forearm Showing the Attachments of Muscles (Posterior View)

Labels (Fig. 81, right):
- Med. intermuscular septum
- Triceps m. (med. head)
- Brachioradialis m.
- Articularis cubiti (triceps)
- Triceps m.
- Med. epicondyle
- Common flexor origin
- Anconeus m.
- Flex. carpi ulnaris m.
- Ext. carpi radialis long. m.
- Lat. epicondyle
- Ext. carpi radialis brev. m.
- Ext. digitorum m.
- Ext. carpi ulnaris m.
- Course of deep radial nerve
- Supinator m.
- Flex. digit. profundus m.
- Ext. carpi ulnaris m.
- Pronator teres m.
- Abductor pollicis long. m.
- Ext. pollicis long. m.
- Ext. pollicis brevis m.
- Ext. indicis m.
- Abductor pollicis long. m.
- Ext. pollicis brevis m.
- Ext. digiti minimi m.
- Ext. pollicis long. m.
- Ext. digitorum m.
- Ext. carpi radialis long. m.
- Ext. carpi ulnaris m.
- Ext. carpi radialis brevis m.

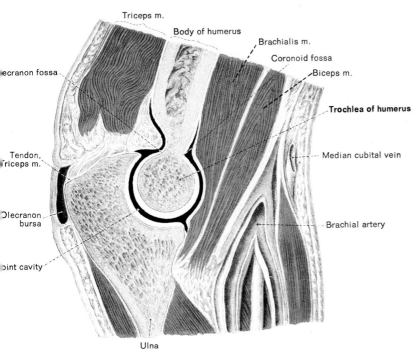

Labels (Fig. 82):
- Triceps m.
- Body of humerus
- Brachialis m.
- Coronoid fossa
- Biceps m.
- Olecranon fossa
- **Trochlea of humerus**
- Tendon, Triceps m.
- Median cubital vein
- Olecranon bursa
- Joint cavity
- Brachial artery
- Ulna

Fig. 82: Sagittal Section of the Left Elbow Joint

NOTE: 1) the trochlea of the humerus articulates with the trochlear notch of the ulna to form a ginglymus or hinge joint. The adaptation of these two articular surfaces is such that only flexion and extension can take place and not lateral displacement.

2) the posterior aspect of the olecranon process is separated from the skin by a subcutaneous bursa, and the insertion of the triceps on the olecranon.

3) that the brachialis muscle lies immediately adjacent to the joint capsule anteriorly, and courses to insert on the roughened depression on the anterior surface of the coronoid process and onto the tuberosity of the ulna.

4) fractures of the distal extremity of the humerus most frequently occur from falls on the outstretched hand because the resulting force is transmitted through the bones of the forearm to the brachium, while fracture of the olecranon generally results from direct trauma to the bone by a fall on the point of the elbow. Posterior dislocation of the ulna and attached radius is the most common dislocation at the elbow joint, again frequently from falls on the outstretched and abducted hand.

Figs. 80, 81, 82   I

Figs. 83 and 84: The Left Humerus

NOTE: 1) the humerus consists of a body and two extremities. The head of the humerus is shaped as a hemisphere and articulates with the scapula at the glenoid cavity.

2) the anatomical neck is a constricted zone just distal to the head of the humerus, and the surgical neck, where fractures frequently occur, lies just below the two tubercles.

3) the greater and lesser tubercles are roughened prominences which allow the insertion of muscles: the supraspinatus, infraspinatus, and the teres minor on the greater tubercle and the subscapularis on the lesser.

4) within the intertubercular sulcus passes the tendon of the long head of the biceps.

5) adjacent to the radial groove courses the radial nerve, which is therefore endangered by fractures of the humerus. If the radial nerve does become injured by a fracture, a clinical condition called *wrist drop* develops because this nerve supplies all the extensors of the wrist and fingers.

6) the distal extremity affords articulation with the radius and ulna; the rounded capitulum (Fig. 84) articulates with the head of the radius, while the grooved trochlea fits into the trochlear notch of the ulna.

7) the radial fossa above the capitulum (Fig. 84) within which the radial head is received upon flexion of the forearm. Additionally, note the coronoid fossa which receives the coronoid process of the ulna.

8) the olecranon fossa (Fig. 83) for the olecranon process of the ulna. Finally, observe the medial and lateral epicondyles which allow attachment of muscles.

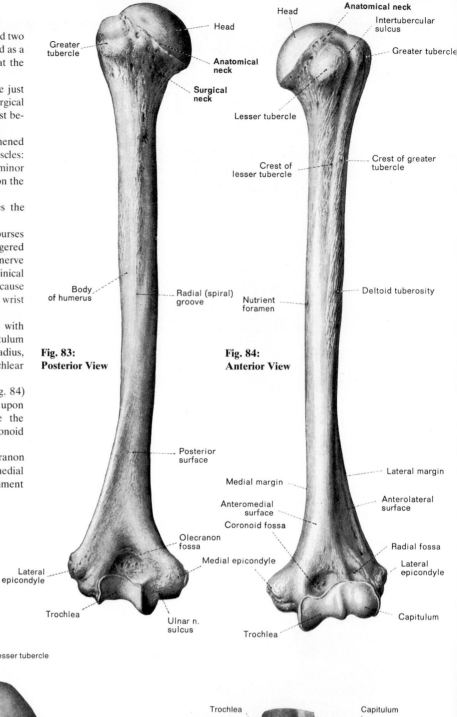

Fig. 83: Posterior View

Fig. 84: Anterior View

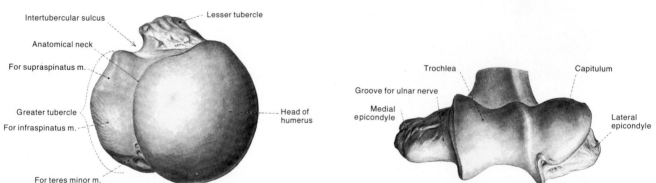

Fig. 85: The Head of the Left Humerus, Viewed from Above

NOTE the sequential sites of attachment for the supraspinatus muscle, infraspinatus muscle, and teres minor muscle on the greater tubercle. The humeral head is coated with hyaline cartilage, which is more abundant in the central part and becomes thinner nearer the circumference.

Fig. 86: The Distal Extremity of the Left Humerus, Viewed from Below

NOTE that the medial epicondyle is larger than the lateral epicondyle and affords attachment for the flexor muscles in the anterior forearm compartment. The ulnar nerve courses along a groove on the dorsal surface of the medial epicondyle and enters the forearm between the two heads of the flexor carpi ulnaris.

Figs. 83–86

Fig. 87: Anterior Fig. 88: Lateral Fig. 89: Anterior Fig. 90: Posterior

Figs. 87–90 I

The Left Ulna (Figs. 87 and 88)

NOTE: 1) the ulna is the medial bone of the forearm. It presents a superior extremity, a body or shaft and an inferior extremity.

2) the superior extremity is marked by two processes, the olecranon and coronoid processes and two concave cavities, the radial notch for articulation with the radius, and the trochlear notch which serves for articulation with the trochlea of the humerus. The brachialis muscle inserts on the tuberosity of the ulna.

3) the tapering body of the ulna affords attachment of the interosseous membrane. The distal extremity is marked by the head of the ulna laterally, and the styloid process postero-medially. The head of the ulna is attached to an articular disc which, in turn, articulates with the triquetral bone. Onto the styloid process of the ulna is attached the ulnar collateral ligament of the wrist joint.

The Left Radius (Figs. 89 and 90)

NOTE: 1) the radius is situated lateral to the ulna in the forearm. It has a body and two extremities. The proximal extremity articulates with both the humerus and ulna. The larger distal extremity articulates inferiorly with the carpal bones (scaphoid, lunate and triquetrum) and medially with the ulna.

2) the proximal extremity is marked by a cylindrical head which articulates with both the capitulum of the humerus and the radial notch of the ulna. Just beneath the neck on the anteromedial aspect is found the radial tuberosity on which is inserted the biceps tendon.

3) the interosseous membrane is attached along the interosseous crest of the shaft.

4) the styloid process distally gives attachment to the brachioradialis muscle and the radial collateral ligament of the radiocarpal joint.

Fig. 91: The Left Elbow Joint, Anterior View

NOTE: 1) the elbow joint is a hinge (ginglymus) joint in which the trochlear notch of the ulna receives the trochlea of the humerus, and the shallow fovea on the head of radius articulates with the capitulum of the humerus.

2) the entire joint is encased by an articular capsule which tends to be loose to allow flexion and extension of the forearm. The capsule is thickened medially by the ulnar collateral ligament and laterally by the radial collateral ligament.

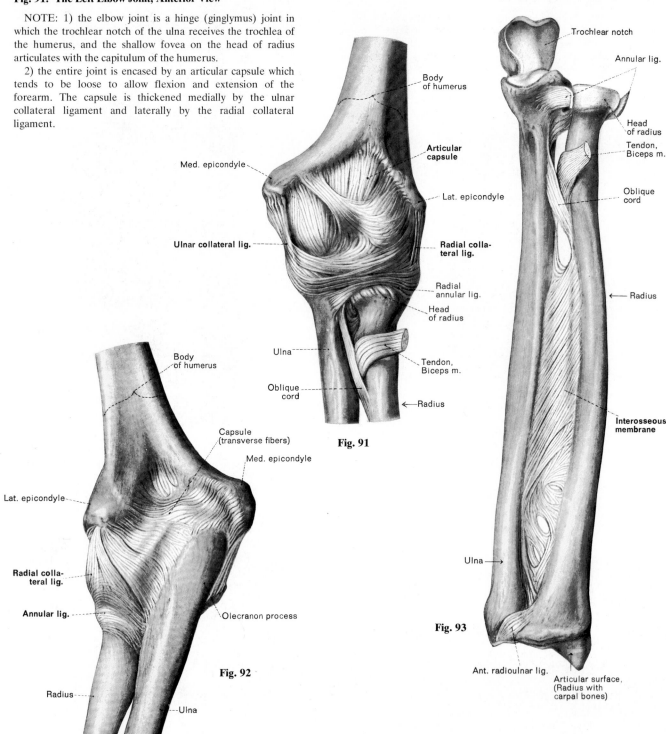

Fig. 91

Fig. 92

Fig. 93

Fig. 92: The Left Elbow Joint, Posterolateral View

NOTE: 1) the fan-shaped form of the radial collateral ligament. It attaches superiorly to the lateral epicondyle and blends inferiorly with the capsule of the joint.

2) the superior portion of the radial annular ligament also blends with the articular capsule.

3) the transverse fibers of the articular capsule forming a band between the medial and lateral epicondyles and bridging the olecranon fossa.

Fig. 93: Radioulnar Joints, Anterior View (left)

NOTE: 1) articulations between the radius and ulna occur proximally, along the shafts of the two bones and distally.

2) the proximal joint is a pivot (trochoid) type joint and consists of the head of the radius which rotates within the radial notch of the ulna. This joint is protected by the lower part of the capsule of the elbow joint and by an underlying annular ligament attached at both ends to the ulna and forming a circular band around the head of the radius.

3) the broad, fibrous interosseous membrane extends obliquely between the bones, while distally the head of the ulna articulates with the ulnar notch of the radius.

Figs. 91, 92, 93

Fig. 94: Roentgenogram of the Elbow Joint of 5½ Year Old Boy

NOTE: 1) the shaft of a long bone is called the *diaphysis* while a center of ossification, distinct from the shaft and usually at the extremity of a long bone, is known as an *epiphysis*.

2) the epiphysis of the head of the radius is as yet not formed in the 5½-year old, while ossification has commenced in the humeral capitulum.

Diaphysis of humerus

Epiphysis of capitulum (humerus)

Coronoid process (ulna)

Ulnar diaphysis

Radial diaphysis

Diaphysis of humerus

Epiphyseal line

Capitulum of humerus

Head of radius

Epiphyseal line

Radial diaphysis

Epiphyseal line

Epiphysis of med. epicondyle

Olecranon process

Ulnar diaphysis

Fig. 95: Roentgenogram of the Elbow Joint of 17 Year Old Male

NOTE: 1) an epiphyseal line (containing cartilage) can be identified in roentgenograms at the plane of junction between the main part of a bone and independently ossifying centers, the epiphyses.

2) by the 17th year ossification of the epiphyseal centers and their coalescence to the diaphyses of the bones of the elbow joint are nearly complete.

Fig 96: Roentgenogram of the Left Elbow Joint in an Adult, Lateral Projection

NOTE the following bony structures:

1. Body of humerus	7. Body of radius
2. Radial fossa	8. Radial tuberosity
3. Olecranon fossa	9. Neck of radius
4. Medial epicondyle	10. Head of radius
5. Coronoid process of ulna	11. Capitulum of humerus
6. Trochlea of humerus	12. Trochlear notch
	13. Olecranon

Fig. 97: Roentgenogram of the Right Elbow Joint in an Adult (A–P Projection)

NOTE the following bony structures:

1. Body of humerus
2. Olecranon fossa
3. Olecranon
4. Lateral epicondyle
5. Medial epicondyle
6. Capitulum of humerus
7. Trochlea of humerus
8. Head of radius
9. Coronoid process of ulna
10. Neck of radius
11. Ulna
12. Radial tuberosity
13. Body of radius

(Figures 96 and 97 come from Wicke, L. *Atlas of Radiologic Anatomy*, 3rd Edition, Urban & Schwarzenberg, Baltimore, 1982).

Figs. 94–97   I

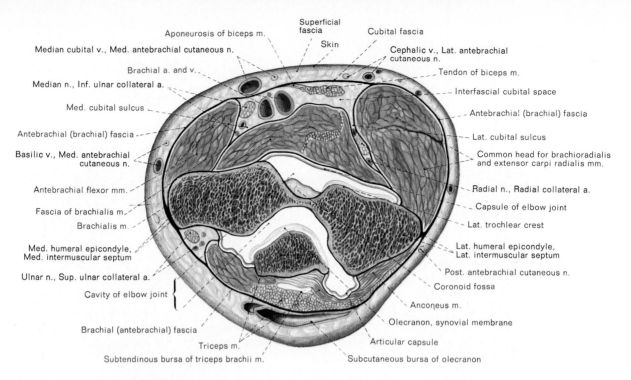

Fig. 98: Cross Section Through the Right Upper Extremity at the Level of the Elbow Joint

NOTE: 1) the position of the ulnar nerve and superior ulnar collateral artery behind the medial epicondyle of the humerus and medial to the olecranon of the ulna (see also Figs. 58, 60 and 76).

2) that the median nerve lies to the ulnar (medial) side of the brachial vein and artery in the cubital fossa (see also Figs. 54, 56 and 70), and that all three of these structures lie deep to the cubital fascia and median cubital vein (see also Figs. 40 and 41).

3) that at this level the radial nerve and radial collateral artery lie between the common origins of the brachioradialis and extensors carpi radialis longus and brevis muscles *and* the deeply located brachialis muscle, which is about to insert on the ulna (see also Figs. 67 and 68).

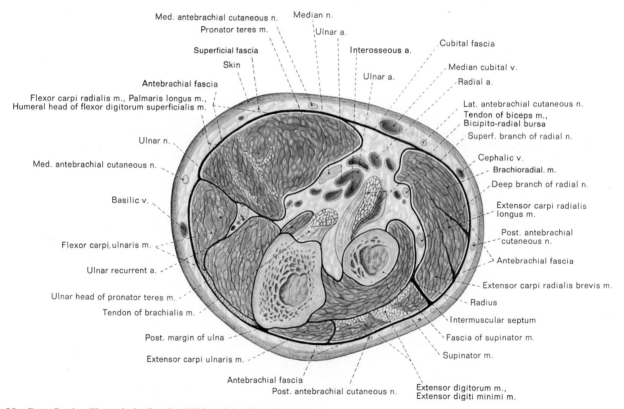

Fig. 99: Cross Section Through the Proximal Third of the Right Forearm

NOTE: 1) that this section is cut at the level at which the common interosseous artery branches from the ulnar artery (see also Fig. 70), and at the sites at which the tendons of insertion of the biceps brachii and brachialis muscles attach to the radius and ulna, respectively (see also Fig. 80).

2) that at this level the radial nerve has already divided into its superficial and deep branches (see also Fig. 67 and 68) and that the ulnar nerve lies under cover of the flexor carpi ulnaris (see also Fig. 70).

Figs. 98, 99

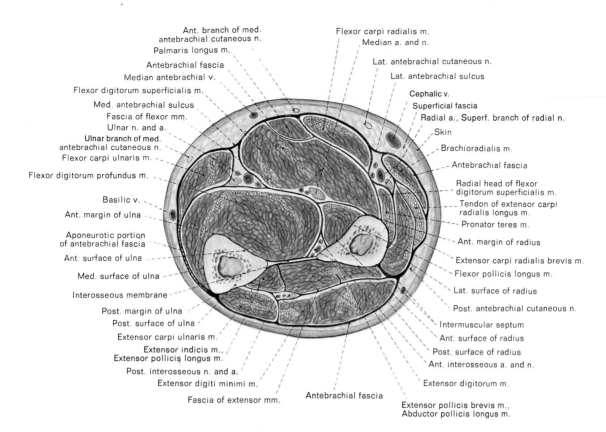

Ant. branch of med. antebrachial cutaneous n.
Palmaris longus m.
Antebrachial fascia
Median antebrachial v.
Flexor digitorum superficialis m.
Med. antebrachial sulcus
Fascia of flexor mm.
Ulnar n. and a.
Ulnar branch of med. antebrachial cutaneous n.
Flexor carpi ulnaris m.
Flexor digitorum profundus m.
Basilic v.
Ant. margin of ulna
Aponeurotic portion of antebrachial fascia
Ant. surface of ulna
Med. surface of ulna
Interosseous membrane
Post. margin of ulna
Post. surface of ulna
Extensor carpi ulnaris m.
Extensor indicis m., Extensor pollicis longus m.
Post. interosseous n. and a.
Extensor digiti minimi m.
Fascia of extensor mm.

Flexor carpi radialis m.
Median a. and n.
Lat. antebrachial cutaneous n.
Lat. antebrachial sulcus
Cephalic v.
Superficial fascia
Radial a., Superf. branch of radial n.
Skin
Brachioradialis m.
Antebrachial fascia
Radial head of flexor digitorum superficialis m.
Tendon of extensor carpi radialis longus m.
Pronator teres m.
Ant. margin of radius
Extensor carpi radialis brevis m.
Flexor pollicis longus m.
Lat. surface of radius
Post. antebrachial cutaneous n.
Intermuscular septum
Ant. surface of radius
Post. surface of radius
Ant. interosseous a. and n.
Extensor digitorum m.

Antebrachial fascia
Extensor pollicis brevis m., Abductor pollicis longus m.

Fig. 100: Cross Section Through the Middle Third of the Right Forearm

NOTE: 1) that in the middle of the forearm, the ulna, radius, interosseous membrane, and intermuscular septa quite clearly delineate the posterior compartment, extending posteriorly and laterally, from the anterior compartment (located anteriorly and medially).

2) the median nerve coursing down the forearm deep to the flexor digitorum superficialis and anterior to the flexor digitorum profundus and flexor pollicis longus (see also Figs. 68–70).

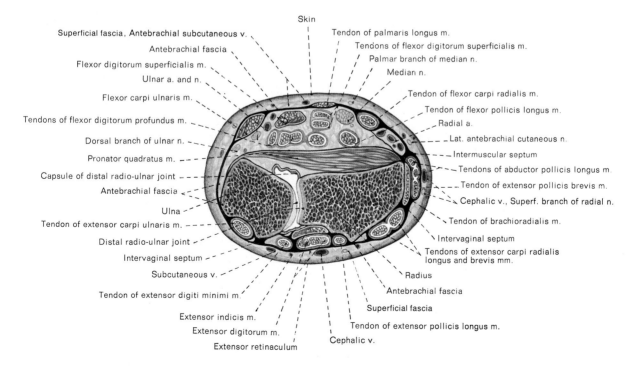

Skin
Superficial fascia, Antebrachial subcutaneous v.
Antebrachial fascia
Flexor digitorum superficialis m.
Ulnar a. and n.
Flexor carpi ulnaris m.
Tendons of flexor digitorum profundus m.
Dorsal branch of ulnar n.
Pronator quadratus m.
Capsule of distal radio-ulnar joint
Antebrachial fascia
Ulna
Tendon of extensor carpi ulnaris m.
Distal radio-ulnar joint
Intervaginal septum
Subcutaneous v.
Tendon of extensor digiti minimi m.
Extensor indicis m.
Extensor digitorum m.
Extensor retinaculum

Tendon of palmaris longus m.
Tendons of flexor digitorum superficialis m.
Palmar branch of median n.
Median n.
Tendon of flexor carpi radialis m.
Tendon of flexor pollicis longus m.
Radial a.
Lat. antebrachial cutaneous n.
Intermuscular septum
Tendons of abductor pollicis longus m.
Tendon of extensor pollicis brevis m.
Cephalic v., Superf. branch of radial n.
Tendon of brachioradialis m.
Intervaginal septum
Tendons of extensor carpi radialis longus and brevis mm.
Radius
Antebrachial fascia
Superficial fascia
Tendon of extensor pollicis longus m.
Cephalic v.

Fig. 101: Cross Section Through the Distal Third of the Right Forearm

NOTE: 1) that at this level the ulnar nerve has already given off its dorsal branch, which supplies the ulnar part of the dorsum of the hand and the dorsal surfaces of the little finger and half of the ring finger (see also Fig. 102).

2) the extreme vulnerability of the ulnar nerve and artery, median nerve, radial artery, as well as all of the flexor tendons on the anterior aspect of the wrist (see also Fig. 68), and the extensor tendons and cephalic vein dorsally.

Dorsal digital
nerves

Cephalic vein

Intercapitular
veins

Dorsal venous
network

Dorsal branch,
Ulnar n.

Basilic vein

Post antebrach.
cutan. nn. (from radial)

**Superficial branch,
Radial n.**

Cephalic
vein

Tendons,
Ext. digi-
torum m.

1st dorsal
interosseous m.

Intertendinous
connections

Synov. sheath,
Ext. digiti
minimi

Synov. sheath,
Ext. carpi
ulnaris

Common
synov. sheath,
Ext. digitorum
and ext.
indicis

Synov. sheath,
Ext. pollicis
long.

Synov. sheaths,
Abd. pollicis long.;
Ext. pollicis brev.

**Extensor
retinaculum**

Synov. sheaths,
Ext. carpi
radialis long.
and brev. mm.

Fig. 102: Superficial Veins and Nerves of the Dorsum of the Left Hand

NOTE: 1) the *cephalic vein* originates on the radial side of the dorsum of the hand while the *basilic vein* arises on the ulnar side.

2) the *superficial radial nerve* supplies the skin of the dorsum of the radial 3½ digits, while the *dorsal branch of the ulnar nerve* supplies the dorsum of the ulnar 1½ digits.

3) the distal phalanx of the dorsum of the radial 3½ digits (not dissected) receives cutaneous innervation from the median nerve while the same region on the ulnar 1½ digits is supplied by the ulnar nerve.

4) all of the structures depicted in this figure pass between the forearm and the hand superficial to the extensor retinaculum.

5) that morphologic adaptation of the superficial venous drainage of the hand has resulted in a profuse venous plexus on the dorsal surface, but very few and quite small superficial veins on the palmar surface. This is obviously of advantage because of the frequent mechanical pressures to which the palmar surface of the hand and fingers is subjected.

6) that communications between adjacent branches of the radial and ulnar nerves occur frequently and that the posterior antebrachial cutaneous branches generally terminate at the wrist.

Fig. 103: Extensor Tendons and Their Synovial Sheaths, the Left Dorsal Wrist

NOTE: 1) a synovial sheath is a double-lined tubular envelope which surrounds a tendon, thereby allowing it to move more freely and with less friction beneath the retinaculum.

2) there are six such synovial compartments on the extensor surface of the wrist, from radial to ulnar: *the first* transmits the tendons of the extensor pollicis brevis and the abductor pollicis longus; *the second*, the extensor carpi radialis longus and brevis; *the third*, the extensor pollicis longus; *the fourth*, the extensor digitorum and extensor indicis; *the fifth*, the extensor digiti minimi; *the sixth*, the extensor carpi ulnaris.

3) the compartments commence just proximal and terminate somewhat distal to the extensor retinaculum.

Figs. 102, 103

Palmar digital aa.
(dorsum branches)

Dors. digital aa.

Dorsal metacarpal aa.

Dorsal digital
artery
(of thumb)

1st dorsal interos-
seous m.

Dorsal digital
nerve (of thumb)

Tendon,
Ext. pollicis
brev. m.

**Tendon,
Ext. pollicis
long. m.**

Radial artery

Dors.
carpal br.,
radial art.

Radial artery

Tendon,
Ext. carpi rad.
long. m.

Tendon, Ext. carpi
rad. brev. m.

**Tendons,
Ext. digitorum m.**

Dors. carpal br.,
Ulnar art.

Ext. retinaculum

Dors. carpal network

Fig. 104: Tendons, Arteries and Digital Nerves. Dorsum of the Left Hand

NOTE: 1) that the radial artery achieves the dorsum of the hand by passing deep to the tendons of the extensors pollicis brevis and longus muscles.

2) the radial artery is the principal source of blood supply to the dorsum of the hand. From its dorsal carpal branch stem the dorsal metacarpal arteries which, in turn, divide into the digital branches.

3) the dorsal digital artery of the thumb comes directly from the radial, while the ulnar side of the little finger receives blood from the ulnar artery through its dorsal carpal branch. Three slender dorsal metacarpal arteries arise directly from the dorsal carpal branch of radial artery and course distally on the surface of the 2nd, 3rd, and 4th dorsal interosseous muscles.

4) the distal portions of the dorsal aspect of the digits receive both arterial and nerve branches which curve around to the dorsum from the palmar aspect of the fingers.

Dorsal metacarpal aa.

Adductor
pollicis m.

Tendon,
Ext. pollicis
long. m.

1st. dorsal
interosseous
muscle

**Princeps pollicis
artery**

**Perforating br.,
Radial art.**

Radial artery

Dors. carpal br.,
Radial art.

Dorsal carpal
network

Extensor
retinaculum

Tendons,
abductor pollicis
long. m.

Ext. pollicis
brevis m.

Dorsal
carpal br.,
Ulnar art.

Post. interos-
seous br.,
Deep radial n.

Post. br.,
ant. interos-
seous art.

Ext. carpi ulnaris m.

Interosseous
membrane

Perforating br.,
Ant. interosseous art.

Fig. 105: Arteries of the Left Dorsal Wrist and Hand, Deep View

NOTE: 1) the extensor retinaculum and most of the tendons of the extensor muscles have been cut in order to reveal the radial artery and its branches at the dorsal wrist and hand.

2) the transverse course of the dorsal carpal artery after it branches from the radial and its anastomosis with branches from the anterior interosseous and ulnar arteries.

3) the course of the princeps pollicis artery dorsal to the adductor pollicis muscle and between that muscle and the 1st dorsal interosseous muscle.

4) the manner in which the dorsal metacarpal arteries divide to form dorsal digital vessels.

Figs. 104, 105   **I**

Transverse fascicles

Superf. trans. metacarpal lig.

Proper palmar digit. aa.

Common palmar digit. aa.

Proper palmar digit. nn.

Cutaneous branches, Median and ulnar nn.

Cutan. br., Ulnar n.

Palmaris brevis m.

Ulnar nerve

Ulnar artery

Antebrachial fascia

Palmar cutan. branches, ulnar nerve

Proper palmar digit. a. (to thumb)

Palmar aponeurosis

Lat. antebrach. cutan. n.

Palmar branch, Median n.

Fig. 106: Superficial Nerves and Arteries of the Palm of the Left Hand

NOTE: 1) the thick fibrous longitudinally oriented, palmar aponeurosis which protects the palmar vessels and nerves and which strengthens the deep fascia in the midportion of the palm. It is a direct continuation of the tendon of the palmaris longus.

2) the radial two-thirds of the palm is innervated by the median nerve, while the ulnar one-third is supplied by the ulna nerve.

3) the more superficial exposure of the vessels and nerves in the distal palm where the palmar aponeurosis is deficient.

1st lumbrical m.

Syn. sheaths of digit. tendons

Syn. sheath of flexor tendons (ulnar bursa)

Opponens d minimi m.

Adductor pollicis muscle

Abductor pollicis brevis m.

Syn. sheath, Flex. pollicis longus m. (radial bursa)

Opponens pollicis m.

Syn. sheath, Flex. carpi radialis m.

Synov. sheath Abd. pollicis long.

Abductor digit. minimi m.

Flexor retinaculum

Tendon Flex. carpi ulnaris m.

Syn. sheath of flexor tendons (ulnar bursa)

Syn. sheath of flex. pollicis longus (radial bursa)

Fig. 107: Muscles, Synovial Sheaths and Tendons Left Wrist and Palm

NOTE: 1) the long flexor tendons enter the palmar aspect of the hand beneath the flexor retinaculum through the carpal tunnel. The median nerve also traverses the tunnel but is not shown in this figure.

2) two synovial-lined tendon compartments pass from the forearm into the hand. The larger of the two (the ulnar bursa) contains the tendons of the superficial and deep flexor muscles, while the smaller one (the radial bursa) contains the tendon of the flexor pollicis longus. A third compartment containing the tendon of the flexor carpi radialis does not pass into the hand but terminates at the wrist.

3) although the ulnar bursa continues into the little finger, the sheaths of the index, middle and ring fingers are interrupted at the metacarpophalangeal joint.

Figs. 106, 107

Tendon, Flex. digitorum profundus m.

Fibrous digital sheath, Cruciform part

Fibrous digital sheath, Anular part

Tendon, Flex. digitorum superficialis m.

Palmar interosseous mm.

Fibrous digital sheath, Anular part

Dorsal interosseous mm.

Tendon sheath, Flex. pollicis long. m.

Transverse head ⎱ Adductor
Oblique head ⎰ pollicis m.

Flex. pollicis brevis m.

Tendons, Flex. digitorum superficialis m.

Abductor pollicis brevis m.

Synovial sheath, Flexor tendons

Opponens pollicis m.

Opening in flexor synovial sheath

Flexor retinaculum

Tendon, Abductor pollicis longus m.

Radial foveola

Synovial sheath, Flexor carpi radialis tendon

Synovial sheath, Flexor pollicis long. tendon

Deep fascia (volar carpal ligament)

Tendon, Palmaris longus m.

Tendon, Abductor pollicis long. m.

Radial artery

Pronator quadratus m.

Probe traversing carpal canal

Tendon, Flex. digit. profundus m.

Vinculum

Crossed insertion fibers, (Flex. digit. superficialis tendon)

Tendon, Flex. digit. superficialis m.

Tendon, Flex. digit. profundus m.

Tendon, Flex. digit. superficialis m.

Fibrous sheath, Digiti minimi

Deep transverse metacarpal lig.

Lumbrical muscles (four)

Synovial sheath, Digiti minimi

Opponens digit. minimi m.

Flex. digit. minimi brev. m.

Abductor digiti minimi m.

Hamulus of hamate bone

Pisiform bone

Tendon, Flex. carpi ulnaris m.

Synovial sheath, Flexor tendons

Tendons, Flex. digitorum superficialis m.

Ulnar nerve, artery and vein

Median nerve

Tendon, Flex. carpi radialis m.

Fig. 108: Muscles of the Right Hand

NOTE: 1) how the flexor digit. profundus achieves its insertion on the distal phalanx. The tendon of the flexor digit. superficialis divides into two slips, allowing the corresponding deep flexor tendon to pass.

2) that along the fingers, the tendons are encased in a synovial sheath and then they are bound by both crossed and transverse (cruciate and annular) fibrous sheaths.

3) the muscles of the thenar eminence: abductor pollicis brevis, flexor pollicis brevis and the underlying opponens pollicis muscle.

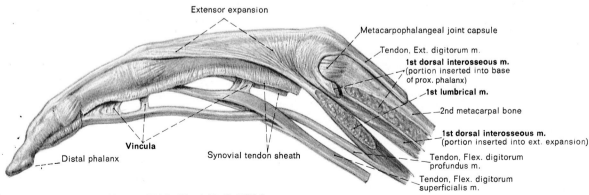

Extensor expansion

Metacarpophalangeal joint capsule

Tendon, Ext. digitorum m.

1st dorsal interosseous m. (portion inserted into base of prox. phalanx)

1st lumbrical m.

2nd metacarpal bone

1st dorsal interosseous m. (portion inserted into ext. expansion)

Tendon, Flex. digitorum profundus m.

Tendon, Flex. digitorum superficialis m.

Vincula

Distal phalanx

Synovial tendon sheath

Fig. 109: Tendon Insertions, Index Finger of Right Hand (Radial Side)

NOTE: 1) the flexor digit. superficialis inserts on the middle phalanx while the flexor digit. profundus inserts on the distal phalanx.

2) the dorsal interosseous and lumbrical muscles join the diverging extensor fibers in the formation of the extensor expansion on the dorsum of the finger.

3) the vincula are remnants of mesotendons and attach both superficial and deep flexor tendons to the digital sheath.

Figs. 108, 109 **I**

Fig. 110: Nerves and Arteries of the Left Palm, Superficial Palmar Arch

NOTE: 1) the median nerve enters the palm beneath the flexor retinaculum and supplies the muscles of the thenar eminence: abductor pollicis brevis, opponens pollicis and flexor pollicis brevis (superficial head). Additionally, it supplies the two most lateral lumbrical muscles and the palmar surface of the lateral three and one-half fingers.

2) the superficial location of the small but important "recurrent" branch of the median nerve which supplies several of the thenar muscles. Its location, just below the deep fascia on the thenar eminence, makes it vulnerable to injury.

3) the ulnar nerve enters the palm superficial to the flexor retinaculum, supplies the medial one and one-half fingers and all the remaining musculature of the hand: three hypothenar muscles, seven interosseous muscles, two medial lumbrical muscles, the adductor pollicis and the flexor pollicis brevis (deep head).

4) the superficial palmar arch is derived principally from the ulnar artery. It crosses the palm to the radial side superficial to the nerves and tendons and is joined by a palmar branch of the radial artery. Three or four common palmar digital arteries arise from the arch, proceed distally and divide into proper palmar digital arteries which course along the fingers with corresponding digital nerves.

Fig. 111: Nerves and Arteries of the Left Palm, Deep Palmar Arch

NOTE: 1) the radial artery at the wrist courses dorsally beneath the tendons of the abductor pollicis longus and the extensors pollicis longus and brevis, through the "anatomical snuff box" (see figures 104 and 105), then passes distally to perforate to the palm of the hand through the two heads of the 1st dorsal interosseous muscle. In the palm it forms the deep palmar arch which crosses the palm to the ulnar side to unite with the deep palmar branch of the ulnar artery.

2) palmar metacarpal arteries stem from the deep arch as does the princeps pollicis artery. There is rich anastomosis between the superficial and deep palmar arches.

3) the deep branch of the ulnar nerve coursing with the deep palmar arch to supply all of the muscles in the deep palm.

4) the palmar carpal anastomosis between the ulnar and radial arteries.

Figs. 110, 111

Dorsal digital nerve to index finger (from radial n.)

Proper palmar digit. nerve (from median n.) to index finger; Radial indicis artery

Anastomosing branch to proper palmar digital artery

Dorsal metacarpal arteries

Second metacarpal bone

Tendons, Extensor digit. m.

Perfor. br., Radial a.

Tendon, Ext. carpi rad. brev. m.

Dorsal carpal br., Radial a.

Dorsal carpal network

Post. antebrach. cutan. n.

1st lumbrical m.

1st dors. interosseous m.

Adductor pollicis m.

Dorsal digital nerves and artery of thumb

Abd. pollicis brevis m.

Opponens pollicis m.

Tendon, Ext. poll. long. m.

Tendon, Ext. carp. rad. brev. m.

Tendon, Abd. poll. long. m.

Tendon, Ext. carp. rad. long. m.

Radial artery

Superficial palmar br., Radial a.

Extensor retinaculum

Synovial sheath, Flexor carpi radialis m.

Radial artery

Superficial branches, Radial nerve

Fig. 112: Superficial Nerves, Arteries and Tendons on the Radial Aspect of the Right Hand

I–IV = Synovial tendon sheaths
   I = Abductor pollicis longus and extensor pollicis brevis tendon sheaths
  II = Extensor carpi radialis longus and brevis tendon sheaths
 III = Extensor pollicis longus tendon sheath
  IV = Extensor digitorum and extensor indicis tendon sheath

NOTE: 1) that only the skin and superficial fascia have been removed in the dissection and the cutaneous nerves and superficial arteries to the thumb, radial side of the index finger, and dorsum of the hand have been preserved.

2) the superficial branches of the radial nerve to the hand (see also Figs. 41, 76 and 102). These supply the dorsum of the thumb, nearly to the tip, as well as the lateral (radial) half of the dorsum of the hand. Additionally, the radial nerve supplies the proximal part of the dorsum of the index, middle, and lateral half of the ring fingers, as far as the proximal interphalangeal joint, since the median nerve sends branches around the digits to supply the more distal parts of the fingers.

3) the distribution of the radial artery to the thumb and dorsum of the hand (see also Figs. 104 and 105). Observe the dorsal digital branch to the thumb, the radial indicis branch to the index finger, the perforating branch that penetrates between the two heads of the first dorsal interosseous muscle and the dorsal carpal branch from which the dorsal metacarpal arteries arise.

Fig. 113: An Arteriogram of the Hand

❶ Radial indicis artery
❷ Proper palmar digital arteries
❸ Common palmar digital arteries
❹ Superficial palmar arch
❺ Princeps pollicis artery
❻ Deep palmar arch
❼ Deep palmar branch of ulnar artery
❽ Ulnar artery
❾ Radial artery
❿ Anterior interosseous artery

NOTE: 1) that the radial artery (9), after crossing the palm to form the deep palmar arch (6), anastomoses with the ulnar artery (8) near the base of the 4th matacarpal bone. Frequently, this anastomosis occurs more medially near the base of the 5th metacarpal bone.

2) that the ulnar artery (8) enters the hand medial to the pisiform bone and hamulus of the hamate bone and then descends to about the mid-metacarpal level before turning radially to form the superficial palmar arch (4) (From Wicke, L., *Atlas of Radiologic Anatomy,* 3rd Edition, Urban & Schwarzenberg, Baltimore, 1982).

Dorsal inter-osseous mm. (four)

Tendon sheath, Flex. pollicis long. m.

Adductor pollicis m.

Flex. pollicis brevis m.

Abductor pollicis brevis m.

Opponens pollicis m.

Flex. pollicis brevis m.

Abductor pollicis brevis m.

Flexor retinaculum

Tendon sheath, Abductor pollicis long. m.

Deep fascia (volar carpal lig.)

Synovial sheath, Flex. carpi radialis tendon

Tendon, Flex. pollicis long. m.

Pronator quadratus m.

Tendon, Brachio-radialis m.

Tendons, Flex. digitorum superficialis

Palmar interosseous mm. (three)

Articular capsule, Metacarpophalangeal joint

Abductor digiti minimi m.

Lumbrical mm. (four)

Opponens digiti minimi m.

Flex. digiti minimi brevis m.

Abductor digiti minimi m.

Pisiform bone; Tendon, Flex. carpi ulnaris m.

Tendons, Flex. digitorum profundus m.

Palmar radiocarpal lig.

Styloid process of ulna

Ulna

Fig. 114: The Deep Muscles of the Right Hand, Palmar View

NOTE: the origins and insertions of the lumbrical muscles and the deeper muscles which contribute to form both the thenar and hypothenar eminences.

Interosseous membrane

Radius

Tendons, Lumbrical mm.

Tendons, Ext. digitoru

Tendons, Palmar interosseus mm.

4th dorsal interosseus m.

3rd dorsal interosseus m.

1st dorsal interosseus m.

2nd dorsal interosseus m.

Fig. 115: The Three Palmar Interosseus Muscles (left, Palmar View)

Fig. 116: The Four Dorsal Interosseus Muscles (left, Dorsal View)

NOTE: whereas the three palmar interosseus muscles (figure 115) are adductors of the fingers, the four dorsal interosseus muscles (figure 116) are abductors. All of the interossei flex the metacarpophalangeal joint and extend the interphalangeal joints, and they are all supplied by the ulnar nerve.

Figs. 114, 115, 116

Fig. 117: The Four Lumbrical Muscles (left, Palmar View) ▲

Tendons, Flex. digitorum superficialis m.

Tendons, Flex. digitorum profundus m.

1st lumbrical m.

2 nd lumbrical m.

3rd lumbrical m.

4th lumbrical m.

Tendons, Flex. digitorum profundus m.

Distal phalanx

Middle phalanx

Proximal phalanx

Tuberosity, Distal phalanx

Distal phalanx

Head
Body — Middle phalanx
Base

Head — Proximal phalanx
Body

Head, 2nd meta-carpal bone

Distal phalanx, Thumb

Sesamoid bone

Proximal phalanx, Thumb

Head, 1st meta-carpal bone

Sesamoid bones

1st meta-carpal bone

Trapezoid

Trapezium

Capitate

Scaphoid

Styloid process, Radius

Lunate

Radius

Phalanges

Sesamoid bone

Metacarpal bones

Hamulus of hamate

Hamate

Carpal bones

Pisiform

Triquetrum

Styloid process, Ulna

Head of ulna

Ulna

Fig. 118: The Skeleton of the Right Wrist and Hand, Palmar View

NOTE: 1) there are 8 carpal bones, 5 metacarpal bones and 14 phalanges. The thumb contains only two phalanges, whereas each of the other fingers have three.

2) the carpal bones are arranged in two rows of four bones each. The proximal row from lateral to medial include the scaphoid, lunate, triquetrum and pisiform. The distal row include the trapezium, trapezoid, capitate and hamate. This latter row of carpal bones articulates with the metacarpals.

3) the first metacarpal (thumb) is the shortest, while the 2nd (index finger) is the longest. Each metacarpal has a base or carpal extremity, a body, and a head or digital extremity which is directed toward the phalanges. In the spaces between the metacarpals are found the interossei muscles.

4) the phalanges of the four medial fingers are arranged in transverse rows and are individually called proximal (1st), middle (2nd) and distal (3rd) phalanx. The thumb has only a proximal and a distal phalanx. Dorsally the phalanges are somewhat convex, while on their palmar surface they are slightly concave.

Flexor digitorum profundus

Palmar interossei

Flexor digitorum superficialis

Flexor digiti minimi brevis; Abductor digiti minimi

Opponens digiti minimi

Adductor pollicis, transverse head

Flexor carpi ulnaris

Opponens digiti minimi

Flexor digiti minimi brevis

Abductor digiti minimi

Flexor carpi ulnaris

Pronator quadratus

Flexor pollicis longus

Adductor pollicis

Flexor pollicis brevis

Abductor pollicis brevis

Flexor carpi radialis

Opponens pollicis

Abductor pollicis longus

Flexor pollicis brevis

Opponens pollicis

Abductor pollicis brevis

Adductor pollicis, oblique head

Fig. 119: Bones of the Right Wrist and Hand (Palmar View) Showing the Attachments of Muscles

NOTE: the origins of muscles are in RED while the insertions are in BLUE.

Figs. 117, 118, 119   **I**

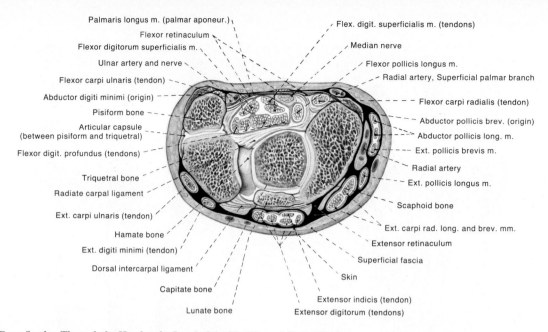

Fig. 120: Cross Section Through the Hand at the Level of the First Row of Carpal Bones

Palmaris longus m. (palmar aponeur.)
Flexor retinaculum
Flexor digitorum superficialis m.
Ulnar artery and nerve
Flexor carpi ulnaris (tendon)
Abductor digiti minimi (origin)
Pisiform bone
Articular capsule (between pisiform and triquetral)
Flexor digit. profundus (tendons)
Triquetral bone
Radiate carpal ligament
Ext. carpi ulnaris (tendon)
Hamate bone
Ext. digiti minimi (tendon)
Dorsal intercarpal ligament
Capitate bone
Lunate bone

Flex. digit. superficialis m. (tendons)
Median nerve
Flexor pollicis longus m.
Radial artery, Superficial palmar branch
Flexor carpi radialis (tendon)
Abductor pollicis brev. (origin)
Abductor pollicis long. m.
Ext. pollicis brevis m.
Radial artery
Ext. pollicis longus m.
Scaphoid bone
Ext. carpi rad. long. and brev. mm.
Extensor retinaculum
Superficial fascia
Skin
Extensor indicis (tendon)
Extensor digitorum (tendons)

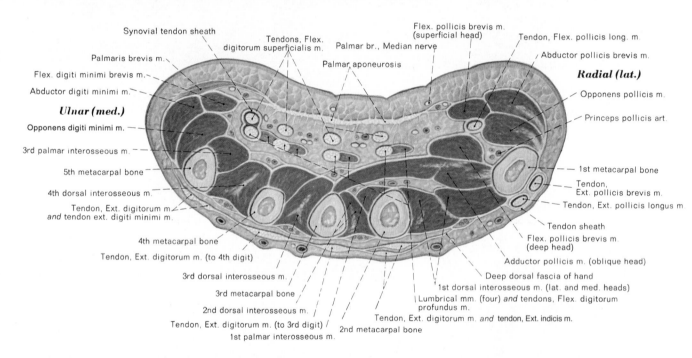

Fig. 121: Cross Section of the Right Hand Through the Metacarpal Bones

Synovial tendon sheath
Palmaris brevis m.
Flex. digiti minimi brevis m.
Abductor digiti minimi m.
Ulnar (med.)
Opponens digiti minimi m.
3rd palmar interosseous m.
5th metacarpal bone
4th dorsal interosseous m.
Tendon, Ext. digitorum m. *and tendon ext. digiti minimi m.*
4th metacarpal bone
Tendon, Ext. digitorum m. (to 4th digit)
3rd dorsal interosseous m.
3rd metacarpal bone
2nd dorsal interosseous m.
Tendon, Ext. digitorum m. (to 3rd digit)
1st palmar interosseous m.

Tendons, Flex. digitorum superficialis m.
Palmar br., Median nerve
Palmar aponeurosis
Flex. pollicis brevis m. (superficial head)
Tendon, Flex. pollicis long. m.
Abductor pollicis brevis m.
Radial (lat.)
Opponens pollicis m.
Princeps pollicis art.
1st metacarpal bone
Tendon, Ext. pollicis brevis m.
Tendon, Ext. pollicis longus m
Tendon sheath
Flex. pollicis brevis m. (deep head)
Adductor pollicis m. (oblique head)
Deep dorsal fascia of hand
1st dorsal interosseous m. (lat. and med. heads)
Lumbrical mm. (four) *and* tendons, Flex. digitorum profundus
Tendon, Ext. digitorum m. *and* tendon, Ext. indicis m.
2nd metacarpal bone

IDENTIFY a) the four dorsal interossei which act as abductors of the fingers and which fill the intervals between the metacarpal bones, b) the three palmar interossei which act as adductors of the fingers, c) the thenar and hypothenar muscles and d) the tendons and lumbrical muscles in the palmar compartment.

Dorsal digital nerve
Dorsal digital artery
Proper palmar digtal nerve
Proper palmar digital artery
Common palmar digital artery

Fig. 122: Nerves and Arteries of the Index Finger

NOTE: the dorsal digital nerve and artery extend only two-thirds the length of the finger. The palmar digital nerve and artery supply not only the entire palmar surface but also the distal one-third of the dorsal surface.

Figs. 120, 121, 122

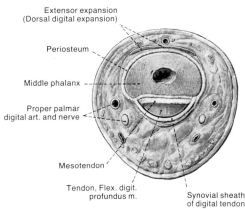

Fig. 123: Cross Section of the Middle Finger Through the Proximal Phalanx

NOTE: 1) the extensor expansion (also called dorsal digital expansion or extensor hood) over the dorsal aspect of the proximal phalanx and part of the middle phalanx. Into this triangular-shaped aponeurosis blend the digital tendon of the extensor digitorum, as well as the tendons of insertion of the adjacent interossous muscles and those of the lumbrical muscles (see also Fig. 109)

2) the synovial sheath on the palmar aspect of the phalanx and the disposition of the superficial and deep flexor tendons of the digit.

Fig. 124: Cross Section of the Middle Finger Through the Middle Phalanx

NOTE: 1) the location of the proper palmar digital arteries and nerves within the subcutaneous fibrous tissue on the lateral aspects of the deep flexor tendon (see also Figs. 110, 122 and 123). Knowing the location of these structures is important both for the application of local anesthesia to the digit and for the cessation of severe bleeding (hemostasis).

2) that the tendon of only the flexor digitorum profundus is present on the palmar aspect of the middle phalanx (see also Figs. 108, 109).

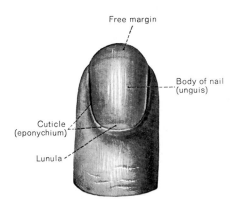

Fig. 125: Finger Nail, Normal Position (Dorsal View)

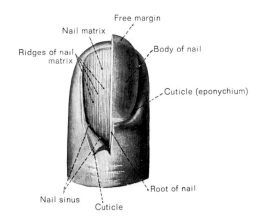

Fig. 126: Left Half of Finger Nail Bed Exposed

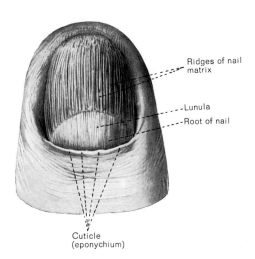

Fig. 127: Nail Bed of Thumb after Removal of Nail

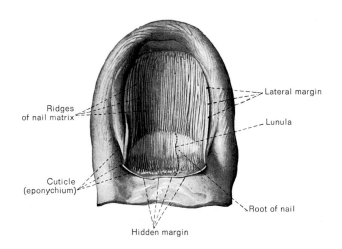

Fig. 128: Nail Bed of Thumb and Reflection of Cuticle

Figs. 123–128   I

Articular capsule,
3rd metacarpophalangeal joint

Collateral
ligaments

**Dorsal
metacarpal
ligaments**

**Dorsal
carpometacarpal
ligaments**

Capitate bone

Trapezoid
bone

Hamate bone

Dorsal
intercarpal
ligament

**Dorsal
intercarpal
ligament**

Scaphoid
bone

Triquetral bone

Styloid
process
(radius)

Styloid process
(ulna)

**Dorsal
radiocarpal
ligament**

Ulna

Radius

Fig. 129: Joints and Ligaments of the Wrist and Hand (Dorsal View, Left Hand)

NOTE: 1) generally the ligaments of the joints in the wrist and hand are named according to the bones they connect.

2) the dorsal radiocarpal ligament strengthens the dorsal aspect of the capsule of the radiocarpal joint. It is joined both medially and laterally by ulnar and radial collateral ligaments (shown but not labelled in the figure), which are seen to extend distally from the styloid processes of both the radius and ulna.

3) the various intercarpal and carpometacarpal ligaments are principally short, dense, connective tissue strands extending between adjacent bones.

4) the articular capsule has been cut on the dorsal aspect of the 3rd metacarpophalangeal joint to reveal the rounded head of the metacarpal bone which fits into the concavity of the base of the proximal phalanx.

Deep transverse
metacarpal lig.

Grooves for
flexor tendons

Sesamoid bones

Palmar metacarpa
ligaments

Hamulus of
hamate bone

Hamatometacarpal
ligament

Articular capsule,
Carpometacarpal joint
(thumb)

Pisometacarpal
ligament

Capitate bone

Pisohamate
ligament

Radiate carpal
ligament

Pisiform bone

**Palmar radiocarpal
ligament**

**Palmar ulno-
carpal lig.**

Styloid process,
Ulna

Lunate bone

Capsule,
distal radioulnar
joint

Styloid process,
Radius

Articular
capsule

Radius

Ulna

Collateral
ligament

Fig. 131: Joints and Ligaments of the Wrist and Hand (Palmar View, Left Hand)

NOTE: 1) the radiocarpal and ulnocarpal ligamentous bands strengthening the palmar aspect of the radiocarpal joint.

2) identify several strong ligaments in the palmar hand including the pisohamate, pisometacarpal and the radiate ligament surrounding the capitate bone.

3) the bases of the metacarpal bones are joined by the palmar metacarpal ligaments, while the more distal heads of these bones are interconnected by the deep transverse metacarpal ligament.

Collateral
ligament

Articular
capsule

Fig. 130: Joints and Ligaments of the Middle Finger

NOTE: the articular capsules of the metacarpophalangeal and interphalangeal joints are strengthened by longitudinally oriented collateral ligaments.

Figs. 129, 130, 131

Collateral ligaments

Base of distal phalanx

Head of middle phalanx

Middle phalanx

prox. alanx; amoid bone

Tuberosity, distal phalanx

Distal interphalang. joint

Proximal phalanx

Proximal interphalang. joint

d of 1st acarpal bone

Head, 4th metacarp. bone

Metacarpophalangeal joint capsule

Deep transverse metacarpal lig.

Body of 1st acarpal bone

Body, 5th metacarpal bone

Base, 3rd metacarpal bone (styloid process)

Base of 1st metacarpal bone

Hamate bone

rapezium bone

Capitate bone

Trapezoid bone

Triquetral bone

Scaphoid bone

Lunate bone

Articular disc

Sulci for tendons

Styloid process of ulna

Head of ulna

Interosseous membrane

Posterior surface of radius

Interosseous margin of ulna

Interosseous margin of radius

Posterior surface of ulna

Fig. 132: Joints of the Right Wrist and Fingers, Viewed from the Dorsal Aspect

NOTE that several of the joints at the wrist and in the fingers have been partially opened by severing the joint capsules transversely, thereby revealing the apposing articular surfaces.

Fig. 133: X-ray of the Right Wrist, Dorso-ventral Projection

NOTE the following numbered structures:

1. Base of 1st metacarpal bone (thumb)
2. Trapezium bone
3. Trapezoid bone
4. Capitate bone
5. Hamate bone
6. Hamulus of hamate bone
7. Base of 5th metacarpal bone (little finger)
8. Scaphoid bone
9. Lunate bone
10. Pisiform bone
11. Triquetral bone
12. Styloid process of radius
13. Ulnar notch (distal radioulnar joint)
14. Styloid process of ulna
15. Radius
16. Ulna

(From Wicke, L., *Atlas of Radiologic Anatomy,* 3rd Edition, Urban & Schwarzenberg, Baltimore, 1982).

Fig. 134: Coronal (Frontal) Section Through the Left Wrist Joints

NOTE: 1) the articular disc situated at the distal end of the ulna. Thus, the radiocarpal joint consists of the radius and articular disc proximally and the scaphoid, lunate and triquetrum distally.

2) the ulnar and radial collateral ligaments which provide the wrist joints with strong longitudinally oriented fibrous bands both laterally and medially.

Interosseous metacarpal ligaments

Carpometacarpal joint of little finger

1st metacarpal bone

Carpometacarpal joint of thumb

Trapezium bone

Trapezoid bone

Radial collateral lig.

Scaphoid bone

Capitate bone

Radiocarpal joint

Lunate bone

Radius

Ulna

Hamate bone

Mediocarpal joint (between two rows of carpal bones)

Triquetral bone

Ulnar collateral ligament

Articular disc

Distal radioulnar joint

Head of ulna

Figs. 132, 133, 134   I

Distal phalanges

Middle phalanges

Proximal phalanges

Heads of
metacarpal bones;
Sesamoid bone
of forefinger

Sesamoid bone

Bases of metacarpal bones

Trapezoid bone

Trapezium bone

Tuberosity of scaphoid bone

Radius

Hamulus of hamate bone

Triquetral bone;
Pisiform bone

Capitate bone

Lunate bone

Styloid process of ulna

Ulna

Fig. 135: X-ray on Adult Left Hand

NOTE: 1) the expanded distal surface of the radius and its articulation inferolaterally with the scaphoid bone and inferomedially with the lunate. The distal extremity of the ulna is lengthened by the styloid process and has an interposed fibrocartilaginous articular disc between it, the radius, and the triquetral bone;

2) the shadow of the pisiform overlies that of the triquetrum. Thus, the proximal row of carpal bones includes the scaphoid, lunate, and triquetrum (with its superimposed pisiform);

3) the articulation of the scaphoid with the trapezium and trapezoid distally and the lunate and capitate laterally;

4) the size and central location of the capitate bone within the wrist. In addition to the capitate, the distal row of carpal bones includes the trapezium, trapezoid, and hamate.

Fig. 135

PART II: THE THORAX

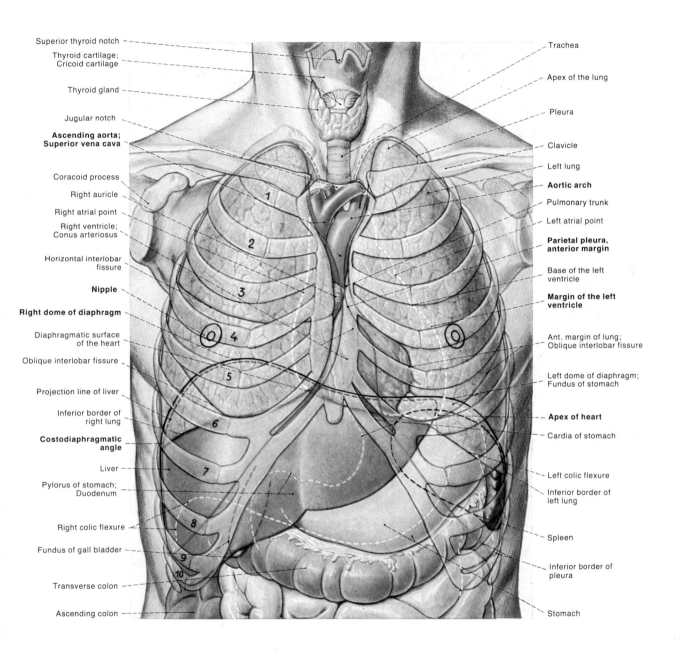

Superior thyroid notch

Thyroid cartilage;
Cricoid cartilage

Thyroid gland

Jugular notch

Ascending aorta;
Superior vena cava

Coracoid process

Right auricle

Right atrial point

Right ventricle;
Conus arteriosus

Horizontal interlobar
fissure

Nipple

Right dome of diaphragm

Diaphragmatic surface
of the heart

Oblique interlobar fissure

Projection line of liver

Inferior border of
right lung

Costodiaphragmatic
angle

Liver

Pylorus of stomach;
Duodenum

Right colic flexure

Fundus of gall bladder

Transverse colon

Ascending colon

Trachea

Apex of the lung

Pleura

Clavicle

Left lung

Aortic arch

Pulmonary trunk

Left atrial point

Parietal pleura,
anterior margin

Base of the left
ventricle

Margin of the left
ventricle

Ant. margin of lung;
Oblique interlobar fissure

Left dome of diaphragm;
Fundus of stomach

Apex of heart

Cardia of stomach

Left colic flexure

Inferior border of
left lung

Spleen

Inferior border of
pleura

Stomach

Fig. 136: Thoracic and Upper Abdominal Viscera Viewed from the Anterior Aspect

NOTE: 1) the outline of the heart and great vessels (white broken line) deep to the anteromedial portion of the lungs;

2) that the liver, lying below the diaphragm, extends superiorly as high as the fourth interspace on the right and to the fifth interspace on the left (red broken line);

3) the superficial position of the superior vena cava and ascending aorta just deep to the manubrium of the sternum in the superior mediastinum;

4) that an upper triangular region containing the great vessels and a lower triangular region overlying the heart (area of superficial cardiac dullness) are not covered by pleura.

5) the reflections of the pleura (blue lines) over both lungs. Observe that the anterior margins of the lung and pleura on the left side are indented to form the cardiac notch (see also Fig. 153 and 173).

6) the position of the nipple over the 4th rib (or 4th intercostal space) in the male and in the young female. Observe also the apex of the heart, oriented toward the left and deep to the 5th intercostal space (i.e. between the 5th and 6th ribs; see also Fig. 173)

Fig. 136   **II**

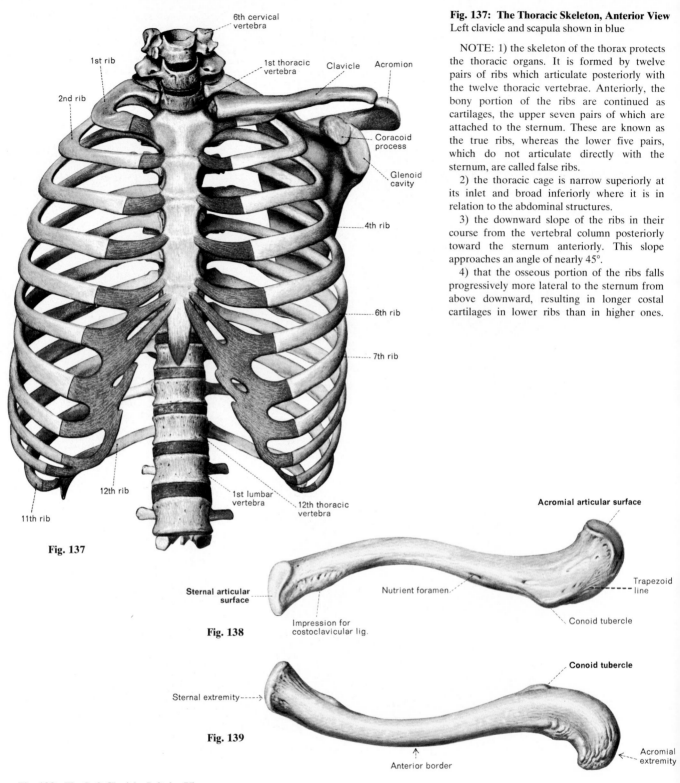

6th cervical
vertebra

1st rib

1st thoracic
vertebra

Clavicle   Acromion

2nd rib

Coracoid
process

Glenoid
cavity

4th rib

6th rib

7th rib

12th rib

1st lumbar
vertebra

12th thoracic
vertebra

11th rib

Fig. 137

Fig. 137: The Thoracic Skeleton, Anterior View
Left clavicle and scapula shown in blue

NOTE: 1) the skeleton of the thorax protects the thoracic organs. It is formed by twelve pairs of ribs which articulate posteriorly with the twelve thoracic vertebrae. Anteriorly, the bony portion of the ribs are continued as cartilages, the upper seven pairs of which are attached to the sternum. These are known as the true ribs, whereas the lower five pairs, which do not articulate directly with the sternum, are called false ribs.

2) the thoracic cage is narrow superiorly at its inlet and broad inferiorly where it is in relation to the abdominal structures.

3) the downward slope of the ribs in their course from the vertebral column posteriorly toward the sternum anteriorly. This slope approaches an angle of nearly 45°.

4) that the osseous portion of the ribs falls progressively more lateral to the sternum from above downward, resulting in longer costal cartilages in lower ribs than in higher ones.

Acromial articular surface

Sternal articular
surface

Nutrient foramen

Trapezoid
line

Conoid tubercle

Impression for
costoclavicular lig.

Fig. 138

Conoid tubercle

Sternal extremity

Fig. 139

Acromial
extremity

Anterior border

Fig. 138: The Left Clavicle, Inferior View

NOTE: 1) the clavicle is a double-curved bone which articulates medially with the sternum just above the first rib and laterally with the acromion of the scapula.

2) the inferior surface has roughened areas for the attachment of the costoclavicular ligament medially and the conoid and trapezoid fascicles of the coracoclavicular ligament laterally. The subclavius muscle attaches along the middle third of the inferior surface.

Fig. 139: The Left Clavicle, Superior View

NOTE: 1) the superior surface of the clavicle affords attachment of the pectoralis major and sternocleidomastoid muscles medially and the deltoid and trapezius muscles laterally.

2) the acromioclavicular articulation associates the clavicle with all the movements of the scapula, while the sternal articulation of the clavicle is a more secure and less movable joint.

Figs. 137, 138, 139

Fig. 140: The Thoracic Skeleton, Posterior View
Left clavicle and scapula shown in blue

NOTE: 1) posteriorly, the skeleton of the thoracic cage consists of the twelve thoracic vertebrae and the posterior parts of the twelve pairs of ribs. Observe the mode of articulation of the ribs to the vertebral column. On an articulated skeleton, confirm that the extremity on the head of typical ribs possesses two articular facets separated by a crest (see Fig. 143: 8th rib). These two facets articulate with the bodies of two adjacent vertebrae, while the crest is attached to the intervertebral disc. The lower of these two facets articulates with the vertebra that numerically corresponds with the rib, and the more superior of the two facets articulates with the adjacent vertebra above.

2) that the scapula affords bony protection posteriorly to the upper lateral aspect of the thoracic cage, but the more medial portions of the intercostal spaces are protected only by soft tissues and, therefore, are vulnerable, as they are in the mid-axillary line and anteriorly. Recall that the medial (vertebral) border of the scapula is attached to the spinal column and thoracic cage by muscles and connective tissue only, and its articulations are to the clavicle and humerus, thus forming the pectoral girdle.

Fig. 141

Fig. 142

Fig. 141: The Sternum, Anterior View

NOTE: 1) the sternum consists of three parts: the manubrium, the body and the xiphoid process and forms the middle portion of the anterior wall of the thorax.

2) the manubrium articulates with the body of the sternum at somewhat of an angle called the sternal angle. The xiphoid process is thin and usually cartilaginous.

3) the concave jugular notch which marks the superior border of the manubrium. Lateral to this are the two clavicular notches, each of which receives the medial end of the respective clavicle.

4) the entire sternum measures between 15 and 20 cm (6 to 7 inches). Its anterior surface is roughened and affords attachment to the sternocleidomastoid and pectoralis major muscles.

Fig. 142: The Sternum, Lateral View

NOTE: 1) the clavicle and the 1st rib articulate with the manubrium. The 2nd rib articulates at the sternal angle where the sternal manubrium and body join. The 3rd to the 6th ribs articulate with the body of the sternum, while the 7th joins the sternum inferiorly at the junction of the xiphoid process.

2) A line projected posteriorly through the sternal angle would meet the vertebral column at the 4th thoracic vertebral level, while the xiphisternal junction lies at vertebral level T-9.

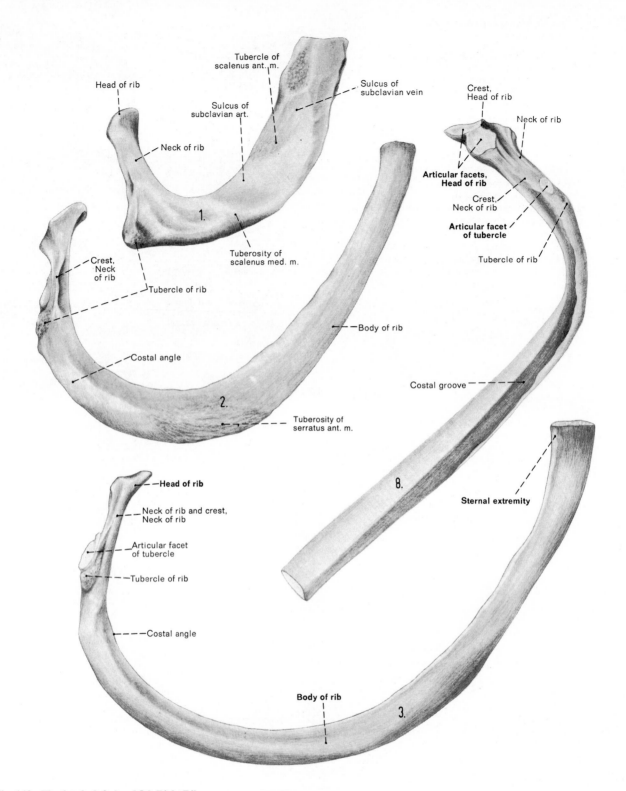

Fig. 143: The 1st, 2nd, 3rd and 8th Right Ribs

NOTE: 1) the superior surfaces of the first, second and third ribs are illustrated in this figure, while the inferior surface of the eighth rib is shown.

2) each rib has a vertebral extremity directed posteriorly, and a sternal extremity directed anteriorly. The body of the rib is the shaft which stretches between these two extremities.

3) the vertebral extremity is marked by a head, a neck and a tubercle. The head contains two facets for articulation with the bodies of the thoracic vertebrae, while the tubercle consists of a non-articular roughened elevation and an articular facet for connection with the transverse process of the thoracic vertebrae.

4) the 1st, 2nd, 10th, 11th and 12th ribs present somewhat different structural characteristics from the 3rd through the 9th ribs. The 1st rib is the most curved of all the ribs and has only a single articular facet on the head of the rib. The 10th, 11th and 12th ribs also have only a single facet on the rib head. The 2nd rib is shaped similar to the 1st rib but is longer.

Fig. 143

NOTE: 1) the sternoclavicular joint is formed by the junction of the clavicle with a) the upper lateral aspect of the manubrium and b) the cartilage of the first rib. A flat articular disc is interposed between the clavicle and the sternum. An articular capsule and fibrous ligamentous bands protect the joint.

2) the cartilages of the 2nd through the 7th ribs articulate with the sternum by means of movable diarthrodial joints, whereas the cartilage of the 1st rib is directly joined to the sternum and, without a joint cavity, forms an immovable articulation (synarthrosis).

Clavicle

Articular disc

Interclavicular lig.

Costoclavicular lig.

Costoclavicular lig.

Articular capsule

1st costal cartilage

Ant. sternoclavicular lig.

Manubrium

Radiate sternocostal lig.

Fig. 144

Sternomanubrial joint (also sternal angle)

2nd costal cartilage

Intercostal spaces (1st and 2nd)

Osseous part of ribs (1st and 2nd)

Angle of 3rd, 4th and 5th ribs.

Manubrium of sternum

First rib

Body of sternum

Fig. 145

Xiphoid process

Fig. 145: The Sternum of an Eleven Year Old Child, Showing Centers of Ossification

NOTE that ossification in the sternum (shown in yellow) commences first in the manubrium during the 5th or 6th prenatal month. Other centers of ossification develop in the sternal body between the 7th prenatal month and the end of the 1st postnatal year. The xiphoid process may commence to ossify as early as the 3rd postnatal year, but more often, much later. Ossification is usually complete in the sternum by the age of 25.

Fig. 146: The Twelve Right Ribs, Showing the Natural Contour of the Thoracic Cage; Lateral View

Fig. 146

Costal cartilages (8th, 9th and 10th)

Figs. 144, 145, 146   II

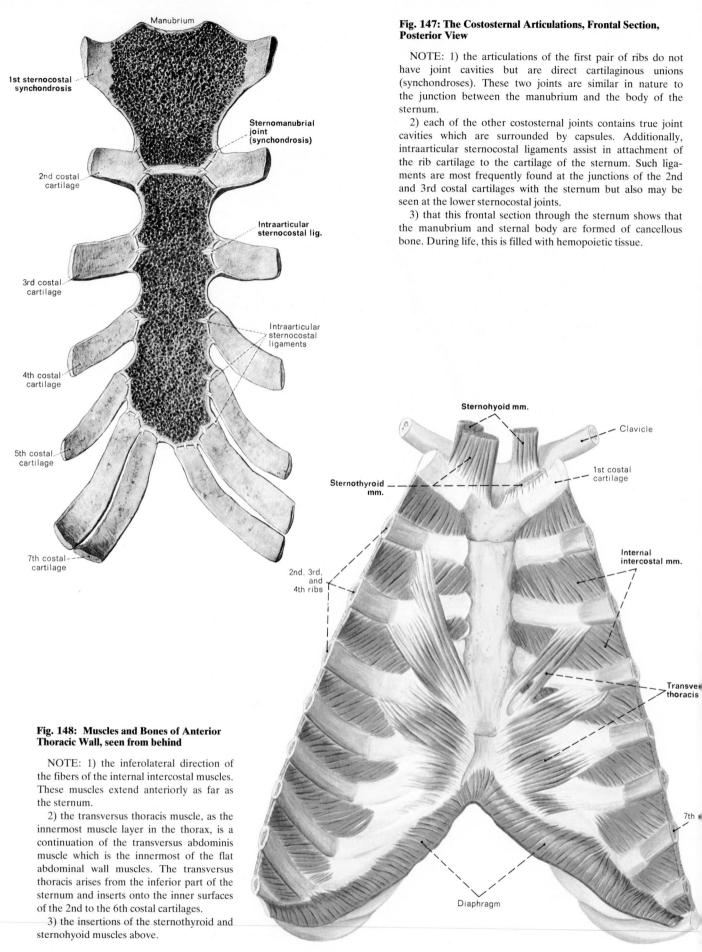

Manubrium

1st sternocostal
synchondrosis

Sternomanubrial
joint
(synchondrosis)

2nd costal
cartilage

Intraarticular
sternocostal lig.

3rd costal
cartilage

Intraarticular
sternocostal
ligaments

4th costal
cartilage

5th costal
cartilage

7th costal
cartilage

Fig. 147: The Costosternal Articulations, Frontal Section, Posterior View

NOTE: 1) the articulations of the first pair of ribs do not have joint cavities but are direct cartilaginous unions (synchondroses). These two joints are similar in nature to the junction between the manubrium and the body of the sternum.

2) each of the other costosternal joints contains true joint cavities which are surrounded by capsules. Additionally, intraarticular sternocostal ligaments assist in attachment of the rib cartilage to the cartilage of the sternum. Such ligaments are most frequently found at the junctions of the 2nd and 3rd costal cartilages with the sternum but also may be seen at the lower sternocostal joints.

3) that this frontal section through the sternum shows that the manubrium and sternal body are formed of cancellous bone. During life, this is filled with hemopoietic tissue.

Sternohyoid mm.

Clavicle

Sternothyroid
mm.

1st costal
cartilage

Internal
intercostal mm.

2nd, 3rd,
and
4th ribs

Transve
thoracis

7th

Diaphragm

Fig. 148: Muscles and Bones of Anterior Thoracic Wall, seen from behind

NOTE: 1) the inferolateral direction of the fibers of the internal intercostal muscles. These muscles extend anteriorly as far as the sternum.

2) the transversus thoracis muscle, as the innermost muscle layer in the thorax, is a continuation of the transversus abdominis muscle which is the innermost of the flat abdominal wall muscles. The transversus thoracis arises from the inferior part of the sternum and inserts onto the inner surfaces of the 2nd to the 6th costal cartilages.

3) the insertions of the sternothyroid and sternohyoid muscles above.

Figs. 147, 148

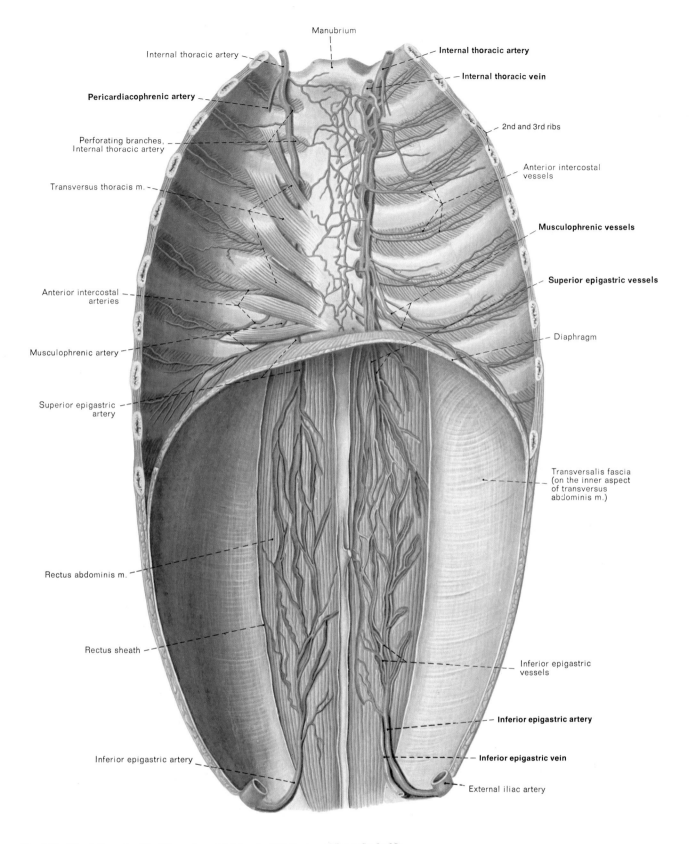

Manubrium

Internal thoracic artery

Internal thoracic artery

Internal thoracic vein

Pericardiacophrenic artery

2nd and 3rd ribs

Perforating branches, Internal thoracic artery

Anterior intercostal vessels

Transversus thoracis m.

Musculophrenic vessels

Superior epigastric vessels

Anterior intercostal arteries

Diaphragm

Musculophrenic artery

Superior epigastric artery

Transversalis fascia (on the inner aspect of transversus abdominis m.)

Rectus abdominis m.

Rectus sheath

Inferior epigastric vessels

Inferior epigastric artery

Inferior epigastric vein

Inferior epigastric artery

External iliac artery

Fig. 149: Blood Vessels of the Thoracic and Abdominal Wall, viewed from the inside

NOTE: 1) the principal vessels dissected include the internal thoracic and inferior epigastric arteries and veins and their terminal branches.

2) the internal thoracic artery branches from the subclavian artery and descends behind the costal cartilages on the inner aspect of the anterior thoracic wall parallel to the lateral margin of the sternum. In its course the internal thoracic artery gives rise to the pericardiacophrenic artery, small anterior mediastinal vessels to the thymus and bronchial structures, perforating branches to the chest wall, anterior intercostal branches which anastomose with the intercostal arteries, and finally it terminates as the musculophrenic and superior epigastric arteries.

3) the superior epigastric artery anastomoses with the inferior epigastric artery, which is a branch of the external iliac artery and which ascends in the abdominal wall from below. The anastomosis occurs in the substance of the rectus abdominis muscle.

Fig. 149 **II**

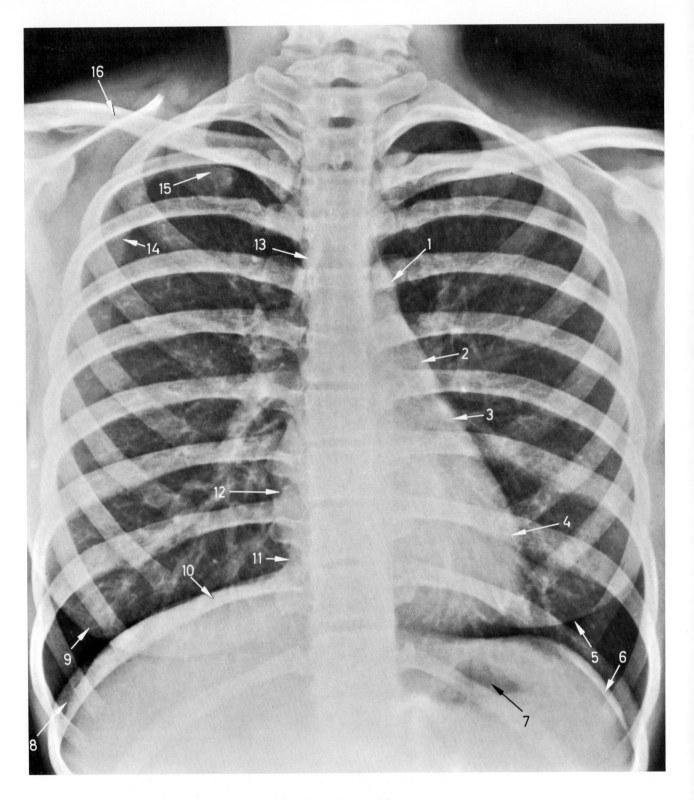

Fig. 150: Posterior-Anterior Radiograph of the Thorax Showing the Heart and Lungs

NOTE the contour of the heart and great vessels (arch of aorta 1, pulmonary trunk 2, inferior vena cava 11, and superior vena cava, 13) and the relationship of these structures to the vertebral column. Observe that the left margin of the heart is formed by the left auricle (3) and left ventricle (4) and that it slopes toward the apex which usually lies about 9 centimeters to the left of the midsternal line, deep to the 5th intercostal space. The right margin of the heart (12) projects as a curved line slightly to the right of the vertebral column (and sternum). Also observe that the heart rests on the diaphragm (6) and note the obvious contours of the left (5) and right (9) breasts. (From Wicke, L. *Atlas of Radiographic Anatomy,* 3rd Edition, Urban & Schwarzenberg, Baltimore, 1982).

1. Arch of aorta	5. Contour of left breast	9. Contour of right breast	13. Superior vena cava
2. Pulmonary trunk	6. Diaphragm	10. Diaphragm	14. Medial border of scapula
3. Left auricle	7. Air in fundus of stomach	11. Inferior vena cava	15. First rib
4. Left ventricle	8. Costodiaphragmatic recess	12. Right atrium	16. Right clavicle

Fig. 150

Fig. 151: Anterior Cervical, Thoracic and Abdominal Musculature

NOTE: 1) on the right side the muscles of the shoulder and upper arm are demonstrated following the removal of the pectoralis major muscle. The anterior layer of the rectus sheath has been opened.

2) on the left side the upper limb has been removed, as have all of the more superficial trunk and cervical musculature, revealing the thoracic cage and the deeper soft tissues.

Fig. 151   II

Labels (left side, top to bottom):
- Stylohyoid m.
- Post. belly, Digastric m.
- Longissimus capitis m.
- Levator scapulae m.
- Scalenus medius m.
- Longus capitis m.
- **Sternocleidomastoid m.**
- Omohyoid m. (sup. and inf. bellies)
- Trapezius m.
- Scalenus medius m.
- Levator scapulae m.
- Superior transverse scapular lig.
- Conoid ligament
- Clavicle
- Acromion
- Trapezoid ligament
- Deltoid m.
- Coracoacromial ligament
- Coracoid process
- Tendons, Supraspinatus and subscapularis muscles
- Subclavius m.
- Tendon and synovial sheath, Long head, Biceps m.
- Pectoralis major m.
- Superior part, Serratus anterior m.
- Deltoid m.
- Short head, Biceps m.
- Subscapularis m.
- Coracobrachialis m.
- Teres major m.
- Latissimus dorsi m.
- **Pectoralis minor m.**
- Serratus anterior m.
- Pectoralis major m.
- Sternalis m. (anomoly)
- Ext. oblique m.
- **Rectus abdominis m.**
- Aponeurosis, Ext. oblique m.
- Tendinous intersection, Rectus abdominis m.
- Anterior layer, Rectus sheath
- Rectus abdominis m. and tendinous intersection

Labels (right side, top to bottom):
- Digastric m., Ant. belly
- Mylohyoid m.
- Hyoid bone and hyoglossus m.
- Rectus capitis anterior m.
- Rectus capitis lateralis m.
- Longus capitis m.
- Atlas and vertebral artery
- Scalenus medius m.
- Longus colli muscle
- Carotid tubercle, 6th cervical vertebra
- Larynx and trachea
- Sternohyoid m.
- Pretracheal layer, Cervical fascia
- Scalenus anterior m.
- Vertebral artery
- Left subclavian artery
- Sternothyroid m.
- Left common carotid artery
- Scalenus posterior m.
- Apex of lung
- Serratus anterior m.
- Articular disc, Sternoclavicular joint
- Interclavicular ligament
- **Ext. intercostal muscle**
- **Pectoralis major muscle**
- Pectoralis minor muscle
- **Serratus anterior muscle**
- External intercostal membrane
- **Serratus anterior m. (slips of origin)**
- External oblique m. (slips of origin)
- Tendon, Rectus abdominis m.
- Ext. intercostal m.
- Costoxiphoid ligaments
- **Posterior layer, Rectus sheath**
- Transversus abdominis m.
- Internal oblique m.
- Anterior layer, Rectus sheath (opened)

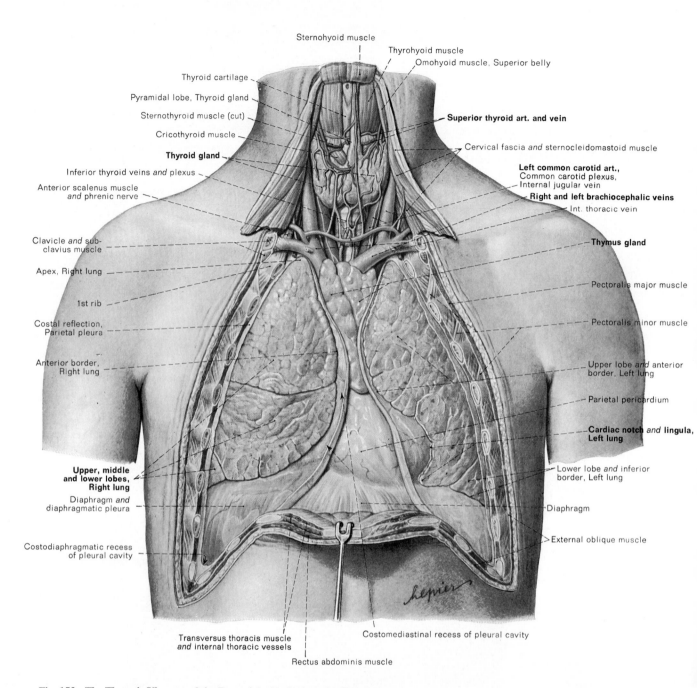

Sternohyoid muscle

Thyrohyoid muscle

Omohyoid muscle, Superior belly

Thyroid cartilage

Pyramidal lobe, Thyroid gland

Sternothyroid muscle (cut)

Cricothyroid muscle

Superior thyroid art. and vein

Cervical fascia *and* sternocleidomastoid muscle

Thyroid gland

Inferior thyroid veins *and* plexus

Anterior scalenus muscle *and* phrenic nerve

Left common carotid art., Common carotid plexus, Internal jugular vein

Right and left brachiocephalic veins

Int. thoracic vein

Clavicle *and* sub-clavius muscle

Thymus gland

Apex, Right lung

Pectoralis major muscle

1st rib

Pectoralis minor muscle

Costal reflection, Parietal pleura

Anterior border, Right lung

Upper lobe *and* anterior border, Left lung

Parietal pericardium

Cardiac notch *and* lingula, Left lung

Upper, middle and lower lobes, Right lung

Diaphragm *and* diaphragmatic pleura

Lower lobe *and* inferior border, Left lung

Diaphragm

External oblique muscle

Costodiaphragmatic recess of pleural cavity

Transversus thoracis muscle *and* internal thoracic vessels

Costomediastinal recess of pleural cavity

Rectus abdominis muscle

Fig. 152: The Thoracic Viscera and the Root of the Neck, Anterior Exposure

NOTE: 1) the anterior thoracic wall has been removed along with the medial portion of both clavicles to reveal the normal position of the heart, lungs, thymus and thyroid gland. The great vessels at the superior aperture to the thorax are also exposed.

2) the parietal pleura, likewise, has been removed arteriorly. The thymus is situated between the two lungs superiorly, whereas inferiorly is found the bare area of the heart. With the heart's apex directed more toward the left, a deficiency can be observed along the border of the left lung. This is called the cardiac notch.

3) the basal surface of both lungs and the inferior aspect of the heart rest on the diaphragm. Superiorly, the apex of each lung extends slightly above the level of the first rib.

4) at the root of the neck, the common carotid artery and internal jugular vein lie lateral and somewhat posterior to the thyroid gland.

5) the rather transverse course in the superior mediastinum of the left brachiocephalic vein in contrast to the nearly vertical course of the right brachiocephalic vein. On either side each of these vessels is formed by a junction of the internal jugular and subclavian veins. The two brachiocephalic veins join (deep to the thymus) to form the superior vena cava.

Fig. 152

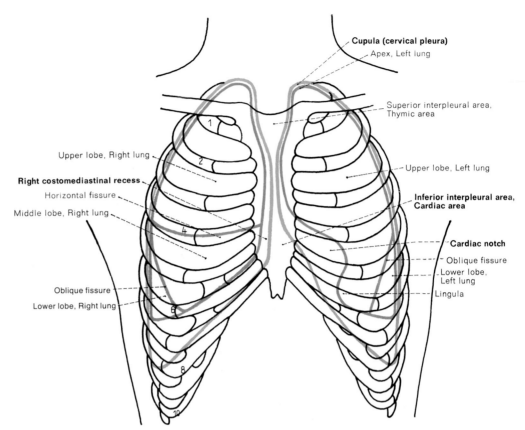

Fig. 153 and 154:
Pleural Reflections (blue) and Lungs (red)
Projected onto Thoracic Wall

Fig. 153: Anterior View

NOTE: 1) each lung is invested by two layers of pleural membrane which are continuous with each other at the hilum of the lung, thereby forming an invaginated sac. The parietal layer of pleura (represented in blue) is the outermost of the two layers and lines the inner surface of the thoracic wall and the superior surface of the diaphragm. The visceral, innermost layer of pleura closely invests and adheres to the surfaces of the lungs (represented in red).

2) the potential space between the two pleural layers is called the pleural cavity and contains only a small amount of serous fluid in the healthy individual, but may contain considerable fluid and blood in pathological conditions.

3) although the parietal pleura is a continuous sheet for each lung, portions of it are described in relation to their adjacent surfaces. Thus, lining the inner surface of the ribs is the costal pleura, while the diaphragmatic and mediastinal pleurae are applied onto the surfaces of the diaphragm and mediastinal structures. Superiorly, the apex of each lung extends above the clavicle into the root of the neck. This is covered by the cupula, or cervical pleura.

4) because of the curvature of the diaphragm, a narrow recess is formed around its periphery into which the surface of the lung (visceral pleura) does not extend. This potential space, lying between reflections of the costal and diaphragmatic pleurae, is called the costodiaphragmatic recess and is of clinical importance, since it may be punctured and drained without damage to lung tissue.

5) similarly, the costomediastinal recess is another pleural space which is situated anterior to the heart, and which is formed at that site by the reflections of the costal and mediastinal pleurae.

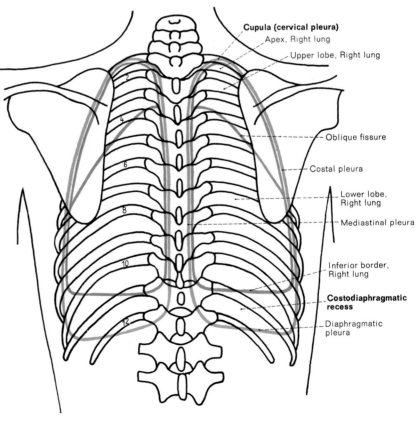

Fig. 154: Posterior View

Figs. 153, 154   **II**

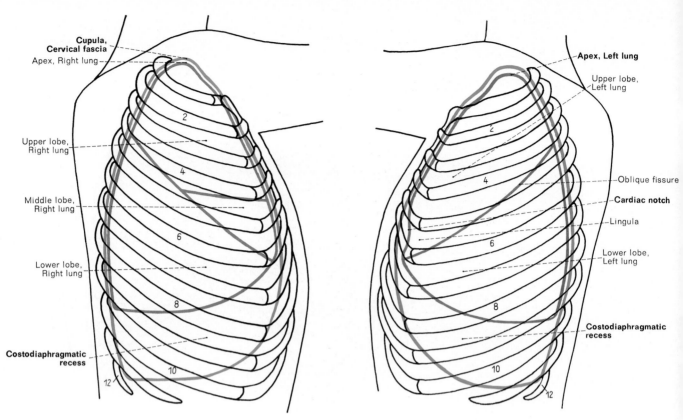

Fig. 155: Right Lateral View

Fig. 156: Left Lateral View

Pleural Reflections (blue) and Lungs (red) Projected onto Thoracic Wall

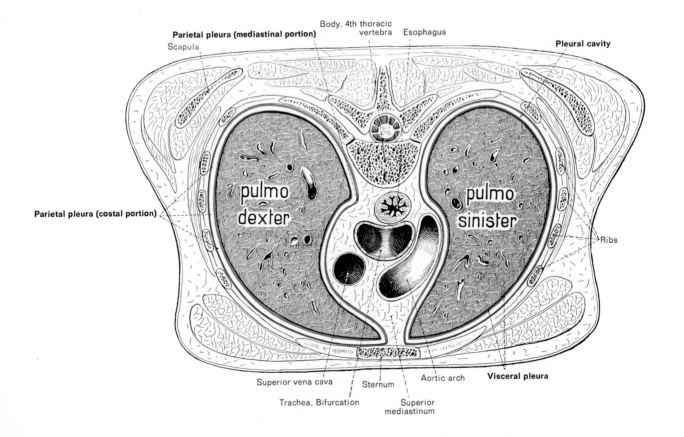

Fig. 157: Cross Section of Thorax at the Level of the Tracheal Bifurcation and the 4th Thoracic Vertebra (Pleura is shown in red)

Figs. 155, 156, 157

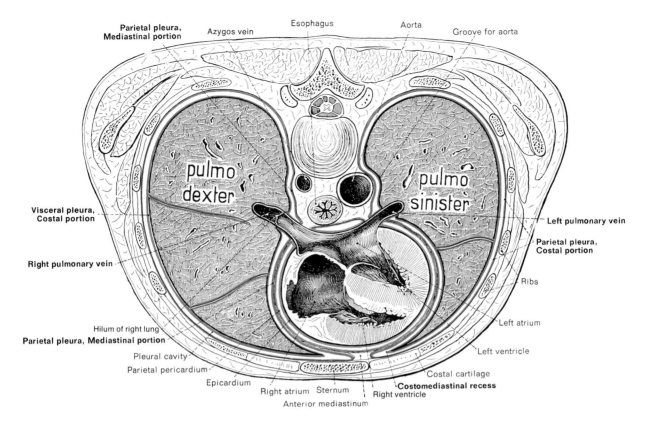

Parietal pleura, Mediastinal portion — Azygos vein — Esophagus — Aorta — Groove for aorta

pulmo dexter

pulmo sinister

Visceral pleura, Costal portion

Left pulmonary vein

Parietal pleura, Costal portion

Right pulmonary vein

Ribs

Left atrium

Hilum of right lung
Parietal pleura, Mediastinal portion

Left ventricle

Pleural cavity

Parietal pericardium

Costal cartilage

Epicardium

Costomediastinal recess

Right atrium — Sternum — Right ventricle

Anterior mediastinum

Fig. 158: Cross Section of Thorax Through the Hilum of the Lung at the Level of the Pulmonary Vein (Pleura in red, Pericardium in blue)

Pulmonary ligament — Azygos vein — Esophagus — Thoracic vertebra — Posterior mediastinum — Descending aorta

pulmo dexter

pulmo sinister

Left ventricle

Epicardium (visceral pericardium)

Pericardial cavity

* Costomediastinal sinus

Right atrium

Parietal pericardium

Left atrium

* Right ventricle — Anterior mediastinum

Visceral pleura

Fig. 159: Cross Section of the Thorax Inferior to the Hilum at the Level of the Pulmonary Ligament (Pleura in red, Pericardium in blue)

Figs. 158, 159   **II**

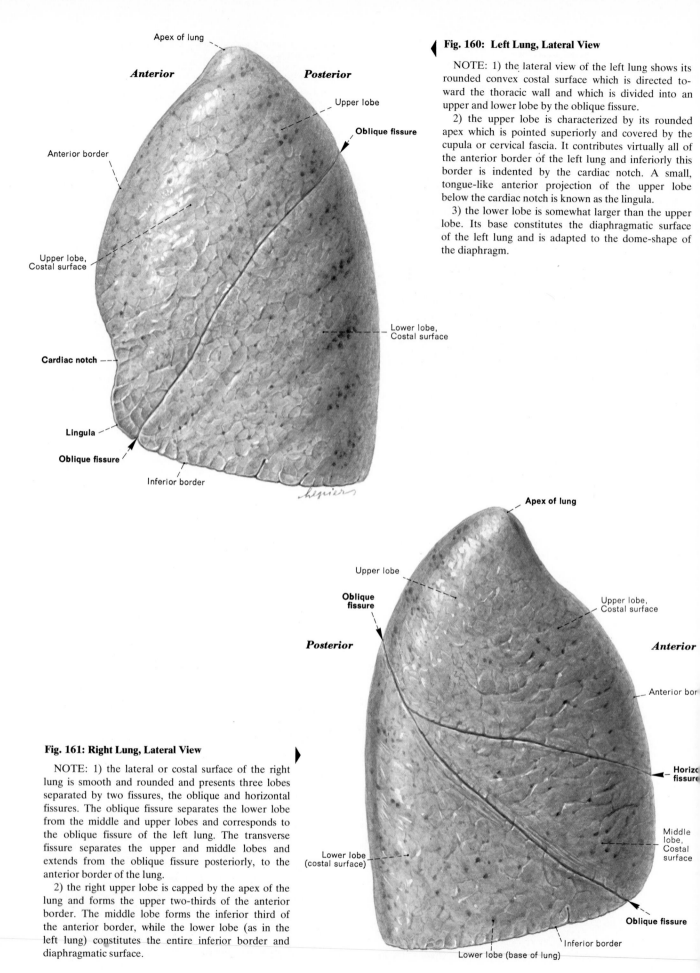

Apex of lung

Anterior

Posterior

Upper lobe

Oblique fissure

Anterior border

Upper lobe,
Costal surface

Lower lobe,
Costal surface

Cardiac notch

Lingula

Oblique fissure

Inferior border

Fig. 160: Left Lung, Lateral View

NOTE: 1) the lateral view of the left lung shows its rounded convex costal surface which is directed toward the thoracic wall and which is divided into an upper and lower lobe by the oblique fissure.

2) the upper lobe is characterized by its rounded apex which is pointed superiorly and covered by the cupula or cervical fascia. It contributes virtually all of the anterior border of the left lung and inferiorly this border is indented by the cardiac notch. A small, tongue-like anterior projection of the upper lobe below the cardiac notch is known as the lingula.

3) the lower lobe is somewhat larger than the upper lobe. Its base constitutes the diaphragmatic surface of the left lung and is adapted to the dome-shape of the diaphragm.

Apex of lung

Upper lobe

Oblique fissure

Upper lobe,
Costal surface

Posterior

Anterior

Anterior bor

**Horiz
fissure**

Middle
lobe,
Costal
surface

Lower lobe
(costal surface)

Oblique fissure

Inferior border

Lower lobe (base of lung)

Fig. 161: Right Lung, Lateral View

NOTE: 1) the lateral or costal surface of the right lung is smooth and rounded and presents three lobes separated by two fissures, the oblique and horizontal fissures. The oblique fissure separates the lower lobe from the middle and upper lobes and corresponds to the oblique fissure of the left lung. The transverse fissure separates the upper and middle lobes and extends from the oblique fissure posteriorly, to the anterior border of the lung.

2) the right upper lobe is capped by the apex of the lung and forms the upper two-thirds of the anterior border. The middle lobe forms the inferior third of the anterior border, while the lower lobe (as in the left lung) constitutes the entire inferior border and diaphragmatic surface.

Figs. 160, 161

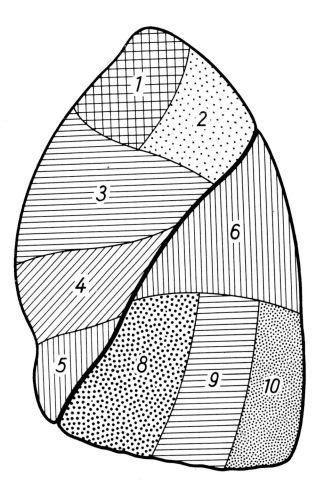

NOTE: 1) bronchopulmonary segments are anatomical subdivisions of the lung, each of which is supplied by its own segmental tertiary bronchus and artery, and drained by intersegmental veins.

2) the trachea divides into two primary bronchi, each of which supplies an entire lung. Each primary bronchus divides into secondary or lobar bronchi. There are two lobar bronchi on the left and three on the right, each supplying a single lobe. The secondary bronchi divide into the segmental or tertiary bronchi, which are distributed to the bronchopulmonary segments. Usual descriptions of the bronchopulmonary segments enumerate 8 to 10 segments in the left lung.

3) the bronchopulmonary segments of the left lung are numbered and named as follows:

Upper lobe
1 Apical ⎱ Frequently considered as a single segment
2 Posterior ⎰
3 Anterior
4 Superior ⎱ Lingular
5 Inferior ⎰

Lower lobe
6 Superior
7 Medial basal ⎱ Usually considered as a single segment;
8 Anterior basal ⎰ Medial basal cannot be seen from lateral view.
9 Lateral basal
10 Posterior basal

4) in the left lower lobe the medial basal bronchus arises separate from the anterior basal in only about 13 % of humans studied. Thus, in most instances the medial basal and anterior basal segments combine as an anteromedial basal segment.

Fig. 163: Right Lung, Bronchopulmonary Segments, Lateral View

NOTE: 1) the concept of subdividing the lungs into functional bronchopulmonary segments allows the surgeon to determine whether segments of lung might be resected in operations in preference to entire lobes.

2) although minor variations exist in the division of the bronchial tree, a significant consistency has become recognized in the bronchopulmonary segmentation. The nomenclature utilized here was offered by Jackson and Huber in 1943 (Dis. of Chest 9: 319–326) and has now become generally accepted because it is the simplest and most straightforward of the many suggested.

3) the bronchopulmonary segments of the right lung are numbered and named as follows:

Upper lobe   **Middle lobe**
1 Apical   4 Lateral
2 Posterior   5 Medial
3 Anterior

Lower lobe
6 Superior
7 Medial basal (cannot be seen from lateral view)
8 Anterior basal
9 Lateral basal
10 Posterior basal

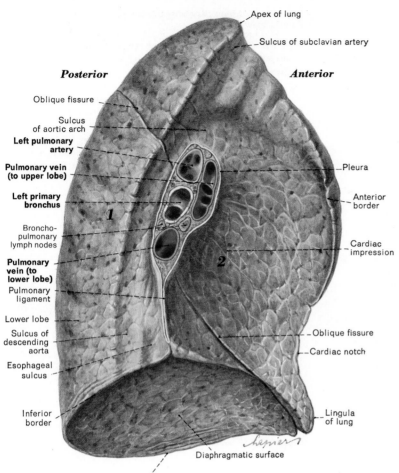

Apex of lung
Sulcus of subclavian artery

Posterior *Anterior*

Oblique fissure
Sulcus of aortic arch
Left pulmonary artery
Pulmonary vein (to upper lobe)
Left primary bronchus
Broncho-pulmonary lymph nodes
Pulmonary vein (to lower lobe)
Pulmonary ligament
Lower lobe
Sulcus of descending aorta
Esophageal sulcus
Inferior border

1
2

Pleura
Anterior border
Cardiac impression
Oblique fissure
Cardiac notch
Lingula of lung

Diaphragmatic surface
Inferior border

Fig. 164: Left Lung, Mediastinal and Diaphragmatic Surfaces

NOTE: 1) the pulmonary arteries are shown in blue since their blood contains less oxygen than that in the pulmonary veins which are shown in red.

2) the concave diaphragmatic surface of the left lung is shaped to cover most of the convex dome of the diaphragm which is completely covered by diaphragmatic pleura. However, the lung does not completely fill the peripheral rim of the diaphragm, thereby forming the costodiaphragmatic recess.

3) the mediastinal (or medial) surface of the left lung is also concave and presents the contours of the adjacent organs in the mediastinum. The large anterior concavity is the cardiac impression. Also found are grooves for the aortic arch and the descending aorta as well as the subclavian artery superiorly and the esophagus inferiorly.

4) the structures which form the root of the left lung at the hilum include the left pulmonary artery, found most superior and below which is found the left bronchus. The left pulmonary veins lie anterior and inferior to the artery and bronchus. The oblique fissure extends across the mediastinal surface from the costal surface to the diaphragm, completely dividing the lung into its two lobes.

PA PV
LB
PV

Fig. 165: Right Lung, Mediastinal and Diaphragmatic Surfaces

NOTE: 1) the diaphragmatic surface of the right lung, similar to that on the left, is shaped to the contour of the diaphragm, while the mediastinal surface superiorly shows grooves for the superior vena cava and subclavian artery. Just above the hilum of the right lung is the arched sulcus for the azygos vein, and this is continued inferiorly behind the root of the lung. The cardiac impression on the right lung is somewhat more shallow than on the left.

2) since the right bronchus frequently branches before the right pulmonary artery it is not unusual for the most superior structure at the root of the right lung to be the bronchus to the upper lobe (eparterial bronchus). The pulmonary artery lies anterior to the bronchus, while the pulmonary veins are located anterior and inferior to these structures.

3) the hilum of the lung is ensheathed by parietal pleura, the layers of which come into contact inferiorly to form the pulmonary ligament. It extends from the inferior border of the hilum to a point just above the diaphragm.

4) the numbers 1 and 2 on this figure and on Fig. 164 refer to the costal and mediastinal portions of the medial surface of the lung.

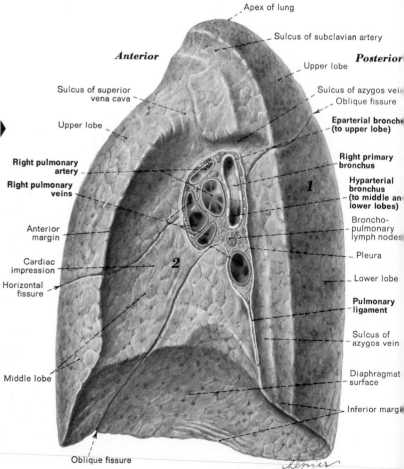

Apex of lung
Sulcus of subclavian artery

Anterior *Posterior*

Upper lobe
Sulcus of azygos vein
Oblique fissure
Eparterial bronchus (to upper lobe)
Right primary bronchus
Hyparterial bronchus (to middle and lower lobes)
Broncho-pulmonary lymph nodes
Pleura
Lower lobe
Pulmonary ligament
Sulcus of azygos vein
Diaphragmatic surface
Inferior margin

Sulcus of superior vena cava
Upper lobe
Right pulmonary artery
Right pulmonary veins
Anterior margin
Cardiac impression
Horizontal fissure
Middle lobe
Oblique fissure

1
2

Figs. 164, 165

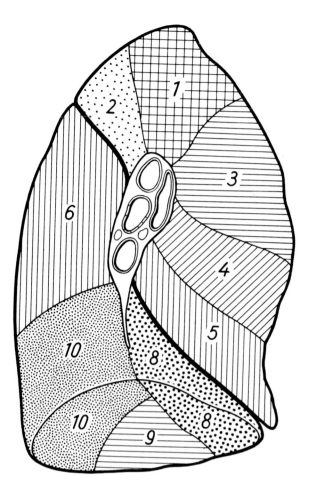

Fig. 166: Left Lung, Bronchopulmonary Segments, Medial View

NOTE: the bronchopulmonary segments of the left lung have been identified as follows:

Upper lobe			Lower lobe	
1	Apical	⎫ Frequently	6	Superior
2	Posterior	⎬ considered as one segment	7	Medial basal*
3	Anterior		8	Anterior basal*
4	Superior	⎫ Lingular	9	Lateral basal
5	Inferior	⎭	10	Posterior basal

* the medial basal and anterior basal segments were at one time frequently considered as a single bronchopulmonary segment. Today, however, they have been recognized as separate segments in a majority of left lungs. Therefore, on this figure that portion of segment 8 just inferior to the oblique fissure should be marked 7 and identified as medial basal.

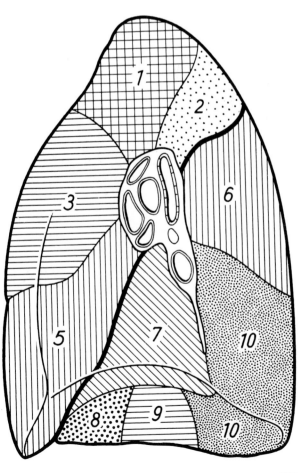

Fig. 167: Right Lung, Bronchopulmonary Segments, Medial View

NOTE: the bronchopulmonary segments of the right lung have been identified as follows:

Upper lobe
1 Apical
2 Posterior
3 Anterior

Middle lobe
4 Lateral (not seen from this view)
5 Medial

Lower lobe
6 Superior
7 Medial basal
8 Anterior basal
9 Lateral basal
10 Posterior basal

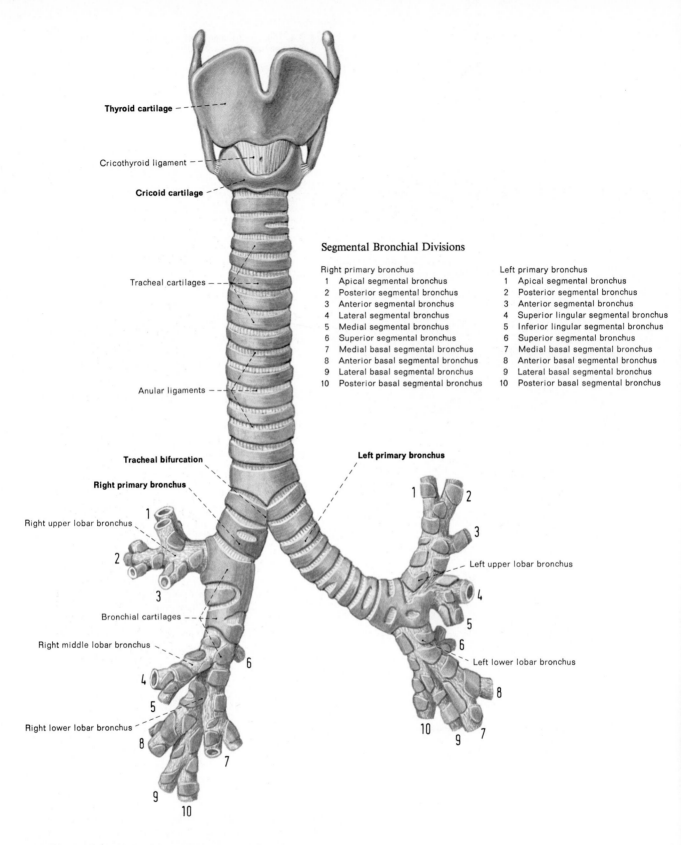

Thyroid cartilage

Cricothyroid ligament

Cricoid cartilage

Tracheal cartilages

Anular ligaments

Tracheal bifurcation

Right primary bronchus

Right upper lobar bronchus

Bronchial cartilages

Right middle lobar bronchus

Right lower lobar bronchus

Left primary bronchus

Left upper lobar bronchus

Left lower lobar bronchus

Segmental Bronchial Divisions

Right primary bronchus
1 Apical segmental bronchus
2 Posterior segmental bronchus
3 Anterior segmental bronchus
4 Lateral segmental bronchus
5 Medial segmental bronchus
6 Superior segmental bronchus
7 Medial basal segmental bronchus
8 Anterior basal segmental bronchus
9 Lateral basal segmental bronchus
10 Posterior basal segmental bronchus

Left primary bronchus
1 Apical segmental bronchus
2 Posterior segmental bronchus
3 Anterior segmental bronchus
4 Superior lingular segmental bronchus
5 Inferior lingular segmental bronchus
6 Superior segmental bronchus
7 Medial basal segmental bronchus
8 Anterior basal segmental bronchus
9 Lateral basal segmental bronchus
10 Posterior basal segmental bronchus

Fig. 168: Anterior Aspect of Larynx, Trachea, and Bronchi

NOTE: 1) the trachea bifurcates into two principal (primary) bronchi. These then divide into lobar (secondary) bronchi which in turn give rise to segmental (tertiary) bronchi.

2) the larynx is located in the anterior aspect of the neck, and its thyroid and cricoid cartilages can be felt through the skin.

3) the thyroid cartilage, projected posteriorly, lies at the level of the 4th and 5th cervical vertebrae, while the cricoid cartilage is at the 6th cervical level. The trachea commences at the lower end of the cricoid and extends slightly more than four inches before bifurcating into the two primary bronchi at the level of T-4. Two inches of trachea lie above the suprasternal notch in the neck, while about two inches of trachea are intrathoracic above its bifurcation.

Fig. 168

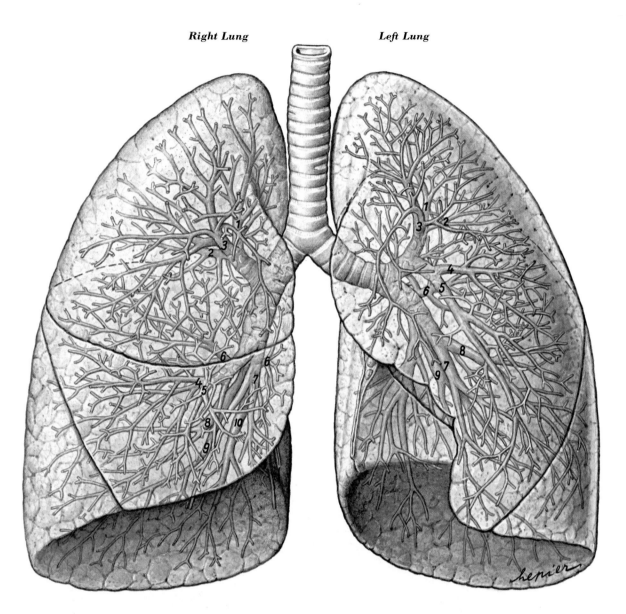

Right Lung   *Left Lung*

Fig. 169: Diagram of the Brochial Tree and its Lobar and Bronchopulmonary Divisions, Anterior View

NOTE: 1) as the trachea divides, the left primary bronchus diverges at a more abrupt angle than the right primary bronchus to reach their respective lungs. Thus, the left bronchus is directed more transversely and the right bronchus more inferiorly.

2) on the right side the upper lobar bronchus branches from the primary bronchus almost immediately, even above the pulmonary artery (eparterial), while the bronchus directed toward the middle and lower lobes branches below the position of the main stem of the pulmonary artery (hyparterial).

3) on the left side the initial lobar bronchus, branching from the primary bronchus, is directed upward and lateralward to the upper lobe segments and its lingular segments. The remaining lobar bronchus is directed inferiorly and soon divides into the segmental bronchi of the lower lobe.

4) the segmental bronchi numbered above are as follows:

Right lung:

1	Apical	6	Superior
2	Posterior	7	Medial basal
3	Anterior	8	Anterior basal
4	Lateral	9	Lateral basal
5	Medial	10	Posterior basal

Left lung:

1	Apical	6	Superior
2	Posterior	7	Medial basal
3	Anterior	8	Anterior basal
4	Superior lingular	9	Lateral basal
5	Inferior lingular	10	Posterior basal

Fig. 169   **II**

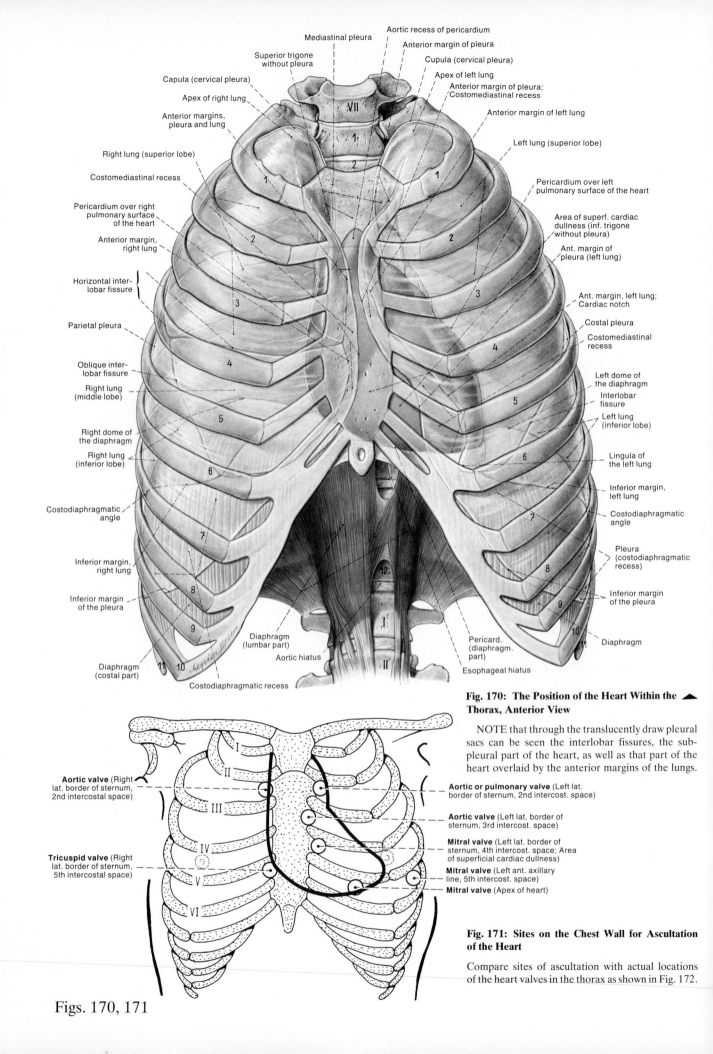

Mediastinal pleura

Aortic recess of pericardium

Superior trigone without pleura

Anterior margin of pleura

Capula (cervical pleura)

Cupula (cervical pleura)

Apex of right lung

Apex of left lung

Anterior margin of pleura; Costomediastinal recess

Anterior margins, pleura and lung

Anterior margin of left lung

Right lung (superior lobe)

Left lung (superior lobe)

Costomediastinal recess

Pericardium over left pulmonary surface of the heart

Pericardium over right pulmonary surface of the heart

Area of superf. cardiac dullness (inf. trigone without pleura)

Anterior margin, right lung

Ant. margin of pleura (left lung)

Horizontal inter-lobar fissure

Ant. margin, left lung; Cardiac notch

Parietal pleura

Costal pleura

Costomediastinal recess

Oblique inter-lobar fissure

Left dome of the diaphragm

Right lung (middle lobe)

Interlobar fissure

Left lung (inferior lobe)

Right dome of the diaphragm

Lingula of the left lung

Right lung (inferior lobe)

Inferior margin, left lung

Costodiaphragmatic angle

Costodiaphragmatic angle

Inferior margin, right lung

Pleura (costodiaphragmatic recess)

Inferior margin of the pleura

Inferior margin of the pleura

Diaphragm (lumbar part)

Pericard. (diaphragm. part)

Diaphragm

Diaphragm (costal part)

Aortic hiatus

Esophageal hiatus

Costodiaphragmatic recess

Fig. 170: The Position of the Heart Within the Thorax, Anterior View

NOTE that through the translucently draw pleural sacs can be seen the interlobar fissures, the subpleural part of the heart, as well as that part of the heart overlaid by the anterior margins of the lungs.

Aortic valve (Right lat. border of sternum, 2nd intercostal space)

Aortic or pulmonary valve (Left lat. border of sternum, 2nd intercost. space)

Aortic valve (Left lat. border of sternum, 3rd intercost. space)

Mitral valve (Left lat. border of sternum, 4th intercost. space; Area of superficial cardiac dullness)

Mitral valve (Left ant. axillary line, 5th intercost. space)

Tricuspid valve (Right lat. border of sternum, 5th intercostal space)

Mitral valve (Apex of heart)

Fig. 171: Sites on the Chest Wall for Ascultation of the Heart

Compare sites of ascultation with actual locations of the heart valves in the thorax as shown in Fig. 172.

Figs. 170, 171

Fig. 172: Projection of the Heart and its Valves onto Anterior Thoracic Wall

NOTE: 1) the broken lines indicate the limits of the area of deep cardiac dullness from which a dull resonance can be obtained by percussion. Lung tissue covers the area of deep cardiac dullness but does not cover the area limited by the dotted lines from which a less resonant superficial cardiac dullness can be obtained by percussion.

2) the apex of the normal heart is usually found in the 5th interspace about 9 centimeters to the left of the midline.

3) that the *pulmonary valve* lies behind the sternal end of the third left costal cartilage. The *aortic valve* is behind the sternum at the level of the 3rd intercostal space. The *bicuspid valve* lies behind the 4th left sternocostal joint, and the *tricuspid valve* lies posterior to the middle of the sternum at the level of the 4th intercostal space.

Rt. common carotid artery — Left common carotid artery
Rt. int. jugular vein — Left int. jugular vein
Rt. subclavian artery — Left subclavian art.
Rt. subclavian vein — Left subclavian vein
Right brachio-cephalic vein — Left brachio-cephalic vein
Brachiocephalic artery — Aortic arch
Superior vena cava — Pulmonary artery trunk
Ascending aorta — **Pulmonary valve**
Aortic valve
Left atrio-ventricular valve (bicuspid)
(Nipple) M — M (Nipple)
Rt. atrio-ventricular valve (tricuspid)
(Diaphragm) D — (Diaphragm)

Fig. 173 (Inspiration)

Fig. 174 (Expiration)

Fig. 173 and 174: Positions of the Heart During Full Inspiration (Fig. 173) and During Full Expiration (Fig. 174)

NOTE: 1) during full inspiration (Fig. 173), the thorax is enlarged by a lowering of the diaphragm due to contraction of its muscle fibers and by elevation and expansion of the thoracic cage (ribs and sternum). The thorax expands antero-posteriorly, transversely and vertically and, therefore, during inspiration the shape of the heart becomes more oblong (i.e. its transverse diameter is decreased), and its apex and diaphragmatic surface are lowered. Inspiration must be accompanied by relaxation of the muscles of the anterior abdominal wall, allowing protrusion of the abdomen and a lowering of the abdominal viscera.

2) full expiration (Fig. 174) occurs because of an elevation of the diaphragm which results from relaxation of its muscle fibers and because the ribs and sternum are lowered. Thus, the capacity of the thoracic cage is diminished, causing an elevation in the diaphragmatic surface of the heart, as well as the apex of the heart, with a concomitant increase in the heart's transverse diameter. Expiration is accompanied by contraction of the muscles of the anterior abdominal wall and an elevation of abdominal viscera, which push the relaxed diaphragm upward.

3) an excellent account of the movements of the thoracic cage during respiration is presented by Professor R.J. Last: *Anatomy, Regional and Applied*, 7th edition, Churchill-Livingstone, 1984, pages 219 – 223).

Figs. 172, 173, 174   II

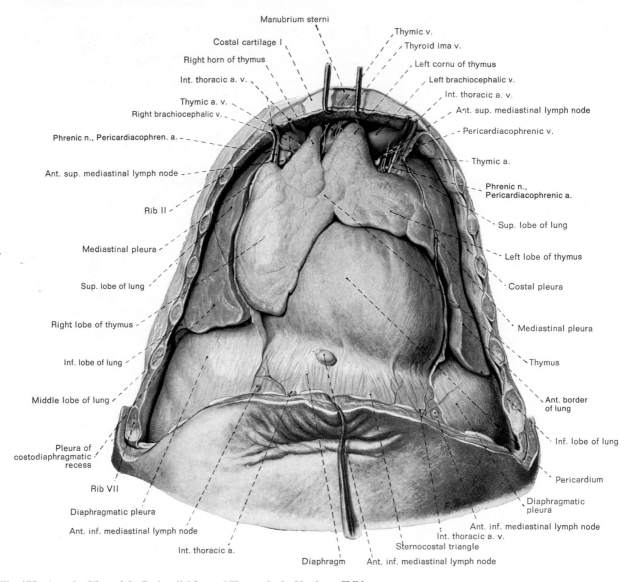

Fig. 175: Anterior View of the Pericardial Sac and Thymus in the Newborn Child

NOTE that the great vessels of the superior mediastinum and the parietal pericardium over the base of the heart are covered by the thymus gland. The thymus also extends into the root of the neck in the newborn child.

Fig. 176: Anterior View of the Heart and Great Vessels of a Newborn Child After Removal of the Thymus

NOTE that the ductus arteriosus is still an enlarged structure immediately after birth.

Figs. 175, 176

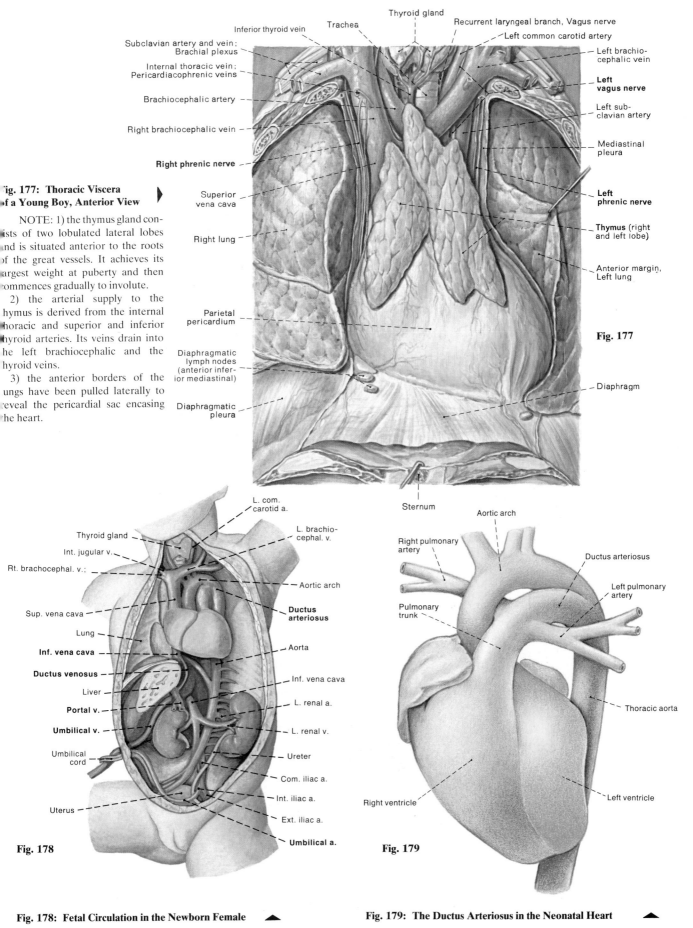

Fig. 177: Thoracic Viscera of a Young Boy, Anterior View

NOTE: 1) the thymus gland consists of two lobulated lateral lobes and is situated anterior to the roots of the great vessels. It achieves its largest weight at puberty and then commences gradually to involute.

2) the arterial supply to the thymus is derived from the internal thoracic and superior and inferior thyroid arteries. Its veins drain into the left brachiocephalic and thyroid veins.

3) the anterior borders of the lungs have been pulled laterally to reveal the pericardial sac encasing the heart.

Inferior thyroid vein

Subclavian artery and vein; Brachial plexus

Internal thoracic vein; Pericardiacophrenic veins

Brachiocephalic artery

Right brachiocephalic vein

Right phrenic nerve

Superior vena cava

Right lung

Parietal pericardium

Diaphragmatic lymph nodes (anterior inferior mediastinal)

Diaphragmatic pleura

Thyroid gland
Trachea
Recurrent laryngeal branch, Vagus nerve
Left common carotid artery

Left brachiocephalic vein

Left vagus nerve

Left subclavian artery

Mediastinal pleura

Left phrenic nerve

Thymus (right and left lobe)

Anterior margin, Left lung

Fig. 177

Diaphragm

Sternum

L. com. carotid a.

Thyroid gland

Int. jugular v.

Rt. brachiocephal. v.;

Sup. vena cava

Lung

Inf. vena cava

Ductus venosus

Liver

Portal v.

Umbilical v.

Umbilical cord

Uterus

L. brachiocephal. v.

Aortic arch

Ductus arteriosus

Aorta

Inf. vena cava

L. renal a.

L. renal v.

Ureter

Com. iliac a.

Int. iliac a.

Ext. iliac a.

Umbilical a.

Fig. 178

Aortic arch

Right pulmonary artery

Ductus arteriosus

Left pulmonary artery

Pulmonary trunk

Thoracic aorta

Right ventricle

Left ventricle

Fig. 179

Fig. 178: Fetal Circulation in the Newborn Female ▲

NOTE that the shades of color depict the oxygen level in the blood. Observe the umbilical vein, ductus arteriosus and umbilical artery – all structures peculiar to fetal circulation.

Fig. 179: The Ductus Arteriosus in the Neonatal Heart ▲

NOTE that the blood in the thoracic aorta is a mixture, part of it coming from the right heart by way of the ductus arteriosus and part of it coming from the left heart through the aorta.

Figs. 177, 178, 179   **II**

Fig. 180: The Opened Right Atrium in a 310 mm Human Fetus

NOTE that in the fetus blood pressure is greater in the right atrium than in the left and foramen ovale II is covered by the septum primum on the left side of septum secundum. This allows blood to pass easily from right to left. After birth, pressure is greater in the left atrium, which results in closure of the foramen.

Fig. 181: Circulation in the Fetus

NOTE: 1) that some oxygenated blood from the umbilical vein flows through the foramen ovale to the left ventricle and out the aorta to the head and limbs. A considerable amount of oxygenated blood also goes through the right ventricle, pulmonary trunk, and then through the ductus arteriosus to the aorta.

2) the shunt formed by the ductus venosus to bypass the liver.

Sup. vena cava

Remainder of foramen ovale I

Septum secundum

Interatrial septum

Right A-V valve

Septum primum; Foramen ovale II

Inf. vena cava

Valve of the Inf. vena cava

Valve of the coronary sinus

Opening of coronary sinus

Vagina

Amniotic cavity

Rectouterine pouch

Posterior lip, external os of uterus

Left atrium

Internal uterine orifice

Margin of placenta

Serous coat of uterus

Marginal sinus of placenta

Uterine veins

Intervillous placental space

Placental septum

Chorionic villi

Attachment of umbilical cord

Uteroplacental arteries

Decidua basalis

Uterine musculature

Amnion

Umbilical arteries and veins

Chorion

Placental septum

Marginal sinus of placenta

Margin of placenta

Anterior lip, external os of uterus

Uterovesical fossa

Ductus arteriosus

Ascending aorta

Superior vena cava

Pulmonary trunk

Foramen ovale

Right atrium

Ductus venosus

Inf. vena cava

Celiac trunk

Umbilical vein

Portal vein

Umbilical ring

Decidua capsularis and parietalis

Umbilical arteries

Chorion laeve

Amnion

Figs. 180, 181

Fig. 182: Diagram of Main Arteries; The Adult Systemic Circulation

NOTE that the heart is outlined in red dots. The black dots are sites along the course of main arteries which may be used as pressure points to interrupt blood flow in the pelvis and limbs during surgery.

Middle meningeal a.
Maxillary a.
External carotid a.
Internal carotid a.
Facial a.
Lingual a.
Thyrocervical trunk
Subclavian a.
Brachiocephalic trunk
Internal thoracic a.
Axillary a.
Lateral thoracic a.
Circumflex humeral a.
Subscapular a.
Intercostal aa.
Deep brachial a.
Brachial a.
Subcostal a.
Abdominal aorta
Radial a.
Ulnar a.
Deep palmar arch
Superficial palmar arch

Vertebral a.
Common carotid a.
Supreme thoracic a.
Arch of aorta
Thoracoacromial a.
Thoracic aorta
Celiac trunk
Gastric a., left
Common hepatic a.
Splenic a.
Sup. mesenteric a.
Renal a.
Spermatic a.
Lumbar aa.
Inferior mesenteric a.
Inferior epigastric a.
Common iliac a.
Middle sacral a.
External iliac a.
Internal iliac a.
Superior gluteal a.
Obturator a.
Inferior gluteal a.
Femoral a.
Lateral circumflex femoral a.
Medial circumflex femoral a.
Deep femoral a.
Perforating a. I
Perforating a. II
Perforating a. III
Descending genicular a.

Popliteal a.

Anterior tibial a.
Posterior tibial a.

Peroneal (fibular) a.

Dorsalis pedis a.

Arcuate a.
Medial plantar a.
Dorsal metatarsal aa.

Pulmonary circulation
Opening of thoracic duct
From head and arm
Hepatic vein
Thoracic duct
Cisterna chyli

To head and arm
Pulmonary artery
Aorta
Liver
Portal vein
Lymph channels
Systemic circulation

Fig. 183: Schema of Normal Blood Flow in the Adult Body

NOTE: 1) that lymph from the abdomen and much of the lower region of the body flows through the thoracic duct. This duct has its origin at the cisterna chyli and subsequently opens into the left subclavian vein close to its junction (with the internal jugular vein) into the left brachiocephalic vein. In this manner circulating lymph in the tissues is returned to the general circulation.

2) the systemic, pulmonary and portal circulatory channels.

Figs. 182, 183   II

Subclavian artery

Brachial plexus

Clavicle

2nd thoracic sympathetic ganglion

Subclavius muscle

Recurrent laryngeal branch,
Right vagus nerve

Scalenus anterior muscle

Cardiac plexus, Vagus nerve

Subclavian vein

Ant. pulmonary plexus,
Vagus nerve

1st rib; Intercostal fascia

Internal thoracic artery

Arch of the azygos vein

Phrenic nerve

Vagus nerve,
Post. pulmonary plexus

Rt. brachiocephalic vein

Pericardiacophrenic art.

Thymus gland

Intercostal vein,
artery and nerve

Superior vena cava

Pulmonary artery

Right phrenic nerve,
Pericardiacophrenic artery

**Sympathetic
trunk ganglia**

Right primary bronchus,
Dorsal bronchial art. and vein

Pulmonary veins

Pericardium
(covered by
mediastinal pleura)

**Greater
splanchnic nerve**

Pulmonary ligament

Esophagus,
Esophageal plexus

Costal pleura

Costal pleura

Central tendon
of diaphragm

Diaphragm

Fig. 184: The Right Side of the Mediastinum

NOTE: 1) with the right lung removed and the structures at its hilum transected, the organs of the mediastinum are exposed and their right lateral surface viewed.

2) the right side of the heart covered by the pericardium and the course of the phrenic nerve and pericardiacophrenic vessels.

3) the ascending course of the azygos vein, its arch and its junction with the superior vena cava.

4) that the right vagus nerve descends in the thorax behind the root of the right lung to form the posterior pulmonary plexus. It then helps form the esophageal plexus and leaves the thorax on the posterior aspect of the esophagus.

5) the dome of the diaphragm on the right side, taking the rounded form of the underlying liver. The inferior (diaphragmatic) surface of the heart rests on the diaphragm.

6) the position of the thoracic sympathetic chain of ganglia coursing longitudinally along the inner surface of the thoracic wall. Observe the greater splanchnic nerve.

Fig. 184

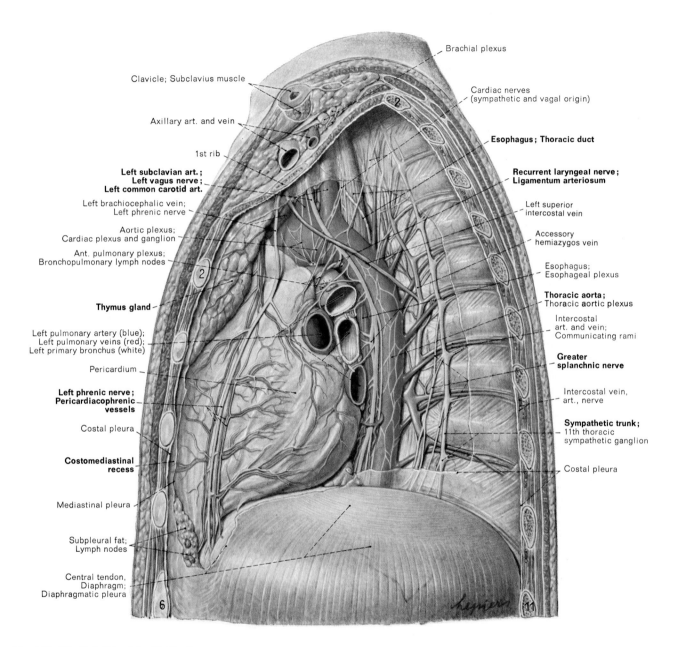

Brachial plexus

Clavicle; Subclavius muscle

Cardiac nerves
(sympathetic and vagal origin)

Axillary art. and vein

Esophagus; Thoracic duct

1st rib

Left subclavian art.;
Left vagus nerve;
Left common carotid art.

Recurrent laryngeal nerve;
Ligamentum arteriosum

Left brachiocephalic vein;
Left phrenic nerve

Left superior
intercostal vein

Aortic plexus;
Cardiac plexus and ganglion

Accessory
hemiazygos vein

Ant. pulmonary plexus;
Bronchopulmonary lymph nodes

Esophagus;
Esophageal plexus

Thoracic aorta;
Thoracic aortic plexus

Thymus gland

Intercostal
art. and vein;
Communicating rami

Left pulmonary artery (blue);
Left pulmonary veins (red);
Left primary bronchus (white)

Greater
splanchnic nerve

Pericardium

Intercostal vein,
art., nerve

Left phrenic nerve;
Pericardiacophrenic
vessels

Sympathetic trunk;
11th thoracic
sympathetic ganglion

Costal pleura

Costal pleura

Costomediastinal
recess

Mediastinal pleura

Subpleural fat;
Lymph nodes

Central tendon,
Diaphragm;
Diaphragmatic pleura

Fig. 185: The Left Side of the Mediastinum

NOTE: 1) with the left lung removed along with most of the mediastinal pleura, the structures of the mediastinum are observed from their left side.

2) the left phrenic nerve and pericardiacophrenic vessels coursing to the diaphragm along the pericardium covering the left side of the heart.

3) the aorta ascends about two inches before it arches posteriorly and to the left of the vertebral column. The descending thoracic aorta commences at about the level of the 4th thoracic vertebra and as it descends, it comes to lie directly anterior to the vertebral column. The intercostal arteries branch directly from the thoracic aorta.

4) the left vagus nerve lies lateral to the aortic arch and gives off its recurrent laryngeal branch which passes inferior to the ligamentum arteriosum. The left vagus then continues to descend, contributes to the esophageal plexus, and enters the abdomen on the anterior aspect of the esophagus.

5) the position of the thymus gland anterior to the root of the great vessels at their attachments to the heart.

6) that the typical intercostal artery and vein course along the inferior border of their respective rib. Because the superior border of the ribs is free of vessels and nerves, it is a safer site for injection or drainage of the thorax.

Fig. 185   II

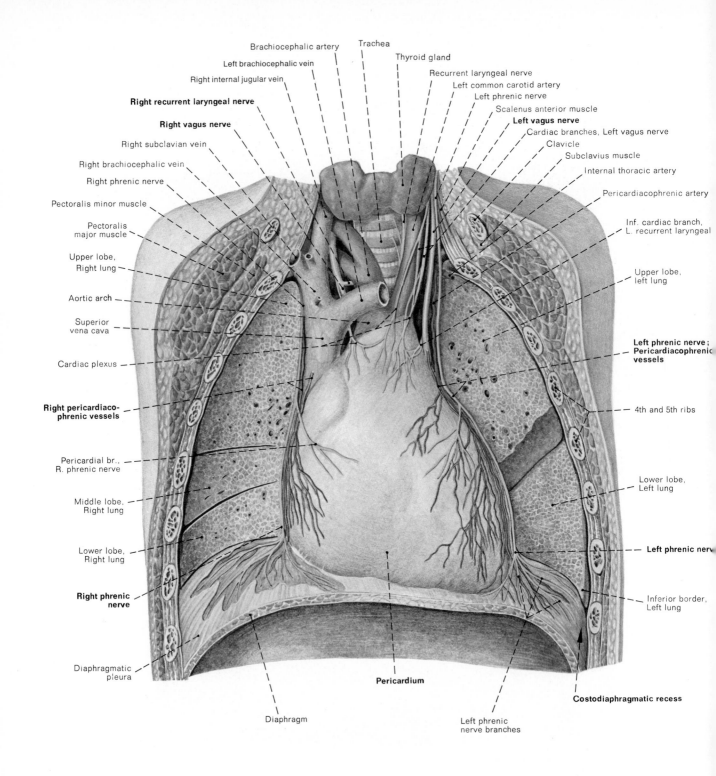

Fig. 186: The Adult Heart, Pericardium and Superior Mediastinal Structures, Anterior View

NOTE: 1) in this frontal section through the thorax, the anterior thoracic wall and the anterior aspect of the lungs and diaphragm have been removed, leaving the pericardium, its contents and its associated vessels and nerves intact. The courses of the vagus nerves and their branches in the superior mediastinum are also demonstrated.

2) the phrenic nerves originate in the neck (C3, 4, 5) and descend almost vertically to innervate the diaphragm. In the superior mediastinum they join the pericardiacophrenic vessels, travel along the lateral surfaces of the pericardium and are distributed principally to the diaphragm, sending some sensory fibers to the pericardium as well.

3) the pericardium is formed by an outer fibrous layer which is lined by an inner serous sac. As the heart develops it invaginates into the inner serous sac, thereby being covered by a visceral layer of serous pericardium (epicardium) and a parietal layer of serous pericardium. The outer fibrous pericardium has only a parietal layer.

Fig. 186

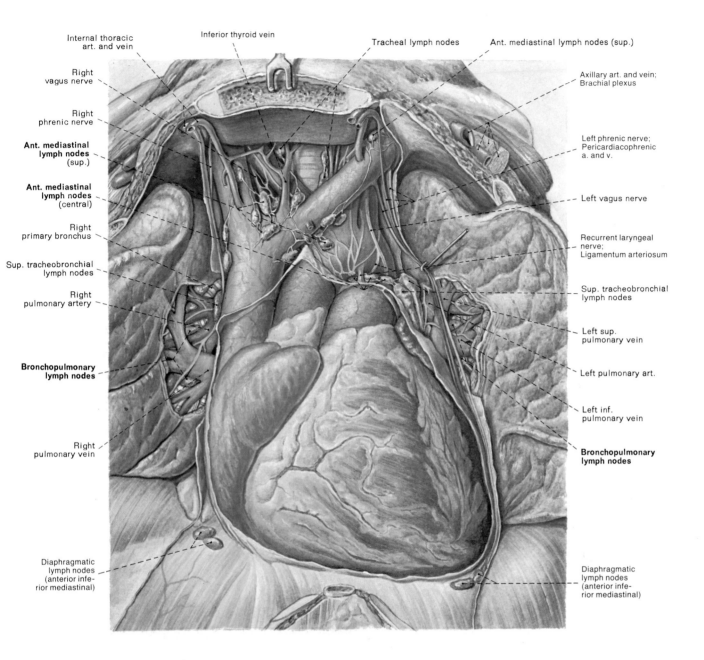

Internal thoracic art. and vein

Inferior thyroid vein

Tracheal lymph nodes

Ant. mediastinal lymph nodes (sup.)

Right vagus nerve

Right phrenic nerve

Ant. mediastinal lymph nodes (sup.)

Ant. mediastinal lymph nodes (central)

Right primary bronchus

Sup. tracheobronchial lymph nodes

Right pulmonary artery

Bronchopulmonary lymph nodes

Right pulmonary vein

Diaphragmatic lymph nodes (anterior inferior mediastinal)

Axillary art. and vein; Brachial plexus

Left phrenic nerve; Pericardiacophrenic a. and v.

Left vagus nerve

Recurrent laryngeal nerve; Ligamentum arteriosum

Sup. tracheobronchial lymph nodes

Left sup. pulmonary vein

Left pulmonary art.

Left inf. pulmonary vein

Bronchopulmonary lymph nodes

Diaphragmatic lymph nodes (anterior inferior mediastinal)

Fig. 187: Lymphatics of the Thorax, Anterior Aspect

NOTE: 1) in this dissection the anterior thoracic wall was removed along with the ventral portion of the pericardium. Further, the anterior borders of the lungs have been pulled laterally to reveal the lymphatic channels at the roots of the lungs. The thymus has also been removed and the manubrium reflected superiorly to expose the organs at the thoracic inlet and their associated lymphatics.

2) the lymph nodes in the anterior aspect of the thoracic cavity might be divided into those associated with the thoracic cage (parietal) and those associated with the organs (visceral). Probably all of the nodes indicated in this figure are visceral nodes.

3) situated ventrally are the *anterior mediastinal nodes* which include a superior group lying ventral to the brachiocephalic veins along their course in the superior mediastinum and at their junction to form the superior vena cava. A more centrally located group lies ventral to the arch of the aorta. Inferiorly, anterior diaphragmatic nodes are sometimes also classified as part of the anterior mediastinal nodes.

4) large numbers of lymph nodes are associated with the trachea, the bronchi and the other structures at the root of the lung. These nodes have been aptly named tracheal, tracheobronchial, bronchopulmonary and pulmonary.

Fig. 187   II

Trachea

Sternum

Inferior thyroid vein

Paratracheal lymph nodes

Common carotid a.; Sup. cardiac n. (of vagus)

Internal thoracic a. and v.

Brachioceph. trunk; Sup. card. nerve

Internal thoracic a. and v.

Inferior cardiac branch, vagus n.

Right phrenic nerve; Pericardiacophrenic a.

Mediastinal pleura

Ant. mediastin. lymph nodes

Right lung

Rt. brachiocephalic vein

Thymic vein; Sup. mediastinal nodes

Aortic pericard. recess

Azygos vein

Hilum of lung

Rt. pulmonary artery; Lymph nodes

Superior vena cava

Pulmonary artery

Ant. bronchial a. and v.

Superior vena cava

Ascending aorta

Rt. phrenic nerve; Pericardiacophrenic a.

Sup. pulmonary vein

Mediastinal pleura

Sulcus terminalis

Pulmon. pericard. recess

Right auricle

Pulmonary trunk

Pericardium

Coronary sulcus

Mediastinal pleura

Adipose tissue

Lymph nodes

Right ventricle

Diaphragmatic pleura

Clavicle

Subclavius muscle

Axillary a. and v.; Brachial plexus

L. brachiocephalic v.; Ant. mediastinal lymph chain

L. phrenic nerve; Pericardiacophrenic a.

Left vagus nerve; Inf. cardiac branch, vagus n.

L. subclavian artery; Sup. cardiac branch, vagus n.

L. superior intercostal v.

Aortic arch; Superficial cardiac plexus

Mediastinal pleura

L. recurrent laryngeal n. Ligamentum arteriosum

Pulmonary plexus

Left pulmonary artery

Hilum of lung

A small pericardial vein

Ant. bronchial a. and v.

Sup. pulmonary vein

Left auricle

Pericardium

Left (obtuse) margin of heart

Conus arteriosus, rt. vent.

Ant. interventric. sulcu

Left lung

Left ventricle, sternocostal surface

Diaphragmatic pleura

Left phrenic nerve

Apex of heart

Inferior mediastinal lymph nodes

Diaphragmatic pleura

Apical incisure of heart

Pericardium

Diaphragm

Acute margin of the heart

Xiphoid process

Diaphragm

Fig. 188: The Heart and Great Vessels, Anterior View

   NOTE that the anterior portion of the pericardium has been removed along with the remnants of the thymus to reveal the heart in its normal position within the middle mediastinum. The arrow is in the transverse pericardial sinus.

Fig. 188

Inferior thyroid vein — Thymic vein — Left recurrent laryngeal nerve

Right vagus nerve — Trachea — Left brachiocephalic vein

Aortic arch; Brachiocephalic artery; Left common carotid artery; Left subclavian artery

Right brachiocephalic vein; Right internal thoracic vein

Superior vena cava

Mediastinal pleura

Right lung

Transverse pericardial sinus

Transition of parietal and visceral pericardium

Right sup. pulmonary vein

Right inf. pulmonary vein

Esophagus (beneath pericardium)

Fat tissue
Diaphragmatic pleura
Diaphragm

Inferior vena cava

Phrenic nerve; Pericardiacophrenic vessels

Superficial cardiac plexus

Left vagus nerve; Left recurrent laryngeal nerve

Left and right pulmonary arteries

Left lung

Mediastinal pleura

Left sup. pulmonary vein

Left inf. pulmonary vein

Oblique pericardial sinus

Parietal pericardium

Sternocostal part of pericardium

Diaphragmatic part of pericardium

Fig. 189: Interior of the Pericardium, Anterior View

NOTE: 1) the pericardium has been opened anteriorly and the heart has been severed from the great vessels and removed. Eight vessels have been cut: the superior and inferior venae cavae, the four pulmonary veins, the pulmonary artery and the aorta.

2) the oblique pericardial sinus is located in the central portion of this posterior wall and is bounded by the pericardial reflections over the pulmonary veins and the venae cavae (venous mesocardium). With the heart in place, the oblique pericardial sinus may be palpated by inserting several fingers behind the heart and probing superiorly until the blind pouch of the sinus is felt.

3) the transverse pericardial sinus lies behind the pericardial reflection surrounding the aorta and pulmonary artery (arterial mesocardium). It may be located by probing from right to left with the index finger immediately posterior to the pulmonary trunk.

4) the site of bifurcation of the pulmonary trunk beneath the arch of the aorta and the course of the left recurrent laryngeal nerve beneath the ligamentum arteriosum (not labelled).

Fig. 189   II

Fig. 190: The Coronary Vessels, Anterior View

NOTE: 1) both the left and right coronary arteries arise from the ascending aorta. The *left coronary* is directed toward the left and soon divides into a *descending anterior interventricular branch* which courses toward the apex and a circumflex branch which passes posteriorly as far as the posterior interventricular sulcus.

2) the right coronary artery is directed toward the right, passing to the posterior aspect of the heart within the coronary sulcus. In its course, branches from the right coronary supply the anterior surface of the right side (anterior cardiac artery). Its largest branch is the posterior interventricular artery which courses toward the apex on the posterior or diaphragmatic surface of the heart.

3) the principal veins of the heart drain into the coronary sinus which in turn flows into the right atrium. The distribution and course of the veins is generally similar to the arteries.

Fig. 191: The Valves of the Heart and the Origin of the Coronary Vessels, Superior View

NOTE that the left coronary artery arises from the aortic sinus behind the left semilunar cusp and the right coronary artery stems from the aortic sinus behind the right semilunar cusp.

Figs. 190, 191

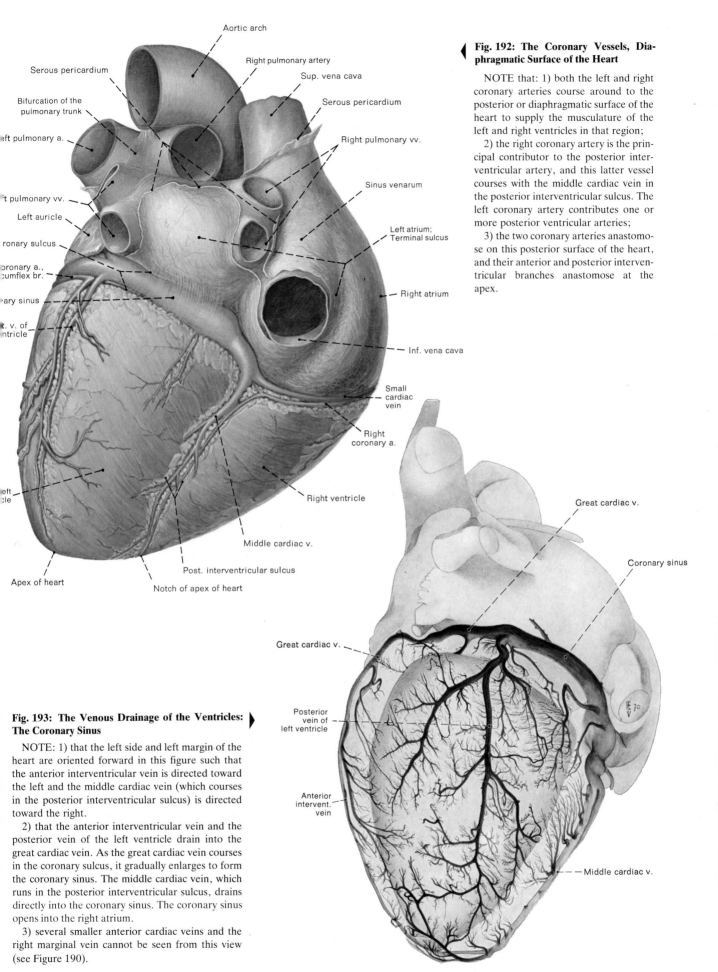

Aortic arch

Serous pericardium

Right pulmonary artery

Sup. vena cava

Serous pericardium

Bifurcation of the pulmonary trunk

Right pulmonary vv.

eft pulmonary a.

t pulmonary vv.

Left auricle

Sinus venarum

ronary sulcus

Left atrium;
Terminal sulcus

oronary a.,
cumflex br.

ary sinus

Right atrium

t. v. of
ntricle

Inf. vena cava

Small
cardiac
vein

Right
coronary a.

eft
cle

Right ventricle

Apex of heart

Middle cardiac v.

Post. interventricular sulcus

Notch of apex of heart

Fig. 192: The Coronary Vessels, Dia-phragmatic Surface of the Heart

NOTE that: 1) both the left and right coronary arteries course around to the posterior or diaphragmatic surface of the heart to supply the musculature of the left and right ventricles in that region;

2) the right coronary artery is the principal contributor to the posterior interventricular artery, and this latter vessel courses with the middle cardiac vein in the posterior interventricular sulcus. The left coronary artery contributes one or more posterior ventricular arteries;

3) the two coronary arteries anastomose on this posterior surface of the heart, and their anterior and posterior interventricular branches anastomose at the apex.

Great cardiac v.

Coronary sinus

Great cardiac v.

Posterior
vein of
left ventricle

Anterior
intervent.
vein

Middle cardiac v.

Fig. 193: The Venous Drainage of the Ventricles: The Coronary Sinus

NOTE: 1) that the left side and left margin of the heart are oriented forward in this figure such that the anterior interventricular vein is directed toward the left and the middle cardiac vein (which courses in the posterior interventricular sulcus) is directed toward the right.

2) that the anterior interventricular vein and the posterior vein of the left ventricle drain into the great cardiac vein. As the great cardiac vein courses in the coronary sulcus, it gradually enlarges to form the coronary sinus. The middle cardiac vein, which runs in the posterior interventricular sulcus, drains directly into the coronary sinus. The coronary sinus opens into the right atrium.

3) several smaller anterior cardiac veins and the right marginal vein cannot be seen from this view (see Figure 190).

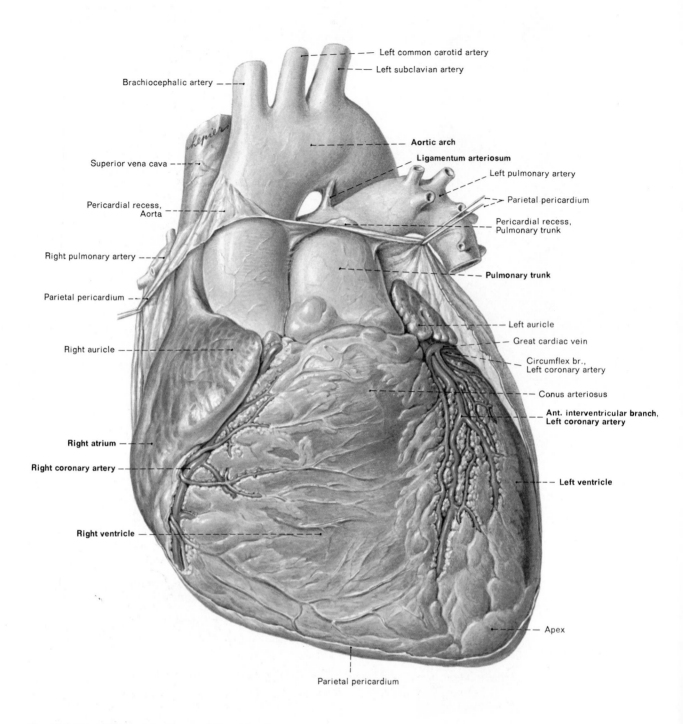

Left common carotid artery
Left subclavian artery
Brachiocephalic artery
Aortic arch
Ligamentum arteriosum
Superior vena cava
Left pulmonary artery
Parietal pericardium
Pericardial recess, Aorta
Pericardial recess, Pulmonary trunk
Right pulmonary artery
Pulmonary trunk
Parietal pericardium
Left auricle
Great cardiac vein
Right auricle
Circumflex br., Left coronary artery
Conus arteriosus
Ant. interventricular branch, Left coronary artery
Right atrium
Right coronary artery
Left ventricle
Right ventricle
Apex
Parietal pericardium

Fig. 194: Ventral View of the Heart and Great Vessels

NOTE: 1) the heart is a muscular organ with its apex pointed inferiorly, toward the left and slightly anteriorly. The base of the heart is opposite to the apex and is, therefore, directed superiorly and toward the right. The great vessels attach to the heart at its base, and the pericardium is reflected over these vessels at their origin.

2) the anterior surface of the heart is its sternocostal surface. The auricular portion of the right atrium and especially the right ventricle is seen from this anterior view; also a small part of the left ventricle is visible on the left side.

3) the pulmonary trunk originates from the right ventricle. To its right and slightly behind can be seen the aorta which arises from the left ventricle. The superior vena cava can be seen opening into the upper aspect of the right atrium.

4) the ligamentum arteriosum. This fibrous structure, attaching the left pulmonary artery to the arch of the aorta, is the postnatal remnant of the fetal ductus arteriosus which, before birth, acted as a shunt diverting some of the blood directed for the lungs back into the aorta for general systemic distribution.

Fig. 194

Left brachiocephalic vein

Left common carotid artery

Right vertebral vein

Left subclavian artery

Right brachiocephalic vein

Aortic arch

Brachiocephalic artery

Descending thoracic aorta;
intercostal arteries

Azygos vein

Ligamentum arteriosum

Superior vena cava

Ascending aorta

Left pulmonary artery

Pericardium (arterial mesocardium)

Right pulmonary artery

* Transverse pericardial sinus

Pulmonary
trunk

Left pulmonary veins

Left auricle

Right pulmonary veins

Great cardiac vein and circumflex br.,
Left coronary art.

Left atrium

Sinus venarum

Pericardium
(venous mesocardium)

Posterior ventricular veins

Oblique veins
of left atrium

Left ventricle

Right atrium

Coronary sinus

Sulcus terminalis

Inferior vena cava

Apex

Coronary sulcus

Right coronary artery and post.
interventricular branch

Middle cardiac vein in posterior
interventricular sulcus

Right ventricle

Fig. 195: Posterior View of the Heart and Great Vessels

NOTE: 1) the two pericardial sinuses. The long transverse arrow indicates the *transverse pericardial sinus* which lies between the arterial mesocardium and the venous mesocardium. The double arrows lie in the *oblique pericardial sinus*, the boundaries of which are actually demarcated by the pericardial reflections around the pulmonary veins.

2) the transverse sinus can be identified by placing your index finger behind the pulmonary artery and aorta with the heart *in situ*. The oblique sinus is open inferiorly, while superiorly it forms a closed sac. This sinus can also be felt by cupping your fingers behind the heart and pushing superiorly.

3) the coronary sinus separates the posterior surface regions of the atria (above and to the right) and the ventricles (below and to the left). The posterior atrial surface principally consists of the left atrium, into which flow the pulmonary veins, although below and to the right can be seen the right atrium and its inferior vena cava. The posterior atrial surface lies anterior to the vertebral column. The posterior ventricular surface is formed principally by the left ventricle and this surface lies over the diaphragm.

Fig. 195   II

Fig. 196 labels (top illustration):

Right coronary artery
Branch to SA node
Branch to pulmonary trunk
Right atrial branch
Right ventricular branch
Right marginal branch
Branch to AV node
Posterior interventricular branch
Right posterolateral branch

Left atrial branch
Left coronary artery
Circumflex branch
Branch to pulmonary trunk
Left marginal branch
Diagonal branch
Anterior septal branch
Diagonal branch
Anterior septal branch
Anterior interventricular branch

H.S.

Fig. 196: The Complete Coronary Arterial Syst

NOTE: 1) this drawing was made from an inject
specimen prepared by Professor Helmut Ferner
the University of Vienna.

2) anastomoses between branches from the l
and right coronary arteries (LCA and RCA) a
visible in the substance of the posterior wall of t
heart. They are especially prominent between t
posterior interventricular branch of the RCA a
the anterior interventricular branch of the LC
which courses from the anterior heart wall arou
the apex to the posterior wall. Additionally, vess
from the circumflex and left marginal branches of t
LCA anastomose with branches from the RCA in t
posterior wall.

3) in this specimen, vessels supplying the si
atrial (SA) node and the atrioventricular (AV) no
arise from the RCA. In about 35% of cases, howev
the artery to the SA node comes from the circumfl
branch of the LCA. Similarly, in about 20%
specimens, the vessel to the AV node is derived fr
the circumflex branch of the LCA.

Fig. 197: A Balanced Left vs. Right Coronary Artery Distribution

NOTE that coronary angiography has demo
strated that in some hearts the proportion of he
muscle supplied by the left and right corona
arteries is nearly balanced. In other hearts, t
balance may be shifted more toward a left (see. F
198) or right (see Fig. 199) coronary arte
dominance.

Fig. 197 labels (bottom illustration):

Rt. coronary artery
SA nodal branch
Branch to pulmonary trunk
Rt. atrial branch
Right ventricular branch
Rt. marginal branch
AV nodal branch
Right atrio-ventricular branch
Post. inter-ventricular branch
Post. septal branch
Rt. posterolat. branch

Left coronary artery
Circumflex branch
Ant. interventricular branch
Ant. septal branch
Diagonal branch
Left marginal branch
Diagonal branch
Left atrial branch
Left posterolat. branch
Left atriovent. branch

Figs. 196, 197

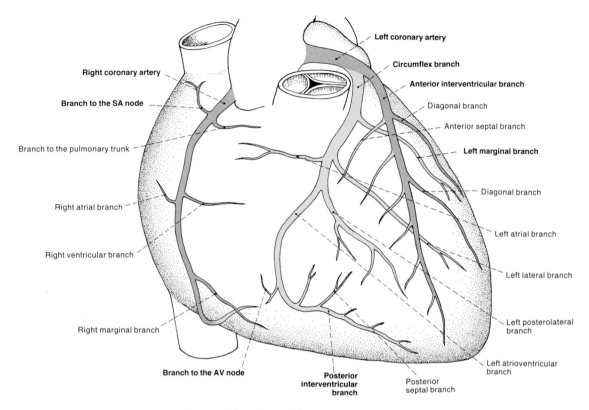

Fig. 198: A Dominant Distribution to the Heart Wall from the Left Coronary Artery

Observe that in hearts containing a dominant left coronary artery, there is very little contribution of blood from the right coronary artery to the posterior wall of the left ventricle. In these cases the posterior interventricular artery arises from the left coronary artery as a continuation of the enlarged circumflex branch.

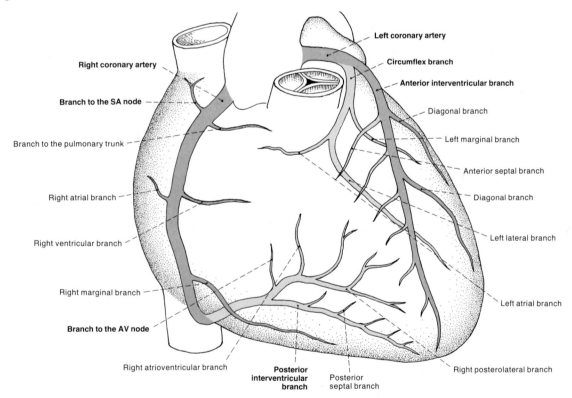

Fig. 199: A Dominant Distribution to the Heart Wall from the Right Coronary Artery

NOTE that in hearts containing a dominant right coronary artery, the posterior wall of the left ventricle receives a larger share of its blood from the right coronary artery when compared with a more balanced coronary distribution (see Fig. 197). In these instances the posterior interventricular artery arises from the right coronary, and the circumflex and marginal branches of the left coronary are relatively smaller. (Drawings in Figures 197, 198 and 199 come from data published by M. Kaltenbach and F. Spahn of Frankfurt, West-Germany: Z. Kardiol., **64**: 193–202, 1975.)

Fig. 200: Left Coronary Arteriogram

NOTE that this arteriogram of the left coronary artery is viewed from a right antero-oblique direction. (From Wicke, L. *Atlas of Radiographic Anatomy,* 3rd Edition, Urban & Schwarzenberg, Baltimore, 1983).

1. Catheter	4. Circumflex branch	7. Left posterolateral branch of circumflex	10. Septal branches
2. Left coronary artery	5. Left marginal branch of circumflex	8. Posterior ventricular branches	11. Diaphragm
3. Anterior interventricular branch	6. Posterior atrial branch	9. Posterior interventricular branch	

Fig. 200

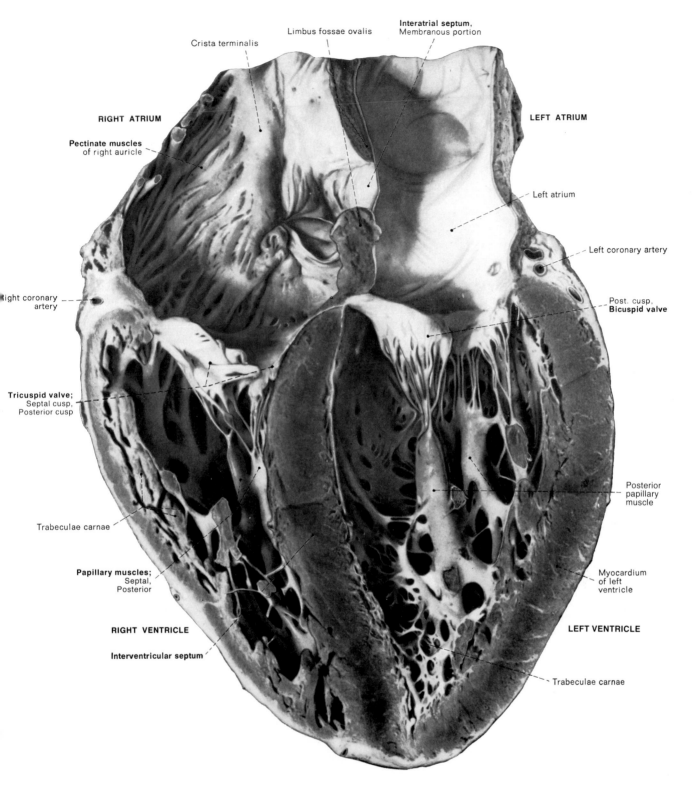

Fig. 201: Frontal Section Through the Heart, Showing Dorsal Half of Heart

NOTE: 1) the human heart is a four-chambered muscular organ consisting of an atrium and a ventricle on each side. The walls of the ventricles are thicker than those of the atria. The atrial chambers are separated by an interatrial septum, and this is continuous with the interventricular septum dividing the two ventricles. Blood passes simultaneously from the two atria into their respective ventricles through the atrioventricular valves.

2) on the right side the atrioventricular valve (AV valve) consists of three cusps and is called the tricuspid valve. On the left side the AV valve has two cusps and is called the bicuspid or mitral valve.

3) the inner surfaces of the atria are relatively smooth, whereas muscular projections, the papillary muscles, protrude from the inner walls of the ventricles to attach to the cusps of the AV valves by way of fibrous, thin cords, the chordae tendineae. (These cords are shown but not labelled.)

4) other elevated muscular bundles on the inner heart wall do not attach to the valves. In the ventricles these are called the trabeculae carnae, while in the right auricle they are named the pectinate muscles.

Fig. 201   II

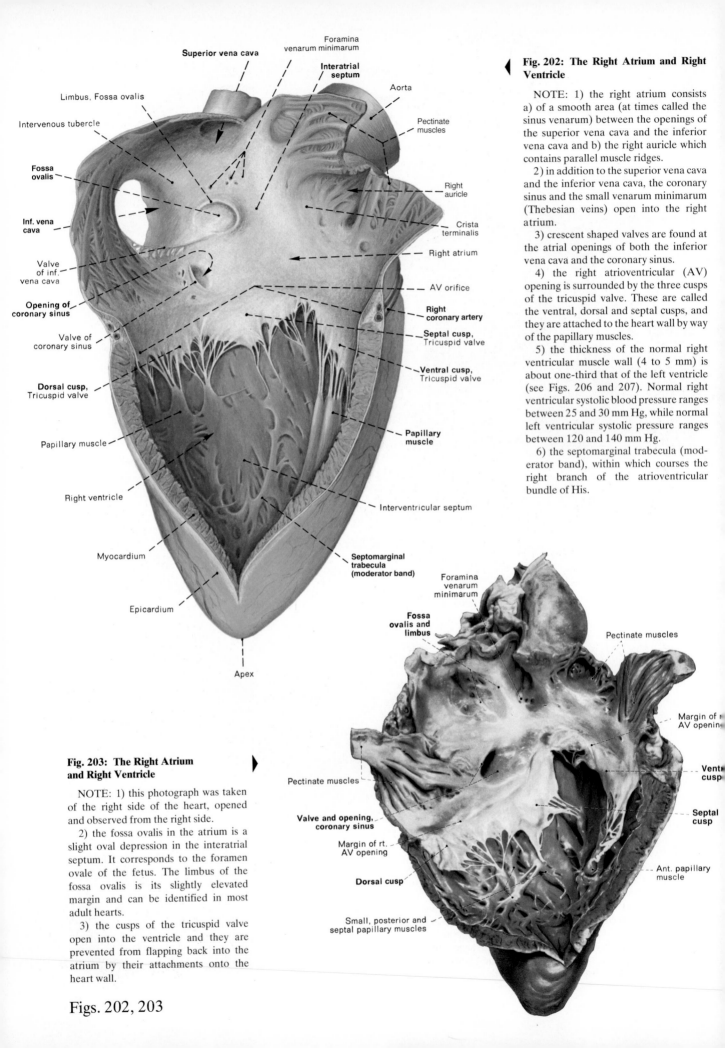

Superior vena cava
Foramina venarum minimarum
Interatrial septum
Aorta
Limbus, Fossa ovalis
Pectinate muscles
Intervenous tubercle
Right auricle
Fossa ovalis
Crista terminalis
Inf. vena cava
Right atrium
Valve of inf. vena cava
AV orifice
Opening of coronary sinus
Right coronary artery
Valve of coronary sinus
Septal cusp, Tricuspid valve
Dorsal cusp, Tricuspid valve
Ventral cusp, Tricuspid valve
Papillary muscle
Papillary muscle
Right ventricle
Interventricular septum
Myocardium
Septomarginal trabecula (moderator band)
Epicardium
Apex

Foramina venarum minimarum
Fossa ovalis and limbus
Pectinate muscles
Pectinate muscles
Margin of AV opening
Valve and opening, coronary sinus
Vent cusp
Margin of rt. AV opening
Septal cusp
Dorsal cusp
Ant. papillary muscle
Small, posterior and septal papillary muscles

Fig. 202: The Right Atrium and Right Ventricle

NOTE: 1) the right atrium consists a) of a smooth area (at times called the sinus venarum) between the openings of the superior vena cava and the inferior vena cava and b) the right auricle which contains parallel muscle ridges.

2) in addition to the superior vena cava and the inferior vena cava, the coronary sinus and the small venarum minimarum (Thebesian veins) open into the right atrium.

3) crescent shaped valves are found at the atrial openings of both the inferior vena cava and the coronary sinus.

4) the right atrioventricular (AV) opening is surrounded by the three cusps of the tricuspid valve. These are called the ventral, dorsal and septal cusps, and they are attached to the heart wall by way of the papillary muscles.

5) the thickness of the normal right ventricular muscle wall (4 to 5 mm) is about one-third that of the left ventricle (see Figs. 206 and 207). Normal right ventricular systolic blood pressure ranges between 25 and 30 mm Hg, while normal left ventricular systolic pressure ranges between 120 and 140 mm Hg.

6) the septomarginal trabecula (moderator band), within which courses the right branch of the atrioventricular bundle of His.

Fig. 203: The Right Atrium and Right Ventricle

NOTE: 1) this photograph was taken of the right side of the heart, opened and observed from the right side.

2) the fossa ovalis in the atrium is a slight oval depression in the interatrial septum. It corresponds to the foramen ovale of the fetus. The limbus of the fossa ovalis is its slightly elevated margin and can be identified in most adult hearts.

3) the cusps of the tricuspid valve open into the ventricle and they are prevented from flapping back into the atrium by their attachments onto the heart wall.

Figs. 202, 203

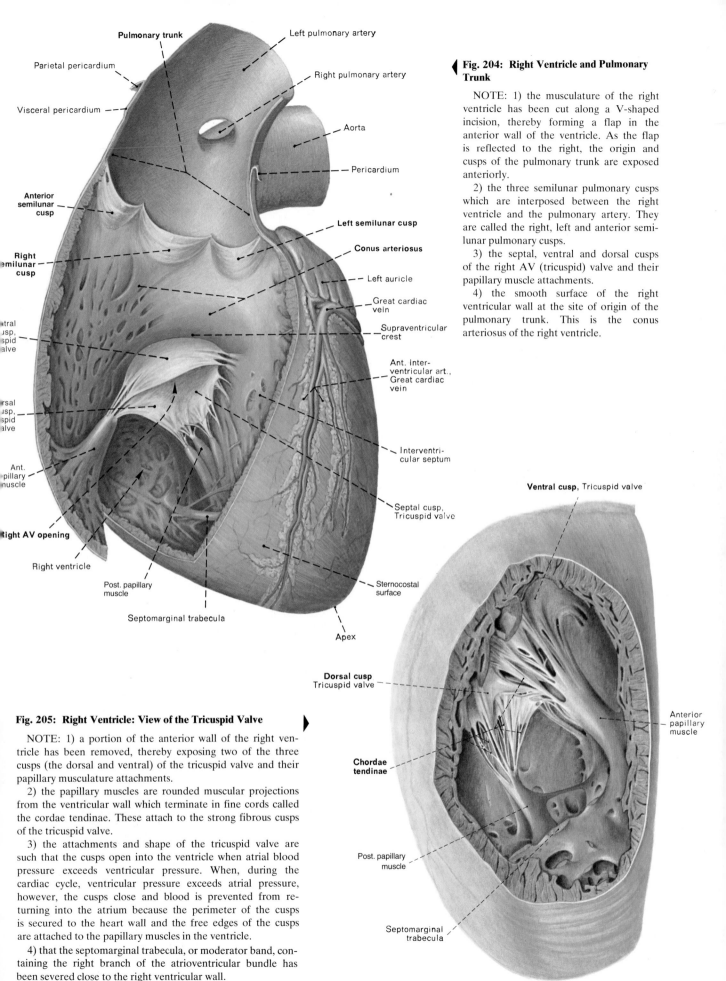

Pulmonary trunk
Parietal pericardium
Visceral pericardium
Left pulmonary artery
Right pulmonary artery
Aorta
Pericardium

Anterior semilunar cusp
Right semilunar cusp

Left semilunar cusp
Conus arteriosus
Left auricle
Great cardiac vein
Supraventricular crest

Ventral cusp, Tricuspid valve
Dorsal cusp, Tricuspid valve

Ant. inter-ventricular art., Great cardiac vein
Interventricular septum

Ant. papillary muscle
Right AV opening
Right ventricle
Post. papillary muscle
Septomarginal trabecula

Septal cusp, Tricuspid valve

Sternocostal surface
Apex

Fig. 204: Right Ventricle and Pulmonary Trunk

NOTE: 1) the musculature of the right ventricle has been cut along a V-shaped incision, thereby forming a flap in the anterior wall of the ventricle. As the flap is reflected to the right, the origin and cusps of the pulmonary trunk are exposed anteriorly.

2) the three semilunar pulmonary cusps which are interposed between the right ventricle and the pulmonary artery. They are called the right, left and anterior semilunar pulmonary cusps.

3) the septal, ventral and dorsal cusps of the right AV (tricuspid) valve and their papillary muscle attachments.

4) the smooth surface of the right ventricular wall at the site of origin of the pulmonary trunk. This is the conus arteriosus of the right ventricle.

Ventral cusp, Tricuspid valve
Dorsal cusp Tricuspid valve
Chordae tendinae
Anterior papillary muscle
Post. papillary muscle
Septomarginal trabecula

Fig. 205: Right Ventricle: View of the Tricuspid Valve

NOTE: 1) a portion of the anterior wall of the right ventricle has been removed, thereby exposing two of the three cusps (the dorsal and ventral) of the tricuspid valve and their papillary musculature attachments.

2) the papillary muscles are rounded muscular projections from the ventricular wall which terminate in fine cords called the cordae tendinae. These attach to the strong fibrous cusps of the tricuspid valve.

3) the attachments and shape of the tricuspid valve are such that the cusps open into the ventricle when atrial blood pressure exceeds ventricular pressure. When, during the cardiac cycle, ventricular pressure exceeds atrial pressure, however, the cusps close and blood is prevented from returning into the atrium because the perimeter of the cusps is secured to the heart wall and the free edges of the cusps are attached to the papillary muscles in the ventricle.

4) that the septomarginal trabecula, or moderator band, containing the right branch of the atrioventricular bundle has been severed close to the right ventricular wall.

Figs. 204, 205   II

Fig. 206: The Left Atrium and Left Ventricle

NOTE: 1) in this specimen a longitudinal section has been made through the left side of the heart, thereby exposing the smooth-walled left atrium above and the thickened, muscular-walled left ventricle below. The left atrium opens into the left ventricle through the left atrioventricular (AV) orifice at which is located the left AV valve. This valve is also called the mitral or bicuspid valve.

2) the mitral valve consists of two cusps, an anterior cusp and a posterior cusp, and these are attached to the left ventricular wall by means of papillary muscles in a manner similar to that seen on the right side of the heart. Observe the chordae tendineae interposed between the cusps and the papillary muscles.

3) the interatrial septum is marked by the valve of the foramen ovale (falx septi), which represents the remnant of the septum primum during the development of the interatrial septum.

4) the left atrium receives the four pulmonary veins (two from each lung) while the left ventricle leads into (indicated by arrow) the aorta.

5) the thick muscular layer of the heart, called the myocardium, is lined on its inner surface by a layer of endothelium, consistent and continuous with the inner lining of blood vessels that enter and leave the heart. The outer covering, called the epicardium, is a serous membrane which serves as the visceral layer of pericardium.

Fig. 207: The Left Ventricle and Ascending Aorta

NOTE: 1) the heart has been cut longitudinally in such a manner that the left ventricular cavity is exposed along with the origin of the ascending aorta.

2) the aortic opening is guarded by three semilunar cusps. These are named the posterior, left and right semilunar aortic cusps. Behind each cusp a small *cul de sac* is formed by the cusp and the wall of the aorta. These small dilated pockets are called the aortic sinuses (sinuses of Valsalva) and from the aortic sinuses behind the left and right semilunar aortic cusps, the left and right coronary arteries arise.

3) during ventricular contraction the blood pressure in the left ventricle is elevated over that in the aorta, thereby causing the aortic valve to open and blood to pass into the aorta. Soon, however, the aortic pressure exceeds ventricular pressure and blood then tends to rush back into the ventricle. In the normal heart, the aortic sinuses trap the regurgitating blood and thereby force the aortic cusps to close.

Figs. 206, 207

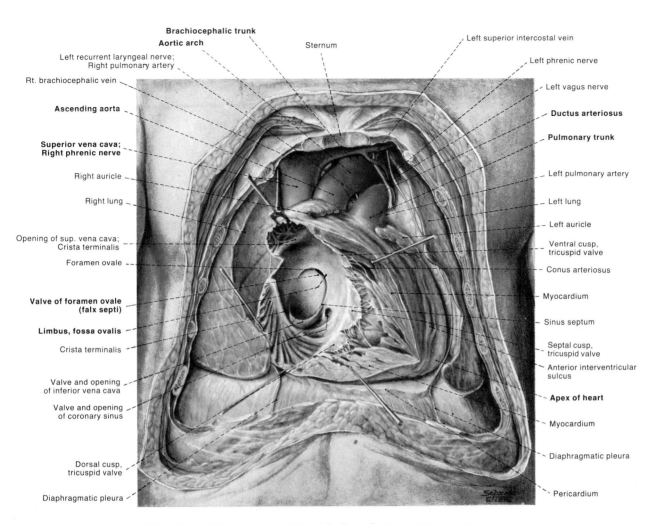

Brachiocephalic trunk
Aortic arch
Left recurrent laryngeal nerve;
Right pulmonary artery
Rt. brachiocephalic vein
Ascending aorta
Superior vena cava;
Right phrenic nerve
Right auricle
Right lung
Opening of sup. vena cava;
Crista terminalis
Foramen ovale
Valve of foramen ovale
(falx septi)
Limbus, fossa ovalis
Crista terminalis
Valve and opening
of inferior vena cava
Valve and opening
of coronary sinus
Dorsal cusp,
tricuspid valve
Diaphragmatic pleura

Sternum

Left superior intercostal vein
Left phrenic nerve
Left vagus nerve
Ductus arteriosus
Pulmonary trunk
Left pulmonary artery
Left lung
Left auricle
Ventral cusp,
tricuspid valve
Conus arteriosus
Myocardium
Sinus septum
Septal cusp,
tricuspid valve
Anterior interventricular
sulcus
Apex of heart
Myocardium
Diaphragmatic pleura
Pericardium

Fig. 208: Heart of Newborn Child: View of Right Atrium and Ventricle, Fossa Ovalis and Tricuspid Valve

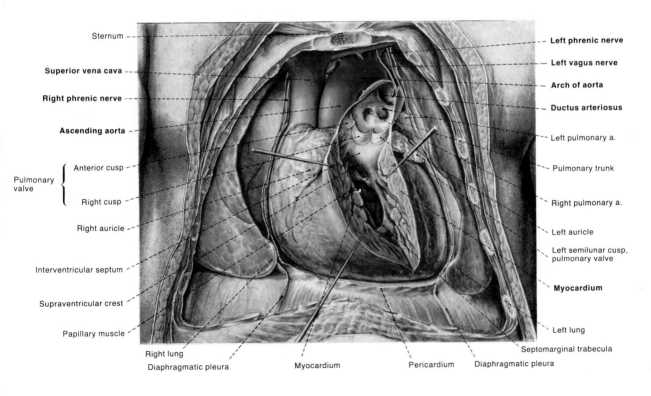

Sternum
Superior vena cava
Right phrenic nerve
Ascending aorta
Pulmonary
valve { Anterior cusp
       Right cusp
Right auricle
Interventricular septum
Supraventricular crest
Papillary muscle

Right lung
Diaphragmatic pleura

Myocardium

Pericardium

Left phrenic nerve
Left vagus nerve
Arch of aorta
Ductus arteriosus
Left pulmonary a.
Pulmonary trunk
Right pulmonary a.
Left auricle
Left semilunar cusp,
pulmonary valve
Myocardium
Left lung
Septomarginal trabecula
Diaphragmatic pleura

Fig. 209: Heart of Newborn Child: View of Pulmonary Trunk and Opened Right Ventricle

Figs. 208, 209   II

**Atrioventricular bundle
and its AV node origin**

Membranous part,
Interventricular septum

Right branch,
AV bundle

valva
atrioventricularis
dextra

pars muscularis
septi
ventricularis

trabeculae
carneae

Fig. 210: The Atrioventricular Bundle
Dissected in the Right Ventricle

NOTE: 1) the atrioventricular (AV) bundle forms a part of the conduction system of the heart and is composed of modified cardiac muscle fibers called Purkinje fibers. This AV bundle commences at the AV node in the interatrial septum near the opening of the coronary sinus of the right atrium.

2) the AV bundle is then directed toward the membranous part of the interventricular septum where it divides into right and left branches. The right branch, which is dissected in this figure, courses in the wall of the right ventricle and is distributed toward the apex.

3) in this dissection the bundle was severed at its site of entrance into the anterior papillary muscle.

aorta ascendens

valva aortae

Membranous part,
Interventricular septum

Left branch, AV bundle

Left
atrium

Mitr
valv

Muscular
part,
Inter-
ventricular
septum

Papillary muscles

Trabeculae
carnae

Fig. 211: The Atrioventricular Bundle
Dissected in the Left Ventricle

NOTE: 1) the left branch of the atrioventricular bundle is dissected on the left side of the interventricular wall. It is seen to commence as a rather wide band of tissue and soon it divides into several strands. These fan out to become distributed among the papillary muscles and trabeculae carnae of the inner left ventricle and ramify among the cardiac muscle fibers.

2) the conduction system of the heart transmits to the cardiac musculature the rhythmic impulses characteristic of the rate of heart beat. This rhythm is superimposed on the natural contractile property of cardiac musculature, and the rate responds to regulation by the cardiac nerves which innervate the heart.

Figs. 210, 211

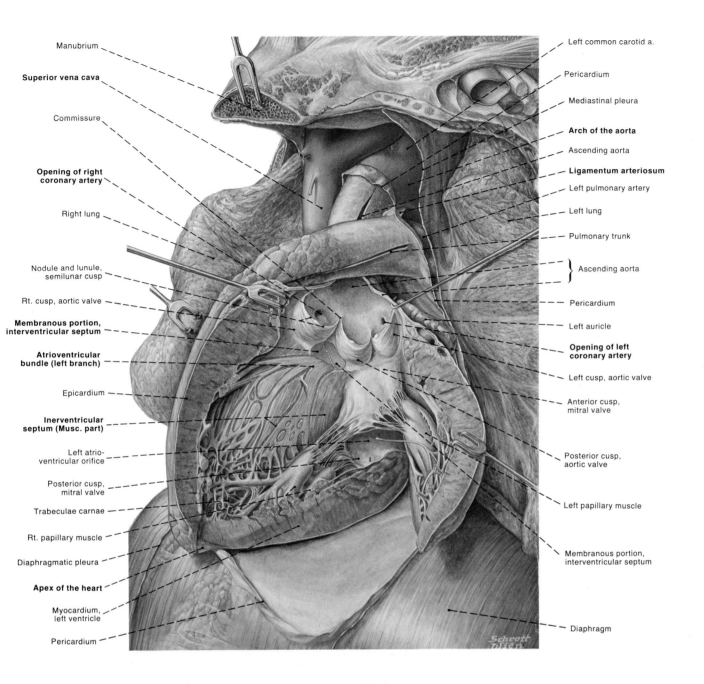

Manubrium

Superior vena cava

Commissure

**Opening of right
coronary artery**

Right lung

Nodule and lunule,
semilunar cusp

Rt. cusp, aortic valve

**Membranous portion,
interventricular septum**

**Atrioventricular
bundle (left branch)**

Epicardium

**Inerventricular
septum (Musc. part)**

Left atrio-
ventricular orifice

Posterior cusp,
mitral valve

Trabeculae carnae

Rt. papillary muscle

Diaphragmatic pleura

Apex of the heart

Myocardium,
left ventricle

Pericardium

Left common carotid a.

Pericardium

Mediastinal pleura

Arch of the aorta

Ascending aorta

Ligamentum arteriosum

Left pulmonary artery

Left lung

Pulmonary trunk

} Ascending aorta

Pericardium

Left auricle

**Opening of left
coronary artery**

Left cusp, aortic valve

Anterior cusp,
mitral valve

Posterior cusp,
aortic valve

Left papillary muscle

Membranous portion,
interventricular septum

Diaphragm

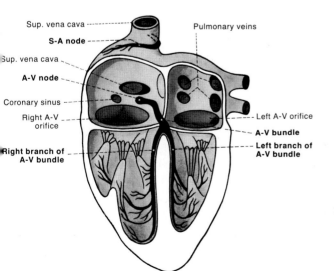

Sup. vena cava

S-A node

Sup. vena cava

A-V node

Coronary sinus

Right A-V
orifice

**Right branch of
A-V bundle**

Pulmonary veins

Left A-V orifice

A-V bundle

**Left branch of
A-V bundle**

Fig. 212: Lateral View of the Atrioventricular Bundle (Left Branch)

NOTE: 1) that in this dissection the left branch of the A-V bundle
has been dissected (and shown in yellow) in its course along the left side
of the interventricular septum. It is observed from within the opened
left ventricle;

2) the anterior and posterior cusps and the associated papillary muscles of the mitral valve, and the right, posterior and left cusps of the aortic valve.

Fig. 213: Diagram of the Conduction System of the Heart

NOTE that the sinoatrial node (S-A node) is located in the wall of
the right atrium at the junction of the superior vena cava with the right
atrium. The atrioventricular node (A-V node) lies in the septal wall of
the right atrium near the opening of the coronary sinus.

Figs. 212, 213   II

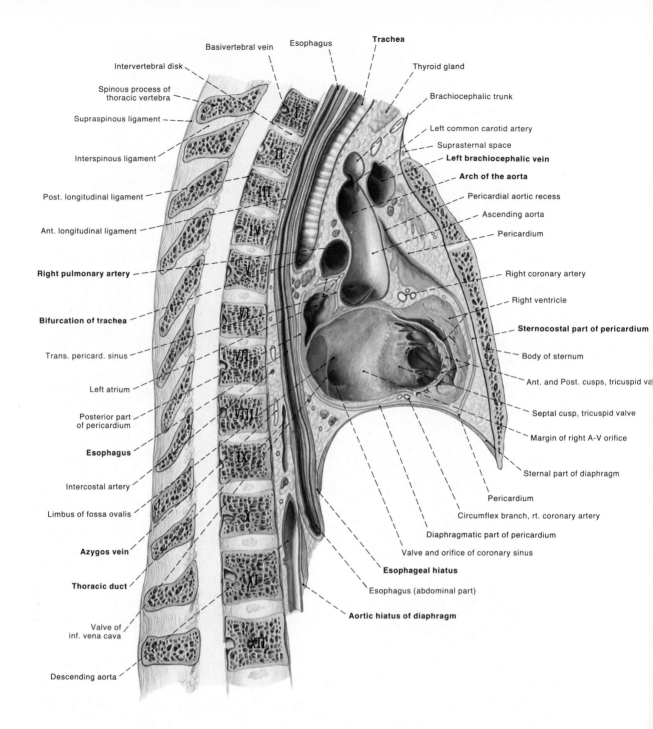

Labels (left side, top to bottom):
- Intervertebral disk
- Spinous process of thoracic vertebra
- Supraspinous ligament
- Interspinous ligament
- Post. longitudinal ligament
- Ant. longitudinal ligament
- Right pulmonary artery
- Bifurcation of trachea
- Trans. pericard. sinus
- Left atrium
- Posterior part of pericardium
- Esophagus
- Intercostal artery
- Limbus of fossa ovalis
- Azygos vein
- Thoracic duct
- Valve of inf. vena cava
- Descending aorta

Labels (top):
- Basivertebral vein
- Esophagus
- Trachea
- Thyroid gland

Labels (right side, top to bottom):
- Brachiocephalic trunk
- Left common carotid artery
- Suprasternal space
- Left brachiocephalic vein
- Arch of the aorta
- Pericardial aortic recess
- Ascending aorta
- Pericardium
- Right coronary artery
- Right ventricle
- Sternocostal part of pericardium
- Body of sternum
- Ant. and Post. cusps, tricuspid valve
- Septal cusp, tricuspid valve
- Margin of right A-V orifice
- Sternal part of diaphragm
- Pericardium
- Circumflex branch, rt. coronary artery
- Diaphragmatic part of pericardium
- Valve and orifice of coronary sinus
- Esophageal hiatus
- Esophagus (abdominal part)
- Aortic hiatus of diaphragm

Fig. 214: A Median Sagittal Section of the Thorax and Vertebral Column Viewed from the Right Side

NOTE that: 1) the bodies of the thoracic vertebrae have been numbered from I to XII;

2) a line drawn directly back from the manubriosternal joint (not labelled) to the spinal column crosses the lower end of the body of the 4th thoracic vertebra, whereas the superior border of the sternum projects back to the 2nd thoracic vertebra, and the lowest point of the xiphoid process lies at the level of the 9th thoracic vertebra;

3) the trachea bifurcates at the level of the upper border of the 5th thoracic vertebra. The esophageal hiatus lies at the upper border of the 10th thoracic vertebra, while somewhat lower, the aortic hiatus is seen at the 11th or between the 11th and 12th thoracic vertebra;

4) because the diaphragmatic opening for the inferior vena cava is to the right of the midline, it cannot be seen in this section; however, the vena caval foramen lies at a level between the 8th and 9th thoracic vertebrae.

5) a median sagittal section of the thorax goes through the right atrium and right ventricle. This is because only one-third of the normal heart lies to the right of the midsternal line, while two-thirds lies to the left of the midline.

6) the transverse pericardial sinus posterior to the aorta. This sinus also courses across the midline posterior to the pulmonary trunk, but in this figure the pulmonary trunk has already bifurcated and, thus, the sinus is shown below the right pulmonary artery.

7) in its course to the right atrium, the left brachiocephalic vein crosses the midline anterior to the arch of the aorta, at the site at which the brachiocephalic trunk arises from the aortic arch (see also Fig. 186, 188).

Fig. 214

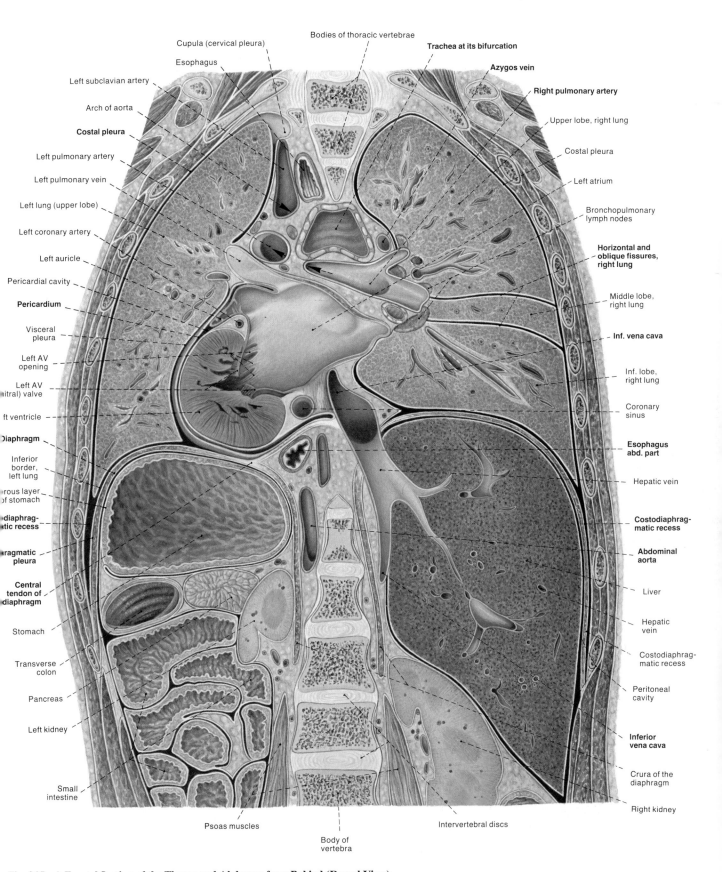

Cupula (cervical pleura)

Esophagus

Left subclavian artery

Arch of aorta

Costal pleura

Left pulmonary artery

Left pulmonary vein

Left lung (upper lobe)

Left coronary artery

Left auricle

Pericardial cavity

Pericardium

Visceral pleura

Left AV opening

Left AV (mitral) valve

ft ventricle

Diaphragm

Inferior border, left lung

rous layer of stomach

diaphrag- tic recess

ragmatic pleura

Central tendon of diaphragm

Stomach

Transverse colon

Pancreas

Left kidney

Small intestine

Bodies of thoracic vertebrae

Trachea at its bifurcation

Azygos vein

Right pulmonary artery

Upper lobe, right lung

Costal pleura

Left atrium

Bronchopulmonary lymph nodes

Horizontal and oblique fissures, right lung

Middle lobe, right lung

Inf. vena cava

Inf. lobe, right lung

Coronary sinus

Esophagus abd. part

Hepatic vein

Costodiaphrag- matic recess

Abdominal aorta

Liver

Hepatic vein

Costodiaphrag- matic recess

Peritoneal cavity

Inferior vena cava

Crura of the diaphragm

Right kidney

Psoas muscles

Body of vertebra

Intervertebral discs

Fig. 215: A Frontal Section of the Thorax and Abdomen from Behind (Dorsal View)

NOTE: 1) that from this dorsal view, the right side of the specimen is on the reader's right. Observe also that the pulmonary arteries and their branches are indicated in blue, as are veins (such as the hepatic veins) that also carry blood with low levels of oxygen saturation.

2) that the A-P plane of this frontal section in the thorax lies in front of the descending aorta but at the plane of etrance into the thorax of the inferior vena cava through the vena caval foramen. Observe that the esophagus is seen only in the superior mediastinum and at its entrance into the stomach just below the diaphragm, while the trachea has been cut at its point of bifurcation.

Fig. 215   **II**

Right common carotid artery
Trachea
Right subclavian artery
Left common carotid artery
Left subclavian artery
Esophagus
Brachiocephalic trunk
Aortic arch
Right primary bronchus
Ligamentum arteriosum
Tracheal bifurcation
Left primary bronchus
Right upper lobe bronchus
Thoracic aorta
Esophagus, Thoracic part
Esophageal hiatus
Inf. vena cava foramen
Esophagus, Abdominal part
Central tendon, Diaphragm
Right crus, Diaphragm
Cardiac antrum, Stomach
Inferior phrenic aa.
Aortic hiatus
Celiac trunk
Left crus, Diaphragm
Abdominal aorta

Fig. 216: The Aorta and Lower Esophagus at the Tracheal Bifurcation and Diaphragm

NOTE: 1) at the level of the bifurcation of the trachea (T-5), the esophagus lies between the trachea and the thoracic aorta. The esophagus then descends into the thorax with the aorta somewhat to its left. In the lower thorax the esophagus bends to the left and thus crosses over the aorta anteriorly from right to left.

2) the esophagus enters the abdomen through the esophageal hiatus of the diaphragm, while the aorta passes through the aortic hiatus.

Figs. 216, 217

Fig. 217: The Relationship or the Esophagus to the Aorta and Trachea, Viewed from Right Side

NOTE: the esophagus commences above as an inferior extension of the pharynx. Superiorly, the esophagus is in relationship with the larynx and thyroid gland. Its middle third courses in relation to the trachea, bronchi and the arch of the aorta, while its lower third descends with the thoracic aorta.

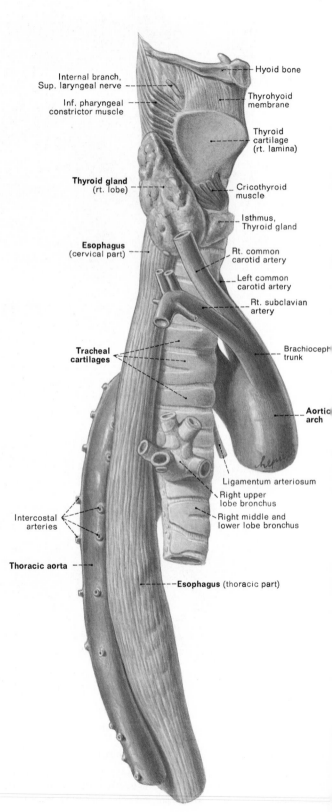

Internal branch, Sup. laryngeal nerve
Hyoid bone
Inf. pharyngeal constrictor muscle
Thyrohyoid membrane
Thyroid cartilage (rt. lamina)
Thyroid gland (rt. lobe)
Cricothyroid muscle
Isthmus, Thyroid gland
Esophagus (cervical part)
Rt. common carotid artery
Left common carotid artery
Rt. subclavian artery
Tracheal cartilages
Brachioceph. trunk
Aortic arch
Ligamentum arteriosum
Right upper lobe bronchus
Intercostal arteries
Right middle and lower lobe bronchus
Thoracic aorta
Esophagus (thoracic part)

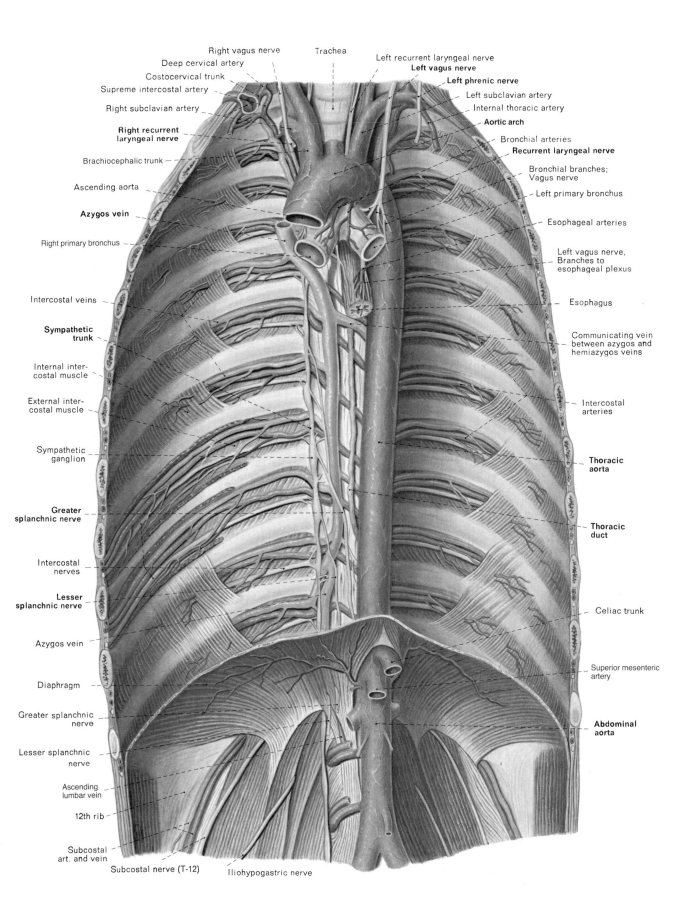

Fig. 218: Vessels and Nerves of the Dorsal Thoracic Wall

NOTE that the aorta ascends from the left ventricle, arches to the left behind the left pulmonary hilum, and descends through most of the thorax, just to the left side of the vertebral column. In this course through the posterior mediastinum, the aorta gradually shifts toward the midline, which it achieves by the time it traverses the aortic hiatus to enter the abdomen.

Fig. 218   **II**

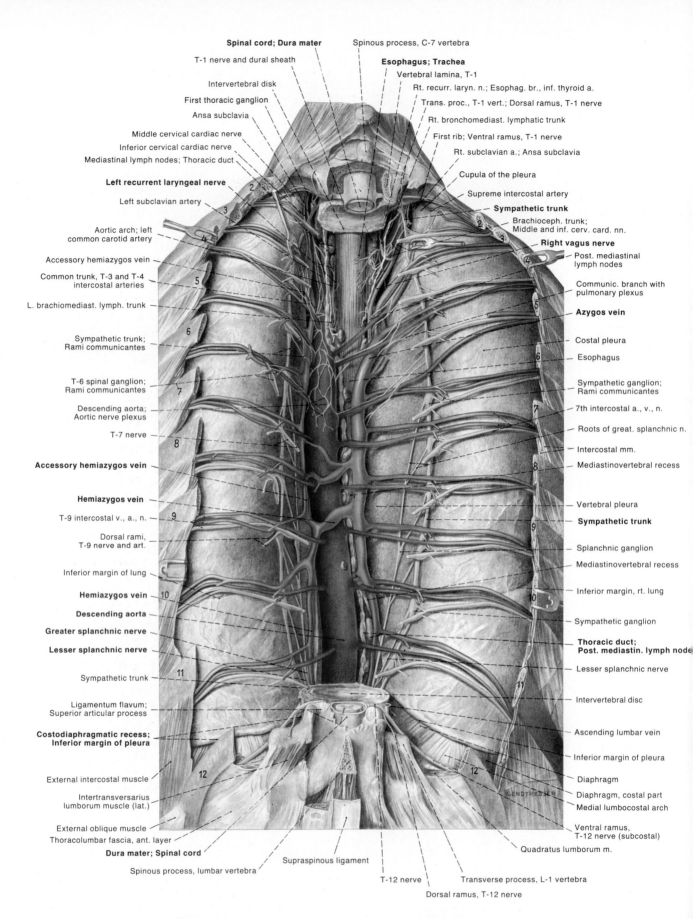

Fig. 219: Dorsal View of the Mediastinum and Lungs with the Thoracic Vertebral Column Removed

NOTE the azygos, hemiazygos and accessory azygos venous pattern that flows in the mediastinum but drains the intercostal spaces. Observe also the relationship of the thoracic sympathetic chain and its ganglia to the intercostal nerves.

Fig. 219

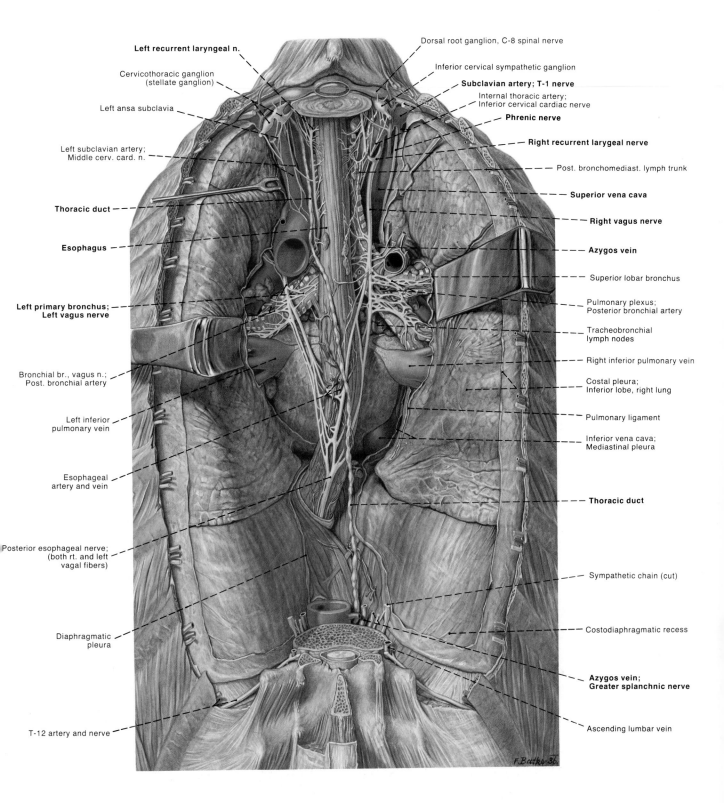

Left recurrent laryngeal n.

Cervicothoracic ganglion (stellate ganglion)

Left ansa subclavia

Left subclavian artery; Middle cerv. card. n.

Thoracic duct

Esophagus

Left primary bronchus; Left vagus nerve

Bronchial br., vagus n.; Post. bronchial artery

Left inferior pulmonary vein

Esophageal artery and vein

Posterior esophageal nerve; (both rt. and left vagal fibers)

Diaphragmatic pleura

T-12 artery and nerve

Dorsal root ganglion, C-8 spinal nerve

Inferior cervical sympathetic ganglion

Subclavian artery; T-1 nerve

Internal thoracic artery; Inferior cervical cardiac nerve

Phrenic nerve

Right recurrent larygeal nerve

Post. bronchomediast. lymph trunk

Superior vena cava

Right vagus nerve

Azygos vein

Superior lobar bronchus

Pulmonary plexus; Posterior bronchial artery

Tracheobronchial lymph nodes

Right inferior pulmonary vein

Costal pleura; Inferior lobe, right lung

Pulmonary ligament

Inferior vena cava; Mediastinal pleura

Thoracic duct

Sympathetic chain (cut)

Costodiaphragmatic recess

Azygos vein; Greater splanchnic nerve

Ascending lumbar vein

F.Batke 36

Fig. 220: Dorsal View of the Mediastinum after Removal of the Vertebral Column and Retraction of the Lungs

NOTE: 1) that in addition to the vertebral column, the descending thoracic aorta has been removed in order to reveal the mediastinal course of the thoracic duct and esophagus. Observe the gradual right to left course of the thoracic duct as it ascends in the mediastinum;

2) that the esophagus descends behind the trachea in the superior mediastinum, but lies directly behind the pericardium below the bifurcation of the trachea;

3) the autonomic plexus of nerves, lymph nodes and bronchial vessels which characterize the hilum of each lung;

4) the course of the right vagus nerve, and observe that the right recurrent laryngeal nerve arches behind the right subclavian artery in order to achieve the neck in its ascent to the larynx.

Fig. 220   II

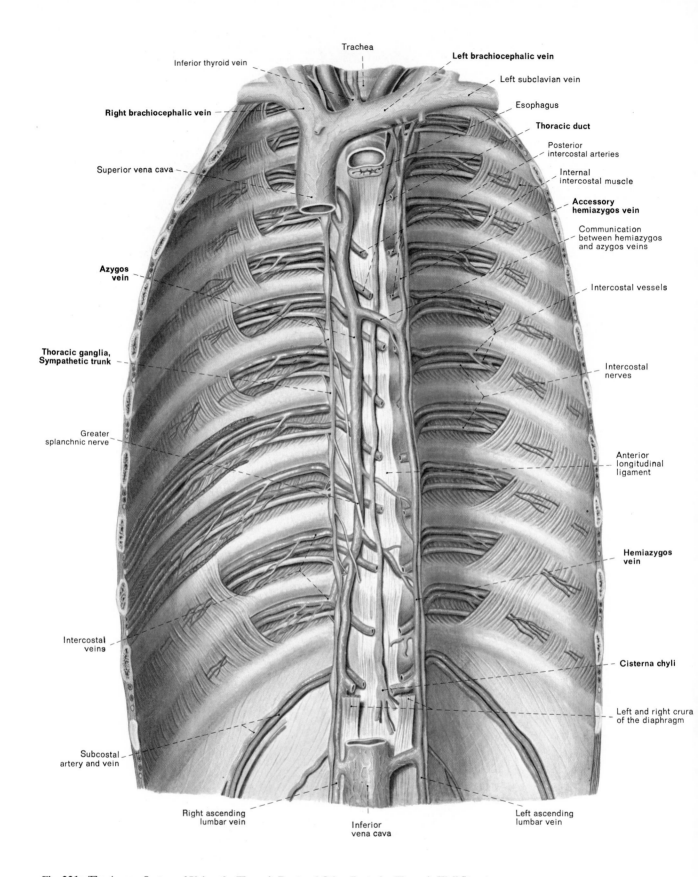

Trachea

Inferior thyroid vein

Left brachiocephalic vein

Left subclavian vein

Right brachiocephalic vein

Esophagus

Thoracic duct

Posterior intercostal arteries

Superior vena cava

Internal intercostal muscle

Accessory hemiazygos vein

Communication between hemiazygos and azygos veins

Azygos vein

Intercostal vessels

Thoracic ganglia, Sympathetic trunk

Intercostal nerves

Greater splanchnic nerve

Anterior longitudinal ligament

Hemiazygos vein

Intercostal veins

Cisterna chyli

Left and right crura of the diaphragm

Subcostal artery and vein

Right ascending lumbar vein

Left ascending lumbar vein

Inferior vena cava

Fig. 221: The Azygos System of Veins, the Thoracic Duct and Other Posterior Thoracic Wall Structures

NOTE: 1) with all the organs of the thorax and mediastinum removed or cut, the hemiazygos and accessory hemiazygos veins to the left of the vertebral column are seen communicating across the midline with the larger azygos vein. This latter vessel also ascends in the thorax to flow into the superior vena cava.

2) the thoracic duct as it arises from the cisterna chyli at the 1st lumbar level.

Fig. 221

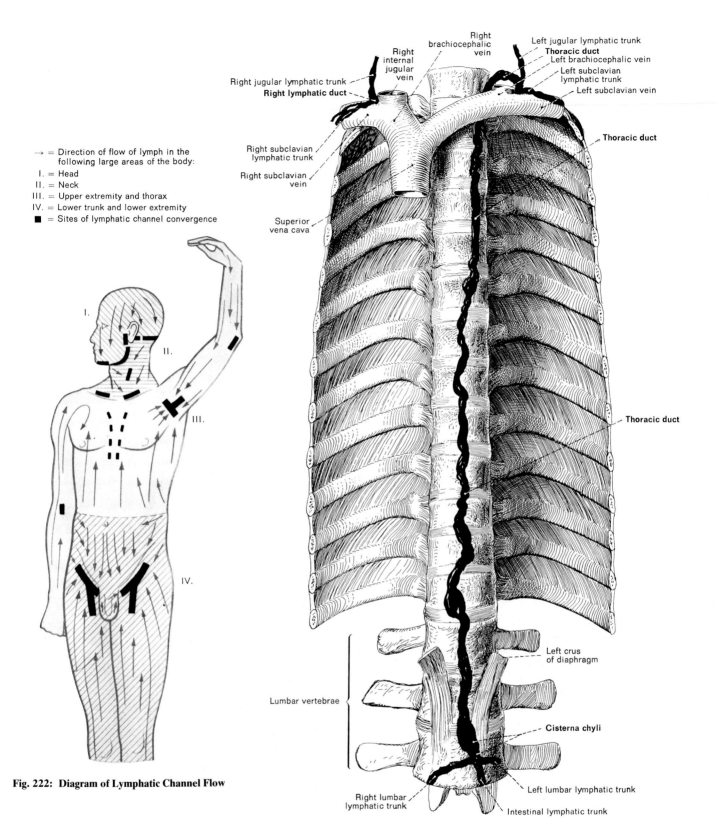

Fig. 222: Diagram of Lymphatic Channel Flow

→ = Direction of flow of lymph in the following large areas of the body:
I. = Head
II. = Neck
III. = Upper extremity and thorax
IV. = Lower trunk and lower extremity
■ = Sites of lymphatic channel convergence

Right internal jugular vein
Right brachiocephalic vein
Right jugular lymphatic trunk
Right lymphatic duct
Left jugular lymphatic trunk
Thoracic duct
Left brachiocephalic vein
Left subclavian lymphatic trunk
Left subclavian vein
Right subclavian lymphatic trunk
Right subclavian vein
Thoracic duct
Superior vena cava
Thoracic duct
Left crus of diaphragm
Lumbar vertebrae
Cisterna chyli
Right lumbar lymphatic trunk
Left lumbar lymphatic trunk
Intestinal lymphatic trunk

Fig. 223: The Thoracic Duct: Its Origin and Course

NOTE: 1) the thoracic duct collects the lymph from most of the body tissues and transmits it back into the blood stream. It originates in the abdomen anterior to the 2nd lumbar vertebra at the cisterna chyli. The duct then ascends into the thorax through the aortic hiatus of the diaphragm slightly to the right of the midline. Within the posterior mediastinum of the thorax and still coursing just ventral to the vertebral column, it gradually crosses the midline to the left. The duct then ascends into the root of the neck on the left side and opens into the left subclavian vein near the junction of the right internal jugular vein.

2) the right lymphatic duct receives lymph from the right side of the head, neck and trunk and from the right upper extremity. It empties into the right subclavian vein.

Figs. 222, 223   II

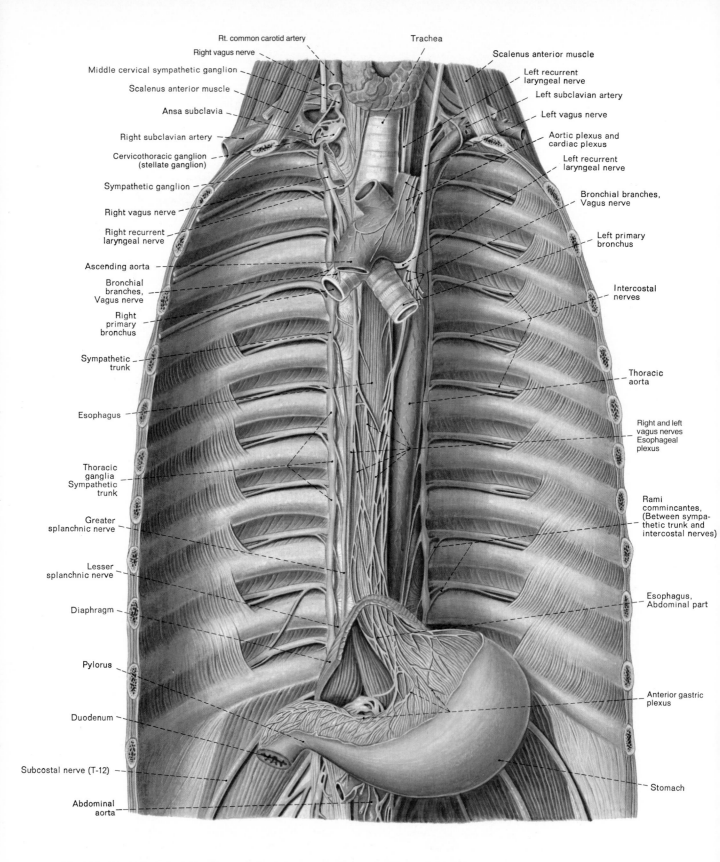

Fig. 224: The Symphathetic Trunks and Vagus Nerves in the Thorax and Upper Abdomen

NOTE: 1) that the ganglionated sympathetic trunks on each side lie lateral to the bodies of the thoracic vertebrae and they are continued into the cervical region above the ribs and into the lumbar region below the diaphragm. Observe that each ganglion is connected to the intercostal nerves by means of rami communicantes. *White rami* communicantes mostly carry preganglionic symphatetic neurons to the ganglia, while the *gray rami* communicantes carry postganglionic fibers back to the spinal nerves. (This figure does not specifically label the white and gray rami.)

2) the course of the vagus nerves in the lower thorax. Below the aortic arch these nerves send branches to the bronchi and then descend to form much of the esophageal plexus. Below the diaphragm most of the fibers of the left vagus contribute to the formation of the anterior gastric nerve plexus, while most of the fibers of the right vagus form the posterior gastric nerve plexus.

Fig. 224

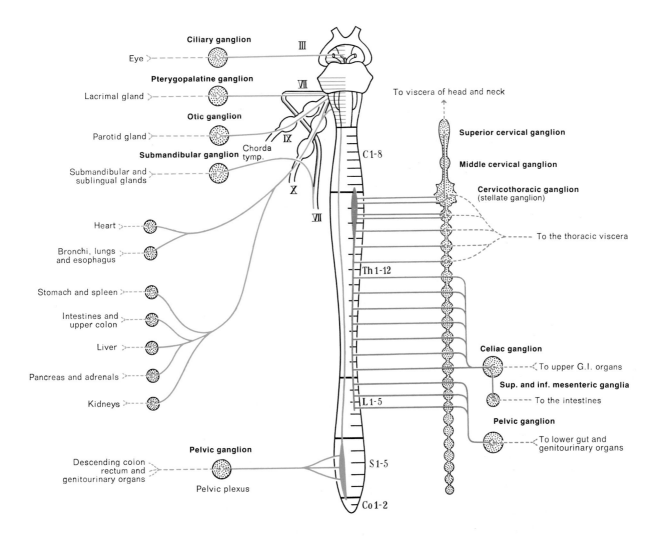

Fig. 225: Diagram of the Autonomic Nervous System. Blue = parasympathetic; red = sympathetic; solid lines = presynaptic neurons; broken lines = postsynaptic neurons.

NOTE: 1) the autonomic nervous system, by definition, is a two motor neuron system with the neuron cell bodies of the *presynaptic neurons* (solid lines) somewhere within the central nervous system, and the cell bodies of the *postsynaptic neurons* (broken lines) located in ganglia distributed peripherally in the body.

2) the autonomic nervous system is comprised of the nerve fibers which supply all the glands and blood vessels of the body including the heart. In so doing, all the smooth and cardiac muscle tissues (sometimes called involuntary muscles) are thereby innervated.

3) the autonomic nervous system is composed of two major divisions called the parasympathetic (in blue) and sympathetic (in red) divisions. The autonomic regulation of visceral function is, therefore, a dualistic control, i.e., most organs receive postganglionic fibers of both parasympathetic and sympathetic source.

4) the *parasympathetic division* is sometimes called a craniosacral outflow because the preganglionic cell bodies of this division lie in the brainstem and in the sacral segments of the spinal cord. Parasympathetic preganglionic fibers are found in four cranial nerves, III (oculomotor), VII (facial), IX (glossopharyngeal) and X (vagus) and in the 2nd, 3rd and 4th sacral nerves.

5) these *preganglionic* parasympathetic fibers then synapse with *postganglionic* parasympathetic cell bodies in peripheral ganglia. From these ganglia the *post*ganglionic nerve fibers innervate the various organs.

6) the *sympathetic division* is sometimes called the thoracolumbar outflow because the *preganglionic* sympathetic neuron cell bodies are located in the lateral horn of the spinal cord between the 1st thoracic spinal segment and the 2nd or 3rd lumbar spinal segment, (i.e., from T-1 to L-3).

7) these *preganglionic* fibers emerge from the cord with their corresponding spinal roots and communicate with the sympathetic trunk and its ganglia where some *presynaptic* sympathetic fibers synapse with *post*ganglionic sympathetic neurons. Other presynaptic fibers (especially those of the upper thoracic segments) ascend in the sympathetic chain and synapse with *post*ganglionic neurons in the cervicothoracic, middle and superior cervical ganglia. *Post*ganglionic fibers from these latter ganglia are then distributed to the viscera of the head and neck. Still other *presynaptic* sympathetic fibers do not synapse in the sympathetic chain of ganglia at all, but collect to form the splanchnic nerves. These nerves course to the collateral sympathetic ganglia (celiac, superior and inferior mesenteric and pelvic ganglia) where synapse with the *post*ganglionic neuron occurs. The *post*ganglionic neurons of the sympathetic division then course to the viscera to supply sympathetic innervation.

8) the functions of the parasympathetic and sympathetic divisions of the autonomic nervous system are antagonistic to each other. The parasympathetic division constricts the pupil, decelerates the heart, lowers blood pressure, relaxes the sphincters of the gut and contracts the longitudinal musculature of the hollow organs. It is the division which is active during periods of calm and tranquility and aids in digestion and absorption. In contrast, the *sympathetic division* dilates the pupil, accelerates the heart, increases blood pressure, contracts the sphincters of the gut and relaxes the longitudinal musculature of hollow organs. It is active when the organism is challenged. It prepares for fight and flight and generally comes to the individual's defense during periods of stress and adversity.

Fig. 225 **II**

Costocervical trunk;
Supreme intercostal artery

Dura mater

Vertebral (sympathetic) nerve
(courses with vertebral art. and vein)

Intercostal branch of
T-1 thoracic nerve

Middle cervical ganglion

Inferior thyroid artery;
Thyroid ansa

Meningeal branch of
intercostal nerve

Stellate ganglion (also called
cervicothoracic ganglion; i. e.
the combined T-1 and inferior
cervical ganglion)

Ansa subclavia (coursing
around the subclavian artery)

Radicular (spinal) branch
of intercostal artery

Inferior cervical cardiac n.

Internal vertebral venous
plexus

Dura mater (opened)

Arachnoid membrane

Ventral root of T-5
thoracic nerve

T-5 intercostal nerve

Ventral root of T-6
thoracic nerve

Denticulate ligament

Anterior spinal art. and vein

Ventral root of T-7
thoracic nerve;
Radicular (spinal) branch of
intercostal artery and vein

Ventral root of T-8
thoracic nerve

T-7 sympathetic ganglion

Ventral root of T-8
thoracic nerve

Internal vertebral vein

Greater splanchnic nerve

Dorsal root ganglion on
T-9 thoracic nerve

Splanchnic ganglion
(found in about 20% of specimens

Ventral root of T-10
thoracic nerve;
Radicular (spinal) branch of
intercostal artery and vein

Anterior spinal art. and vein

T-11 intercostal nerve

Splanchnic ganglion on
greater splanchnic nerve
(found in about 20% of specimens)

Lesser splanchnic nerve

Subcostal nerve (T-12)

Greater and lesser
splanchnic nerves

Right celiac ganglion

Celiac trunk

Azygos vein

Left celiac ganglion

Right sympathetic trunk

Superior mesenteric art.

Abdominal aortic plexus

Left renal artery

Fig. 226: The Sympathetic Trunks and Intercostal Nerves and Vessels in the Posterior Part of the Thoracic Wall, Anterior View

NOTE: 1) the two sympathetic trunks (located in the posterior mediastinum of the thorax), their ganglia and the rami communicantes that interconnect the ganglia with the segmentally coursing intercostal nerves.

2) that the bodies of the lower 7 or 8 thoracic vertebrae have been removed in order to reveal, in this anterior view, the ventral surface of the spinal cord and the anterior spinal roots that help to form the thoracic nerves.

3) the **greater splanchnic nerve** which is formed from thoracic sympathetic ganglia T-5 to T-9 or T-10 and the **lesser splanchnic nerve** which is formed from sympathetic ganglia T-9 or T-10 and T-11. These nerves descend parallel to the sympathetic trunks and enter the abdomen by perforating the crura of the diaphragm. Most of the fibers of the greater splanchnic nerves terminate on the postganglionic neurons in the *celiac ganglia;* most fibers in the lesser splanchnic nerve synapse in the *aorticorenal ganglia* (shown near the renal arteries but not labelled), while the lowest splanchnic nerve, arising on each side from the T-12 sympathetic ganglion (not shown) ends in the renal autonomic plexus.

Fig. 226

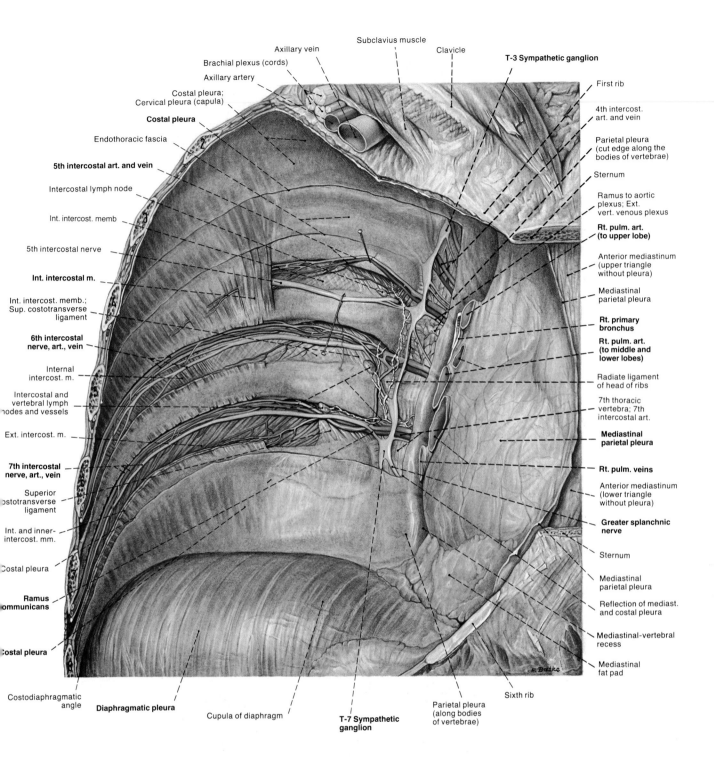

Axillary vein
Subclavius muscle
Clavicle
Brachial plexus (cords)
Axillary artery
T-3 Sympathetic ganglion
Costal pleura;
Cervical pleura (capula)
First rib
Costal pleura
4th intercost.
art. and vein
Endothoracic fascia
Parietal pleura
(cut edge along the
bodies of vertebrae)
5th intercostal art. and vein
Sternum
Intercostal lymph node
Ramus to aortic
plexus; Ext.
vert. venous plexus
Int. intercost. memb
**Rt. pulm. art.
(to upper lobe)**
5th intercostal nerve
Anterior mediastinum
(upper triangle
without pleura)
Int. intercostal m.
Mediastinal
parietal pleura
Int. intercost. memb.;
Sup. costotransverse
ligament
**Rt. primary
bronchus**
**6th intercostal
nerve, art., vein**
**Rt. pulm. art.
(to middle and
lower lobes)**
Internal
intercost. m.
Radiate ligament
of head of ribs
Intercostal and
vertebral lymph
nodes and vessels
7th thoracic
vertebra; 7th
intercostal art.
Ext. intercost. m.
**Mediastinal
parietal pleura**
**7th intercostal
nerve, art., vein**
Rt. pulm. veins
Superior
costotransverse
ligament
Anterior mediastinum
(lower triangle
without pleura)
Int. and inner-
intercost. mm.
**Greater splanchnic
nerve**
Costal pleura
Sternum
**Ramus
communicans**
Mediastinal
parietal pleura
Reflection of mediast.
and costal pleura
Costal pleura
Mediastinal-vertebral
recess
Mediastinal
fat pad
Costodiaphragmatic
angle
Sixth rib
Diaphragmatic pleura
Cupula of diaphragm
**T-7 Sympathetic
ganglion**
Parietal pleura
(along bodies
of vertebrae)

Fig. 227: The Right Posterior Thoracic Wall, the Sympathetic Trunk and the Intercostal Nerves and Vessels, Anterior View

NOTE: 1) that the right lung has been removed from the thoracic cavity, but clearly visible are the cut structures at the right pulmonary hilum; these include the right primary bronchus, the right pulmonary artery (severed distally enough to show its three branches to the lobes of the right lung) and the pulmonary veins.

2) that the costal and mediastinal reflections of parietal pleura have been stripped away to reveal the 5th, 6th and 7th intercostal spaces and the intercostal vessels and nerves that course within them around the thoracic wall. Observe that the intercostal vessels and nerves lie just below the ribs and that usually the nerve is slightly more inferior to the artery and vein within the intercostal space. This close relationship of the intercostal vessels and nerve to the lower border of the ribs in the posterior and lateral chest wall explains why it is safer to guide a needle through the intercostal space along the superior border of the rib when entrance into the thoracic cavity is necessary.

3) the sympathetic trunk and the 3rd and 8th sympathetic ganglia. Observe also that, in addition to the rami communicantes, the sympathetic trunk or ganglia contribute sympathetic fibers to the aortic plexus (seen coursing toward the left from this right sympathetic trunk), as well as to the splanchic nerves.

4) the intercostal and paravertebral lymph nodes and lymphatic channels.

Fig. 227   II

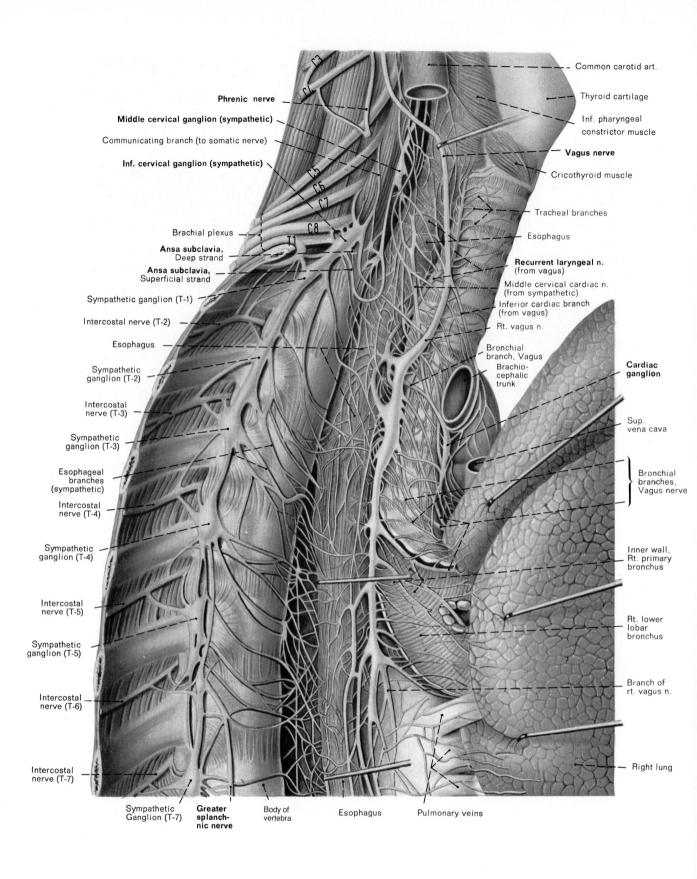

Fig. 228: The Cervical and Upper Thoracic Distribution of Autonomic Nerves

NOTE: the organs of the posterior mediastinum are viewed from the right side by pulling the lungs forward and removing certain of the organs. Observe the two major descending nerve trunks and their associated complexes: the right vagus nerve situated more anteriorly and the right sympathetic trunk descending more posteriorly in the thorax adjacent to the costovertebral joints.

Fig. 228

Azygos vein

Sympathetic ganglion (T-5)

Esophagus

Sympathetic ganglion (T-6)

Inter-ganglionic portion. **Sympathetic trunk**

Sympathetic ganglion (T-7)

Sympathetic ganglion (T-8)

Sympathetic trunk·

Intercostal nerve (T-9)

Sympathetic ganglion (T-9)

Intercostal nerve (T-10)

Sympathetic ganglion (T-10)

Thoracic duct

Inter costal { vein / artery / nerve

Quadratus lumborum muscle

Rt. vagus nerve; Bronchial artery

Rt. middle lobar bronchus

Rt. lower lobar bronchus

Bronchial branches, Vagus nerve (pulmonary plexus)

Esophageal branch, Rt. vagus nerve

Rt. pulmonary veins

Rt. lung

Pericardium

Esophagus

Esophageal branch of rt. vagus n.

Post. vagal trunk

Phrenic nerve

Inf. vena cava

Diaphragm

Lesser splanchnic nerve

Greater splanchnic nerve

Thoracic duct

Aorta and aortic plexus

Vena caval foramen

Fig. 229: Lower Thoracic Portion of Autonomic Nervous System

NOTE: 1) the formation of the greater and lesser splanchnic nerves. The greater splanchnic nerve is derived from preganglionic sympathetic fibers which emerge from sympathetic ganglia T-6 to T-9 or T-10, whereas the lesser splanchnic nerve is derived from ganglia T-10 and T-11.

2) the right vagus nerve after contributing parasympathetic fibers to the esophageal plexus becomes the posterior vagal trunk dorsal to the esophagus as that organ passes through the diaphragm.

Fig. 229   **II**

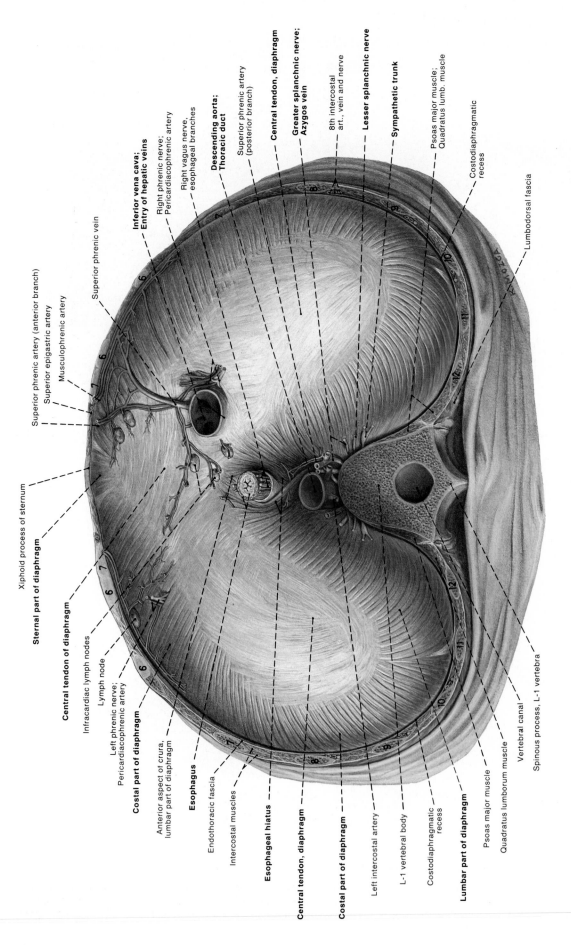

Superior phrenic artery (anterior branch)

Superior epigastric artery

Musculophrenic artery

Superior phrenic vein

Xiphoid process of sternum

Sternal part of diaphragm

Central tendon of diaphragm

Infracardiac lymph nodes

Lymph node

Left phrenic nerve; Pericardiacophrenic artery

Costal part of diaphragm

Anterior aspect of crura, lumbar part of diaphragm

Esophagus

Endothoracic fascia

Intercostal muscles

Esophageal hiatus

Central tendon, diaphragm

Costal part of diaphragm

Left intercostal artery

L-1 vertebral body

Costodiaphragmatic recess

Lumbar part of diaphragm

Psoas major muscle

Quadratus lumborum muscle

Vertebral canal

Spinous process, L-1 vertebra

Inferior vena cava; Entry of hepatic veins

Right phrenic nerve; Pericardiacophrenic artery

Right vagus nerve, esophageal branches

Descending aorta; Thoracic duct

Superior phrenic artery (posterior branch)

Central tendon, diaphragm

Greater splanchnic nerve; Azygos vein

8th intercostal art., vein and nerve

Lesser splanchnic nerve

Sympathetic trunk

Psoas major muscle; Quadratus lumb. muscle

Costodiaphragmatic recess

Lumbodorsal fascia

Fig. 230: The Diaphragm: Its Openings, Blood Vessels and Nerves Viewed From Above

NOTE: 1) that the thoracic cage has been severed transversely in a plane extending from the xiphoid process anteriorly to the body of the first lumbar vertebra posteriorly. The diaphragmatic pleurae and the pericardium have been stripped from the superior (thoracic) surface of the diaphragm;

2) the relative location of the vena caval orifice and the esophageal and aortic hiatuses. The *vena caval opening* lies to the right of the midline, is more anterior and higher (8th to 9th thoracic vertebra) than the other two. The *aortic hiatus* lies in the midline and is the most posterior and the most inferior (L-1) of these large apertures. The *esophageal hiatus*, also in the midline, lies anterior to the aortic hiatus at about the level of the 10th thoracic vertebra.

Fig. 230

PART III: THE ABDOMEN

Fig. 231: Superficial Musculature of the Anterior Abdominal and Thoracic Wall

NOTE: 1) the first layer of abdominal musculature consists principally of the external oblique muscle and its broad, flat aponeurosis which extends medially to the midline (forming the anterior layer of the sheath of the rectus abdominis muscle) and inferiorly as the inguinal ligament.

2) the external oblique arises by means of 7 or 8 fleshy slips from the outer surfaces of the lower ribs (ribs 5 to 12), thereby interdigitating with the fleshy origin of the serratus anterior muscle.

Fig. 231   **III**

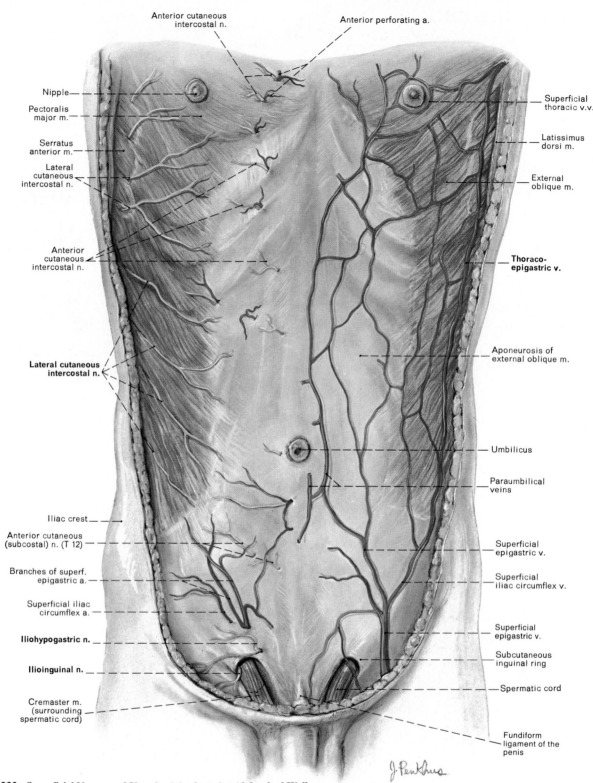

Anterior cutaneous intercostal n.

Anterior perforating a.

Nipple

Pectoralis major m.

Serratus anterior m.

Lateral cutaneous intercostal n.

Anterior cutaneous intercostal n.

Lateral cutaneous intercostal n.

Iliac crest

Anterior cutaneous (subcostal) n. (T 12)

Branches of superf. epigastric a.

Superficial iliac circumflex a.

Iliohypogastric n.

Ilioinguinal n.

Cremaster m. (surrounding spermatic cord)

Superficial thoracic v.v.

Latissimus dorsi m.

External oblique m.

Thoraco-epigastric v.

Aponeurosis of external oblique m.

Umbilicus

Paraumbilical veins

Superficial epigastric v.

Superficial iliac circumflex v.

Superficial epigastric v.

Subcutaneous inguinal ring

Spermatic cord

Fundiform ligament of the penis

J. Penkhus

Fig. 232: Superficial Nerves and Vessels of the Anterior Abdominal Wall

NOTE: 1) the distribution of the superficial vessels and cutaneous nerves is demonstrated upon the removal of the skin and superficial fatty layers over the lower thoracic and anterior abdominal wall.

2) the thoracic intercostal nerves supply the abdominal surface with lateral and anterior cutaneous branches.

3) in the inguinal region, the ilioinguinal and iliohypogastric branches of the 1st lumbar nerve become superficial in the region of the superficial inguinal ring.

4) the branches of superficial epigastric artery (which arises from the femoral artery) as they ascend in the inguinal region toward the umbilicus. Note also the superficial branches of the intercostal arteries.

5) the thoracoepigastric vein which serves as a means of communication between the femoral vein and the axillary vein. In cases of obstruction of the portal vein, these superficial veins become greatly enlarged forming varicose veins over the abdominal wall (sometimes this condition is called *caput medusae*).

Fig. 232

Sternocleidomastoid m.
Semispinalis capitis m.
Stylohyoid m.
Splenius capitis m.
Levator scapulae m.
Longus capitis m.

Hyoglossus m.
Mylohyoid m.
Digastric m. (ant. and post. bellies);
Hyoid bone
Inferior pharyngeal constrictor m.
Thyrohyoid m.
Sternohyoid m.
Omohyoid m. (superior belly)
Sternothyroid m.
Anterior, middle and
posterior scalene mm.

Sternocleidomastoid m.

Omohyoid m.
(inferior belly)
**Clavicle;
Subclavius m.**
**Serratus anterior m.
(upper part)**
Internal intercostal mm.

External intercostal mm.

Pectoralis minor m.
**Serratus anterior m.
(middle part)**
**Pectoralis major m.
(cut margin)**
Costal arch

Linea alba

External oblique m.

Intercrural fibers

Fundiform ligament of penis

Acromion

Deltoid m.
Pectoralis
major m.

Deltoid m.
Biceps brachii m.
(long head)
Biceps brachii m.
(short head)
Coracobrachialis m.

Teres major m.
Subscapularis m.

Latissimus dorsi m.
Serratus anterior m. (lower part)

Rectus abdominis m.

Latissimus dorsi m.

External oblique m.

Superficial layer, aponeurosis
of Internal oblique m.

Deep layer, aponeurosis
of Internal oblique m.

Aponeurosis, External oblique m.

External oblique m.

Internal oblique m.

Anterior superior iliac spine

Aponeurosis, External oblique m.

Internal oblique m.

Cremaster m.

Reflected inguinal ligament

1
2
4
5
6
7
8

Fig. 233: The Deeper Layers of the Musculature of the Trunk, Axilla and Neck

NOTE that: 1) the pectoralis major and minor muscles have been reflected to reveal the underlying digitations of the serratus anterior muscle as these strands attach to the ribs forming the thoracic wall. Observe that the external oblique muscle covers a relatively large portion of the inferolateral thoracic wall as well as stretching across the anterior abdominal wall as its external muscular layer.

2) the external oblique muscle and the lower lateral part of its aponeurosis have been severed in a semicircular manner near their origin in order to reveal the underlying internal oblique muscle. There are certain generalities about the attachments of the external and internal oblique muscles which also apply to the deepest of the anterior abdominal wall muscles, the transversus abdominis muscle: a) they all attach to the last six ribs (the external oblique frequently extending one or two ribs higher), b) they all are attached to both the iliac crest and the inguinal ligament, and c) they all insert into the linea alba.

Fig. 233   III

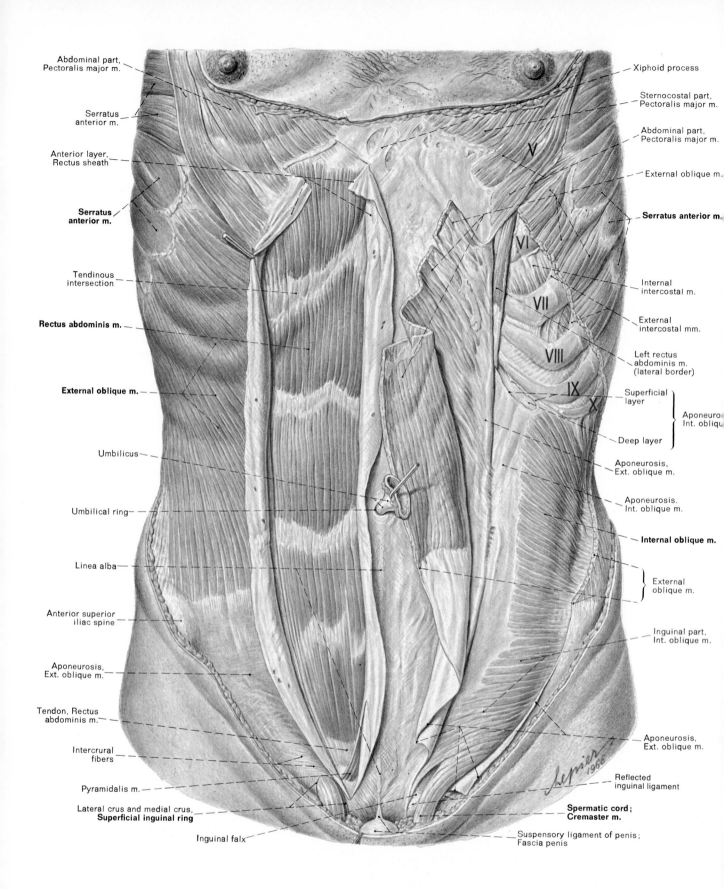

Abdominal part,
Pectoralis major m.

Serratus
anterior m.

Anterior layer,
Rectus sheath

**Serratus
anterior m.**

Tendinous
intersection

Rectus abdominis m.

External oblique m.

Umbilicus

Umbilical ring

Linea alba

Anterior superior
iliac spine

Aponeurosis,
Ext. oblique m.

Tendon, Rectus
abdominis m.

Intercrural
fibers

Pyramidalis m.

Lateral crus and medial crus,
Superficial inguinal ring

Inguinal falx

Xiphoid process

Sternocostal part,
Pectoralis major m.

Abdominal part,
Pectoralis major m.

External oblique m.

Serratus anterior m.

Internal
intercostal m.

External
intercostal mm.

Left rectus
abdominis m.
(lateral border)

Superficial
layer

Aponeuro...
Int. obliqu...

Deep layer

Aponeurosis,
Ext. oblique m.

Aponeurosis,
Int. oblique m.

Internal oblique m.

External
oblique m.

Inguinal part,
Int. oblique m.

Aponeurosis,
Ext. oblique m.

Reflected
inguinal ligament

**Spermatic cord;
Cremaster m.**

Suspensory ligament of penis;
Fascia penis

V

VI

VII

VIII

IX

X

Fig. 234: Anterior Abdominal Wall: Rectus Abdominis and Internal Oblique Muscles

NOTE: 1) the specimen's right rectus sheath has been opened (reader's left) to reveal the right rectus abdominis muscle which is marked by transversely oriented tendinous intersections. On the specimen's left side, the external oblique muscle has been severed to reveal the second muscular layer, the internal oblique muscle. This also reveals ribs 6 through 10.

2) the muscle fibers of the external oblique course inferomedially (or in the same direction as you would put your hands in your side pockets), whereas most of the fibers of the internal oblique course in the opposite direction.

Fig. 234

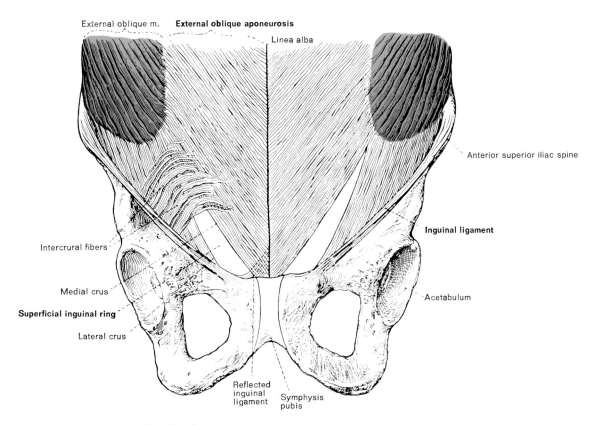

Fig. 235: **The Aponeurosis of the External Oblique Muscle**

NOTE: 1) the superficial inguinal ring is a triangular slit-like opening in the aponeurosis of the external oblique muscle. Observe how the intercrural fibers would strengthen the lateral aspect of the superficial ring by extending between the medial crus and lateral crus.

2) the inguinal ligament which extends between the anterior superior iliac spine and the pubic tubercle. This ligament is formed by the lowermost fibers of the external oblique aponeurosis and lends support to the inferior portion of the anterior abdominal wall.

Fig. 236: **The Superficial Inguinal Ring and Spermatic Cord**

NOTE: 1) the superficial inguinal ring transmits the spermatic cord in the male and the round ligament of the uterus in the female. In this dissection, the right spermatic cord has been lifted in order to show the lateral crus of the inguinal ring.

2) the tendinous fibers of the aponeurosis are continuous with the fleshy fibers of the external oblique. They are directed inferiorly and medially and either decussate or insert into the linea alba.

Figs. 235, 236   **III**

Fig. 237: Middle Layer of Abdominal Musculature: Internal Oblique Muscle

NOTE: 1) on the right side, the external oblique muscle has been severed and reflected to expose the right internal oblique muscle. On the left side, the anterior layer of the rectus sheath has been incised longitudinally to expose the left rectus abdominis muscle with its tendinous intersections and the small pyramidalis muscle.

2) the muscle fibers of the internal oblique muscle arise from the inguinal ligament, the iliac crest and the lumbar aponeurosis. They insert into the lower ribs above, and into an aponeurosis which contributes to the formation of the rectus sheath medially. Inferiorly, the aponeurosis of the internal oblique along with the aponeurosis of the transversus abdominis muscle forms the conjoint tendon, which is also known as the inguinal falx (shown, but not labelled). The conjoint tendon inserts into the pubic crest along with the lower end of the rectus sheath, thereby helping to provide strength to the inherently weak inguinal-pubic region.

3) the cremaster muscle. This muscular covering over the outer surface of the spermatic cord in the male represents an extension of the internal oblique (also possibly the transversus abdominis). It originates on the inguinal ligament and, after its fibers loop around the spermatic cord, inserts onto the pubis. Upon contraction this muscle lifts the testis within the scrotum toward the subcutaneous inguinal ring.

Fig. 237

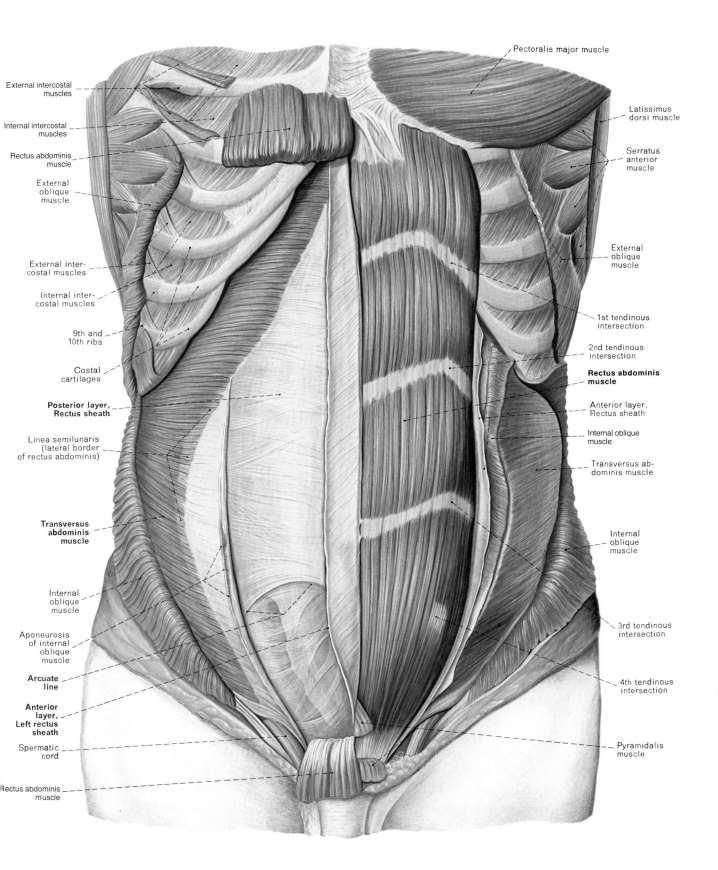

External intercostal muscles

Internal intercostal muscles

Rectus abdominis muscle

External oblique muscle

External intercostal muscles

Internal intercostal muscles

9th and 10th ribs

Costal cartilages

Posterior layer, Rectus sheath

Linea semilunaris (lateral border of rectus abdominis)

Transversus abdominis muscle

Internal oblique muscle

Aponeurosis of internal oblique muscle

Arcuate line

Anterior layer, Left rectus sheath

Spermatic cord

Rectus abdominis muscle

Pectoralis major muscle

Latissimus dorsi muscle

Serratus anterior muscle

External oblique muscle

1st tendinous intersection

2nd tendinous intersection

Rectus abdominis muscle

Anterior layer, Rectus sheath

Internal oblique muscle

Transversus abdominis muscle

Internal oblique muscle

3rd tendinous intersection

4th tendinous intersection

Pyramidalis muscle

Fig. 238: Deep Layer of Abdominal Musculature: The Transversus Abdominis Muscle

NOTE: 1) on the right, the external and internal oblique and rectus abdominis muscles have been resected demonstrating the transversus abdominis muscle. On the left, the rectus abdominis muscle remains intact but the small pyramidalis muscle was severed to show the insertion of the left rectus.

2) on the right, the posterior layer of the rectus sheath is exposed, while on the left, the anterior layer of the sheath has been opened to demonstrate the muscle. Below the arcuate line, the posterior sheath of the rectus abdominis is wanting, and the overlying rectus muscle lies directly anterior to the transversalis fascia.

Fig. 238   III

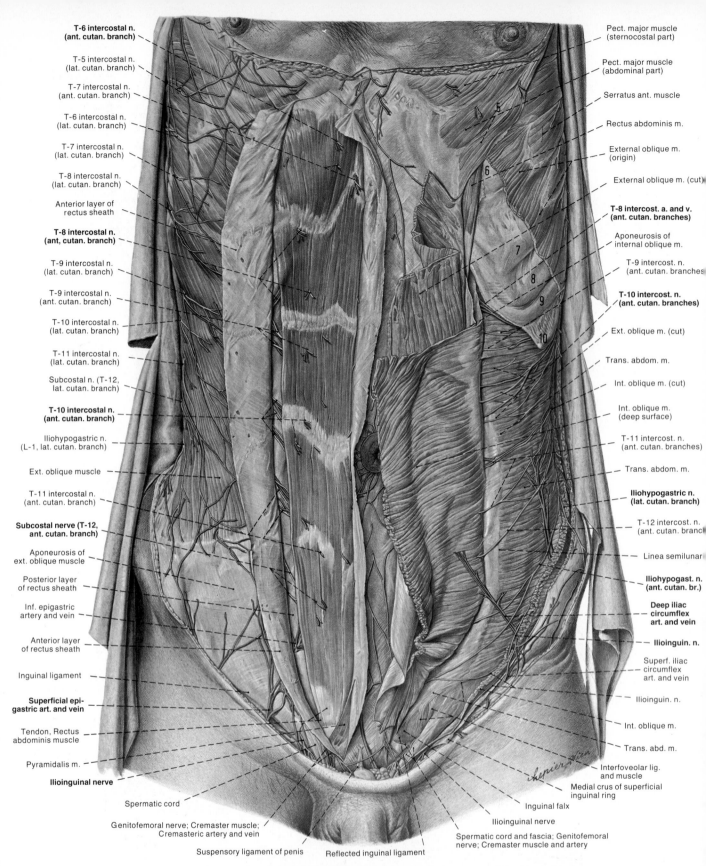

Fig. 239: Vessels and Nerves of the Anterior Abdominal Wall: The Lateral Cutaneous and Anterior Cutaneous Branches

NOTE: 1) that on the right side the *lateral cutaneous branches* of the lower sic thoracic and first lumbar nerves and vessels are shown coursing in an inferomedial direction superficial to the external oblique muscle. On this side also the anterior lamina of the rectus sheath has been opened. The *anterior cutaneous branches* of these nerves supply the rectus abdominis muscle by penetrating the lateral border of the rectus sheath.

2) that on the left side (reader's right) the external and internal oblique muscles have been cut to show more clearly the anterior cutaneous branches in their segmental course around the abdominal wall on the surface of the transversus abdominis muscle. These vessels and nerves supply the three layers of flat abdominal muscles and then penetrante their aponeuroses to gain access to the rectus muscle. Note also that the L-1 nerve divides into the iliohypogastric and ilioinguinal nerves just above the iliac crest.

Fig. 239

Pectoralis major muscle (abdominal part)
T-8 intercostal artery
Rectus abdominis muscle
T-9 intercost. nerve (ant. cutan. branch)
T-8 intercost. nerve (ant. cutan. branch)
T-8 intercost. nerve (lat. cutan. branch)
T-9 intercost. nerve (ant. cutan. branch)
T-9 intercost. vessels (lat. cutan. branch)
T-10 intercost. n. (lat. cutan. branch)
Anterior layer of rectus sheath
T-11 intercost. n. (lat. cutan. branch)
External oblique m.
Subcostal nerve (T-12, lat. cutan. branch)
T-10 intercost. n. (ant. cutan. branch)
Iliohypogastric n. -1, lat. cutan. branch)
T-11 intercost. n. (ant. cutan. branch)
Posterior layer of rectus sheath
Subserous fascia
ubcostal n. (T-12) nt. cutan. branch)
Urachus
reperitoneal fat
Superficial epigastric art.
Transversalis fascia
Sup. vesical art. nd venous plexus; Urinary bladder
T-11 intercost. n. nt. cutan. branch)
T-10 intercost. n. (ant. cutan. branch)
Inguinal falx
Subcostal nerve (T-12)
Adminiculum of linea alba; Symphysis pubis
Anterior layer of rectus sheath

Trans. abdominis muscle (deep to the rectus sheath)
Anastomosis: Superior and inferior epigastric vessels
Serratus ant. muscle
Anterior layer of rectus sheath
External oblique m.
Posterior layer of rectus sheath
Anterior layer of rectus sheath
Linea alba
Umbilicus
Posterior layer of rectus sheath
Umbilical ring; Paraumbilical veins
External oblique m.
Linea semicircularis
Transversalis fascia
Med. umbilical lig. (umbilical artery prenatally)
Aponeurosis, ext. oblique m.
Apponeurosis, ext. oblique m.
Superf. iliac circumflex art.
Transversalis fascia
Inf. epigastric art.
Ilioinguinal nerve
Insertion of rectus abdominis muscle; Inguinal falx
Prevesical space
Pyramidalis muscle
Linea alba

Fig. 240: Vessels and Nerves of the Anterior Abdominal Wall: The Epigastric Anastomosis

NOTE: 1) that the anterior layer of the rectus sheath has been opened on both sides and the two rectus abdominis muscles have been cut.
2) the descending course of the *superior epigastric artery and veins* (from the internal thoracic) and the ascending course of the *inferior epigastric artery and veins (*from the external iliac) found between the posterior layer of the rectus sheath and the rectus abdominis muscle on each side.

Fig. 240   **III**

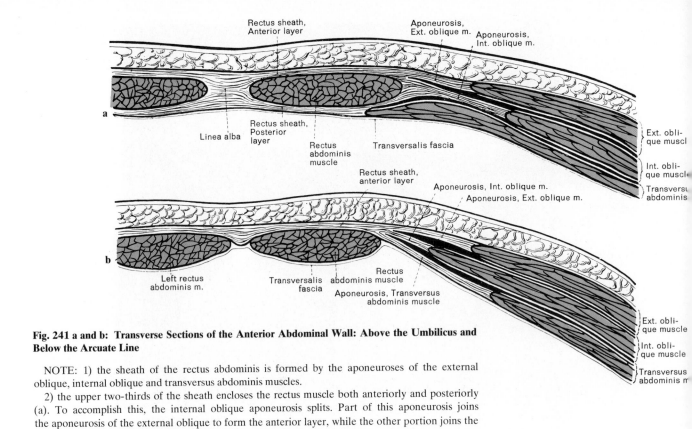

Fig. 241 a and b: **Transverse Sections of the Anterior Abdominal Wall: Above the Umbilicus and Below the Arcuate Line**

NOTE: 1) the sheath of the rectus abdominis is formed by the aponeuroses of the external oblique, internal oblique and transversus abdominis muscles.

2) the upper two-thirds of the sheath encloses the rectus muscle both anteriorly and posteriorly (a). To accomplish this, the internal oblique aponeurosis splits. Part of this aponeurosis joins the aponeurosis of the external oblique to form the anterior layer, while the other portion joins the aponeurosis of the transversus abdominis to form the posterior layer.

3) the lower one-third of the sheath (b), below the arcuate line, is deficient posteriorly, since the aponeuroses of all three muscles pass anterior to the rectus abdominis muscle.

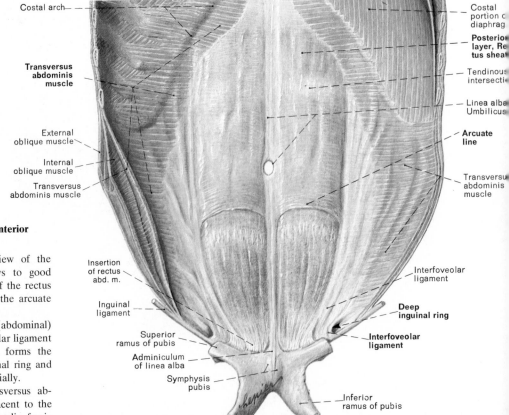

Fig. 242: **Inner Aspect of the Anterior Abdominal Wall**

NOTE: 1) this posterior view of the anterior abdominal wall shows to good advantage the posterior layer of the rectus sheath and the relationship of the arcuate line to the umbilicus.

2) the opening of the deep (abdominal) inguinal ring and the interfoveolar ligament which is a fibrous band that forms the medial edge of the deep inguinal ring and then courses superiorly and medially.

3) the breadth of the transversus abdominis muscle which lies adjacent to the next inner layer, the transversalis fascia (not shown).

Figs. 241 a, 241 b, 242

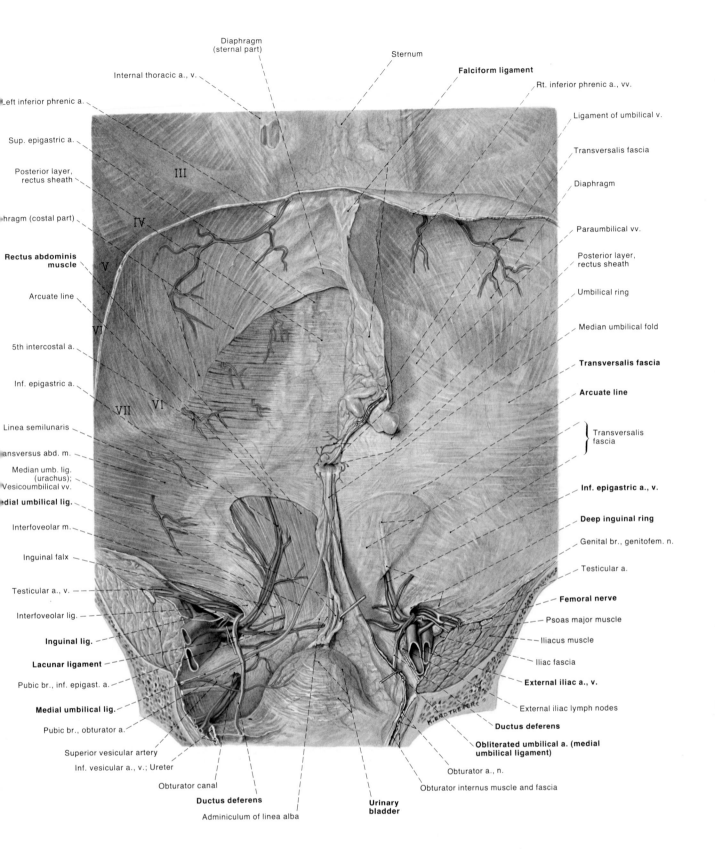

Fig. 243: The Vessels and Umbilical Ligaments on the Inner Aspect of the Anterior Abdominal Wall

NOTE: 1) the course of the *median umbilical ligament* (remnant of the urachus) and the two *medial umbilical ligaments* (remnants of the umbilical arteries) from their origins in the pelvis to the umbilicus. When covered with peritoneum, these structures are called umbilical folds;

2) that the two *lateral umbilical folds* represent peritoneal reflections over the inferior epigastric vessels;

3) the abdominal inguinal rings through each of which course the ductus deferens and the testicular artery and vein;

4) the passage of the external iliac artery and vein beneath the inguinal ligament on each side, thereby achieving the anterior aspect of the thigh, where the vessels become the femoral artery and vein.

Fig. 243   III

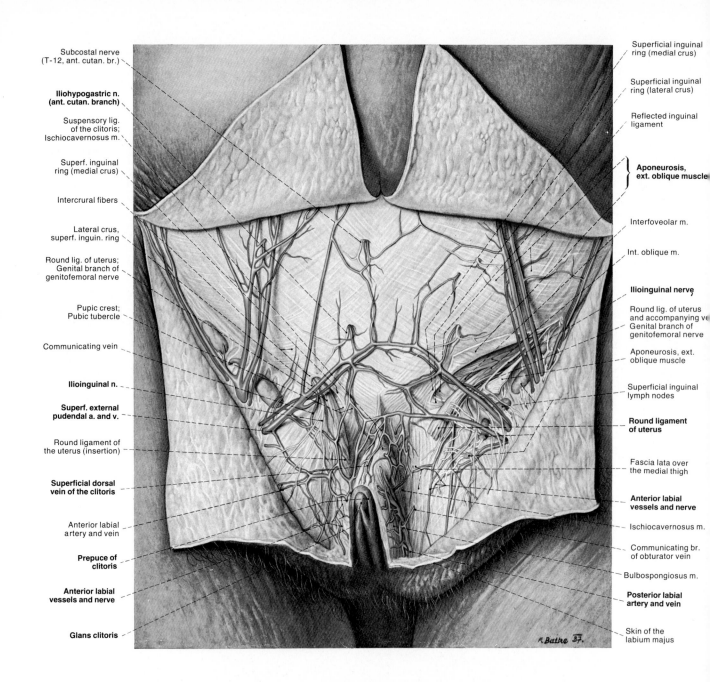

Labels (left side, top to bottom):
Subcostal nerve (T-12, ant. cutan. br.)
Iliohypogastric n. (ant. cutan. branch)
Suspensory lig. of the clitoris; Ischiocavernosus m.
Superf. inguinal ring (medial crus)
Intercrural fibers
Lateral crus, superf. inguin. ring
Round lig. of uterus; Genital branch of genitofemoral nerve
Pupic crest; Pubic tubercle
Communicating vein
Ilioinguinal n.
Superf. external pudendal a. and v.
Round ligament of the uterus (insertion)
Superficial dorsal vein of the clitoris
Anterior labial artery and vein
Prepuce of clitoris
Anterior labial vessels and nerve
Glans clitoris

Labels (right side, top to bottom):
Superficial inguinal ring (medial crus)
Superficial inguinal ring (lateral crus)
Reflected inguinal ligament
Aponeurosis, ext. oblique muscle
Interfoveolar m.
Int. oblique m.
Ilioinguinal nerve
Round lig. of uterus and accompanying ve
Genital branch of genitofemoral nerve
Aponeurosis, ext. oblique muscle
Superficial inguinal lymph nodes
Round ligament of uterus
Fascia lata over the medial thigh
Anterior labial vessels and nerve
Ischiocavernosus m.
Communicating br. of obturator vein
Bulbospongiosus m.
Posterior labial artery and vein
Skin of the labium majus

F. Bathe 37.

Fig. 244: The Inguinal Region of the Anterior Abdominal Wall in the Female (1): Superficial Inguinal Ring and Superficial Vessels and Nerves

NOTE: 1) that the skin and superficial fascia have been reflected upward and laterally from the inguinal region in this female body, thereby exposing the aponeurosis of the external oblique muscle, the superficial inguinal ring, the superficial vessels and nerves of the lower anterior abdominal wall, a few superficial inguinal lymph nodes and the muscles and vessels of the clitoris.

2) that the superficial inguinal ring is an opening in the aponeurosis of the external oblique muscle. On the specimen's left (reader's right), the ring has been opened to reveal the lower course of the round ligament of the uterus and the ilioinguinal nerve and on the specimen's right, the genital branch of the genitofemoral nerve (L-1, L-2). Observe also the iliohypogastric nerve (branch of L-1) as it emerges through the aponeurosis to become a sensory nerve after supplying motor fibers to the underlying musculature.

3) that vessels supplying and draining this region include the superficial external pudendal, superficial iliac circumflex, and superficial epigastric arteries and veins (see labels, Fig. 245). All three of the arteries arise from the femoral artery, while their accompanying veins all drain into the great saphenous vein just before this latter vessel joins the femoral vein in the upper anteromedial aspect of the thigh.

4) that the *superficial external pudendal artery* courses medially across the round ligament (spermatic cord) near the superficial inguinal ring to supply the superficial structures of the lower abdomen and the labium majus (scrotum); the *superficial iliac circumflex artery* penetrates the fascia lata and courses laterally, immediately below the inguinal ligament, toward the anterior superior iliac spine; the *superficial epigastric artery* penetrates the cribriform fascia and ascends over the inguinal ligament within the superficial fascia of the lower abdominal wall between its (the superficial fascia's) superficial (Camper's) and deep (Scarpa's) layers. These two arteries are labelled on Fig. 245.

5) the surface anatomy of the clitoris, its prepuce, and its suspensory ligament (see also Figs. 367, 368 and 370). Observe the superficial dorsal vein of the clitoris; this vessel may drain into either the right or left superficial external pudendal veins, and note that it lies superficial to the (subfascial) dorsal arteries and vein of the clitoris (see Fig. 245).

Fig. 244

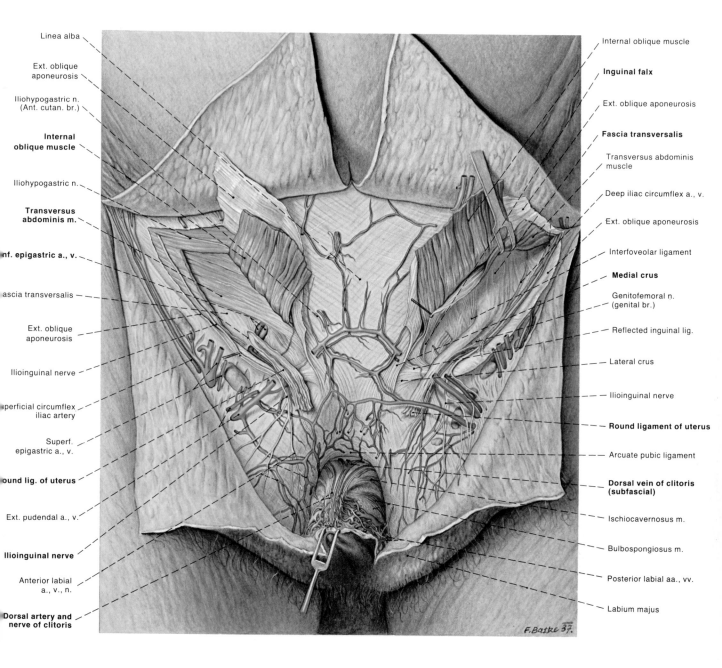

Linea alba

Ext. oblique aponeurosis

Iliohypogastric n. (Ant. cutan. br.)

Internal oblique muscle

Iliohypogastric n.

Transversus abdominis m.

Inf. epigastric a., v.

Fascia transversalis

Ext. oblique aponeurosis

Ilioinguinal nerve

Superficial circumflex iliac artery

Superf. epigastric a., v.

Round lig. of uterus

Ext. pudendal a., v.

Ilioinguinal nerve

Anterior labial a., v., n.

Dorsal artery and nerve of clitoris

Internal oblique muscle

Inguinal falx

Ext. oblique aponeurosis

Fascia transversalis

Transversus abdominis muscle

Deep iliac circumflex a., v.

Ext. oblique aponeurosis

Interfoveolar ligament

Medial crus

Genitofemoral n. (genital br.)

Reflected inguinal lig.

Lateral crus

Ilioinguinal nerve

Round ligament of uterus

Arcuate pubic ligament

Dorsal vein of clitoris (subfascial)

Ischiocavernosus m.

Bulbospongiosus m.

Posterior labial aa., vv.

Labium majus

F. Baske 37.

Fig. 245: The Inguinal Region of the Anterior Abdominal Wall in the Female (2): The Opened Inguinal Canal

NOTE: 1) that in this anterior view, the left (reader's right) inguinal canal has been completely opened by severing the overlying transversus abdominis and internal oblique muscles, as well as the lower lateral portion of the aponeurosis of the external oblique muscle;

2) that the female inguinal canal contains the round ligament of the uterus and the artery and vein which supply that ligament. The ilioinguinal branch of the L-1 spinal nerve, along with the genital branch of the genitofemoral nerve (L-1 and L-2), both emerge from the superficial inguinal ring with the round ligament;

3) that although the genital branch of the genitofemoral nerve enters the inguinal canal with the round ligament at the deep inguinal ring, the ilioinguinal nerve does not. It joins with the contents of the inguinal canal just deep to the aponeurosis of the external oblique;

4) that the ilioinguinal nerve and the genital branch of the genitofemoral nerve, in the female, both supply sensory innervation to the inguinal region and to the labia majora;

5) that the round ligament, when leaving the superficial inguinal ring, splits into a number of fibrous strands which then become enmeshed in the subcutaneous folds of the labium majus on each side. The labia majora are the homologues of the scrotal sacs in the male;

6) the inferior epigastric artery and vein coursing just medial to the deep inguinal ring, as they do in the male;

7) that the principal superficial vessels of the inguinal region are the superficial iliac circumflex, superficial epigastric, and the external pudendal arteries and veins.

8) the dorsal nerve and artery of the clitoris and the (subfascial) dorsal vein of the clitoris. The dorsal nerve of the clitoris comes from the posterior labial branch of the perineal nerve (from the pudendal nerve). The dorsal artery of the clitoris is one of the terminal branches of the internal pudendal artery, while the (subfascial) dorsal vein of the clitoris drains into the vesical plexus on the anterior aspect of the bladder within the pelvis.

Fig. 245   III

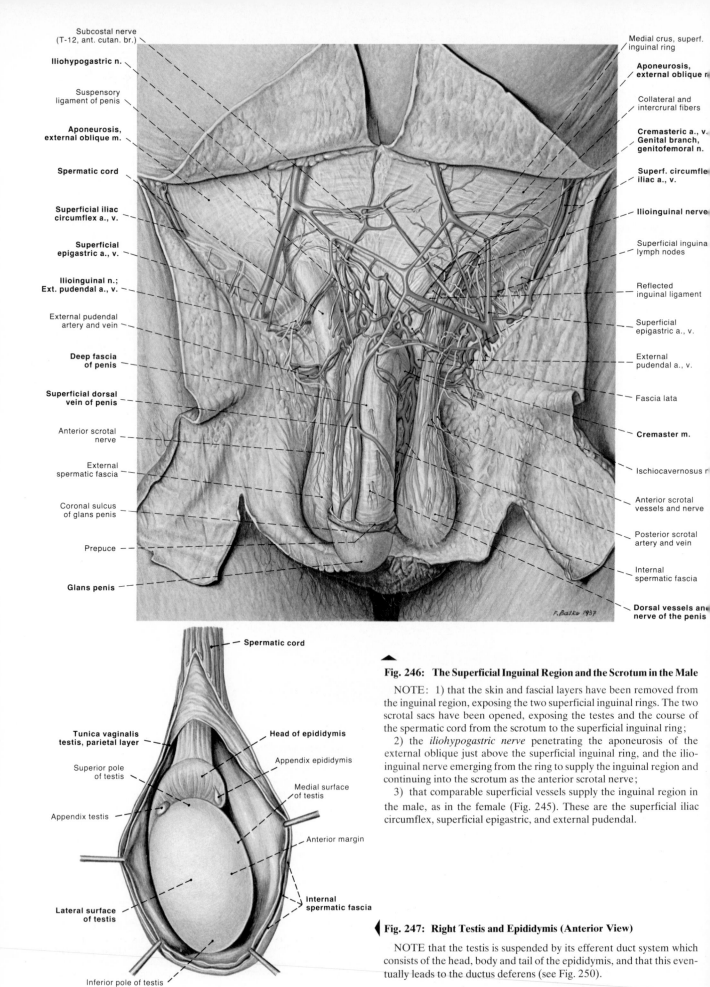

Subcostal nerve
(T-12, ant. cutan. br.)

Iliohypogastric n.

Suspensory
ligament of penis

Aponeurosis,
external oblique m.

Spermatic cord

Superficial iliac
circumflex a., v.

Superficial
epigastric a., v.

Ilioinguinal n.;
Ext. pudendal a., v.

External pudendal
artery and vein

Deep fascia
of penis

Superficial dorsal
vein of penis

Anterior scrotal
nerve

External
spermatic fascia

Coronal sulcus
of glans penis

Prepuce

Glans penis

Medial crus, superf.
inguinal ring

Aponeurosis,
external oblique m.

Collateral and
intercrural fibers

Cremasteric a., v.;
Genital branch,
genitofemoral n.

Superf. circumflex
iliac a., v.

Ilioinguinal nerve

Superficial inguinal
lymph nodes

Reflected
inguinal ligament

Superficial
epigastric a., v.

External
pudendal a., v.

Fascia lata

Cremaster m.

Ischiocavernosus m.

Anterior scrotal
vessels and nerve

Posterior scrotal
artery and vein

Internal
spermatic fascia

Dorsal vessels and
nerve of the penis

F. Batke 1937

Spermatic cord

Tunica vaginalis
testis, parietal layer

Superior pole
of testis

Appendix testis

Lateral surface
of testis

Inferior pole of testis

Head of epididymis

Appendix epididymis

Medial surface
of testis

Anterior margin

Internal
spermatic fascia

Fig. 246: The Superficial Inguinal Region and the Scrotum in the Male

NOTE: 1) that the skin and fascial layers have been removed from the inguinal region, exposing the two superficial inguinal rings. The two scrotal sacs have been opened, exposing the testes and the course of the spermatic cord from the scrotum to the superficial inguinal ring;

2) the *iliohypogastric nerve* penetrating the aponeurosis of the external oblique just above the superficial inguinal ring, and the ilioinguinal nerve emerging from the ring to supply the inguinal region and continuing into the scrotum as the anterior scrotal nerve;

3) that comparable superficial vessels supply the inguinal region in the male, as in the female (Fig. 245). These are the superficial iliac circumflex, superficial epigastric, and external pudendal.

Fig. 247: Right Testis and Epididymis (Anterior View)

NOTE that the testis is suspended by its efferent duct system which consists of the head, body and tail of the epididymis, and that this eventually leads to the ductus deferens (see Fig. 250).

Figs. 246, 247

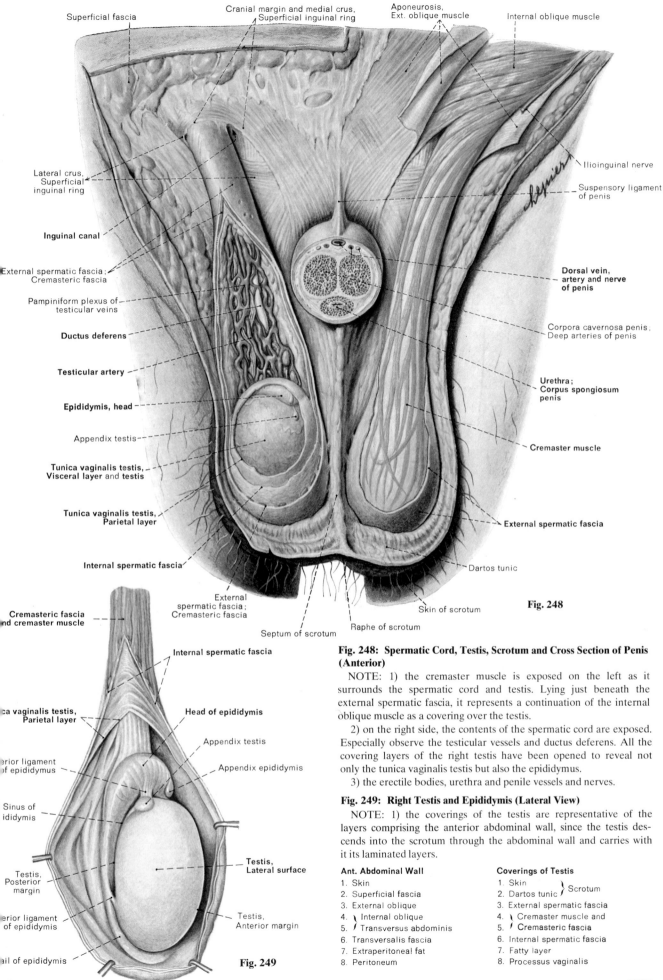

Superficial fascia

Cranial margin and medial crus,
Superficial inguinal ring

Aponeurosis,
Ext. oblique muscle

Internal oblique muscle

Lateral crus,
Superficial
inguinal ring

Ilioinguinal nerve

Suspensory ligament
of penis

Inguinal canal

External spermatic fascia;
Cremasteric fascia

Dorsal vein,
artery and nerve
of penis

Pampiniform plexus of
testicular veins

Ductus deferens

Corpora cavernosa penis;
Deep arteries of penis

Testicular artery

Epididymis, head

Urethra;
Corpus spongiosum
penis

Appendix testis

Tunica vaginalis testis,
Visceral layer and testis

Cremaster muscle

Tunica vaginalis testis,
Parietal layer

Internal spermatic fascia

External spermatic fascia

Dartos tunic

External
spermatic fascia;
Cremasteric fascia

Skin of scrotum

Fig. 248

Septum of scrotum

Raphe of scrotum

Cremasteric fascia
and cremaster muscle

Internal spermatic fascia

Tunica vaginalis testis,
Parietal layer

Head of epididymis

Appendix testis

Superior ligament
of epididymus

Appendix epididymis

Sinus of
epididymis

Testis,
Posterior
margin

Testis,
Lateral surface

Inferior ligament
of epididymis

Testis,
Anterior margin

Tail of epididymis

Fig. 249

Fig. 248: Spermatic Cord, Testis, Scrotum and Cross Section of Penis (Anterior)

NOTE: 1) the cremaster muscle is exposed on the left as it surrounds the spermatic cord and testis. Lying just beneath the external spermatic fascia, it represents a continuation of the internal oblique muscle as a covering over the testis.

2) on the right side, the contents of the spermatic cord are exposed. Especially observe the testicular vessels and ductus deferens. All the covering layers of the right testis have been opened to reveal not only the tunica vaginalis testis but also the epididymis.

3) the erectile bodies, urethra and penile vessels and nerves.

Fig. 249: Right Testis and Epididymis (Lateral View)

NOTE: 1) the coverings of the testis are representative of the layers comprising the anterior abdominal wall, since the testis descends into the scrotum through the abdominal wall and carries with it its laminated layers.

Ant. Abdominal Wall	Coverings of Testis
1. Skin	1. Skin ⎫ Scrotum
2. Superficial fascia	2. Dartos tunic ⎭
3. External oblique	3. External spermatic fascia
4. ⎫ Internal oblique	4. ⎫ Cremaster muscle and
5. ⎭ Transversus abdominis	5. ⎭ Cremasteric fascia
6. Transversalis fascia	6. Internal spermatic fascia
7. Extraperitoneal fat	7. Fatty layer
8. Peritoneum	8. Processus vaginalis

Figs. 248, 249   III

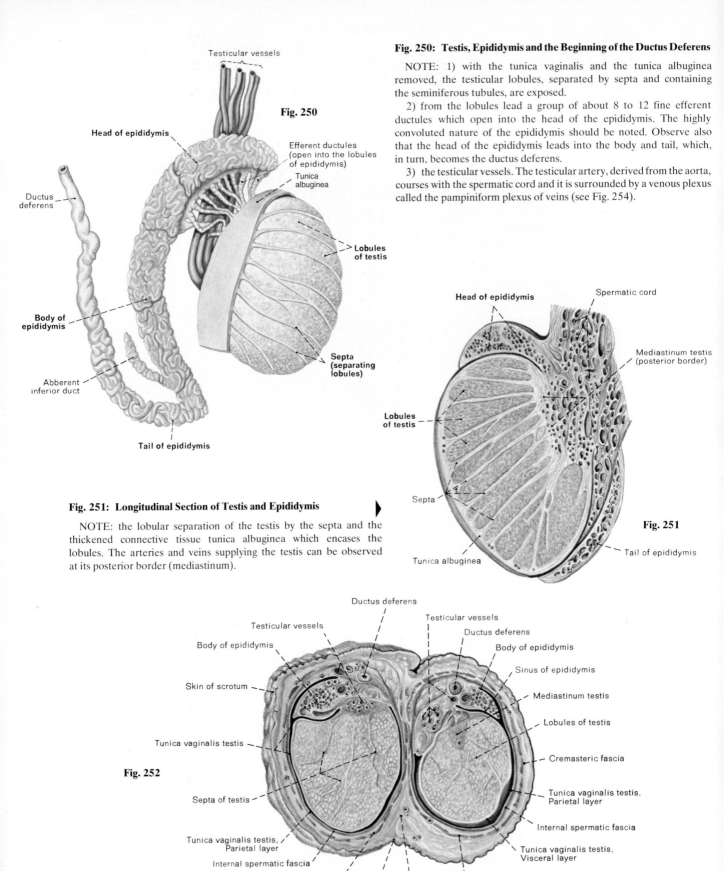

Testicular vessels

Head of epididymis

Ductus deferens

Body of epididymis

Abberent inferior duct

Tail of epididymis

Fig. 250

Efferent ductules (open into the lobules of epididymis)

Tunica albuginea

Lobules of testis

Septa (separating lobules)

Fig. 250: Testis, Epididymis and the Beginning of the Ductus Deferens

NOTE: 1) with the tunica vaginalis and the tunica albuginea removed, the testicular lobules, separated by septa and containing the seminiferous tubules, are exposed.

2) from the lobules lead a group of about 8 to 12 fine efferent ductules which open into the head of the epididymis. The highly convoluted nature of the epididymis should be noted. Observe also that the head of the epididymis leads into the body and tail, which, in turn, becomes the ductus deferens.

3) the testicular vessels. The testicular artery, derived from the aorta, courses with the spermatic cord and it is surrounded by a venous plexus called the pampiniform plexus of veins (see Fig. 254).

Fig. 251: Longitudinal Section of Testis and Epididymis   ▶

NOTE: the lobular separation of the testis by the septa and the thickened connective tissue tunica albuginea which encases the lobules. The arteries and veins supplying the testis can be observed at its posterior border (mediastinum).

Head of epididymis

Spermatic cord

Mediastinum testis (posterior border)

Lobules of testis

Septa

Tunica albuginea

Tail of epididymis

Fig. 251

Ductus deferens

Testicular vessels

Body of epididymis

Skin of scrotum

Tunica vaginalis testis

Fig. 252

Septa of testis

Tunica vaginalis testis, Parietal layer

Internal spermatic fascia

Cremaster muscle

Scrotal raphe

Scrotal septum

Testicular vessels

Ductus deferens

Body of epididymis

Sinus of epididymis

Mediastinum testis

Lobules of testis

Cremasteric fascia

Tunica vaginalis testis, Parietal layer

Internal spermatic fascia

Tunica vaginalis testis, Visceral layer

Cremaster muscle

Fig. 252: Cross Section of Testis and Scrotum

NOTE: the scrotum is divided by the median raphe and septum into two lateral compartments, each surrounding an ovoid-shaped testis. The two scrotal compartments do not communicate.

Figs. 250, 251, 252

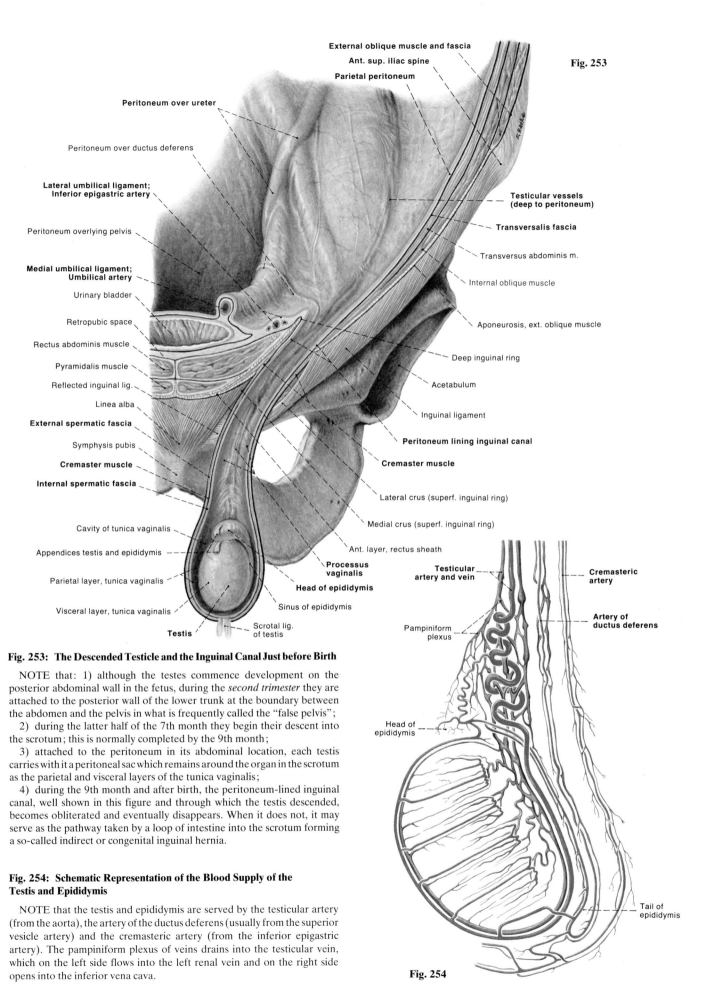

External oblique muscle and fascia
Ant. sup. iliac spine
Parietal peritoneum

Fig. 253

Peritoneum over ureter

Peritoneum over ductus deferens

Lateral umbilical ligament;
Inferior epigastric artery

Peritoneum overlying pelvis

Medial umbilical ligament;
Umbilical artery

Urinary bladder

Retropubic space

Rectus abdominis muscle

Pyramidalis muscle

Reflected inguinal lig.

Linea alba

External spermatic fascia

Symphysis pubis

Cremaster muscle

Internal spermatic fascia

Cavity of tunica vaginalis

Appendices testis and epididymis

Parietal layer, tunica vaginalis

Visceral layer, tunica vaginalis

Testis

Testicular vessels
(deep to peritoneum)

Transversalis fascia

Transversus abdominis m.

Internal oblique muscle

Aponeurosis, ext. oblique muscle

Deep inguinal ring

Acetabulum

Inguinal ligament

Peritoneum lining inguinal canal

Cremaster muscle

Lateral crus (superf. inguinal ring)

Medial crus (superf. inguinal ring)

Ant. layer, rectus sheath

Processus
vaginalis

Head of epididymis

Sinus of epididymis

Scrotal lig.
of testis

Testicular
artery and vein

Pampiniform
plexus

Head of
epididymis

Cremasteric
artery

Artery of
ductus deferens

Tail of
epididymis

Fig. 254

Fig. 253: The Descended Testicle and the Inguinal Canal Just before Birth

NOTE that: 1) although the testes commence development on the posterior abdominal wall in the fetus, during the *second trimester* they are attached to the posterior wall of the lower trunk at the boundary between the abdomen and the pelvis in what is frequently called the "false pelvis";

2) during the latter half of the 7th month they begin their descent into the scrotum; this is normally completed by the 9th month;

3) attached to the peritoneum in its abdominal location, each testis carries with it a peritoneal sac which remains around the organ in the scrotum as the parietal and visceral layers of the tunica vaginalis;

4) during the 9th month and after birth, the peritoneum-lined inguinal canal, well shown in this figure and through which the testis descended, becomes obliterated and eventually disappears. When it does not, it may serve as the pathway taken by a loop of intestine into the scrotum forming a so-called indirect or congenital inguinal hernia.

Fig. 254: Schematic Representation of the Blood Supply of the Testis and Epididymis

NOTE that the testis and epididymis are served by the testicular artery (from the aorta), the artery of the ductus deferens (usually from the superior vesicle artery) and the cremasteric artery (from the inferior epigastric artery). The pampiniform plexus of veins drains into the testicular vein, which on the left side flows into the left renal vein and on the right side opens into the inferior vena cava.

Figs. 253, 254   **III**

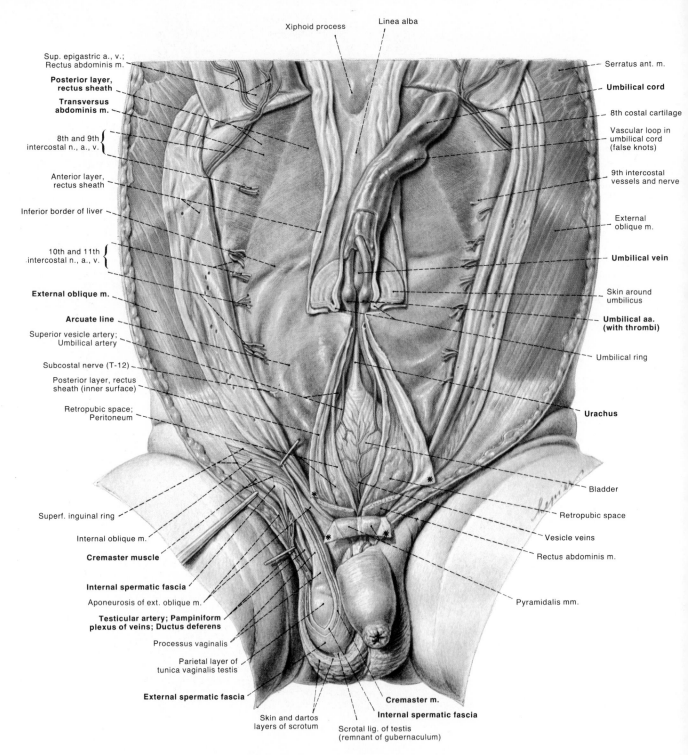

Xiphoid process

Linea alba

Sup. epigastric a., v.;
Rectus abdominis m.

**Posterior layer,
rectus sheath**

**Transversus
abdominis m.**

8th and 9th
intercostal n., a., v.

Anterior layer,
rectus sheath

Inferior border of liver

10th and 11th
intercostal n., a., v.

External oblique m.

Arcuate line

Superior vesicle artery;
Umbilical artery

Subcostal nerve (T-12)

Posterior layer, rectus
sheath (inner surface)

Retropubic space;
Peritoneum

Superf. inguinal ring

Internal oblique m.

Cremaster muscle

Internal spermatic fascia

Aponeurosis of ext. oblique m.

**Testicular artery; Pampiniform
plexus of veins; Ductus deferens**

Processus vaginalis

Parietal layer of
tunica vaginalis testis

External spermatic fascia

Skin and dartos
layers of scrotum

Scrotal lig. of testis
(remnant of gubernaculum)

Cremaster m.

Internal spermatic fascia

Serratus ant. m.

Umbilical cord

8th costal cartilage

Vascular loop in
umbilical cord
(false knots)

9th intercostal
vessels and nerve

External
oblique m.

Umbilical vein

Skin around
umbilicus

**Umbilical aa.
(with thrombi)**

Umbilical ring

Urachus

Bladder

Retropubic space

Vesicle veins

Rectus abdominis m.

Pyramidalis mm.

Fig. 255: A Deep Dissection of the Anterior Abdominal Wall and the Umbilical Region in the Newborn

NOTE: 1) that the anterior layer of the rectus sheath has been severed and reflected laterally on each side. The two rectus abdominis muscles have been severed near the symphysis pubis and reflected superiorly (almost out of view) in order to reveal the posterior layer of the rectus sheath. Observe the arcuate line.

2) that an incision has been made in the linea alba between the umbilical ring and the symphysis pubis exposing the apex of the bladder, the urachus, the paired umbilical arteries and the single umbilical vein.

3) that the anterior aspect of the right spermatic cord and right scrotal sac have been opened to uncover the ductus deferens and the testis, the latter structure surrounded by the tunica vaginalis testis.

4) the severed umbilical cord which is usually between one and two centimeters in diameter and about 50 centimeters (20 inches) long. It contains the two umbilical arteries and the umbilical vein which are surrounded by a mucoid form of connective tissue called Wharton's jelly. Frequently the umbilical vessels form harmless loops in the cord called "false knots" (seen as bulges in this figure). More rarely looping of the cord may be of some functional significance and such "true knots" may alter the circulation to and from the fetus, causing vascular obstruction.

5) the bulges in the umbilical arteries. These are *in situ* blood clots, called thrombi, which occlude the arteries, but which are probably postmortem phenomena in this instance.

Fig. 255

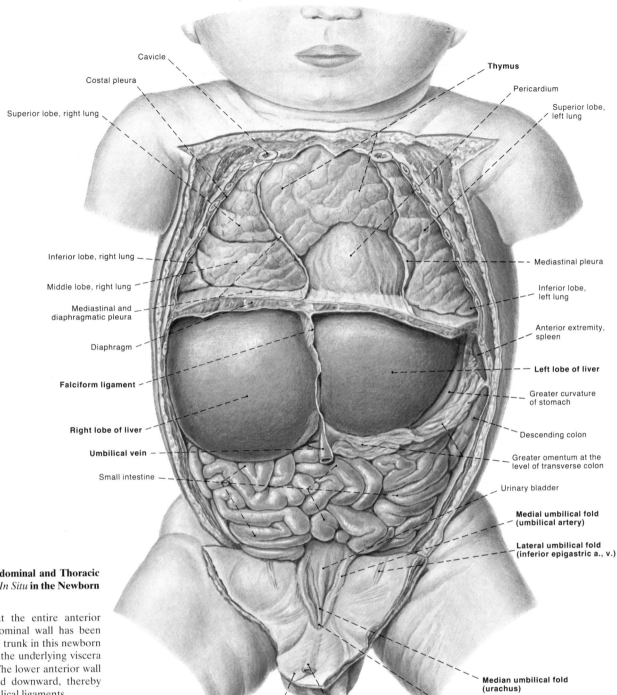

Cavicle

Costal pleura

Superior lobe, right lung

Thymus

Pericardium

Superior lobe, left lung

Inferior lobe, right lung —

Middle lobe, right lung —

Mediastinal and diaphragmatic pleura

Diaphragm —

Falciform ligament —

Right lobe of liver —

Umbilical vein —

Small intestine —

— Mediastinal pleura

Inferior lobe, left lung

Anterior extremity, spleen

Left lobe of liver

Greater curvature of stomach

Descending colon

Greater omentum at the level of transverse colon

Urinary bladder

Medial umbilical fold (umbilical artery)

Lateral umbilical fold (inferior epigastric a., v.)

Median umbilical fold (urachus)

Umbilical ring

Falciform ligament   Umbilical vein

Fig. 256: The Abdominal and Thoracic Viscera Observed *In Situ* in the Newborn Child

NOTE: 1) that the entire anterior thoracic and abdominal wall has been removed from the trunk in this newborn child, uncovering the underlying viscera in both cavities. The lower anterior wall has been reflected downward, thereby exposing the umbilical ligaments.

2) that the average newborn infant weighs about 3300 gr (7 lbs) and measures about 50 cm (20 inches) from the top of the head to the sole of the foot, and the umbilicus is located about 1.5 cm below the mid-point of this crown-heel length.

3) that the transverse diameter of the abdominal cavity in the newborn is greatest above the umbilicus, principally due to the inordinate proportion of the abdomen occupied by the liver. Observe that a greater area (than in the adult) of the anterior surface of both lobes lies immediately deep to the abdominal musculature and that the ribs (cut away in this figure) afford less protection to the upper abdomen.

4) that the average weight of the liver in the newborn is about 120 gr, and it constitutes 4 percent of the body weight at birth. In the adult, the liver weighs 12 to 13 times its weight at birth, but accounts for only 2.5 to 3.5 percent of the total body weight.

5) that most of the anterior surface of the stomach lies deep to the left lobe of the liver, allowing only a small portion of the greater curvature to be visible. The left lobe of the liver almost reaches the spleen.

6) that the loops of intestine form an oval-shaped mass, the greatest diameter of which is transverse in contrast to the adult in which it is vertical.

7) the broad-based truncated shape of the thoracic cavity and the large size of the thymus which weighs about 10 gr at birth (it accounts for 0.42 percent of body weight at birth, compared to 0.03 to 0.05 percent in the adult).

8) that the facts mentioned in 2, 3, 4, 6, and 7 are taken from: Crelin, Edmund S., *Functional Anatomy of the Newborn,* Yale University Press, New Haven, 1973. This is an excellent and short monograph (87 pages) which would be of benefit for any medical student to read.

Fig. 256   III

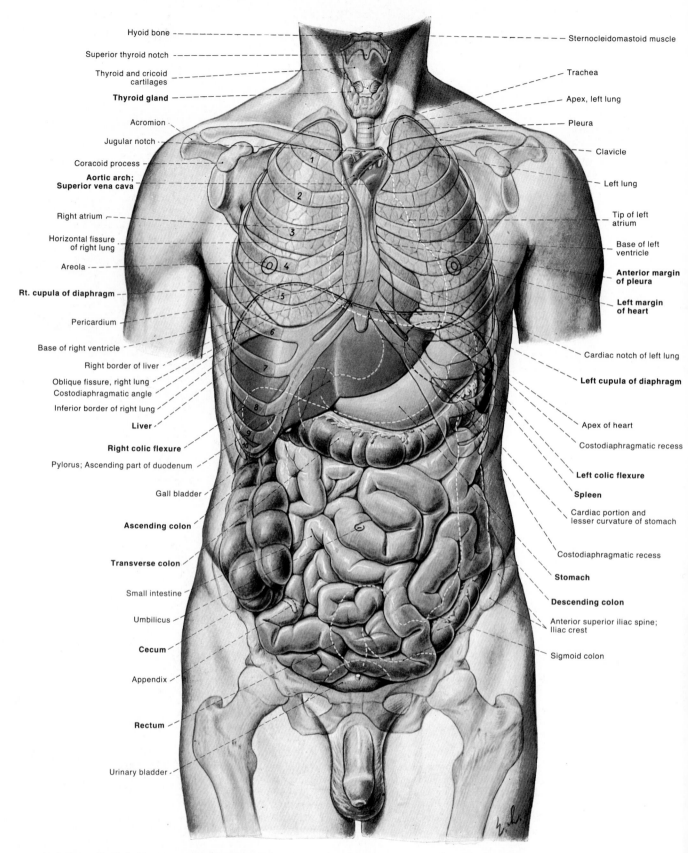

Fig. 257: Frontal View of Thoracic and Abdominal Viscera

NOTE that the surface projections of the heart, stomach, gall bladder, spleen, transverse colon, descending and sigmoid colon, rectum, and urinary bladder are indicated by white broken outlines. The limits of the pleura are shown as solid blue lines and the spleen as a purple broken line. The gall bladder is shown as a broken blue line.

Fig. 257

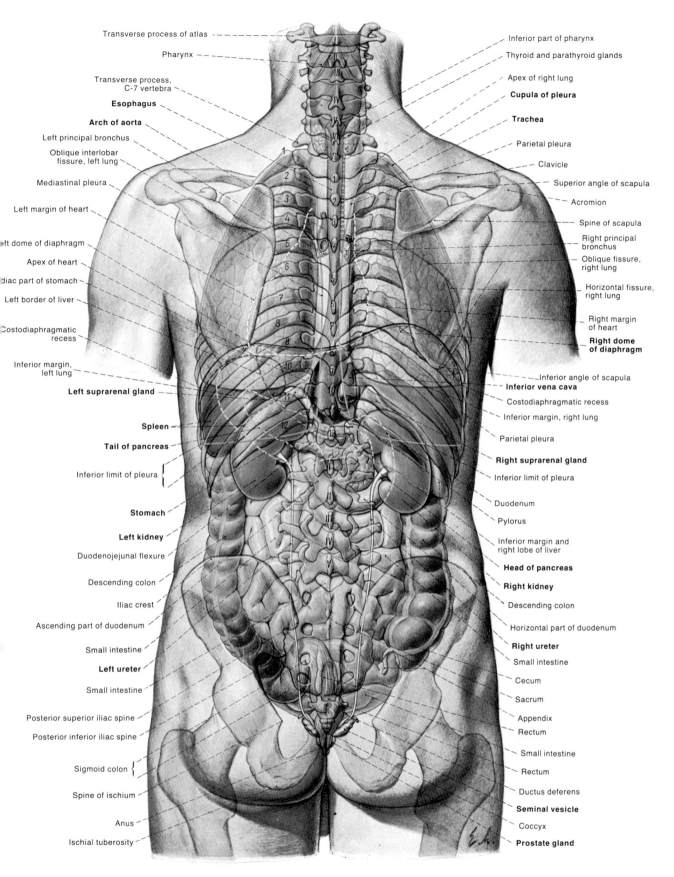

Transverse process of atlas

Pharynx

Transverse process, C-7 vertebra

Esophagus

Arch of aorta

Left principal bronchus

Oblique interlobar fissure, left lung

Mediastinal pleura

Left margin of heart

Left dome of diaphragm

Apex of heart

Cardiac part of stomach

Left border of liver

Costodiaphragmatic recess

Inferior margin, left lung

Left suprarenal gland

Spleen

Tail of pancreas

Inferior limit of pleura

Stomach

Left kidney

Duodenojejunal flexure

Descending colon

Iliac crest

Ascending part of duodenum

Small intestine

Left ureter

Small intestine

Posterior superior iliac spine

Posterior inferior iliac spine

Sigmoid colon

Spine of ischium

Anus

Ischial tuberosity

Inferior part of pharynx

Thyroid and parathyroid glands

Apex of right lung

Cupula of pleura

Trachea

Parietal pleura

Clavicle

Superior angle of scapula

Acromion

Spine of scapula

Right principal bronchus

Oblique fissure, right lung

Horizontal fissure, right lung

Right margin of heart

Right dome of diaphragm

Inferior angle of scapula

Inferior vena cava

Costodiaphragmatic recess

Inferior margin, right lung

Parietal pleura

Right suprarenal gland

Inferior limit of pleura

Duodenum

Pylorus

Inferior margin and right lobe of liver

Head of pancreas

Right kidney

Descending colon

Horizontal part of duodenum

Right ureter

Small intestine

Cecum

Sacrum

Appendix

Rectum

Small intestine

Rectum

Ductus deferens

Seminal vesicle

Coccyx

Prostate gland

Fig. 258: Posterior View of Thoracic and Abdominal Viscera

NOTE that the surface projections of the heart, stomach and duodenum are shown as white broken lines, the body and tail of the pancreas as yellow broken lines, the liver as brown broken lines, the superior pole of the spleen as a purple broken line, and the limits of the pleura as solid blue lines.

Fig. 258   III

Right lobe of liver

Round ligament of liver

Gall bladder

Transverse colon

Peritoneum (through which can be seen the transversus abdominis muscle)

Taenia omentalis

Anterior taenia coli (longitudinal muscle); Haustra (intestinal sacculation)

Ascending colon

Small intestine (ileum)

Pylorus of stomach

Falciform ligament

Left lobe of liver

Greater curvature of stomach

Body of **stomach**

Peritoneum (through which can be seen the rectus abdominis muscle)

Gastrocolic ligament

Greater omentum

Transversus abdominis muscle

Internal oblique muscle

External oblique muscle

Sigmoid colon

Parietal peritoneum

Lateral umbilical fold

Arcuate line

Medial umbilical fold (umbilical artery)

Median umbilical fold (urachus)

Fig. 259: The Abdominal Cavity (1), the Viscera Left Intact

NOTE: 1) the greater omentum, which attaches along the greater curvature of the stomach, covers most of the intestines like an apron, and extends inferiorly almost as far as the pelvis.

2) the falciform ligament and round ligament of the liver (ligamentum teres). The falciform ligament is a remnant of the ventral mesogastrium. It extends between the liver and the anterior wall and separates the left and right lobes of the liver. The round ligament is the remains of the obliterated umbilical vein.

3) on the inner surface of the anterior wall identify

a) *the median umbilical fold* = the remains of the urachus, which in the fetus extends between the bladder and the umbilicus.

b) *the medial umbilical folds* = the obliterated umbilical arteries, which, before birth, coursed from the common iliac arteries to the umbilicus.

c) *the lateral umbilical folds* = which represent a reflection of peritoneum over the inferior epigastric vessels.

Fig. 259

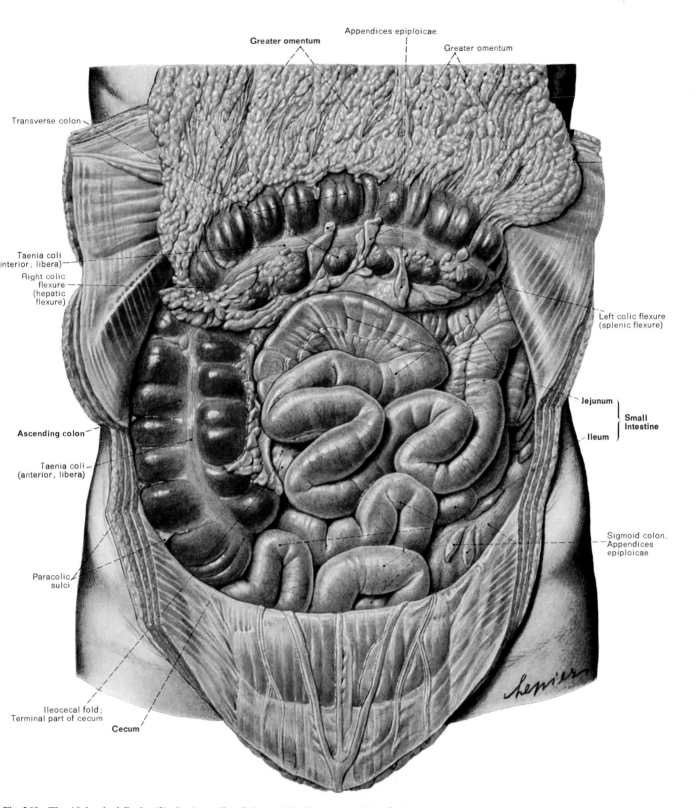

Greater omentum

Appendices epiploicae

Greater omentum

Transverse colon

Taenia coli (anterior; libera)

Right colic flexure (hepatic flexure)

Left colic flexure (splenic flexure)

Jejunum

Ileum

Small Intestine

Ascending colon

Taenia coli (anterior, libera)

Sigmoid colon, Appendices epiploicae

Paracolic sulci

Ileocecal fold; Terminal part of cecum

Cecum

Fig. 260: The Abdominal Cavity (2), the Ascending Colon and the Transverse Colon and its Mesocolon

NOTE: 1) with the greater omentum reflected superiorly, the transverse colon comes into view as it crosses the abdominal cavity from right to left, in continuity with the ascending colon on the right and the descending colon (not shown in this figure; see Fig. 303 and 304) on the left. Observe the longitudinal muscles (taeniae) along the outer surface of the colon. Since these muscles are shorter than the other coats of the large intestine, they cause sacculations which are called haustra.

2) that small, smooth irregular fatty masses called appendices epiploicae are suspended from the large intestine, thereby assisting in its identification.

3) below the mesocolon (inframesocolic) can be seen the small intestine which consists of three portions, the duodenum (see Figs. 285–287), jejunum and ileum. The outer walls of the small intestine are smooth and glistening and are not sacculated.

4) the small intestine measures about 22 feet in length, commencing at the pyloric end of the stomach and terminating at the ileocecal junction, which marks the commencement of the large intestine.

Fig. 260   III

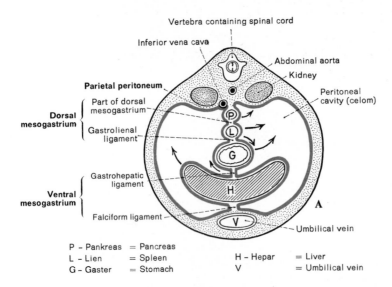

P – Pankreas = Pancreas
L – Lien = Spleen
G – Gaster = Stomach

H – Hepar = Liver
V = Umbilical vein

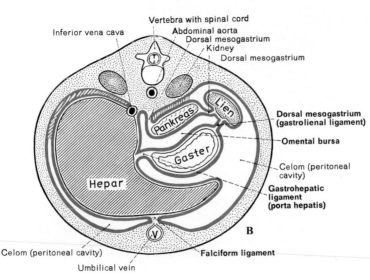

Figs. 261, 262 A, 262 B

Fig. 261: The Developing Gastrointestinal Organs and their Mesenteries

NOTE: 1) as the primitive gastrointestinal tube develops within the abdominal celom, it is suspended to the body wall by primitive peritoneal reflections, both ventrally and dorsally. The early peritoneal attachments to the expanding stomach are called the ventral mesogastrium and dorsal mesogastrium, while the dorsal mesentery develops on the posterior aspect of the primitive small and large intestine.

2) the embryonic liver develops into the ventral mesogastrium, thereby dividing this ventral peritoneal attachment into:

a) a portion between the anterior body wall and the liver which eventually becomes the falciform ligament, and

b) a portion between the liver and the stomach which becomes the lesser omentum.

3) on the dorsal aspect:

a) the pancreas develops in relation to the primitive duodenum, both of which lose their mesenteries during gut rotation to become retroperitoneal;

b) the dorsal mesogastrium, attaching along the greater curvature of the stomach and rotating with the stomach, becomes the greater omentum. This eventually encases the transverse colon;

c) the dorsal mesentery remains attached to the small intestine, while the ascending and descending colon become displaced to the right and left side respectively, becoming adherent to the posterior body wall;

d) the sigmoid colon usually retains its mesentery while that of the rectum becomes obliterated.

4) near the cecal end of the small intestine the developing G.I. canal communicates with the vitelline duct. Before birth, this duct usually becomes resorbed; when it persists (3% of cases), it results in a diverticulum of the ileum called Meckel's diverticulum.

Cross Sectional Diagram of Development of Mesogastria
Fig. 262 A: Early Stage (about six weeks)

NOTE: 1) the primitive peritoneal reflections are indicated in red. The arrows show the direction of growth and, therefore, of movement by the various organs to achieve the positions shown in Fig. 262 B.

2) at this early stage, the peritoneum completely surrounds the organs in the upper abdominal region (visceral peritoneum) and attaches peripherally to the body wall (parietal peritoneum). Attaching along the posterior border of the stomach, the dorsal mesogastrium then surrounds the spleen and pancreas. Anterior to the stomach, the liver becomes interposed between the stomach and the anterior body wall. This forms the gastrohepatic ligament (also called lesser omentum) between the lesser curvature of the stomach and the liver, and the falciform ligament between the liver and the anterior body wall.

Cross Sectional Diagram of Development of Mesogastria
Fig. 262 B: Late Fetal Stage

NOTE: 1) with the rotation of the organs (in the direction of the arrows in Fig. 262 A), the liver grows into the celomic cavity toward the right and contacts the inferior vena cava, while the stomach rotates such that its dorsal mesogastrium (greater curvature) is shifted to the left. The pancreas and spleen still retain their position posterior to the stomach.

2) the reflection of dorsal mesogastrium between the stomach and spleen becomes established as the gastrolienal ligament while one layer of mesogastrium surrounding the pancreas (and duodenum) fuses to the posterior body wall. This latter development fixates these two organs with a layer of peritoneum on their anterior surface, causing them to become retroperitoneal. The omental bursa also develops posterior to the stomach and anterior to the pancreas.

L	= Liver	D	= Duodenum	S	= Symphysis pubis	
P	= Pancreas	J	= Jejunum	I to IV	= The four layers	
M	= Magen (Stomach, in German)	CS	= Sigmoid colon		of the greater omentum	
C. tr.	= Transverse colon	I	= Ileum		(dorsal mesogastrium)	

Fig. 264: Peritoneal Reflections in Adult Female

NOTE: 1) the greater peritoneal sac (red stippled) lies between the layers of visceral and parietal peritoneum. The greater peritoneal sac communicates with the lesser peritoneal sac (omental bursa; black) through the epiploic foramen (of Winslow).

2) dorsally, the roots of three distinct peritoneal mesenteries can be observed: a) the transverse mesocolon, b) the mesentery surrounding the small intestine, and c) the sigmoid mesocolon.

3) behind the stomach and transverse colon, observe the retroperitoneal pancreas and duodenum. Note also that a portion of the liver is not surrounded by peritoneum (bare area of the liver) and lies adjacent to the diaphragm.

Fig. 263 A, B, & C: Stages in the Development of the Omental Bursa (Sagittal Diagrams)

NOTE: 1) at four weeks the dorsal border of the stomach (Magen, M) grows faster than the ventral border assisting in rotation of the stomach on its long axis. The greater curvature and its dorsal mesogastrium becomes directed to the left, while the lesser curvature and the ventral mesogastrium is directed to the right.

2) by eight weeks (Fig. 263 A) the omental bursa (black) forms behind the stomach between the two leaves of dorsal mesogastrium. The pancreas and duodenum are still surrounded by dorsal mesentery. As gut rotation continues the dorsal mesogastrium extends inferiorly (Fig. 263 B, arrow) to form the greater omentum which becomes a double reflection (4 leaves) of the dorsal mesogastrium "trapping" the cavity of the omental bursa between the 2nd and 3rd leaves.

3) continued development (Fig. 263 C) results in a further descent of the greater omentum over the abdominal viscera and a fusion (cross-hatched) of the 2nd and 3rd leaves inferiorly.

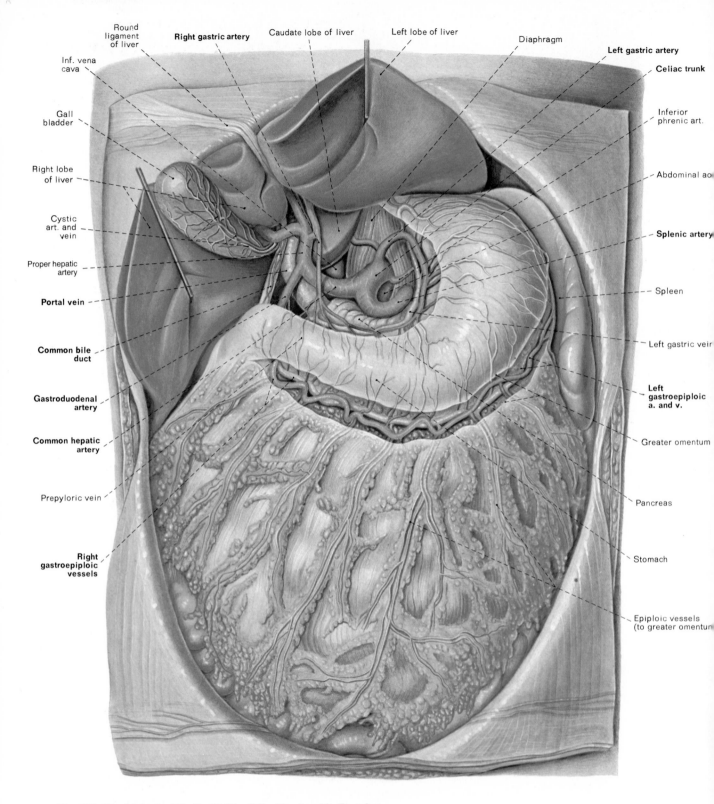

Round ligament of liver

Inf. vena cava

Gall bladder

Right lobe of liver

Cystic art. and vein

Proper hepatic artery

Portal vein

Common bile duct

Gastroduodenal artery

Common hepatic artery

Prepyloric vein

Right gastroepiploic vessels

Right gastric artery

Caudate lobe of liver

Left lobe of liver

Diaphragm

Left gastric artery

Celiac trunk

Inferior phrenic art.

Abdominal ao

Splenic artery

Spleen

Left gastric vein

Left gastroepiploic a. and v.

Greater omentum

Pancreas

Stomach

Epiploic vessels (to greater omentum

Fig. 265: The Abdominal Cavity (3): The Celiac Trunk and its Branches

NOTE: 1) the right and left lobes of the liver have been elevated and the lesser omentum has been removed between the lesser curvature of the stomach and the liver to reveal the celiac trunk and its branches and three major structures at the porta hepatis, the hepatic artery, portal vein and common bile duct.

2) the celiac trunk lies anterior to the 12th thoracic vertebra and almost immediately divides into the left gastric artery, and the hepatic and splenic arteries:

a) the left gastric artery courses along the lesser curvature of the stomach and anastomoses with the right gastric branch of the hepatic artery;

b) the hepatic artery courses to the right and gives off the gastroduodenal artery before dividing to enter the lobes of the liver;

c) the splenic artery courses to the left toward the hilum of the spleen;

d) the gastroduodenal artery gives rise to the right gastroepiploic artery which follows along the greater curvature of the stomach to anastomose with the left gastroepiploic branch of the splenic artery.

Fig. 265

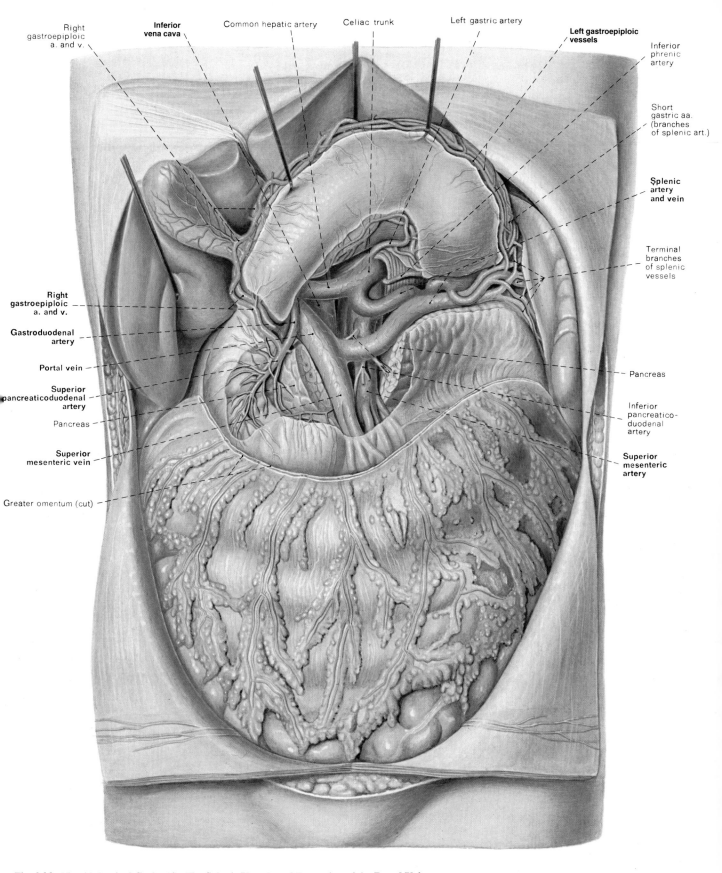

Fig. 266: The Abdominal Cavity (4): The Splenic Vessels and Formation of the Portal Vein

NOTE: 1) the attachment of the greater omentum has been cut along the greater curvature of the stomach. The stomach has been lifted to expose its posterior surface and the underlying pancreas, duodenum and blood vessels. A portion of the body of the pancreas has been removed to reveal the formation of the portal vein by the junction of the splenic and superior mesenteric veins.

2) the splenic artery in its tortuous course across the left upper abdomen to the hilum of the spleen. Observe also how the gastroduodenal artery lies posterior to the pyloric end of the stomach and divides into the right gastroepiploic artery and the superior pancreaticoduodenal artery. The origin of the left gastroepiploic artery from the splenic is also visible.

3) the root of the superior mesenteric artery as it branches from the abdominal aorta just below the celiac trunk.

Fig. 266   **III**

Fig. 267: Inner Surface of the Mucosa of the Stomach (magnified 40×)

This is a dried specimen of the inner surface of the stomach showing the elevated mounds or gastric areas which characterize the mucosal wall. These gastric areas vary from one to five or six mm. in diameter and are marked by many small pits or gastric foveolae. Into the base of these pits empty the gastric glands which are located in the mucosal layer and which form the stomach secretions.

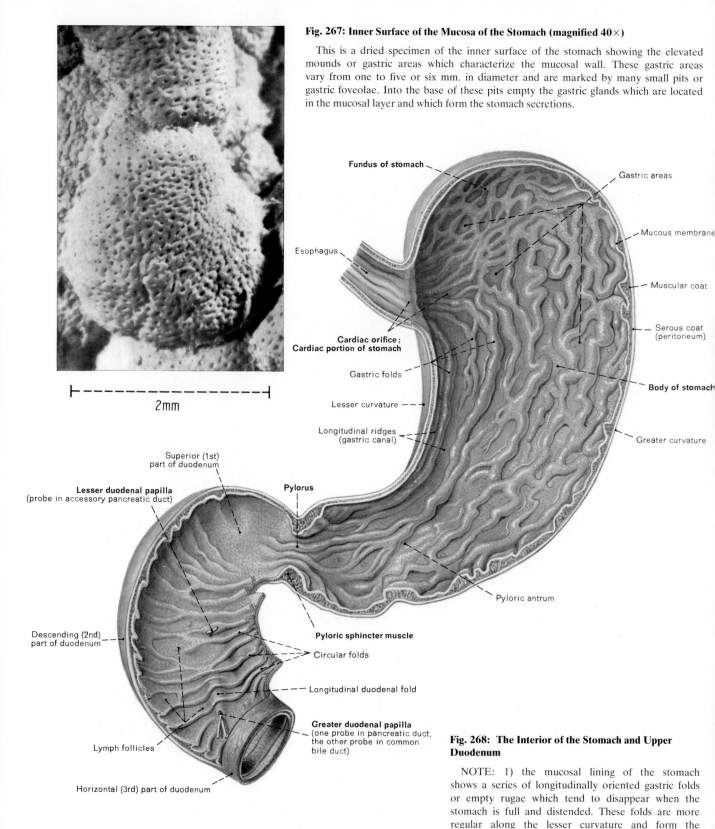

2mm

Fundus of stomach

Gastric areas

Mucous membrane

Esophagus

Muscular coat

Serous coat (peritoneum)

Cardiac orifice; Cardiac portion of stomach

Gastric folds

Body of stomach

Lesser curvature

Longitudinal ridges (gastric canal)

Greater curvature

Superior (1st) part of duodenum

Pylorus

Lesser duodenal papilla (probe in accessory pancreatic duct)

Pyloric antrum

Descending (2nd) part of duodenum

Pyloric sphincter muscle

Circular folds

Longitudinal duodenal fold

Greater duodenal papilla (one probe in pancreatic duct, the other probe in common bile duct)

Lymph follicles

Horizontal (3rd) part of duodenum

Fig. 268: The Interior of the Stomach and Upper Duodenum

NOTE: 1) the mucosal lining of the stomach shows a series of longitudinally oriented gastric folds or empty rugae which tend to disappear when the stomach is full and distended. These folds are more regular along the lesser curvature and form the grooved gastric canal. The concept that food travels along this canal (magenstrasse) is not correct.

2) the surface of the first portion of the duodenum (superior) is smooth, whereas the circular ridges characteristic of the small intestine can be seen to commence in the second or descending portion of the duodenum.

3) the pyloric junction of the stomach with the duodenum. A circular muscle, the pyloric sphincter, guards this junction. It diminishes significantly in size the lumen of the gastrointestinal tract at this point. The pylorus is to the right of midline at the level of the 1st lumbar vertebra.

4) the openings in the wall of the duodenum. The greater duodenal papilla serves as the site of the openings of both the common bile duct and the main pancreatic duct. The accessory pancreatic duct opens two centimeters more proximally through the lesser duodenal papilla.

Figs. 267, 268

1. Esophagus
2. Stomach fundus (air bubble)
3. Body of stomach
   3a Lesser curvature
   3b Greater curvature
4. Peristaltic constriction at angular notch
5. Pyloric antrum (expanded)
6. Bulb of superior duodenum (1st part)
7. Descending duodenum (2nd part)
8. Jejunum
9. Left dome of diaphragm
10. Gas in left colic flexure

Fig. 270: Anterior View of Stomach

NOTE: 1) the stomach is a dilated muscular and mucosal sac situated in the gastrointestinal tract between the esophagus (cardiac end) and duodenum (pyloric end). It consists of an upper dome-shaped portion called the *fundus*, a middle portion, *the body*, and a tapering caudal part referred to as the *pyloric portion.*

2) although the shape of the stomach varies with the amount of its contents, it presents two curvatures. The greater curvature is directed toward the left and to it is attached the greater omentum. The greater curvature forms an acute angle with the esophagus called the cardiac notch. The lesser curvature constitutes the right border of the stomach and along this edge is attached the lesser omentum. Its lower third bends toward the duodenum beyond the angular notch.

3) the blood vessels supplying the stomach include the a) left and right gastric arteries along the lesser curvature, b) the left and right gastroepiploic arteries along the greater curvature, c) the short gastric branches of the splenic artery. Observe the esophageal branches of the left gastric artery supplying the cardiac end of the stomach. ▼

Fig. 269: X-Ray of Lower Esophagus, Stomach, Duodenum, and Proximal Jejunum

NOTE: this is a normal "J-shaped" or "fish-hook" stomach. Observe that the cardiac and pyloric ends of the stomach are more securely attached to the posterior body wall, whereas the body and pyloric part are more mobile. Frequently in the upright position, the greater curvature hangs as low as the brim of the pelvis.

Fig. 271: A Celiac Trunk Arteriogram

NOTE: 1) that this figure is a negative print from an X-ray taken of the upper abdomen following the injection of a contrast medium through a catheter (*21, arrow*), which was introduced into the abdominal aorta and directed upward to the point where the celiac trunk (*3*) branches from the aorta. The principal subbranches of the celiac trunk, therefore, can be visualized.

2) the three primary vessels arising from the celiac trunk (*3*) are the *left gastric artery* (*2*), the *splenic artery* (*4*) which is directed in a tortuous pattern toward the spleen (*1*), and the *common hepatic artery* (*5*) which courses almost directly to the right.

3) that from one of the inferior hilar branches of the splenic artery arises the left gastroepiploic artery (*6*), which then gives origin to epiploic arteries (*7, arrows*) which descend to supply the greater omentum. The left gastroepiploic (*6*) courses along the greater curvature of the stomach to anastomose with the right gastroepiploic artery (*9*). This latter vessel arises from the gastroduodenal artery (*8*) which, in turn, courses inferiorly as a major vessel derived from the common hepatic artery (*5*).

4) that beyond the origin of the gastroduodenal artery (*8*) the common hepatic artery (*5*) is called the proper hepatic artery (*10*).

5) that the proper hepatic artery (*10*) soon divides into the *right hepatic artery* (*11*), from which branches the cystic artery (*12*) which supplies the gall bladder, the *middle hepatic artery* (*13*), and the *left hepatic artery* (*14, arrow*). The hepatic vessels, of course, supply the liver (*16*).

6) that from the right hepatic artery (*14*) in this individual branches the right gastric artery (*15, arrow*). Just as frequently the right gastric artery is found arising from the common hepatic artery (*5*). The right gastric artery courses around the lesser curvature of the stomach to anastomose with the left gastric (*2*). The latter vessel is one of the original branches of the celiac trunk.

7) that inferiorly can be seen the right renal pelvis (*17*) and the right ureter (*18, arrow*). Observe that because of the liver, these structures on the right side are significantly lower than the left renal pelvis (*19*) and the origin of the left ureter (*20, arrow*).

8) that this figure comes from Wicke, L., *Atlas of Radiologic Anatomy,* 3rd Edition, Urban & Schwarzenberg, Baltimore, 1982.

Fig. 271

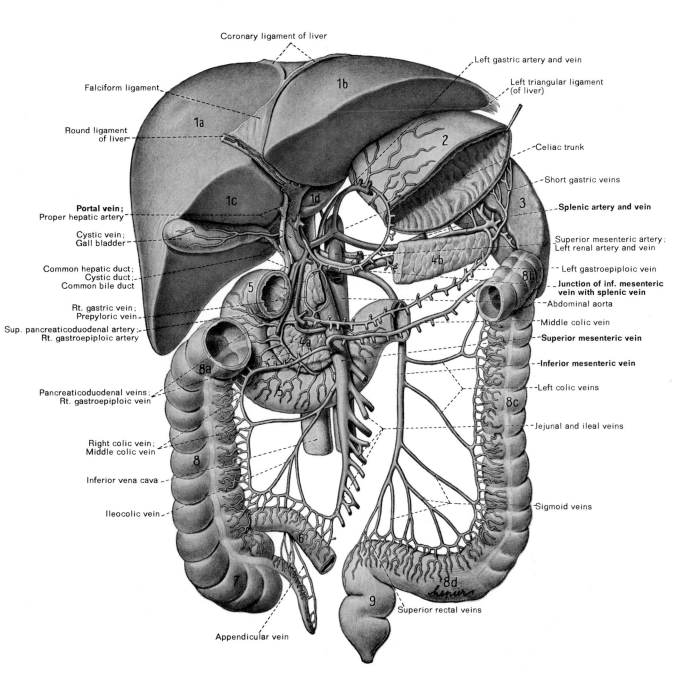

Coronary ligament of liver

Falciform ligament

Round ligament of liver

Portal vein; Proper hepatic artery

Cystic vein; Gall bladder

Common hepatic duct; Cystic duct; Common bile duct

Rt. gastric vein; Prepyloric vein

Sup. pancreaticoduodenal artery; Rt. gastroepiploic artery

Pancreaticoduodenal veins; Rt. gastroepiploic vein

Right colic vein; Middle colic vein

Inferior vena cava

Ileocolic vein

Appendicular vein

Left gastric artery and vein

Left triangular ligament (of liver)

Celiac trunk

Short gastric veins

Splenic artery and vein

Superior mesenteric artery; Left renal artery and vein

Left gastroepiploic vein

Junction of inf. mesenteric vein with splenic vein

Abdominal aorta

Middle colic vein

Superior mesenteric vein

Inferior mesenteric vein

Left colic veins

Jejunal and ileal veins

Sigmoid veins

Superior rectal veins

Fig. 272: Abdominal Portal System of Veins

NOTE: 1) the abdominal portal system of veins drains venous blood from the gastro-intestinal tract, the gall bladder, pancreas and spleen through the liver via the large portal vein. This is done in order to subject this venous blood to the various functions of the liver before it is returned to the general systemic circulation by way of the hepatic veins into the inferior vena cava.

2) the portal vein is formed by the union of the superior mesenteric vein and the splenic vein. The inferior mesenteric vein drains into the splenic vein. At the esophageal end of the stomach (esophageal veins) and at the distal end of the rectum (inferior rectal veins), the portal system of veins anastomoses with the systemic veins. Certain disease states which may cause a reduction of blood flow through the liver result in greater use of these anastomotic channels in the return of blood in the portal system.

3) the functions of the liver are numerous, varied and vital to life. The liver secretes bile which is then stored in the gall bladder and released when food appears in the duodenum. Bile aids in the digestion and absorption of fats. The liver converts glucose to glycogen, stores the glycogen and then reconverts it to glucose again when needed. Further, the liver is involved in the synthesis of Vitamin A, heparin, prothrombin, fibrinogen and other substances. It functions also in detoxification of substances in the blood. It is involved in the breakdown of hemoglobin and stores both iron and copper.

1a Right lobe of liver
1b Left lobe of liver
1c Quadrate lobe of liver
1d Caudate lobe of liver
2   Stomach
3   Spleen
4a Head of pancreas
4b Tail of pancreas
5   Duodenum
6   Ileum
7   Cecum
8   Ascending colon
8a Right colic flexure
8b Left colic flexure
8c Descending colon
8d Sigmoid colon
9   Rectum
↑ = Junction of sup. mesenteric v. and splenic vein to form portal vein

Fig. 272   III

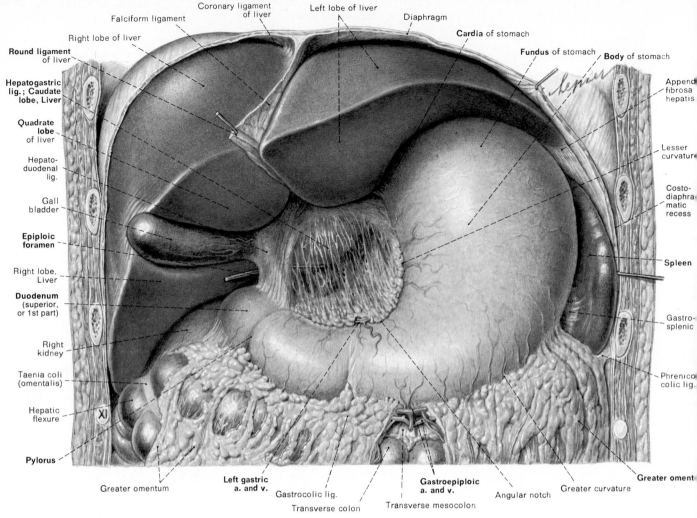

Round ligament of liver

Hepatogastric lig.; Caudate lobe, Liver

Quadrate lobe of liver

Hepato-duodenal lig.

Gall bladder

Epiploic foramen

Right lobe, Liver

Duodenum (superior, or 1st part)

Right kidney

Taenia coli (omentalis)

Hepatic flexure

Pylorus

Right lobe of liver

Falciform ligament

Coronary ligament of liver

Left lobe of liver

Diaphragm

Cardia of stomach

Fundus of stomach — Body of stomach

Append fibrosa hepatis

Lesser curvature

Costo-diaphra-matic recess

Spleen

Gastro-splenic

Phrenico colic lig.

Greater omentum

XI

Greater omentum

Left gastric a. and v.

Gastrocolic lig.

Transverse colon

Transverse mesocolon

Gastroepiploic a. and v.

Angular notch

Greater curvature

Greater oment

Fig. 273: The Lesser Omentum, Stomach, Liver and Spleen

NOTE: 1) with the liver elevated, a probe has been inserted through the epiploic foramen into the vestibule of the omental bursa. By way of this opening, the greater peritoneal sac communicates with the lesser peritoneal sac. Observe that the lesser omentum consists of the hepatogastric and hepatoduodenal ligaments.

2) the epiploic foramen is situated just caudal to the liver and readily admits two fingers. It is bound superiorly by the caudate lobe of the liver, inferiorly by the superior or 1st part of the duodenum, posteriorly by the inferior vena cava, and anteriorly by the lesser omentum which ensheathes the structures of the porta hepatis (hepatic artery, portal vein and bile ducts).

3) the greater omentum extends along the greater curvature from the spleen to the duodenum. The gall bladder is situated between the right and quadrate lobes of the liver and projects just beyond the inferior border of the liver, thereby coming into contact directly with the anterior abdominal wall at this site.

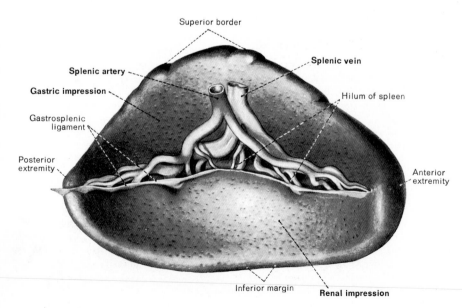

Superior border

Splenic artery

Splenic vein

Gastric impression

Hilum of spleen

Gastrosplenic ligament

Posterior extremity

Anterior extremity

Inferior margin

Renal impression

Fig. 274: The Spleen, Visceral Surface

NOTE that the spleen is situated in the left hypochondriac region between the fundus of the stomach and the diaphragm. Its visceral surface shows the contours of the organs related to it. A gastric impression and a renal impression conform to the shapes of the stomach and left kidney. Additionally, the left colic flexure, the tail of the pancreas and the left adrenal gland, which overlies the left kidney, are related to this visceral surface.

Figs. 273, 274

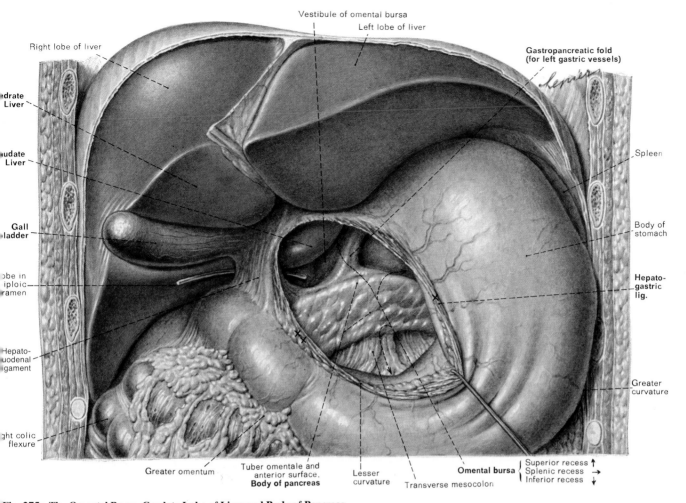

Vestibule of omental bursa
Left lobe of liver

Right lobe of liver

Gastropancreatic fold
(for left gastric vessels)

drate
Liver

udate
Liver

Spleen

Gall
ladder

Body of
stomach

obe in
iploic
ramen

Hepato-
gastric
lig.

Hepato-
uodenal
igament

Greater
curvature

ght colic
flexure

Greater omentum   Tuber omentale and
anterior surface,
Body of pancreas

Lesser
curvature

Transverse mesocolon

Omental bursa { Superior recess ↑
Splenic recess →
Inferior recess ↓

Fig. 275: The Omental Bursa, Caudate Lobe of Liver and Body of Pancreas

NOTE: 1) the liver has been elevated and the lesser curvature of the stomach has been pulled down and to the left in order to enlarge the exposure obtained by opening the omental bursa through the hepatogastric ligament (indicated by x and xx). The superior, splenic and inferior recesses of this bursa have been indicated by the arrows.

2) the portion of the omental bursa adjacent to the epiploic foramen is called the vestibule. Observe the gastropancreatic fold which crosses the dorsal wall of the bursa. This fold is formed by a reflection of peritoneum covering the left gastric artery which courses (from its origin on the celiac trunk) to the left of the superior recess of the omental bursa to achieve its destination, the lesser curvature of the stomach.

3) exposure of the omental bursa in this manner reveals the caudate lobe of the liver which can be seen situated on the dorsal surface of the liver's right lobe as well as the anterior surface of the body of the pancreas coursing transversely behind the stomach.

4) the left lobe of the liver overlies the lesser curvature, the fundus and part of the body of the stomach. While the caudate lobe is situated to the right of the esophagus (not visible in this figure), the quadrate lobe, which lies between the fossa of the gall bladder and the round ligament, comes into contact with the pylorus and the first part of the duodenum.

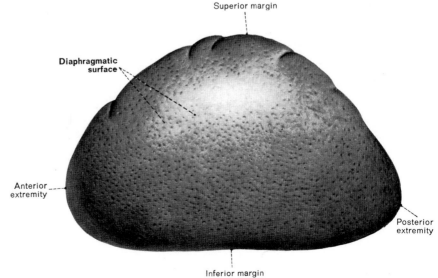

Superior margin

Diaphragmatic
surface

Anterior
extremity

Posterior
extremity

Inferior margin

Fig. 276: The Spleen, Diaphragmatic Surface

NOTE: the diaphragmatic surface of the spleen is directed posterolaterally. It is smooth and convex and conforms to the concave abdominal surface of the adjacent diaphragm. Although the normal adult spleen may vary considerably in size from 100 grams to 400 grams, its proximity to the 9th, 10th and 11th ribs of the left side makes it vulnerable to costal fractures in this region.

Figs. 275, 276   III

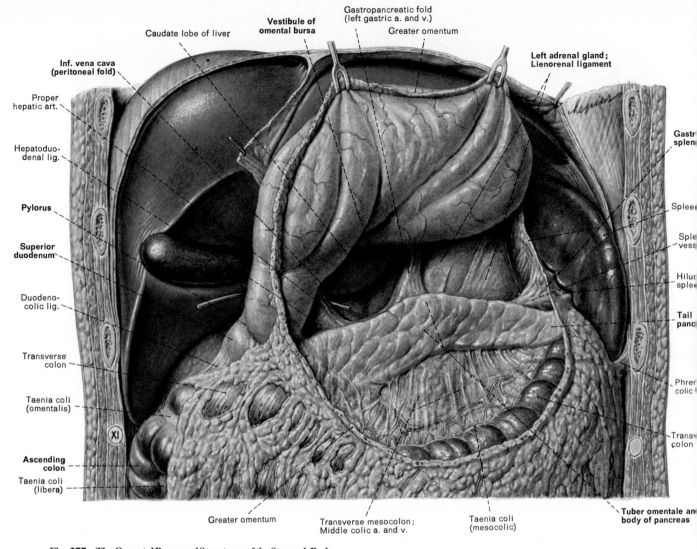

Caudate lobe of liver

Vestibule of omental bursa

Gastropancreatic fold (left gastric a. and v.)

Greater omentum

Left adrenal gland; Lienorenal ligament

Inf. vena cava (peritoneal fold)

Proper hepatic art.

Hepatoduo-denal lig.

Pylorus

Superior duodenum

Duodeno-colic lig.

Transverse colon

Taenia coli (omentalis)

Ascending colon

Taenia coli (libera)

Gastr splen

Splee

Sple vess

Hilu sple

Tail panc

Phre colic

Trans colon

Tuber omentale an body of pancreas

Greater omentum

Transverse mesocolon; Middle colic a. and v.

Taenia coli (mesocolic)

Fig. 277: The Omental Bursa and Structures of the Stomach Bed

NOTE: 1) the attachment of the greater omentum has been cut along the entire greater curvature of the stomach and the stomach has been elevated to expose the dorsal wall of the omental bursa.

2) the transverse course of the pancreas across the posterior abdomen and the pointed direction of the tail of the pancreas toward the hilum of the spleen.

3) the severed peritoneal reflection between the stomach and the spleen, the gastrosplenic ligament and its conti-nuation from the spleen to the kidney, the lienorenal liga-ment. Covering the upper pole of the left kidney, observe the adrenal gland.

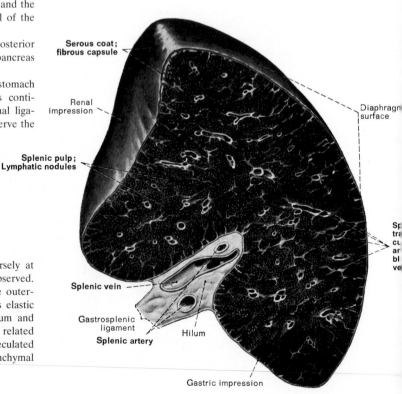

Serous coat; fibrous capsule

Renal impression

Splenic pulp; Lymphatic nodules

Diaphragm surface

Sp tra cu ar bl ve

Splenic vein

Gastrosplenic ligament

Splenic artery

Hilum

Gastric impression

Fig. 278: Spleen, Cross Section

NOTE: 1) the spleen has been sectioned transversely at the hilum where the severed splenic vessels can be observed.

2) covering the spleen are two external coats. The outer-most is a serous coat and beneath this is the fibrous elastic capsule. The serous coat derives from the peritoneum and is continuous at the hilum with the peritoneal folds related to the spleen. The fibrous, elastic coat invests the trabeculated soft masses of splenic pulp which compose the parenchymal tissue of the organ.

Figs. 277, 278

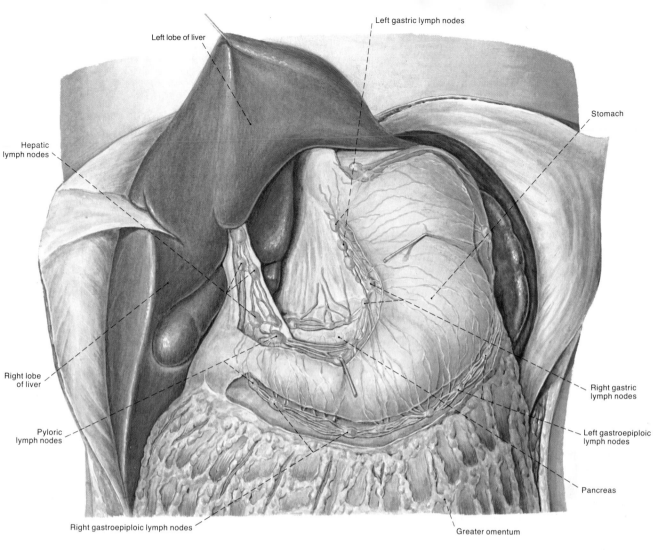

Fig. 279: Lymphatic Vessels and Nodes of the Stomach, the Porta Hepatis and Pancreas

NOTE that lymphatic vessels of the stomach follow the course of the right and left gastroepiploic vessels along the greater curvature and the right and left gastric vessels along the lesser curvature. Those in the porta hepatis course along the branches of the hepatic artery and, behind the stomach, nodes that drain the pancreas follow the course of the splenic artery. The efferent vessels from these nodes pass toward the preaortic nodes surrounding the celiac axis.

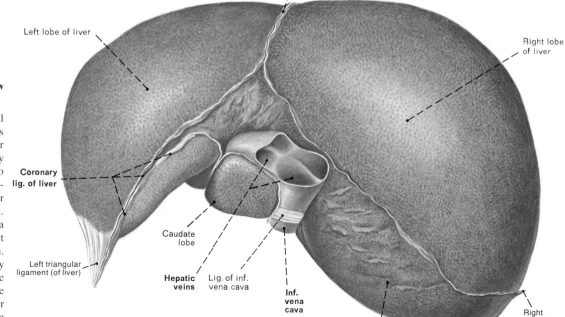

Fig. 280: Dorsocranial View of Liver

NOTE: 1) the visceral peritoneum closely adheres to the surface of the liver and is called the coronary ligament. Between the two leaves of the coronary ligament a portion of the liver is devoid of peritoneum. This is called the bare area of the liver and it is in direct contact with the diaphragm.

2) the hepatic veins as they converge superiorly from the liver lobes to empty into the inferior vena cava; this latter vessel lies in its sulcus on the posterior surface of the liver.

Figs. 279, 280   III

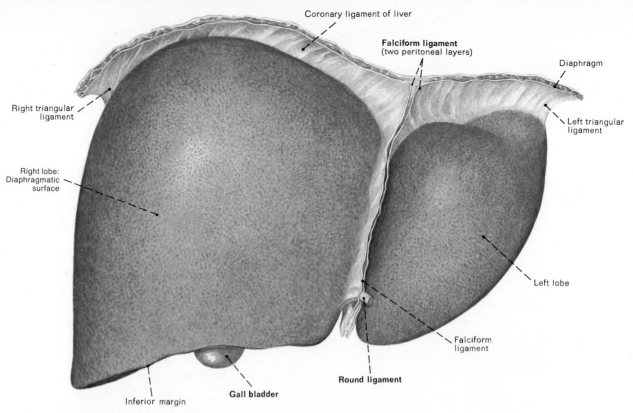

Fig. 281: Anterior Surface of the Liver (with Diaphragmatic Attachment)

NOTE: 1) the falciform ligament (derived from the ventral mesogastrium) separates the large right from the smaller left lobe of the liver. It contains the fibrous cord called the round ligament of the liver which is the resultant structure from the obliteration of the umbilical vein.

2) the fundus of the gall bladder extending below the sharply angled hepatic inferior margin.

Fig. 282: Posterior (Visceral) Surface of Liver and the Gall Bladder

NOTE: 1) the impressions made by the esophagus and stomach on the left lobe of the liver and the right kidney, right suprarenal gland, duodenum and transverse colon on the right lobe.

2) the sulcus formed by the inferior vena cava, which subdivides the caudate lobe from the right lobe. The gall bladder along with the portal vein, hepatic artery and common bile duct bound the quadrate lobe.

3) the continuity of the round ligament (umbilical vein) with the ligamentum venosum (ductus venosus).

Figs. 281, 282

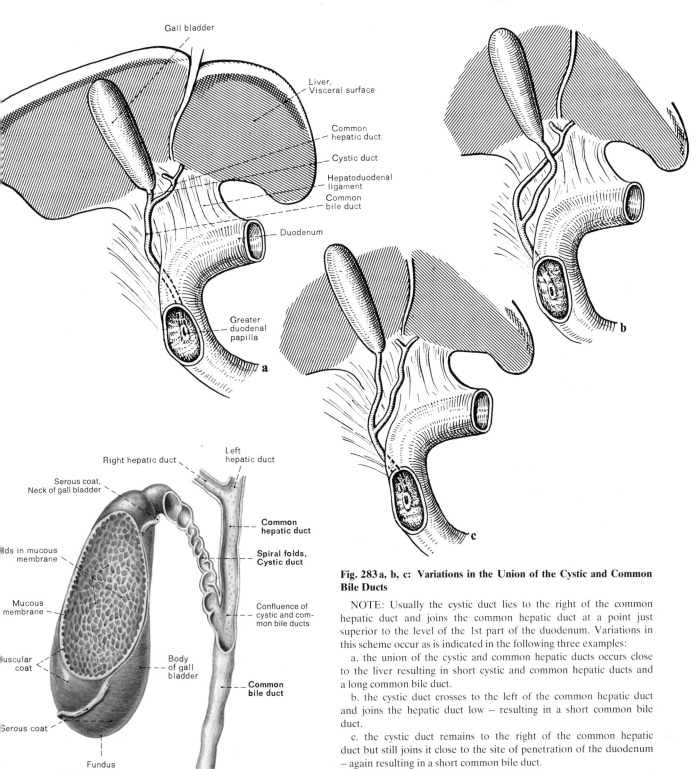

Gall bladder

Liver,
Visceral surface

Common
hepatic duct

Cystic duct

Hepatoduodenal
ligament

Common
bile duct

Duodenum

Greater
duodenal
papilla

a

b

c

Right hepatic duct

Left
hepatic duct

Serous coat,
Neck of gall bladder

**Common
hepatic duct**

**Spiral folds,
Cystic duct**

lds in mucous
membrane

Mucous
membrane

Confluence of
cystic and com-
mon bile ducts

luscular
coat

Body
of gall
bladder

**Common
bile duct**

Serous coat

Fundus
of gall bladder

Circular
duodenal folds

Lymph nodes

**Pancreatic
duct**

Longitudinal
duodenal folds

Orifice of
pancreatic duct

Greater
duodenal papilla

Fig. 283 a, b, c: Variations in the Union of the Cystic and Common Bile Ducts

NOTE: Usually the cystic duct lies to the right of the common hepatic duct and joins the common hepatic duct at a point just superior to the level of the 1st part of the duodenum. Variations in this scheme occur as is indicated in the following three examples:

a. the union of the cystic and common hepatic ducts occurs close to the liver resulting in short cystic and common hepatic ducts and a long common bile duct.

b. the cystic duct crosses to the left of the common hepatic duct and joins the hepatic duct low – resulting in a short common bile duct.

c. the cystic duct remains to the right of the common hepatic duct but still joins it close to the site of penetration of the duodenum – again resulting in a short common bile duct.

Fig. 284: The Gall Bladder and Biliary Duct System

NOTE: 1) the wall of the gall bladder has been opened to reveal the meshwork characteristic of the surface of the mucosal layer. The pear-shaped gall bladder stores bile which reaches it from the liver. Its capacity is about 35 cc.

2) the spiral nature of the cystic duct which leads from the neck of the gall bladder. Normally the cystic duct measures about $1\frac{1}{2}$ inches long and joins the common hepatic duct (which also is about $1\frac{1}{2}$ inches long) to form the common bile duct. The common bile duct descends about 3 inches to open into the 2nd or descending portion of the duodenum.

3) at its point of entrance into the duodenum (the greater duodenal papilla), the common bile duct is joined by the main pancreatic duct (duct of Wirsung).

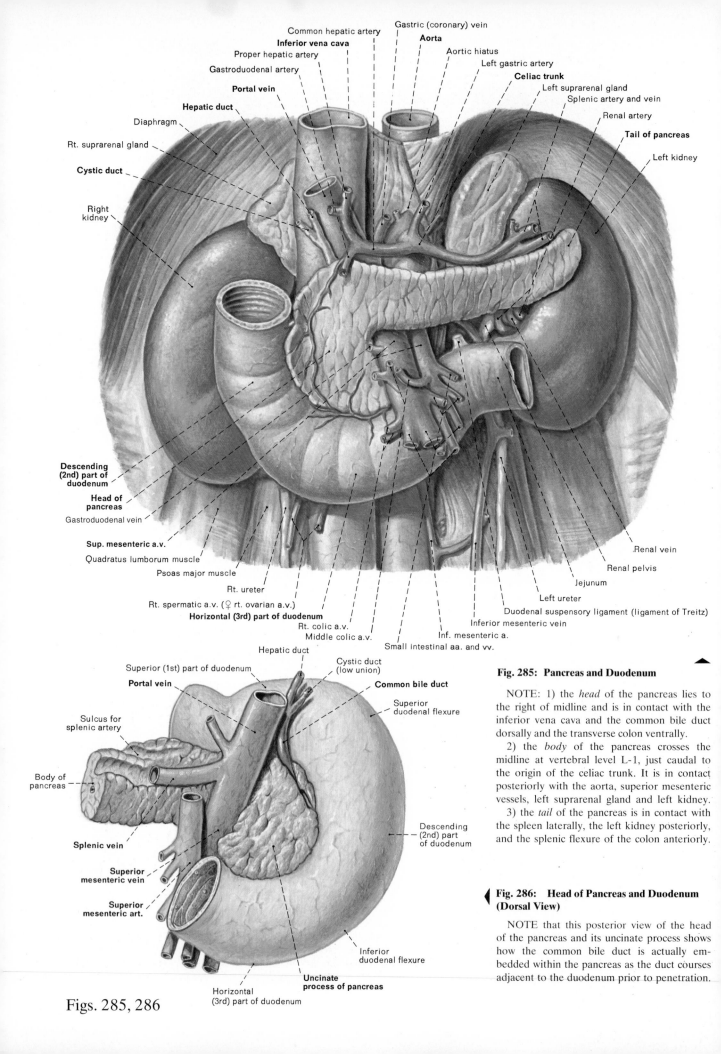

Common hepatic artery
Gastric (coronary) vein
Inferior vena cava
Aorta
Proper hepatic artery
Aortic hiatus
Gastroduodenal artery
Left gastric artery
Portal vein
Celiac trunk
Left suprarenal gland
Hepatic duct
Splenic artery and vein
Diaphragm
Renal artery
Rt. suprarenal gland
Tail of pancreas
Cystic duct
Left kidney
Right kidney

Descending (2nd) part of duodenum
Head of pancreas
Gastroduodenal vein
Sup. mesenteric a.v.
Quadratus lumborum muscle
Psoas major muscle
Rt. ureter
Rt. spermatic a.v. (♀ rt. ovarian a.v.)
Horizontal (3rd) part of duodenum
Rt. colic a.v.
Middle colic a.v.
Small intestinal aa. and vv.
Inf. mesenteric a.
Inferior mesenteric vein
Left ureter
Duodenal suspensory ligament (ligament of Treitz)
Jejunum
Renal pelvis
Renal vein

Hepatic duct
Cystic duct (low union)
Superior (1st) part of duodenum
Common bile duct
Portal vein
Superior duodenal flexure
Sulcus for splenic artery
Body of pancreas
Splenic vein
Descending (2nd) part of duodenum
Superior mesenteric vein
Superior mesenteric art.
Inferior duodenal flexure
Horizontal (3rd) part of duodenum
Uncinate process of pancreas

Fig. 285: Pancreas and Duodenum

NOTE: 1) the *head* of the pancreas lies to the right of midline and is in contact with the inferior vena cava and the common bile duct dorsally and the transverse colon ventrally.

2) the *body* of the pancreas crosses the midline at vertebral level L-1, just caudal to the origin of the celiac trunk. It is in contact posteriorly with the aorta, superior mesenteric vessels, left suprarenal gland and left kidney.

3) the *tail* of the pancreas is in contact with the spleen laterally, the left kidney posteriorly, and the splenic flexure of the colon anteriorly.

◄ **Fig. 286: Head of Pancreas and Duodenum (Dorsal View)**

NOTE that this posterior view of the head of the pancreas and its uncinate process shows how the common bile duct is actually embedded within the pancreas as the duct courses adjacent to the duodenum prior to penetration.

Figs. 285, 286

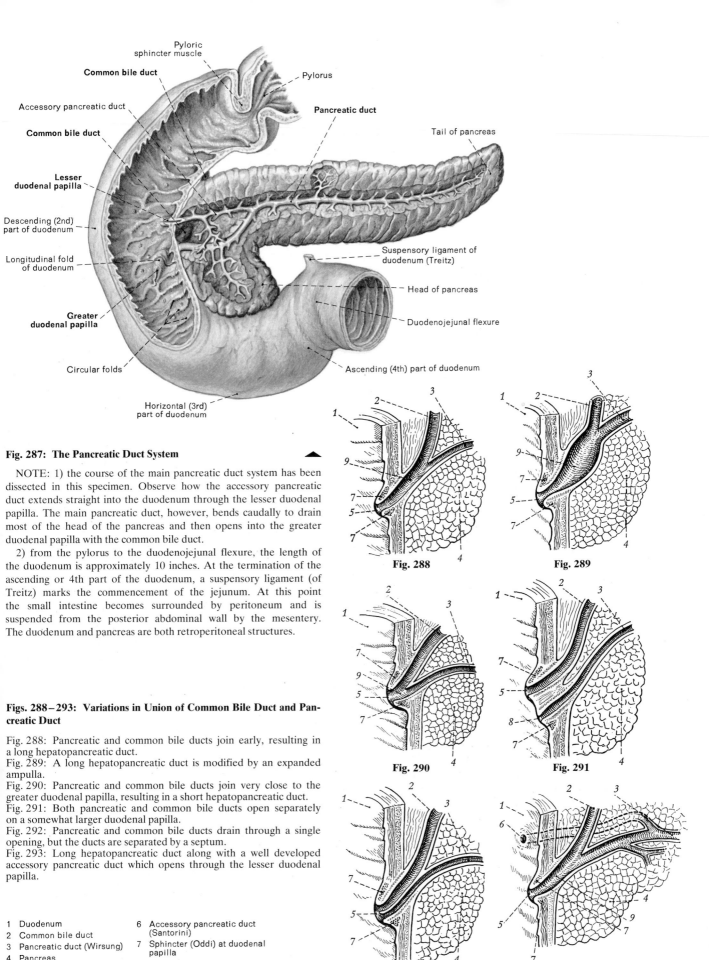

Pyloric
sphincter muscle

Common bile duct

Pylorus

Accessory pancreatic duct

Common bile duct

Pancreatic duct

Tail of pancreas

**Lesser
duodenal papilla**

Descending (2nd)
part of duodenum

Longitudinal fold
of duodenum

Suspensory ligament of
duodenum (Treitz)

Head of pancreas

Duodenojejunal flexure

**Greater
duodenal papilla**

Circular folds

Ascending (4th) part of duodenum

Horizontal (3rd)
part of duodenum

Fig. 288   **Fig. 289**

Fig. 287: The Pancreatic Duct System ▲

NOTE: 1) the course of the main pancreatic duct system has been
dissected in this specimen. Observe how the accessory pancreatic
duct extends straight into the duodenum through the lesser duodenal
papilla. The main pancreatic duct, however, bends caudally to drain
most of the head of the pancreas and then opens into the greater
duodenal papilla with the common bile duct.

2) from the pylorus to the duodenojejunal flexure, the length of
the duodenum is approximately 10 inches. At the termination of the
ascending or 4th part of the duodenum, a suspensory ligament (of
Treitz) marks the commencement of the jejunum. At this point
the small intestine becomes surrounded by peritoneum and is
suspended from the posterior abdominal wall by the mesentery.
The duodenum and pancreas are both retroperitoneal structures.

Fig. 290   **Fig. 291**

Figs. 288–293: Variations in Union of Common Bile Duct and Pancreatic Duct

Fig. 288: Pancreatic and common bile ducts join early, resulting in
a long hepatopancreatic duct.
Fig. 289: A long hepatopancreatic duct is modified by an expanded
ampulla.
Fig. 290: Pancreatic and common bile ducts join very close to the
greater duodenal papilla, resulting in a short hepatopancreatic duct.
Fig. 291: Both pancreatic and common bile ducts open separately
on a somewhat larger duodenal papilla.
Fig. 292: Pancreatic and common bile ducts drain through a single
opening, but the ducts are separated by a septum.
Fig. 293: Long hepatopancreatic duct along with a well developed
accessory pancreatic duct which opens through the lesser duodenal
papilla.

1 Duodenum
2 Common bile duct
3 Pancreatic duct (Wirsung)
4 Pancreas
5 Greater duodenal papilla
6 Accessory pancreatic duct
   (Santorini)
7 Sphincter (Oddi) at duodenal
   papilla
8 Pancreatic duct separate opening
9 Hepatopancreatic duct

Fig. 292   **Fig. 293**

Figs. 287–293   **III**

Fig. 294: X-Ray of the Upper Gastrointestinal Tract.

NOTE: 1) that this figure is a positive print made from an X-ray film and, thus, the contrast medium appears black instead of the conventional white.

2) the sites of junction of the tubular organs comprising the upper gastrointestinal tract. The esophageal orifice at the cardiac end of the stomach (*1 a*) is closed. Observe that this is at the T-11 vertebral level.

3) that the pylorus of the stomach (not numbered) is the narrowed region leading into the superior part of the duodenum (*4*). The superior (*4*), descending (*5 a*), horizontal (*5 b*) and ascending (*5 c*) parts of the duodenum are easily recognizable, as is the duodenojejunal junction (*5 d*).

4) that the contrast medium outlines the internal circular folds or plicae of the jejunum (*6*) and also identifies a peristaltic contraction wave (*7 a, 7 b*).

1   Esophagus. 1a. Cardia closed, contrast medium in creases of mucous membrane
2   Fundus of stomach (filled)
3a Lesser curvature of stomach with longitudinal mucosal folds
3b Greater curvature with gastric folds and areas
4   Duodenal bulb, superior part of duodenum
5a Descending part of duodenum
5b Horizontal part of duodenum
5c Ascending part of duodenum
5d Duodenojejunal flexure
6   Jejunum with circular plicae
7   Peristaltic contraction wave from 7a to 7b

Mesenteric lymph nodes

Root of mesentery

Mesenteric lymph nodes

Mesenteric lymph nodes

Ileum

Lymphatic vessels

Fig. 295: Lymphatic Vessels and Nodes of the Ileum.

NOTE that this loop of ileum, injected with India ink, demonstrates the radial orientation of the lymphatic vessels from the organ to the root of the mesentery. Along the paths of these vessels are found the mesenteric lymph nodes.

Figs. 294, 295

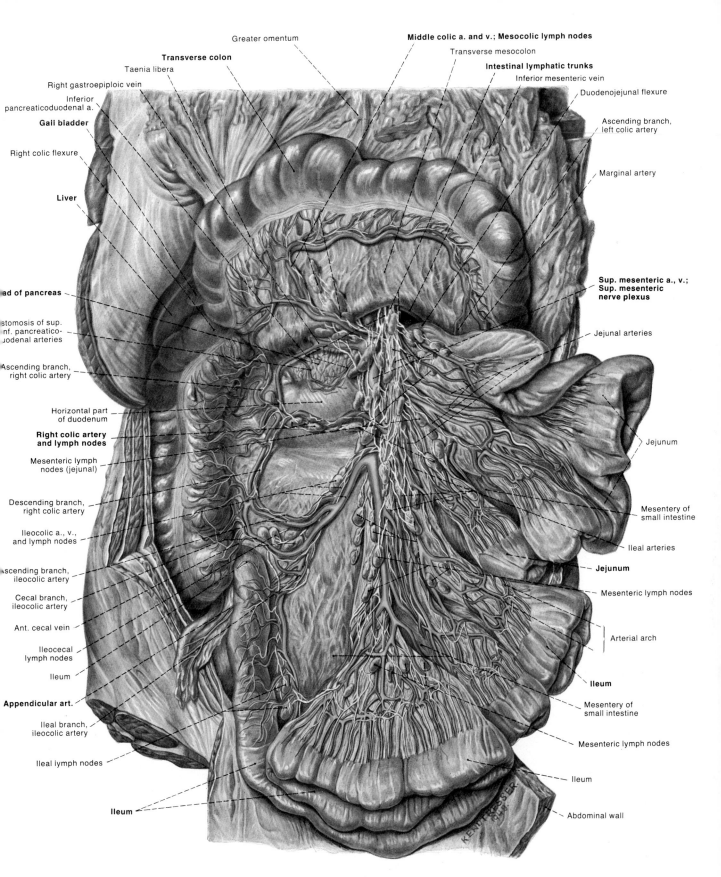

Greater omentum

Middle colic a. and v.; Mesocolic lymph nodes

Transverse colon

Transverse mesocolon

Taenia libera

Intestinal lymphatic trunks

Right gastroepiploic vein

Inferior mesenteric vein

Inferior pancreaticoduodenal a.

Duodenojejunal flexure

Gall bladder

Ascending branch, left colic artery

Right colic flexure

Marginal artery

Liver

ad of pancreas

Sup. mesenteric a., v.; Sup. mesenteric nerve plexus

stomosis of sup. nf. pancreatico- uodenal arteries

Jejunal arteries

Ascending branch, right colic artery

Horizontal part of duodenum

Right colic artery and lymph nodes

Jejunum

Mesenteric lymph nodes (jejunal)

Descending branch, right colic artery

Mesentery of small intestine

Ileocolic a., v., and lymph nodes

Ileal arteries

scending branch, ileocolic artery

Jejunum

Cecal branch, ileocolic artery

Mesenteric lymph nodes

Ant. cecal vein

Arterial arch

Ileocecal lymph nodes

Ileum

Ileum

Appendicular art.

Mesentery of small intestine

Ileal branch, ileocolic artery

Mesenteric lymph nodes

Ileal lymph nodes

Ileum

Ileum

Abdominal wall

Fig. 296: Abdominal Cavity (5); Lymph Nodes, Vessels and Nerves Serving the Jejunum, Ileum, Ascending and Transverse Colon

NOTE that: 1) the transverse colon has been lifted to reveal its mesocolon along with the retroperitoneal head of the pancreas and duodenum. The loops of jejunum and ileum have been reflected to the left to show the root of the mesentery with its complex network of lymphatics, blood vessels and autonomic nerves.

2) chains of mesenteric lymph nodes follow the ileal and jejunal branches of the superior mesenteric artery and vein, as well as the ileocolic, right colic and middle colic branches of the same vessel.

3) the lymphatics from both the small and large intestine drain centrally and superiorly, eventually to interconnect with pre-aortic chains of nodes.

Fig. 296   III

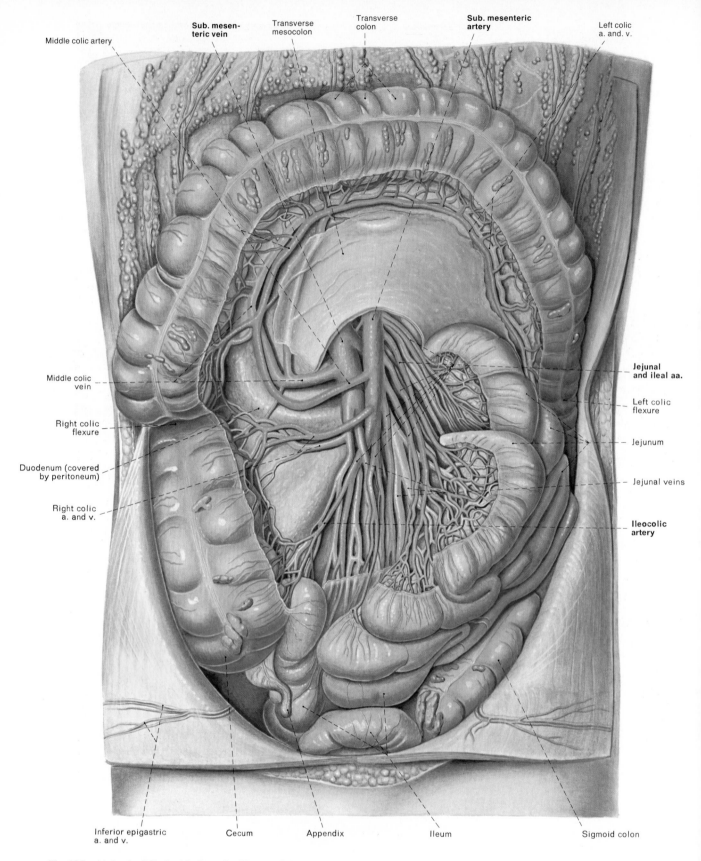

Middle colic artery

Sub. mesen-teric vein

Transverse mesocolon

Transverse colon

Sub. mesenteric artery

Left colic a. and v.

Middle colic vein

Right colic flexure

Duodenum (covered by peritoneum)

Right colic a. and v.

Jejunal and ileal aa.

Left colic flexure

Jejunum

Jejunal veins

Ileocolic artery

Inferior epigastric a. and v.

Cecum

Appendix

Ileum

Sigmoid colon

Fig. 297: Abdominal Cavity (6): Superior Mesenteric Vessels and Branches

NOTE: 1) the transverse colon has been turned upward and the small intestine was pushed to the left. The peritoneal attachment along the coils of small intestine and colon has been dissected to reveal the branches of the superior mesenteric vessels which supply the small intestine, ascending colon and transverse colon.

2) the intestinal arteries (jejunal and ileal) branch from the left side of the superior mesenteric artery. There are about 12 of these vessels and they are distributed to the jejunum and ileum.

3) branching from the right side of the superior mesenteric artery are the ileocolic (to the ileocecal region), right colic (to the ascending colon) and middle colic (transverse colon) arteries. Observe the elaborate branching of these vessels and the rich anastomoses which exist among them.

Fig. 297

Fig. 298: Superior Mesenteric Arteriogram

NOTE: 1) that a catheter (*1*) has been inserted into the common iliac artery and through the abdominal aorta to the point of branching of the superior mesenteric artery (*2*). Contrast medium was injected in order to allow visualization of the principal branches of that vessel. The original radiograph is shown as a negative print.

2) the jejunal (*3*) and ileal (*4*) arteries branching as a sequence of vessels (about fifteen in number) which supply all of the small intestine beyond the duodenum.

3) the ileocolic artery (*5*) and its appendicular branch (*6*), the right colic (*7*), and middle colic (*9*) arteries which supply the cecum, ascending colon (*8*) and transverse colon. Observe that anastomoses among these vessels close to the colon contribute to the formation of the marginal artery (*10*).

4) that other structures can be identified for orientation. These are the right colic flexure (*11*), the left colic flexure (*12*), the sigmoid colon (*13*), the body of the T-12 vertebra and the iliac crest (*14*).

5) that this figure comes from Wicke, L., *Atlas of Radiologic Anatomy*, 3rd Edition, Urban & Schwarzenberg, Baltimore, 1982.

Fig. 298   III

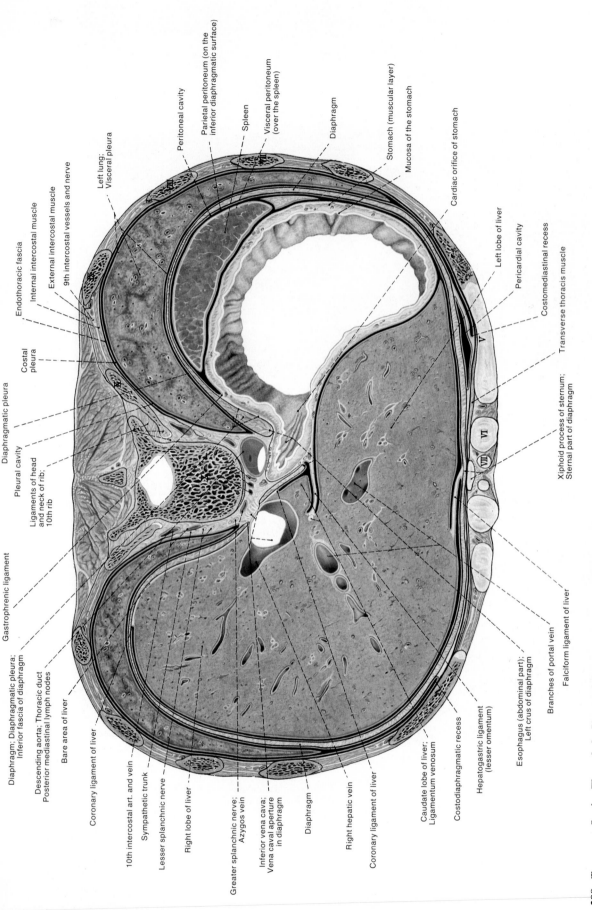

Fig. 299: Transverse Section Through the Upper Abdomen at the Level of the Tenth Thoracic Vertebra

NOTE: 1) that a cross-section through the body of the 10th thoracic vertebra also cuts through the lower part of the thoracic cavity on each side and, therefore, includes the inferior portions of the lower lobes of both lungs (seen in purple). Observe the visceral pleura, closely adherent to the lungs, and the costal and diaphragmatic reflections of parietal pleura. Between the parietal and visceral layers of pleura is the pleural cavity, which extends inferolaterally as the costodiaphragmatic recess (labelled on the specimen's right).

2) that the liver, stomach, and spleen occupy the largest part of the abdominal cavity at this vertebral level. Observe that the esophageal aperture in the right crus of the diaphragm is located at T-10. Through this aperture course the vagal nerve trunks, as well as some esophageal branches of the left gastric vessels.

3) that the descending thoracic aorta, still in the posterior mediastinum, is slightly to the left of the midline and ventral to the T-10 vertebral body. Adjacent to it are found some lymph nodes and the thoracic duct. To the right are found the inferior vena cava, the lower part of the vena caval aperture, and the part of the posterior surface of the liver not covered by peritoneum and called the bare area of the liver. (Note that sections of the 5th to 10th ribs are labelled I to V.)

Fig. 299

Fig. 300: Transverse Section Through the Upper Abdomen at the Level of the Intervertebral Disc Between the Twelfth Thoracic and First Lumbar Vertebrae

NOTE: 1) that a cross-section of the abdomen between T-12 and L-1 goes through the hilum of the stomach, the body of the liver, the spleen and its hilar vessels, the upper pole of the left kidney, and the two suprarenal glands;

2) the quadrate and caudate lobes of the liver (see also Fig. 282). The *quadrate lobe*, located on the posteroinferior hepatic surface, is limited on the left by a fissure within which is found the round ligament of the liver and posteriorly by the hilar structures of the porta hepatis. The *caudate lobe*, located more superiorly on the posterior hepatic surface, is represented here by its caudate and papillary processes;

3) the hepatic artery, portal vein, the cystic duct, and the common bile duct. Also observe the inferior vena cava (into which flow the hepatic veins), the aorta, and the left gastric and splenic vessels;

4) the relationship of the pancreas to the stomach, spleen, left kidney, left suprarenal gland, the left crus of the diaphragm, and the aorta. Observe the many lymph nodes anterior to the aorta, at the hilum of the spleen, and at the porta hepatis. (Note that sections of the 8th to 12th ribs are labelled VIII to XII.)

Fig. 300   III

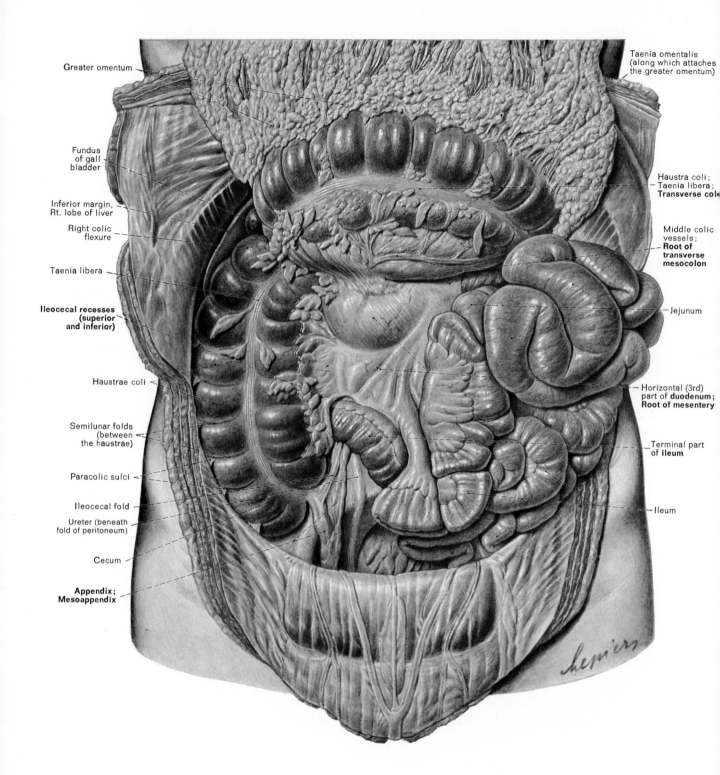

Greater omentum

Fundus
of gall
bladder

Inferior margin,
Rt. lobe of liver

Right colic
flexure

Taenia libera

**Ileocecal recesses
(superior
and inferior)**

Haustrae coli

Semilunar folds
(between
the haustrae)

Paracolic sulci

Ileocecal fold

Ureter (beneath
fold of peritoneum)

Cecum

**Appendix;
Mesoappendix**

Taenia omentalis
(along which attaches
the greater omentum)

Haustra coli;
Taenia libera;
Transverse colon

Middle colic
**vessels;
Root of
transverse
mesocolon**

Jejunum

Horizontal (3rd)
part of **duodenum;
Root of mesentery**

Terminal part
of **ileum**

Ileum

Fig. 301: Abdominal Cavity (7): The Ascending and Transverse Colon

NOTE: 1) the greater omentum has been reflected superiorly and the jejunum and ileum have been pulled to the left in order to expose the root of the mesentery of the small intestine on the right side.

2) the horizontal (3rd) part of the duodenum which is retroperitoneal and which is covered by the smooth and glistening peritoneum. Observe also the distal portion of the ileum at its junction with the cecum. At this ileocecal junction, identify the ileocecal fold, the appendix and the mesoappendix. The appendix may extend cranially behind the cecum, toward the left and behind the ileum, or as demonstrated here, inferiorly over the pelvic brim.

3) the transverse colon and the small intestine beyond the duodenal junction are more mobile than most other organs because they are attached to the transverse mesocolon and the mesentery.

4) the retroperitoneal position of the right ureter as it descends over the pelvic brim on its course toward the bladder in the pelvis.

Fig. 301

Middle colic vessels;
Root of transverse mesocolon

Transverse colon

Greater omentum

Taenia libera

Body
of pancreas

Left colic
flexure

Superior and
inferior
duodenal
recesses

Inferior pole,
Left kidney;
Left ureter

Paracolic sulci

Inferior duodenal
fold

Sigmoid colon;
Sigmoid
mesocolon

Intersigmoid
fossa

Mesentery

Small intestine

Terminal portion
of ileum

Inferior ileocecal
recess

Cecum

Vermiform appendix;
mesoappendix

Fig. 302: Abdominal Cavity (8): The Descending and Sigmoid Colon and the Duodenojejunal Junction

NOTE: 1) the transverse colon and greater omentum have been reflected superiorly and the jejunum and ileum have been pulled to the right
to reveal the duodenojejunal junction and the descending and sigmoid colon.

2) as the ascending (4th) part of the duodenum becomes jejunum, and the small intestine acquires a mesentery at that site, there frequently are
found duodenal fossae or recesses situated in relation to the junction. Look for the inferior and superior duodenal recesses (present in over 50% of
the cases). These are of importance because they represent possible sites of intestinal herniae within the abdomen.

3) the mobility of the sigmoid colon because of its mesocolic attachment, in contrast to the descending colon which is more fixed to the posterior
wall of the abdomen. Observe the intersigmoid fossa located behind the sigmoid mesocolon and between it and the peritoneum reflected over the
external iliac vessels.

Fig. 302   III

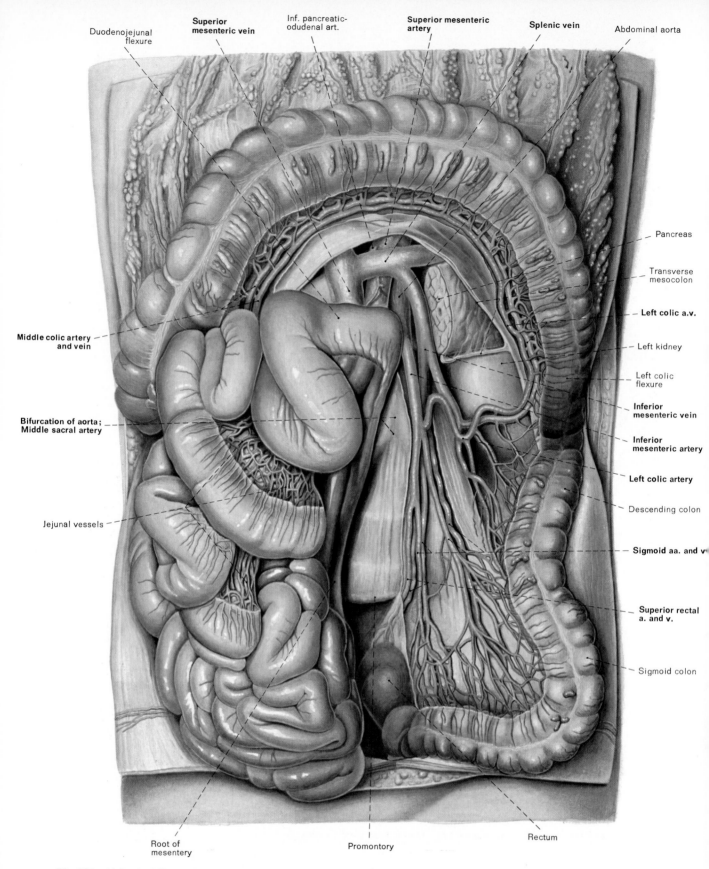

Duodenojejunal flexure — Superior mesenteric vein — Inf. pancreatic-odudenal art. — Superior mesenteric artery — Splenic vein — Abdominal aorta

Pancreas — Transverse mesocolon — Left colic a.v. — Left kidney — Left colic flexure — Inferior mesenteric vein — Inferior mesenteric artery — Left colic artery — Descending colon — Sigmoid aa. and v. — Superior rectal a. and v. — Sigmoid colon

Middle colic artery and vein — Bifurcation of aorta; Middle sacral artery — Jejunal vessels

Root of mesentery — Promontory — Rectum

Fig. 303: Abdominal Cavity (9): The Inferior Mesenteric Vessels and Branches

NOTE: 1) the small intestine has been pushed to the right side of the abdomen to reveal the origin of the inferior mesenteric artery from the aorta, and the drainage of the inferior mesenteric vein into the splenic vein. Also a portion of the body of the pancreas and transverse mesocolon was removed to show these relationships more clearly.

2) the inferior mesenteric artery supplies the descending colon via the left colic artery. Observe the anastomosis around the margin of the large bowel between the left colic artery and the middle colic artery. Somewhat lower, the inferior mesenteric gives rise to the sigmoid arteries and the superior rectal vessels.

3) the bifurcation of the abdominal aorta retroperitoneally and the middle sacral artery descending in the midline.

Fig. 303

1. Catheter
2. Inferior mesenteric artery
3. Left colic artery
4. Ascending branch of left colic artery
5. Descending branch of left colic artery
6. Sigmoid arteries
7. Superior rectal artery
8. Left common iliac artery
9. Barium in appendix
10. Ascending colon
11. Left colic flexure
12. Descending colon
13. Sigmoid colon
14. Right renal pelvis
15. Right ureter

Fig. 304: An Inferior Mesenteric Arteriogram

NOTE that: 1) a catheter *(1)* has been inserted through the right internal iliac artery and directed superiorly into the abdominal aorta to the point of origin of the inferior mesenteric artery *(2)*. A contrast medium was then injected into that artery in order to demonstrate its field of distribution;

2) the branches of the inferior mesenteric artery *(2)* shown in this arteriogram are quite normal. The left colic artery *(3)* shows both an ascending *(4)* and a descending branch *(5)*;

3) several sigmoid arteries *(6)* supply the sigmoid colon *(13)*, and these anastomose above with branches of the left colic artery *(3)* and below with the superior rectal artery *(7)*.

4) that this figure comes from Wicke, L., *Atlas of Radiologic Anatomy*, 3rd Edition, Urban and Schwarzenberg, Baltimore, 1982.

Fig. 304   III

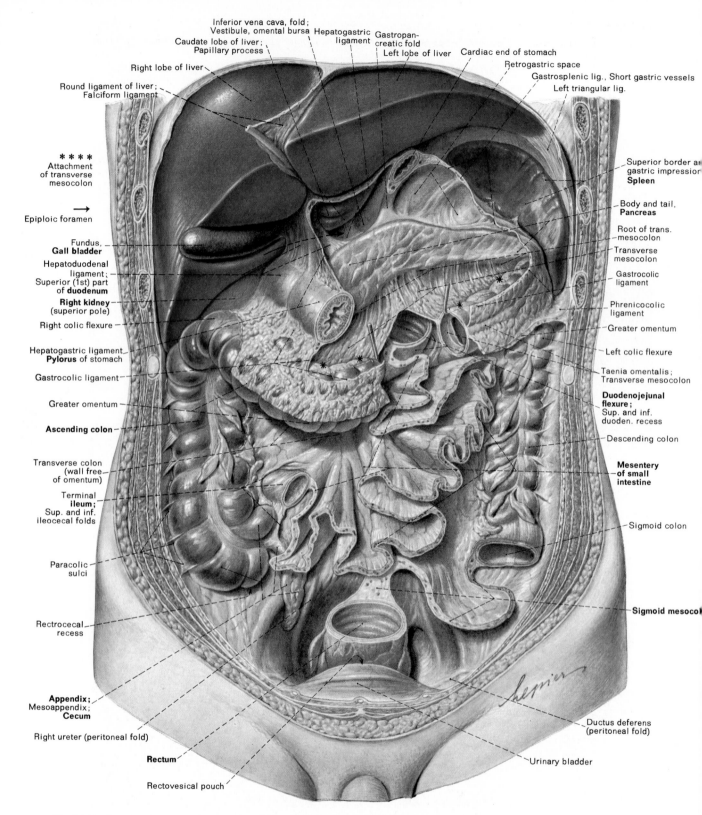

Inferior vena cava, fold;
Vestibule, omental bursa   Hepatogastric   Gastropan-
Caudate lobe of liver;   ligament   creatic fold
Papillary process   Left lobe of liver   Cardiac end of stomach

Right lobe of liver   Retrogastric space

Round ligament of liver;   Gastrosplenic lig., Short gastric vessels
Falciform ligament   Left triangular lig.

Superior border an
gastric impression
Spleen

****
Attachment
of transverse
mesocolon

Body and tail,
Pancreas

→   Root of trans.
Epiploic foramen   mesocolon

Fundus,   Transverse
Gall bladder   mesocolon

Hepatoduodenal   Gastrocolic
ligament;   ligament
Superior (1st) part
of duodenum   Phrenicocolic
ligament
Right kidney
(superior pole)   Greater omentum

Right colic flexure   Left colic flexure

Hepatogastric ligament   Taenia omentalis;
Pylorus of stomach   Transverse mesocolon

Gastrocolic ligament   Duodenojejunal
flexure;
Sup. and inf.
Greater omentum   duoden. recess

Descending colon
Ascending colon

Mesentery
of small
Transverse colon   intestine
(wall free
of omentum)

Terminal
ileum;   Sigmoid colon
Sup. and inf.
ileocecal folds

Paracolic
sulci

Sigmoid mesoco

Rectrocecal
recess

Appendix;
Mesoappendix;   Ductus deferens
Cecum   (peritoneal fold)

Right ureter (peritoneal fold)

Rectum   Urinary bladder

Rectovesical pouch

Fig. 305: Abdominal Cavity (10): The Large Intestine and the Mesenteries

NOTE: 1) the stomach was cut just proximal to the pylorus and the small intestine was severed at the duodenojejunal junction and at the distal ileum and then removed by cutting the mesentery. A portion of the transverse colon was removed along with the greater omentum, and the sigmoid colon was resected to reveal its mesocolon.

2) the mesentery of the small intestine extends obliquely across the posterior abdominal wall from the duodenojejunal flexure to the ilocecal junction. In this distance of about 6 to 7 inches, the mesentery is thrown into many folds to accommodate all the loops of jejunum and ileum.

3) the ascending and descending colon is fused to the posterior abdominal wall, while the transverse and sigmoid colon are suspended by their respective mesocolons.

4) that the vessels and nerves supplying the small intestine course *between* the layers of the mesentery to achieve the organ.

Fig. 305

Fig. 306: The Ileocecal Junction

NOTE: 1) the terminal ileum, cecum and lower ascending colon have been opened anteriorly to reveal the ileocecal junction and the opening of the vermiform appendix.

2) the leaves of the ileocecal valve have been separated. Observe that this valve is formed by two reflected folds of the wall of the large intestine. These folds unite and then project further around the large intestine as the frenulum.

3) the orifice of the appendix opens into the cecum, although the position and the direction of the appendix are quite variable. Observe the semilunar folds, the sacculations (haustrae) and longitudinal muscle bands (taeniae) which characterize the large intestine.

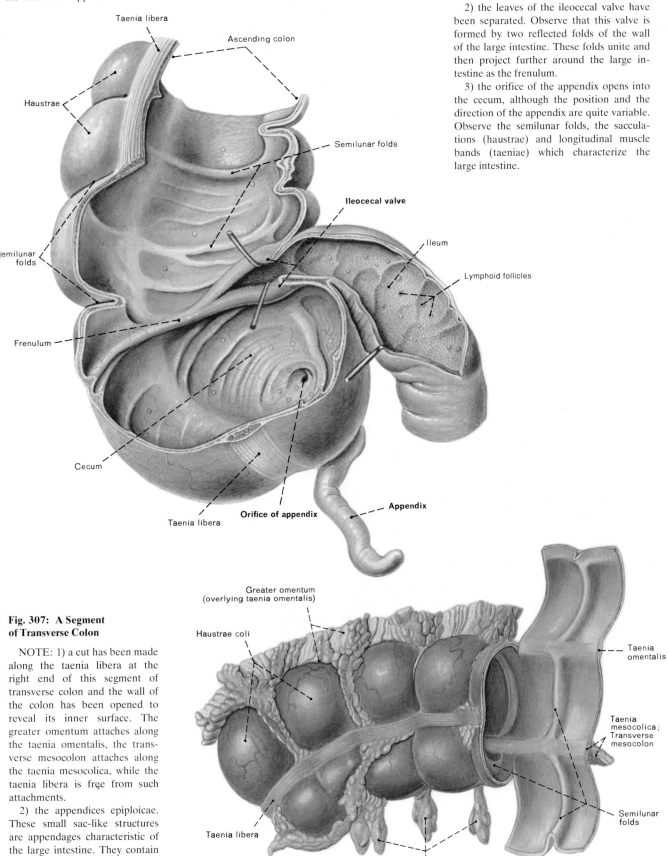

Fig. 307: A Segment of Transverse Colon

NOTE: 1) a cut has been made along the taenia libera at the right end of this segment of transverse colon and the wall of the colon has been opened to reveal its inner surface. The greater omentum attaches along the taenia omentalis, the transverse mesocolon attaches along the taenia mesocolica, while the taenia libera is free from such attachments.

2) the appendices epiploicae. These small sac-like structures are appendages characteristic of the large intestine. They contain fat and their function is unknown.

Figs. 306, 307   III

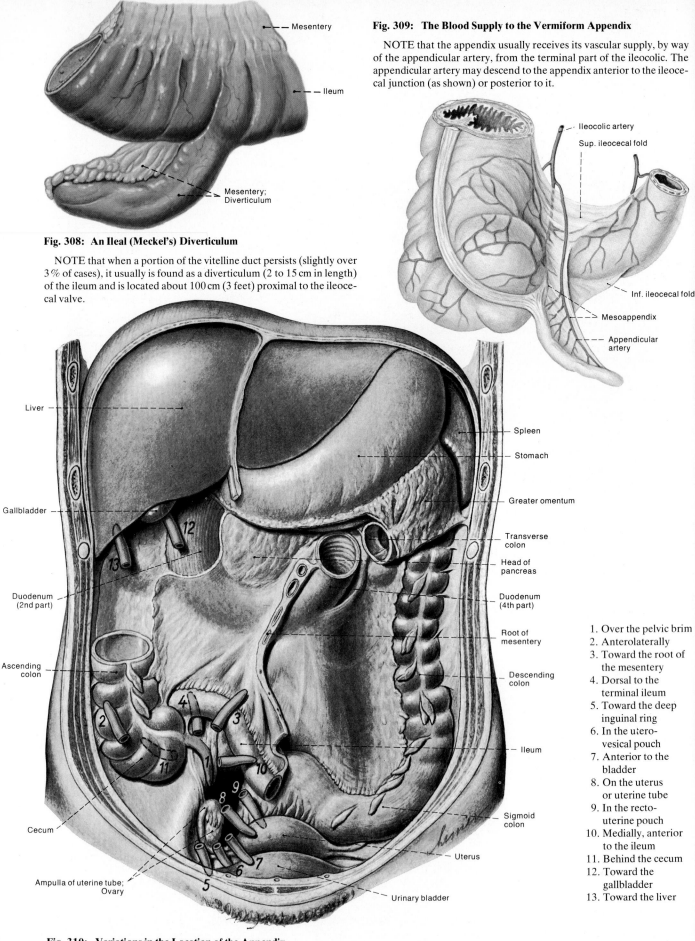

Mesentery

Ileum

Mesentery;
Diverticulum

Fig. 308: An Ileal (Meckel's) Diverticulum

NOTE that when a portion of the vitelline duct persists (slightly over 3% of cases), it usually is found as a diverticulum (2 to 15 cm in length) of the ileum and is located about 100 cm (3 feet) proximal to the ileocecal valve.

Fig. 309: The Blood Supply to the Vermiform Appendix

NOTE that the appendix usually receives its vascular supply, by way of the appendicular artery, from the terminal part of the ileocolic. The appendicular artery may descend to the appendix anterior to the ileocecal junction (as shown) or posterior to it.

Ileocolic artery

Sup. ileocecal fold

Inf. ileocecal fold

Mesoappendix

Appendicular artery

Liver

Gallbladder

Duodenum
(2nd part)

Ascending
colon

Cecum

Ampulla of uterine tube;
Ovary

Spleen

Stomach

Greater omentum

Transverse
colon

Head of
pancreas

Duodenum
(4th part)

Root of
mesentery

Descending
colon

Ileum

Sigmoid
colon

Uterus

Urinary bladder

1. Over the pelvic brim
2. Anterolaterally
3. Toward the root of
   the mesentery
4. Dorsal to the
   terminal ileum
5. Toward the deep
   inguinal ring
6. In the utero-
   vesical pouch
7. Anterior to the
   bladder
8. On the uterus
   or uterine tube
9. In the recto-
   uterine pouch
10. Medially, anterior
    to the ileum
11. Behind the cecum
12. Toward the
    gallbladder
13. Toward the liver

Fig. 310: Variations in the Location of the Appendix

NOTE that at least 13 different locations (shown in blue) for the appendix have been described, the most common being 11, 1, 3 (and 10), and 4.

Figs. 308, 309, 310

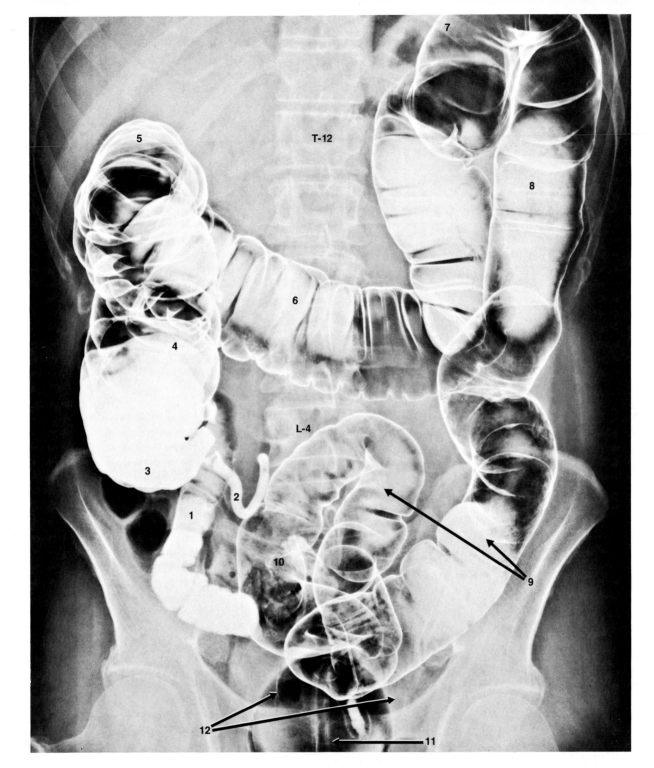

Fig. 311: The Radiographic Anatomy of the Large Intestine (Double Contrast)

NOTE: 1) that an excellent radiographic visualization may be achieved when a thin barium sulfate mixture is administered as an enema. The mixture is then expelled and the colon is insufflated with air (barium-air double contrast method).

2) that the large intestine is about 150 cm (5 feet) in length, and it extends from the ileocecal junction to the anus. Its diameter varies from 3.75 to 7.6 cm (1.5 to 3 inches) and, normally, is of greatest width at its commencement at the cecum, from whence it gradually narrows. Near the distal rectum it dilates once again as the rectal ampulla, and this leads to the anal canal.

3) the cecum (3) is usually located in the iliac fossa of the lower right abdominal quadrant, but because it is enveloped by peritoneum, its position may be variable. Observe that the cecum is a cul-de-sac that opens superiorly into the ascending colon (4). Its junction with the terminal ileum (1) occurs most often on the medial or posterior cecal surface. The appendix (2) extends from the cecum about 2 cm below the ileocecal opening.

4) that the right colic (or hepatic) flexure (5) is oriented inferiorly and anteriorly and continues to the left to become the transverse colon (6). This

5) that the transverse colon, suspended by its mesentery, crosses the abdomen. It ascends in the left upper quadrant toward the left colic (splenic) flexure (7), where it continues inferiorly as the descending colon (8).

6) that the descending colon becomes the sigmoid colon (9) at the inlet to the lesser pelvis. Surrounded by its mesentery, the sigmoid colon leads into the rectum (10), which then descends into the true pelvis.

7) the positions of the bodies of the 12th thoracic (T-12) and 4th lumbar (L-4) vertebrae, the symphysis pubis (11), and an air-filled balloon (12). (From Wicke, L., *Atlas of Radiologic Anatomy*, 3rd Edition, Urban and Schwarzenberg, Baltimore, 1982.)

Fig. 311   III

Fig. 312: The Inner Surface of the Rectum and Anal Canal

NOTE: 1) at about the level of the 3rd sacral vertebra, the sigmoid colon becomes the rectum. Measuring about 5 inches in length, the rectum then becomes the anal canal which is the terminal $1^1/_2$ inches of the intestinal tract. The rectum is dilated near its junction with the anal canal, giving rise to the rectal ampulla.

2) the internal mucosa of the rectum is thrown into transverse folds of which there are usually three in number. They are also known as the valves of Houston.

3) below the rectal ampulla, the mucosa of the anal canal shows a series of longitudinal folds called the anal colums (columns of Morgagni). Each of these folds usually possesses an artery and vein, and between the anal columns are small fossae called the anal sinuses. The veins in this region are dilated and tortuous and can become varicosed, giving rise to a condition called hemorrhoids or piles.

4) distal to the anal column is an abrupt zone of epithelial transition. The stratified squamous of the distalmost part of the anal canal becomes the simple columnar of the rectum. This transition line can be identified in a living person and is referred to as Hilton's line.

Fig. 313: External Surface of Rectum, Lateral View ▶

NOTE: 1) the rectum presents a dorsally directed sacral flexure proximally and a less pronounced ventrally directed perineal flexure distally. Observe that the peritoneum ensheathes the rectum ventrally almost as far as the ampulla (to the bladder in the male and the uterus in the female). Dorsally, much of the rectum is in contact with the posterior pelvic wall and the peritoneum dips only as far as the commencement of the sacral flexure.

2) the fibers of the levator ani muscle (which forms the floor of the pelvis) surround the rectum and are

(con't next page)

Figs. 312, 313

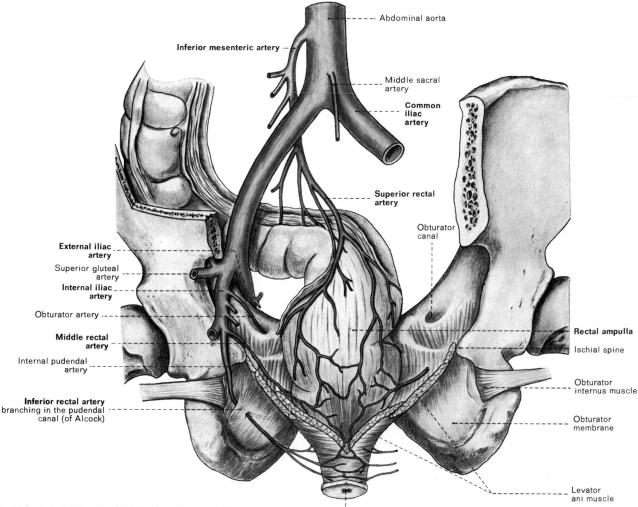

Fig. 314: Arterial Supply of the Rectum, Posterior View

NOTE: 1) this posterior view of the arterial supply of the rectum shows the superior rectal artery which branches from the inferior mesenteric artery, and distributes to the rectum as far as the ampulla. The middle rectal artery coming off the internal iliac artery and the inferior rectal artery branching from the internal pudendal artery supply the more caudal parts of the rectum.

2) from the bifurcation of the aorta, the middle sacral artery descends down the midline of the sacrum. The common iliac arteries branch into external and internal iliac vessels. From the internal iliac (hypogastric), many of the pelvic organs derive their blood supply.

3) the internal pudendal artery coursing within the pudendal canal (of Alcock). The inferior rectal artery branches from the internal pudendal within this canal.

Fig. 315: Distribution Pattern of the Rectal Arteries

This figure shows the distribution of the superior, middle and inferior rectal arteries as they supply the rectum and the anal canal. Observe that the region of distribution of the superior rectal artery is much greater than either the middle or inferior rectal arteries. Note the rich anastomoses among these three vessels.

continued distally as the external sphincter ani muscle. The internal sphincter ani muscle (seen in Figure 312) is composed of smooth muscle and really represents a thickening of the inner circular muscle layer in the wall of the rectum. Oberve also the outer longitudinal (smooth) muscle layer.

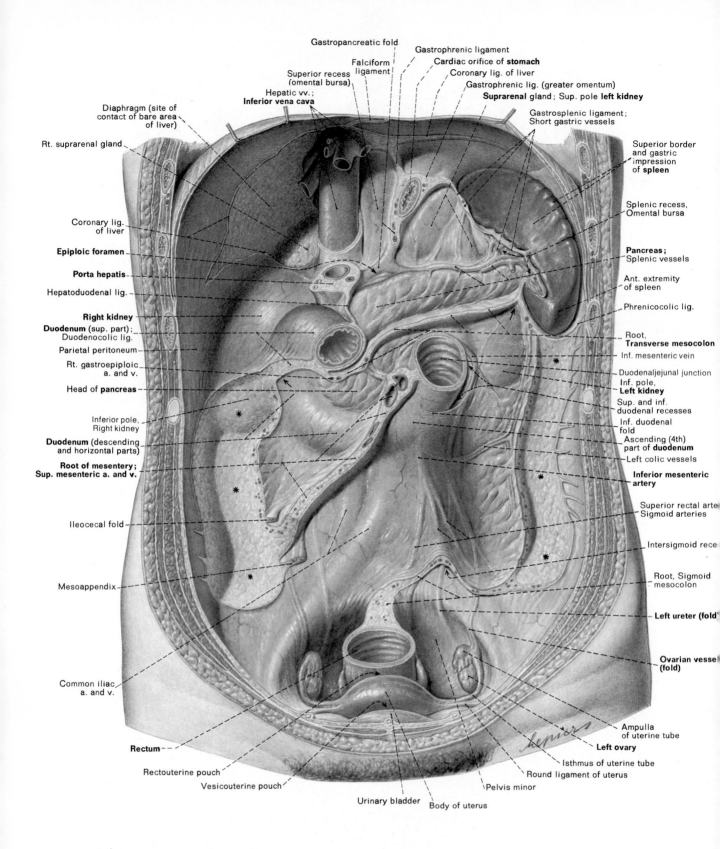

Gastropancreatic fold
Gastrophrenic ligament
Falciform ligament
Cardiac orifice of **stomach**
Superior recess (omental bursa)
Coronary lig. of liver
Hepatic vv.;
Inferior vena cava
Gastrophrenic lig. (greater omentum)
Suprarenal gland; Sup. pole **left kidney**
Gastrosplenic ligament;
Short gastric vessels

Diaphragm (site of contact of bare area of liver)
Rt. suprarenal gland

Superior border and gastric impression of **spleen**
Splenic recess, Omental bursa

Coronary lig. of liver
Epiploic foramen
Porta hepatis
Hepatoduodenal lig.

Pancreas; Splenic vessels
Ant. extremity of spleen
Phrenicocolic lig.

Right kidney
Duodenum (sup. part); Duodenocolic lig.
Parietal peritoneum
Rt. gastroepiploic a. and v.
Head of **pancreas**

Root, **Transverse mesocolon**
Inf. mesenteric vein
Duodenaljejunal junction
Inf. pole, **Left kidney**
Sup. and inf. duodenal recesses
Inf. duodenal fold
Ascending (4th) part of **duodenum**
Left colic vessels

Inferior pole, Right kidney
Duodenum (descending and horizontal parts)
Root of mesentery; **Sup. mesenteric a. and v.**

Inferior mesenteric artery

Superior rectal arte
Sigmoid arteries

Ileocecal fold

Intersigmoid rece

Mesoappendix

Root, Sigmoid mesocolon

Left ureter (fold

Ovarian vesse (fold)

Common iliac a. and v.

Ampulla of uterine tube
Left ovary
Isthmus of uterine tube
Round ligament of uterus
Pelvis minor

Rectum
Rectouterine pouch
Vesicouterine pouch
Urinary bladder
Body of uterus

Fig. 316: The Abdominal Cavity (11): Posterior Abdominal Peritoneum (Female)

NOTE: 1) the stomach and intestine (except duodenum and rectum) have been removed and their associated mesenteries have been cut close to their roots on the posterior abdominal wall. The liver and its attachments and the gall bladder were removed, leaving intact the spleen and the retroperitoneal organs (duodenum, pancreas, adrenal glands, kidneys and ureters, aorta and inferior vena cava).

2) ascending and descending portions of the large intestine are fused to the posterior abdominal wall (sites marked by *) with a peritoneal layer covering their anterior surfaces. Observe the small black arrows at the right and left colic flexures.

3) the course of the ureters and ovarian vessels as they descend over the pelvic brim. Notice the ovary, uterine tubes and uterus located in the pelvis and their relationship to the rectum and bladder.

Fig. 316

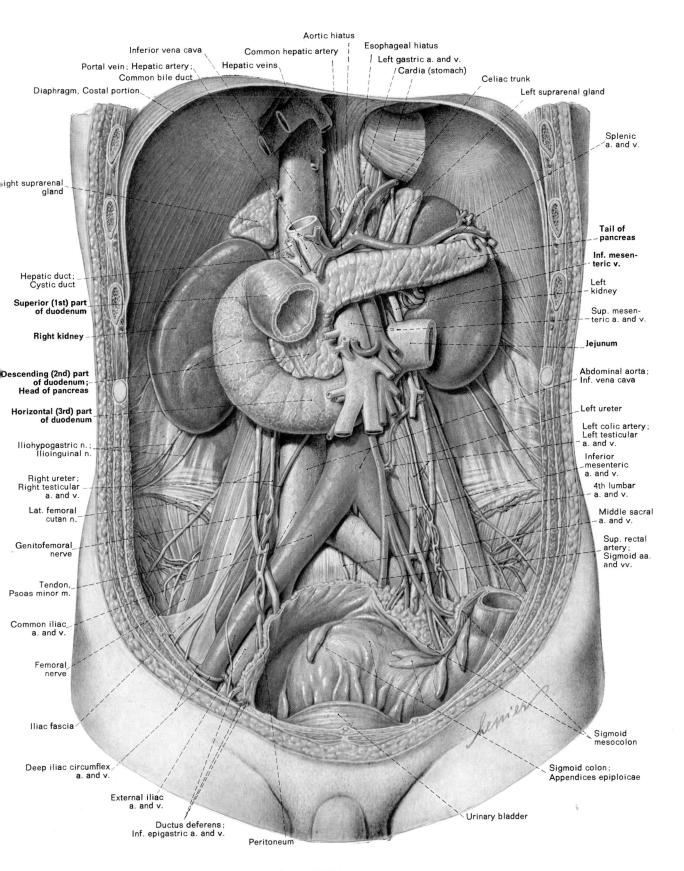

Inferior vena cava
Common hepatic artery
Aortic hiatus
Esophageal hiatus
Left gastric a. and v.
Cardia (stomach)
Portal vein; Hepatic artery;
Common bile duct
Hepatic veins
Celiac trunk
Diaphragm, Costal portion
Left suprarenal gland
Right suprarenal gland
Splenic a. and v.
Tail of pancreas
Inf. mesenteric v.
Hepatic duct; Cystic duct
Left kidney
Superior (1st) part of duodenum
Sup. mesenteric a. and v.
Right kidney
Jejunum
Descending (2nd) part of duodenum; Head of pancreas
Abdominal aorta; Inf. vena cava
Horizontal (3rd) part of duodenum
Left ureter
Iliohypogastric n.; Ilioinguinal n.
Left colic artery; Left testicular a. and v.
Inferior mesenteric a. and v.
Right ureter; Right testicular a. and v.
4th lumbar a. and v.
Lat. femoral cutan n.
Middle sacral a. and v.
Genitofemoral nerve
Sup. rectal artery; Sigmoid aa. and vv.
Tendon, Psoas minor m.
Common iliac a. and v.
Femoral nerve
Iliac fascia
Sigmoid mesocolon
Deep iliac circumflex a. and v.
Sigmoid colon; Appendices epiploicae
External iliac a. and v.
Ductus deferens; Inf. epigastric a. and v.
Peritoneum
Urinary bladder

Fig. 317: The Abdominal Cavity (12): The Retroperitoneal Organs (Male)

NOTE: 1) that the curvature of the duodenum lies ventral to the hilum of the right kidney, while the duodenojejunal junction is situated ventral to the lower medial border of the left kidney. Observe that the right kidney is slightly lower than the left.

2) the head of the pancreas lies ventral to the inferior vena cava and within the curve of the duodenum. A small extension of the head of the pancreas, the uncinate process, projects posterior to the superior mesenteric vessels. Upon crossing the midline at the level of the 1st lumbar vertebra, the posterior surface of the body and tail of the pancreas is in contact with the middle third of the left kidney.

Fig. 317   III

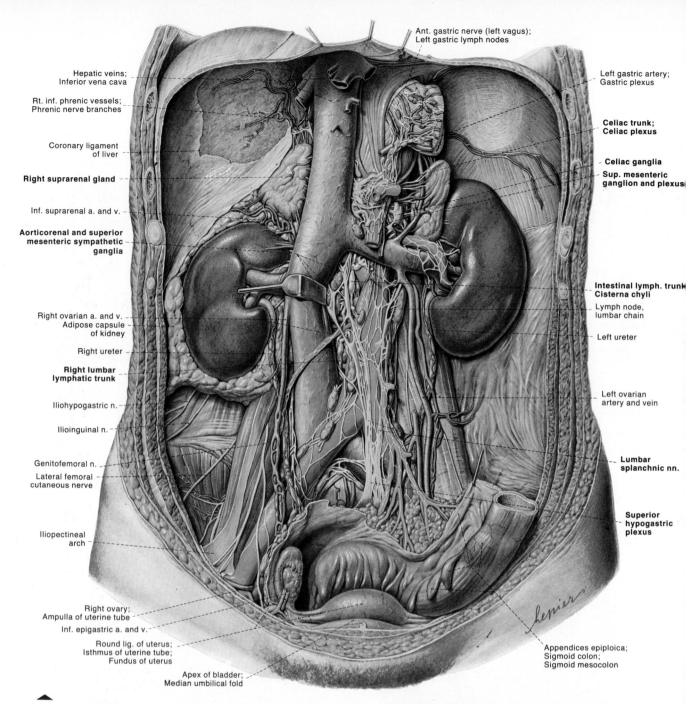

Hepatic veins;
Inferior vena cava

Rt. inf. phrenic vessels;
Phrenic nerve branches

Coronary ligament
of liver

Right suprarenal gland

Inf. suprarenal a. and v.

**Aorticorenal and superior
mesenteric sympathetic
ganglia**

Right ovarian a. and v.
Adipose capsule
of kidney

Right ureter

**Right lumbar
lymphatic trunk**

Iliohypogastric n.

Ilioinguinal n.

Genitofemoral n.
Lateral femoral
cutaneous nerve

Iliopectineal
arch

Right ovary;
Ampulla of uterine tube

Inf. epigastric a. and v.

Round lig. of uterus;
Isthmus of uterine tube;
Fundus of uterus

Apex of bladder;
Median umbilical fold

Ant. gastric nerve (left vagus);
Left gastric lymph nodes

Left gastric artery;
Gastric plexus

**Celiac trunk;
Celiac plexus**

Celiac ganglia

**Sup. mesenteric
ganglion and plexus**

**Intestinal lymph. trunk
Cisterna chyli**

Lymph node,
lumbar chain

Left ureter

Left ovarian
artery and vein

**Lumbar
splanchnic nn.**

**Superior
hypogastric
plexus**

Appendices epiploica;
Sigmoid colon;
Sigmoid mesocolon

**Fig. 318: Abdominal Cavity (13): Lymphatics and
Nerves of the Posterior Abdominal Wall**

NOTE: 1) that lymphatic channels draining pelvic
and posterior abdominal wall structures course along
iliac nodes to right and left chains of lumbar nodes
which parallel the aorta. These lumbar trunks are
joined by intestinal trunks draining the G. I. tract in
helping to form the cysterna chyli;

2) the sympathetic ganglia and plexuses which are
found in relation to the abdominal aorta and its
branches.

**Fig. 319: Posterior Abdominal Wall
in 5 Month Fetus**

NOTE the lobulated appearance of the fetal kidneys. Even at birth this lobulation is obvious, but as
maturation proceeds the surface slowly becomes
smooth. Observe the large suprarenal glands and
ureters, and the location of the testes.

Figs. 318, 319

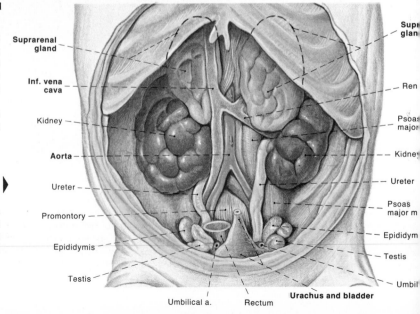

Suprarenal
gland

Inf. vena
cava

Kidney

Aorta

Ureter

Promontory

Epididymis

Testis

Supr
glan

Ren

Psoa
majo

Kidney

Ureter

Psoa
major m

Epididym

Testis

Umbil

Urachus and bladder

Umbilical a.   Rectum

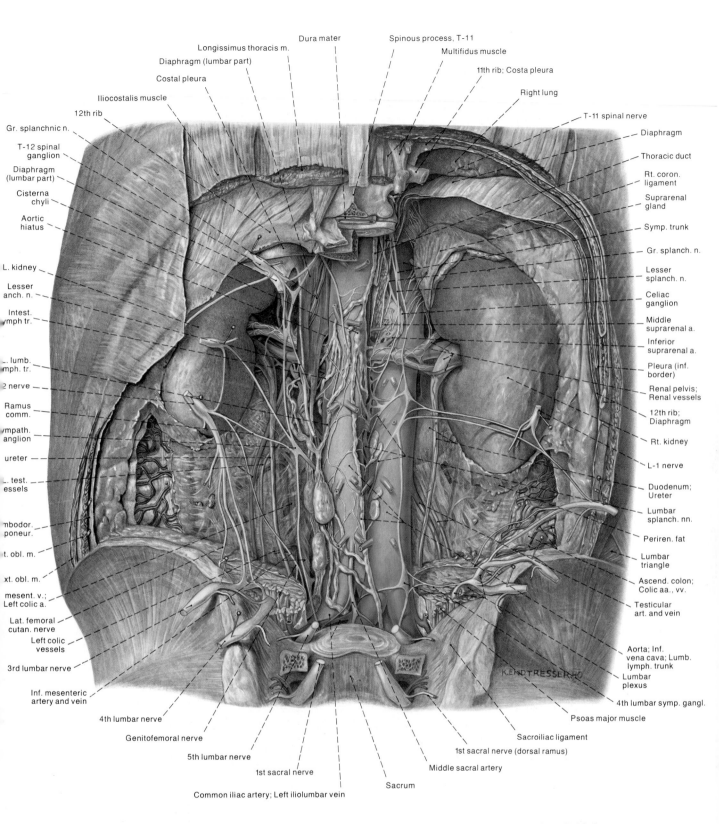

Fig. 320: Abdominal Cavity (14): Posterior Abdominal Retroperitoneal Structures in the Lumbar Region, Viewed from Behind

NOTE: 1) that in this posterior view of the lumbar retroperitoneal space, the vertebral column (vertebrae T-12 to L-5) has been removed, as have the other soft tissue structures that form the posterior abdominal wall. On the right side the 11th and 12th ribs have also been resected in order to visualize the upper pole of the right kidney and the superimposed right suprarenal gland.

2) the inferior vena cava ascending to the right side of the abdominal aorta. Observe that the cut lumbar arteries and veins (unlabelled) join these great vessels at each segmental level in the lumbar region. Also note the lumbar lymphatic trunks ascending toward the cisterna chyli, which is located to the side of the aorta at about the L-1 level near the origin of the right renal artery. Closeby, observe the position of the celiac ganglion.

3) that the renal arteries send ascending branches to the suprarenal glands and descending branches to the ureters.

4) that the lumbar spinal nerves, having been severed from the spinal cord when the vertebral column was removed, are reflected to each side and pinned to surrounding structures. Some of their connections, however, to the lumbar sympathetic ganglia and trunks have been left intact.

Fig. 320   III

Fig. 321: The Abdominal Cavity (15): The Posterior Abdominal Wall

NOTE: 1) the kidneys, ureters, suprarenal glands, and the great vessels and their branches. The kidneys extend between vertebral levels T-12 and L-3. The ureters commence on the posterior aspect of the hilum of the kidneys, course inferiorly over the pelvic brim near the bifurcation of the common iliac arteries, eventually to terminate in the bladder.

2) the suprarenal glands as they cap the upper pole of each kidney. These are highly vascular and vital glands of internal secretion (endocrine).

3) the aorta which enters the abdomen through the aortic hiatus (T-12). The inferior vena cava lies to the right of the vertebral column. It is formed by the confluence of the two common iliac veins (at about L-5) and passes through the caval opening of the diaphragm.

Fig. 321

Superior suprarenal aa.
(from inf. phrenic)

Superior border

Suprarenal gland

Anterior surface

Middle
suprarenal aa.
(from aorta)

Fatty
renal capsule

Right
supra-
renal vv.

Fibrous
al capsule

Medial
border

Inferior
suprarenal art.
(from renal art.)

— Rt. renal art.

— Rt. renal vein

— Rt. ureter

Capsule

Central vein

Glomerulosa
Fasciculata   Zones of
adrenal
cortex
Reticularis

Adrenal cortex

Adrenal medulla

Fig. 324: Section Through Suprarenal Gland ▲

NOTE that the suprarenal gland is composed of an inner medulla and outer cortex. The cells of the medulla secrete epinephrine while the adrenal cortex secretes adrenal corticosteroids.

◀ **Fig. 322: Right Kidney and Suprarenal Gland**

NOTE: 1) the suprarenal (adrenal) gland is an endocrine gland whose secretions are vital to life. The glands are located in the posterior abdominal region and situated adjacent to the superior poles of the kidneys. The right suprarenal gland is pyramidal in shape, and its anterior surface lies behind the inferior vena cava and adjacent to the right lobe of the liver. Posteriorly, it is in contact with the diaphragm and the right kidney.

2) the suprarenal glands are highly vascular, receiving arterial blood from numerous sources. These include arteries branching directly from the aorta and others coming from the inferior phrenic and renal arteries. Most of the venous blood is drained from the adrenal gland by way of single or paired suprarenal veins. On the right side, these veins drain directly into the inferior vena cava, whereas on the left this drainage is into the left renal vein.

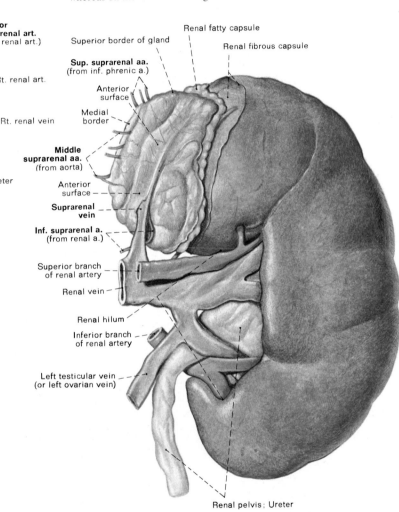

Renal fatty capsule

Superior border of gland

Renal fibrous capsule

Sup. suprarenal aa.
(from inf. phrenic a.)

Anterior
surface

Medial
border

**Middle
suprarenal aa.**
(from aorta)

Anterior
surface

**Suprarenal
vein**

Inf. suprarenal a.
(from renal a.)

Superior branch
of renal artery

Renal vein

Renal hilum

Inferior branch
of renal artery

Left testicular vein
(or left ovarian vein)

Renal pelvis; Ureter

Fig. 323: Left Kidney and Suprarenal Gland ▲

NOTE: 1) the left suprarenal gland is oriented onto the medial surface of the superior part of the left kidney. It presents a crescenteric shape with its concave surface adjacent to the kidney. The anterior surface lies behind the cardiac end of the stomach and the pancreas, i.e. behind the omental bursa, while its posterior surface rests upon the left crus of the diaphragm.

2) the combined weight of both suprarenal glands averages about 10 grams. The glands are each surrounded by an investing fibrous capsule, around which is a variable amount of areolar tissue.

Figs. 322, 323, 324   III

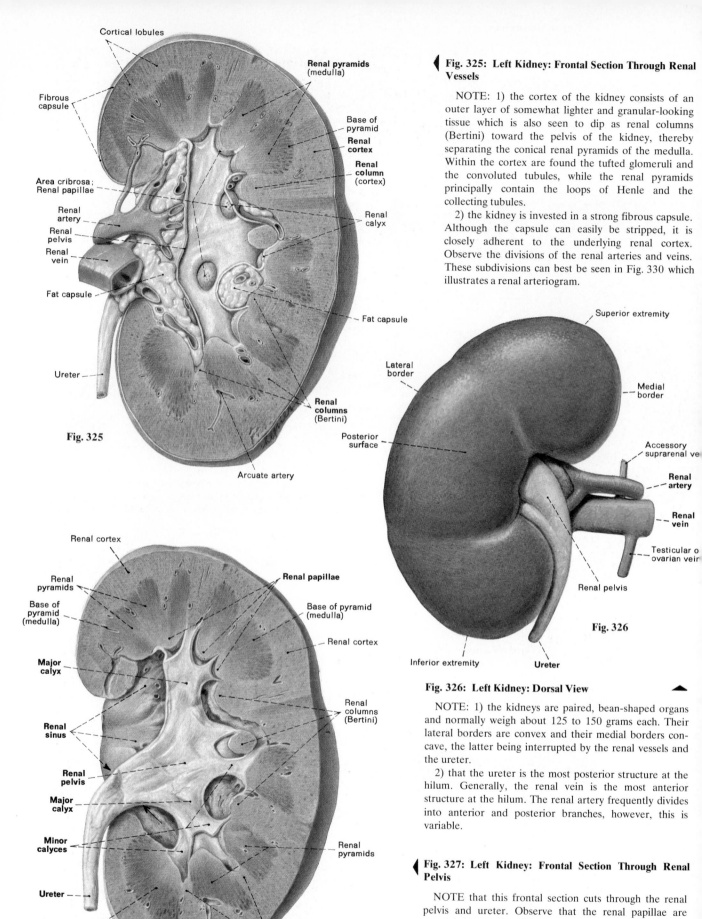

Fig. 325

Fig. 326

Fig. 327

Fig. 325: Left Kidney: Frontal Section Through Renal Vessels

NOTE: 1) the cortex of the kidney consists of an outer layer of somewhat lighter and granular-looking tissue which is also seen to dip as renal columns (Bertini) toward the pelvis of the kidney, thereby separating the conical renal pyramids of the medulla. Within the cortex are found the tufted glomeruli and the convoluted tubules, while the renal pyramids principally contain the loops of Henle and the collecting tubules.

2) the kidney is invested in a strong fibrous capsule. Although the capsule can easily be stripped, it is closely adherent to the underlying renal cortex. Observe the divisions of the renal arteries and veins. These subdivisions can best be seen in Fig. 330 which illustrates a renal arteriogram.

Fig. 326: Left Kidney: Dorsal View

NOTE: 1) the kidneys are paired, bean-shaped organs and normally weigh about 125 to 150 grams each. Their lateral borders are convex and their medial borders concave, the latter being interrupted by the renal vessels and the ureter.

2) that the ureter is the most posterior structure at the hilum. Generally, the renal vein is the most anterior structure at the hilum. The renal artery frequently divides into anterior and posterior branches, however, this is variable.

Fig. 327: Left Kidney: Frontal Section Through Renal Pelvis

NOTE that this frontal section cuts through the renal pelvis and ureter. Observe that the renal papillae are cupped by small collecting tubes, the minor calyces. Several minor calyces unite to form a mayor calyx, while the renal pelvis is formed by the union of two or three major calyces. Leading from the renal pelvis is the somewhat more narrowed ureter.

Figs. 325, 326, 327

Fig. 328: Retrograde Pyelogram

NOTE: 1) a radioopaque substance has been introduced into each ureter and forced in a retrograde manner into the renal pelvis, major calyces and minor calyces of each side. Observe that into the minor calyces project the renal papillae (5), resulting in radiolucent invaginations into the radioopaque minor calyces.

2) the shadow of the superior extremity of the left kidney extending to the top of the body of the T-12 vertebra, while the right kidney is somewhat more inferior.

3) the lateral margins of the psoas major muscles. The ureters course toward the pelvis along the anterior surfaces of these muscles.

1 Descending colon	3 Psoas major muscle	5 Renal papilla	7 Inferior pole of
2 Ascending colon	(lateral border)	6 Ureter	left kidney
	4 Renal pelvis		XII 12th thoracic vertebra

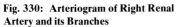

Renal hilum

Fig. 329: Left Kidney: Ventral View

NOTE: 1) although the stem of the renal artery initially lies dorsal to the stem of the renal vein at the hilum, the renal artery divides into anterior and posterior branches. The anterior branch generally enters the kidney ventral to the renal vein, as is shown in this figure.

2) the anterior surfaces of the kidneys are covered by peritoneum and are in relationship to more ventrally located abdominal organs. In contrast, their posterior surfaces lie adjacent to the musculature of the posterior abdominal wall and the diaphragm.

1 Stomach	3 Right renal artery	5 Interlobular arteries	XII 12th thoracic
2 Superior (1st) part	4 Interlobar arteries	K Catheter	vertebra
of duodenum			

Fig. 330: Arteriogram of Right Renal Artery and its Branches

NOTE: 1) an arterial catheter (K) has been inserted into the femoral artery, passed through the abdominal aorta and into the right renal artery. Observe the division of the renal artery successively into interlobar arteries (4).

2) as the interlobar arteries reach the junction of the renal cortex and medulla, they arch over the bases of the pyramids forming the arcuate arteries (not numbered in this figure). From the arcuate arteries branch a series of interlobular arteries which extend through the afferent arterioles which enter the renal glomeruli.

3) the stomach (1) and superior (1st) part of the duodenum (2) which are filled with air.

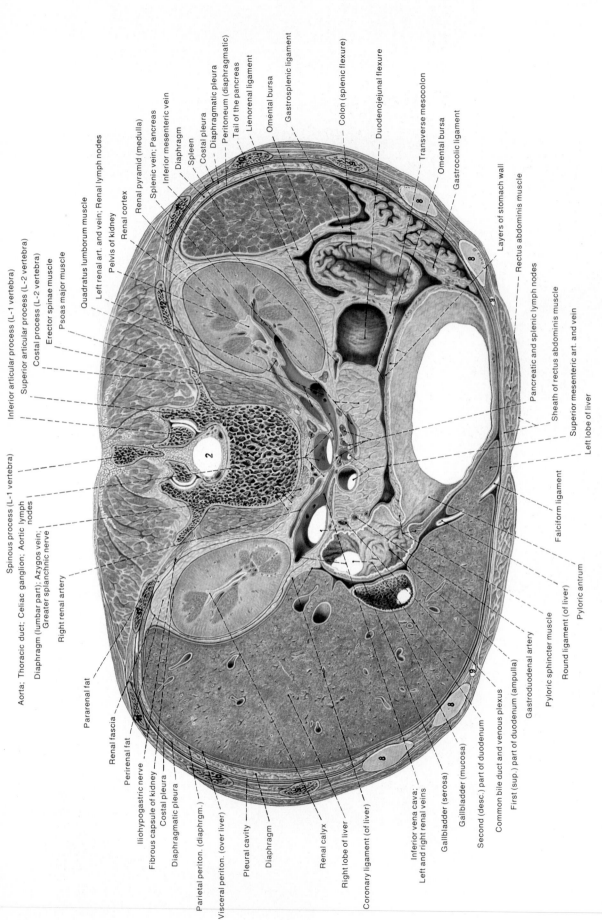

Inferior articular process (L–1 vertebra)
Superior articular process (L–2 vertebra)
Costal process (L–2 vertebra)
Erector spinae muscle
Psoas major muscle
Quadratus lumborum muscle
Left renal art. and vein; Renal lymph nodes
Pelvis of kidney
Renal cortex
Renal pyramid (medulla)
Splenic vein; Pancreas
Inferior mesenteric vein
Diaphragm
Spleen
Costal pleura
Diaphragmatic pleura
Peritoneum (diaphragmatic)
Tail of the pancreas
Lienorenal ligament
Omental bursa
Gastrosplenic ligament
Colon (splenic flexure)
Duodenojejunal flexure
Transverse mesocolon
Omental bursa
Gastrocolic ligament
Layers of stomach wall
Rectus abdominis muscle
Sheath of rectus abdominis muscle
Pancreatic and splenic lymph nodes
Superior mesenteric art. and vein
Left lobe of liver

Spinous process (L–1 vertebra)
Aorta; Thoracic duct; Celiac ganglion; Aortic lymph nodes
Diaphragm (lumbar part); Azygos vein; Greater splanchnic nerve
Right renal artery

Pararenal fat
Renal fascia
Perirenal fat
Iliohypogastric nerve
Fibrous capsule of kidney
Costal pleura
Diaphragmatic pleura
Parietal periton. (diaphrgm.)
Visceral periton. (over liver)
Pleural cavity
Diaphragm
Renal calyx
Right lobe of liver
Coronary ligament (of liver)
Inferior vena cava: Left and right renal veins
Gallbladder (serosa)
Gallbladder (mucosa)
Second (desc.) part of duodenum
Common bile duct and venous plexus
First (sup.) part of duodenum (ampulla)
Gastroduodenal artery
Pyloric sphincter muscle
Round ligament (of liver)
Pyloric antrum
Falciform ligament

Fig. 331: Transverse Section Through the Abdomen at the Level of the Body of the Second Lumbar Vertebra

NOTE: 1) that through a transverse section at this level are found the pylorus of the stomach and the first (or superior) part of the duodenum, from which can be seen continuing inferiorly the second (or descending) part of the duodenum. Observe also the gallbladder, the pancreas (dorsal to which are seen the superior mesenteric vessels), the duodenal-jejunal flexure of the small intestine and the left colic (or splenic) flexure of the large intestine.

2) that the left kidney (reader's right) is sectioned across the lower part of the left renal hilum, whereas the hilum of the right kidney is found below the level of this transection and shows well in Figure 332. Observe the long course of the left renal vein to the inferior vena cava, and that the latter vessel is located retroperitoneally behind the pancreas and duodenum and to the right side of the aorta.

Fig. 331

Fig. 332: Transverse Section Through the Abdomen at the Level of the Body of the Third Lumbar Vertebra

NOTE: 1) the hilum of the right kidney, the descending (2nd) part of the duodenum with its greater duodenal papilla and sphincter of Oddi, the head of the pancreas just to the left of the descending part of the duodenum, and the transverse colon just beyond the right (hepatic) colic flexure. Also observe that the superior mesenteric vessels are anterior to the horizontal (3rd) part of the duodenum.

2) that the kidney is closely invested by a fibrous capsule. External to this capsule is a *perirenal* fatty layer, which lies adjacent to the *renal fascia*. External to the renal fascia is the *pararenal fat* (body), which lies adjacent to the muscular structures of the posterior abdominal wall.

Fig. 332   III

Labels (clockwise from top):

Kidney and fibrous capsule
Taenia omentalis (of descending colon)
Peritoneal cavity
Renal sinus and pelvis
Descending colon
Taenia mesocolica, Left colic artery
Taenia libera
Renal calyx
Left ureter
Jejunum; Mesentery of the small intestine
Greater omentum
Inferior mesenteric vein
Transverse colon
Taenia mesocolica
Omental bursa
Gastrocolic ligament; Taenia omentalis
Layers (or tunics) of the stomach
Transverse mesocolon
Jejunum
Duodenojejunal flexure
Stomach (mucosa)
Mesentery of the small intestine
Para-aortic (lumbar) lymph nodes
Left testicular artery and vein
Mesenteric lymph nodes: Jejunal artery
Superior mesenteric art., vein and ganglion
Linea alba
Falciform ligament (of the liver)
Ligament of umbilical vein
Gastrocolic ligament
Rectus abdominis muscle and sheath
Transverse colon
Omental bursa
Haustrum
Right gastroepiploic vein
Deep fascia (over ext. obl. m.)
Ext. and int. oblique mm.; Transversus abdominis m.
Parietal peritoneum
Visceral peritoneum
Liver (right lobe)
Semilunar folds
Taenia libera
Transverse colon (just beyond rt. colic flexure)
2nd (desc.) part of duodenum
Greater duodenal papilla
Hepatopancreatic duct
Interlobar peritoneum
Renal pyramid
Renal sinus and pelvis
Renal artery (branch)
Hilum of right kidney
Right renal artery and vein
Inferior vena cava
Sympath. trunk (lumb. part); 3rd lumb. art.
Erector spinae muscle
Psoas major m.; L-2 nerve (to lumbar plexus); 3rd lumb. art.
Latissimus dorsi muscle
Lumbar fascia (anterior layer)
Iliohypogastric nerve (L-1)
Serratus posterior inferior muscle
Quad. lumb. m.; Transversal. fascia
Subcostal nerve (T-12)
Pararenal fat (body)
Perirenal fatty layer (or capsule)
Renal fascia
Transverse process (L-3 vertebra)
Gallbladder

Right diaphragmatic pleura
Vena caval foramen
Esophageal hiatus
Subcostales muscles
Diaphragm, Costal portion
Right crus (of diaphragm)
Lateral arcuate ligament
Medial arcuate ligament
Right medial crus
Transversus abdominis muscle
Right lateral crus
Quadratus lumborum muscle
Iliolumbar ligament
Iliacus muscle
Psoas minor muscle
Psoas major muscle
Iliopectineal arch
Iliopsoas muscle
Inguinal ligament
Ischial tuberosity
Pubic tubercle

Left diaphragmatic pleura
Central tendon of diaphragm
Aortic hiatus; Abdominal aorta
Left medial crus
12th rib; Lat. arcuate ligament
Quadratus lumborum m.
Tendinous arches of psoas major m.
Transverse process (lumbar vertebra)
Iliac crest
Sacrotuberous ligament
Linea terminalis
Iliopectineal arch
Sacrospinous ligament
Greater trochanter
Iliofemoral ligament
Obturator membrane
Lesser trochanter
Symphysis pubis

Fig. 333: The Diaphragm and Posterior Abdominal Wall Muscles

NOTE: 1) the posterior attachments of the diaphragm include a) the right and left crura which arise from the anterior and lateral aspects of the bodies of the upper 3 or 4 lumbar vertebrae, b) the right and left medial arcuate ligaments which are thickenings in the psoas fascia, and c) the lateral arcuate ligaments along the 12th rib overlying the quadratus lumborum muscle.

2) the psoas major and minor muscles descending from the lumbar vertebrae to join the iliacus in the lateral wall of the pelvis to insert onto the lesser trochanter of the femur. The iliopsoas is the most powerful flexor of the thigh at the hip joint.

3) the rectangular quadratus lumborum intervening between the 12th rib, the transverse processes of the lumbar vertebrae and the posteromedial iliac crest.

Fig. 334: Posterior View of Diaphragm

NOTE: 1) the posterior half of the bony thorax (ribs and vertebral column) has been removed to reveal the diaphragm from behind. Observe that the caval opening is to the right of midline and more superior to those transmitting the esophagus and aorta.

2) that from their origin around the thoracic outlet, the muscular fibers of the diaphragm converge to insert into a central tendon. Observe the dome-shape of the diaphragm on each side and that the right dome extends more superiorly into the thoracic cavity because of the large right lobe of the liver.

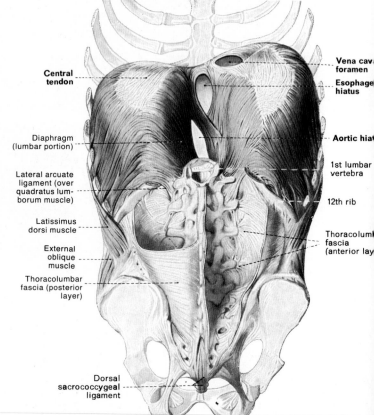

Central tendon
Diaphragm (lumbar portion)
Lateral arcuate ligament (over quadratus lumborum muscle)
Latissimus dorsi muscle
External oblique muscle
Thoracolumbar fascia (posterior layer)
Dorsal sacrococcygeal ligament

Vena caval foramen
Esophageal hiatus
Aortic hiatus
1st lumbar vertebra
12th rib
Thoracolumbar fascia (anterior layer)

Figs. 333, 334

Vena caval foramen

Transversus abdominis m.

Central tendon of diaphragm

Costal part of diaphragm

Esophageal hiatus

Med. lumbocostal arch

Lat. lumbocostal arch

Psoas minor m. (cut)

Quadratus lumborum m.

Transversus abdominis m.

Psoas major m.

Iliacus m.

Promontory of sacrum

Peritoneum

Rectum

Pecten of pubis (pectineal ligament)

Lacunar ligament

Sternal part of the diaphragm

Esophagus (traversing the esophageal hiatus)

Costal part of the diaphragm

Transversus abdominis m.

Central tendon of diaphragm

Aortic hiatus

Abdominal aorta and celiac trunk

Right crus of diaphragm

Quadratus lumborum m.

Transversalis fascia

Lumbar vertebrae

Iliac crest

Tendon of psoas minor m.

Psoas major m.

Iliacus m.

Iliopsoas m.

Urinary bladder

Vascular compartments of the femoral sheath

Femoral art.

Femoral vein

Inguinal ligament

Rectus abdominis m.

Fig. 335: The Psoas Minor, Psoas Major, Iliacus, and Quadratus Lumborum Muscles and the Diaphragm

NOTE: 1) the *psoas minor muscle* lies anterior to the psoas major. It arises from the lateral aspect of the bodies of the T-12 and L-1 vertebrae and its insertion merges with the lower part of the psoas major above the inguinal ligament. It is innervated by the L-1 nerve.

2) the *psoas major muscle* arises from the transverse processes of the 5 lumbar vertebrae, as well as from the lateral aspect of the bodies of the 12th thoracic and all 5 lumbar vertebrae. It descends deep to the inguinal ligament and is joined by the iliacus muscle (see Fig. 333). The psoas major is supplied by the first 3 lumbar nerves, and through it course the lumbar nerves in the formation of the lumbar plexus (see Fig. 336).

3) the *iliacus muscle* arises from the inner aspect of the pelvis within the concavity called the iliac fossa, and from the lateral aspect of the sacrum. It converges with the psoas muscles deep to the inguinal ligament. The iliacus is supplied by branches of the femoral nerve.

4) the *quadratus lumborum muscle* arises from the medial part of the 12th rib and from the transverse processes of the upper 4 lumbar vertebrae. It inserts into the iliolumbar ligament and the iliac crest and is innervated by T-12 and the upper 3 or 4 lumbar nerves.

5) the relative locations of the vena caval, esophageal, and aortic hiatuses in the diaphragm.

Fig. 335   **III**

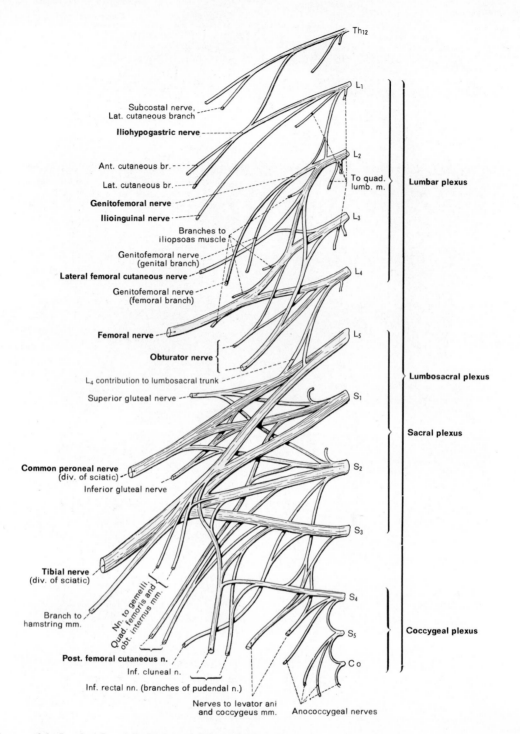

Subcostal nerve, Lat. cutaneous branch

Iliohypogastric nerve

Ant. cutaneous br.

Lat. cutaneous br.

Genitofemoral nerve

Ilioinguinal nerve

Branches to iliopsoas muscle

Genitofemoral nerve (genital branch)

Lateral femoral cutaneous nerve

Genitofemoral nerve (femoral branch)

Femoral nerve

Obturator nerve

L_4 contribution to lumbosacral trunk

Superior gluteal nerve

Common peroneal nerve (div. of sciatic)

Inferior gluteal nerve

Tibial nerve (div. of sciatic)

Branch to hamstring mm.

Nn. to gemelli, Quad. femoris and obt. internus mm.

Post. femoral cutaneous n.

Inf. cluneal n.

Inf. rectal nn. (branches of pudendal n.)

Nerves to levator ani and coccygeus mm.

Anococcygeal nerves

Th_{12}

L_1

L_2

To quad. lumb. m.

L_3

L_4

L_5

S_1

S_2

S_3

S_4

S_5

Co

Lumbar plexus

Lumbosacral plexus

Sacral plexus

Coccygeal plexus

Fig. 336: Diagram of the Lumbar, Sacral, Pudendal and Coccygeal Nerve Plexuses

NOTE: 1) the 12th thoracic (subcostal) and 1st lumbar nerves are distributed principally to the lower abdominal wall. The anterior rami of the remaining segmental nerves of the lumbosacral plexus innervate the muscles and skin of the pelvis, perineum and lower extremity. L_1 divides into the iliohypogastric and ilioinguinal nerves.

2) L_2, L_3 and L_4 are the principal segments forming the lumbar plexus. L_1 contributes some fibers to the genitofemoral nerve. The main peripheral nerves derived from these segments include:

a) the genitofemoral nerve (L_1, L_2) c) the obturator nerve (L_2, L_3, L_4)

b) the lateral femoral cutaneous nerve (L_2, L_3) d) femoral nerve (L_2, L_3, L_4)

3) L_5, S_1, S_2 and S_3 with some contribution from L_4 form the sacral plexus. The principal peripheral nerves derived from these segments include:

a) the superior gluteal nerve (L_4, L_5, S_1)

b) the inferior gluteal nerve (L_5, S_1, S_2) c) the sciatic nerve { common peroneal nerve (L_4, L_5, S_1, S_2) / tibial nerve $(L_4, L_5, S_1, S_2, S_3)$

d) the posterior femoral cutaneous nerve (S_1, S_2, S_3)

4) S_2, S_3 and S_4 also contribute to the pudendal plexus while S_4, S_5 and the coccygeal nerve form fine nerve filaments which innervate the skin of the anococcygeal region. The pudendal nerve is the main sensory and motor nerve of the perineum. Other sensory (inferior cluneal) and motor (nerve to levator ani and coccygeus muscles) branches of the pudendal plexus also come from sacral segments.

Fig. 336

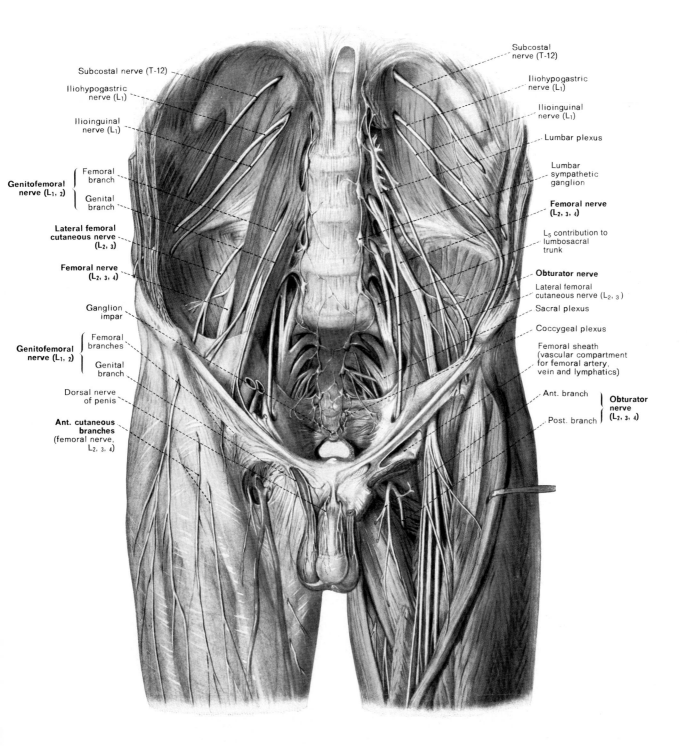

Subcostal nerve (T-12)

Iliohypogastric
nerve (L₁)

Ilioinguinal
nerve (L₁)

Genitofemoral
nerve (L₁, ₂) {
Femoral
branch

Genital
branch
}

Lateral femoral
cutaneous nerve
(L₂, ₃)

Femoral nerve
(L₂, ₃, ₄)

Ganglion
impar

Genitofemoral
nerve (L₁, ₂) {
Femoral
branches

Genital
branch
}

Dorsal nerve
of penis

Ant. cutaneous
branches
(femoral nerve,
L₂, ₃, ₄)

Subcostal
nerve (T-12)

Iliohypogastric
nerve (L₁)

Ilioinguinal
nerve (L₁)

Lumbar plexus

Lumbar
sympathetic
ganglion

Femoral nerve
(L₂, ₃, ₄)

L₅ contribution to
lumbosacral
trunk

Obturator nerve

Lateral femoral
cutaneous nerve (L₂, ₃)

Sacral plexus

Coccygeal plexus

Femoral sheath
(vascular compartment
for femoral artery,
vein and lymphatics)

Ant. branch

Post. branch
} Obturator
nerve
(L₂, ₃, ₄)

Fig. 337: The Lumbosacral Plexus: Posterior Abdominal Wall and Anterior Thigh

NOTE: 1) on the left side, the psoas major and minor muscles have been removed in order to reveal the plexus of lumbar nerves more completely. As can be seen on the right side, these nerves emerge from the spinal cord and descend along the posterior abdominal wall within the substance of the psoas muscles. Observe that the 12th thoracic nerve (subcostal nerve) courses around the abdominal wall below the 12th rib.

2) the 1st lumbar nerve divides into an iliohypogastric and an ilioinguinal branch. The ilioinguinal nerve descends obliquely toward the iliac crest, penetrates through the transversus and internal oblique muscles to join the spermatic cord, becoming cutaneous at the superficial inguinal ring.

3) the genitofemoral nerve can be found coursing superficially on the surface of the psoas major muscle. It divides into a genital branch (which innervates the cremaster muscle and the skin of the scrotum) and a femoral branch (which is sensory to the upper anterior thigh.)

4) the femoral and obturator nerves. These nerves are derived from L₂, L₃ and L₄ and descend to innervate the anterior and medial groups of femoral muscles, respectively. The femoral nerve enters the thigh beneath the inguinal ligament, dividing into both motor and sensory branches, whereas the obturator nerve courses more medially through the obturator foramen to become the principal nerve of the adductor muscle group.

5) L₄ and L₅ nerve roots (lumbosacral trunk) join with the upper three sacral nerves to form the sacral plexus. From most of this plexus is derived the large sciatic nerve which leaves the pelvis through the greater sciatic foramen to achieve the gluteal region and the posterior aspect of the lower limb.

Fig. 337   **III**

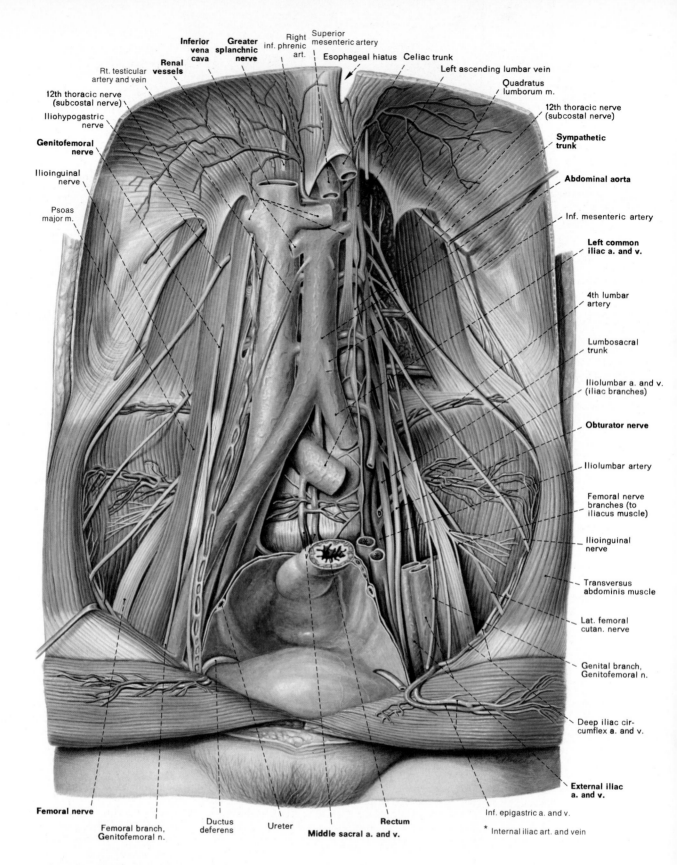

Fig. 338: The Posterior Abdominal Vessels and Nerves

NOTE: 1) the abdominal viscera have been removed as well as the psoas muscles on the left side. Observe the greater splanchnic nerves as they pierce the diaphragmatic crura to enter the abdomen. Also note the inferior phrenic arteries nearby. Identify the abdominal sympathetic chain of ganglia situated anterolaterally on the vertebral column.

2) the testicular arteries arising from the aorta just below the renal arteries. Inferiorly, the testicular artery and vein join the ductus deferens to enter the abdominal inguinal ring just lateral to the inferior epigastric vessels. Observe the middle sacral vessels descending into the pelvis in the midline. The middle sacral artery originates from the aorta at its bifurcation, whereas the vein usually drains into the left common iliac vein.

Fig. 338

Greater splanchnic nerve
Diaphragm
Cardia of stomach
Ramus communicans
11th thoracic nerve
Thoracic sympathetic ganglia
11th rib
Lesser splanchnic nerve
Rt. crus of diaphragm
12th rib
Celiac ganglia and plexus
Renal ganglion and plexus
Renal artery
Sympathetic trunk
Quadratus lumborum m.
Lumbar sympathetic ganglion
Iliac crest
Iliacus muscle
Gray rami communicantes
Sacral sympathetic ganglia
11th rib
12th thoracic nerve (subcostal nerve)
Celiac trunk
Superior mesenteric a.
Superior mesenteric ganglion
1st lumbar nerve
Aortic plexus (abdominal)
2nd lumbar nerve
Inf. mesenteric plexus
Quadratus lumborum muscle
Inferior mesenteric art
3rd lumbar nerve
Iliac plexus
4th lumbar nerve
5th lumbar nerve
Lumbosacral trunk
Sacral plexus
1st sacral nerve
2nd sacral nerve
3rd sacral nerve
Pudendal plexus
Acetabulum
Levator ani muscle
Ganglion·impar
Rectum
5th sacral nerve
Coccygeal nerve
4th sacral nerve
Visceral branches, pudendal nerve

Fig. 339: Lumbar Sympathetic Trunk and Abdominal Autonomic Ganglia

NOTE: 1) in addition to the two sympathetic chains of ganglia descending from the thorax through the abdomen and into the pelvis, the plexuses and their associated ganglia which overlie the major arteries branching from the aorta. Thus, the celiac plexuses along with the superior mesenteric, inferior mesenteric, renal, aortic and iliac plexuses form a dense network of autonomic fibers from which many of the abdominal and pelvic viscera receive sympathetic innervation.

2) the splanchnic nerves (containing preganglionic sympathetic fibers) as they join the upper abdominal ganglia where many of their fibers synapse with postganglionic sympathetic neurons.

3) that below L-2 only gray rami communicantes connect the ganglia of the sympathetic chain to the segmental nerves, since at these lower levels the rami consist only of postganglionic sympathetic fibers.

Fig. 339   III

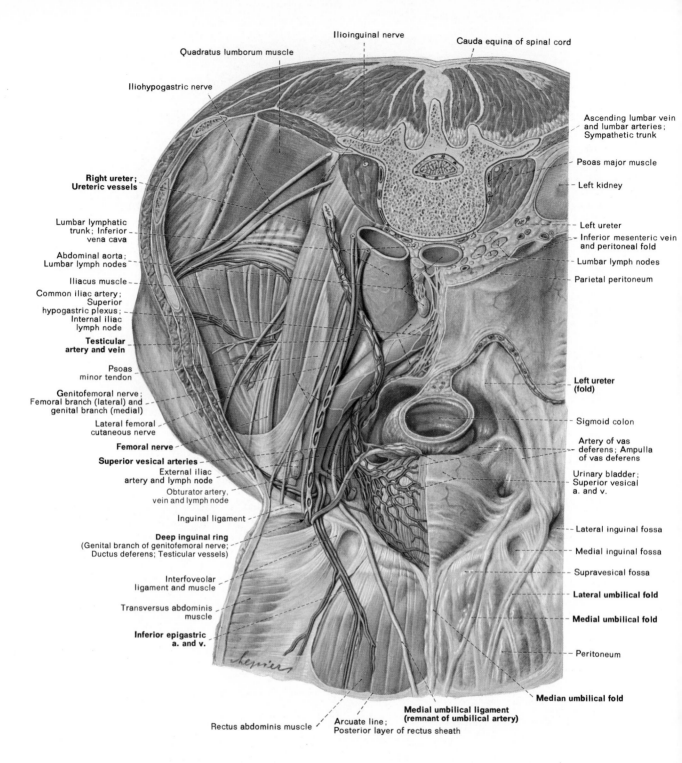

Quadratus lumborum muscle

Ilioinguinal nerve

Cauda equina of spinal cord

Iliohypogastric nerve

Ascending lumbar vein and lumbar arteries; Sympathetic trunk

Psoas major muscle

Right ureter; Ureteric vessels

Left kidney

Lumbar lymphatic trunk; Inferior vena cava

Left ureter

Inferior mesenteric vein and peritoneal fold

Abdominal aorta; Lumbar lymph nodes

Lumbar lymph nodes

Iliacus muscle

Parietal peritoneum

Common iliac artery; Superior hypogastric plexus; Internal iliac lymph node

Testicular artery and vein

Psoas minor tendon

Left ureter (fold)

Genitofemoral nerve; Femoral branch (lateral) and genital branch (medial)

Sigmoid colon

Lateral femoral cutaneous nerve

Artery of vas deferens; Ampulla of vas deferens

Femoral nerve

Urinary bladder; Superior vesical a. and v.

Superior vesical arteries

External iliac artery and lymph node

Obturator artery, vein and lymph node

Lateral inguinal fossa

Inguinal ligament

Medial inguinal fossa

Deep inguinal ring (Genital branch of genitofemoral nerve; Ductus deferens; Testicular vessels)

Supravesical fossa

Lateral umbilical fold

Interfoveolar ligament and muscle

Transversus abdominis muscle

Medial umbilical fold

Inferior epigastric a. and v.

Peritoneum

Median umbilical fold

Medial umbilical ligament (remnant of umbilical artery)

Rectus abdominis muscle

Arcuate line; Posterior layer of rectus sheath

Fig. 340: Vessels and Nerves of the Inferior Abdomen and Pelvis

NOTE: 1) the anterior abdominal wall has been incised vertically on both sides and reflected inferiorly, thereby exposing its inner (posterior) surface. The body has been transected through the lumbar region at the caudal end of the 3rd lumbar vertebra. On the right side, the peritoneum investing the abdominal cavity has been stripped away, whereas on the left it has been left intact.

2) this dissection reveals the intact male pelvic viscera viewed from above. Observe the course of the ureters as they cross the pelvic brim anterior to the common iliac arteries. Within the pelvis, the ureter curves medially toward the bladder. At the lateral angle of the bladder, the ductus deferens courses on its path to the seminal vesicle ventral to the ureter.

3) the convergence of the testicular vessels, ductus deferens and genital branch of the genitofemoral nerve (innervation of cremaster muscle) at the abdominal inguinal ring to form the spermatic cord of the inguinal canal.

4) the origins within the pelvis of the umbilical ligaments of the anterior abdominal wall: a) the median umbilical fold extending from the bladder to the umbilicus (urachus), b) the medial umbilical fold formed by a peritoneal reflection over the obliterated umbilical artery, and c) the lateral umbilical fold formed by peritoneum covering the inferior epigastric vessels.

5) the superior hypogastric plexus or presacral nerve lying anterior to the bifurcation of the aorta and descending behind the peritoneum into the pelvis.

Fig. 340

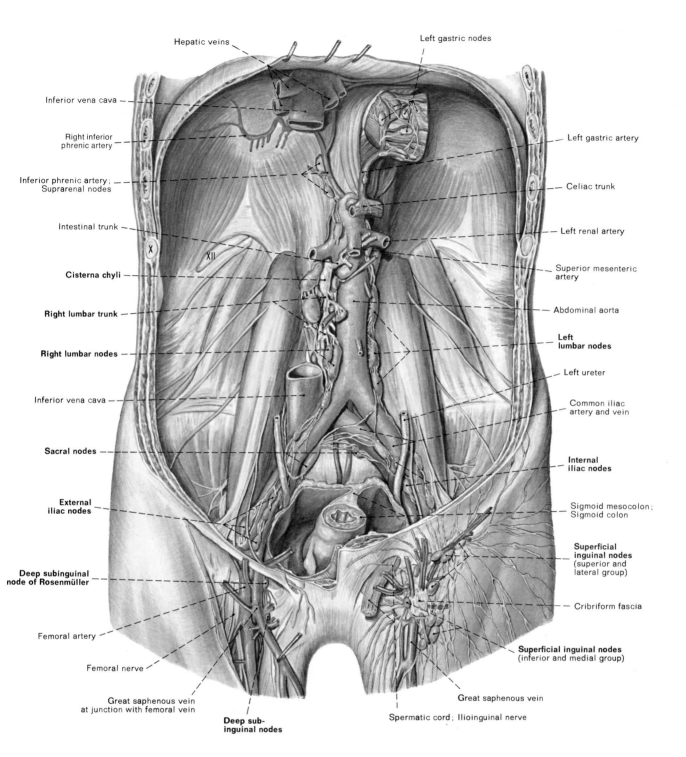

Hepatic veins

Left gastric nodes

Inferior vena cava

Right inferior
phrenic artery

Left gastric artery

Inferior phrenic artery;
Suprarenal nodes

Celiac trunk

Intestinal trunk

Left renal artery

X

XII

Superior mesenteric
artery

Cisterna chyli

Right lumbar trunk

Abdominal aorta

Right lumbar nodes

**Left
lumbar nodes**

Left ureter

Inferior vena cava

Common iliac
artery and vein

Sacral nodes

**Internal
iliac nodes**

**External
iliac nodes**

Sigmoid mesocolon;
Sigmoid colon

**Superficial
inguinal nodes**
(superior and
lateral group)

**Deep subinguinal
node of Rosenmüller**

Cribriform fascia

Femoral artery

Superficial inguinal nodes
(inferior and medial group)

Femoral nerve

Great saphenous vein
at junction with femoral vein

Great saphenous vein

**Deep sub-
inguinal nodes**

Spermatic cord; Ilioinguinal nerve

Fig. 341: The Inguinal, Pelvic and Lumbar (Aortic) Lymph Nodes

NOTE: 1) chains of lymph nodes from the inguinal region to the diaphragm lie along the paths of the major blood vessels. In the inguinal region, the superficial inguinal lymph nodes lie just distal to the inguinal ligament and in the subcutaneous superficial fascia. They range from 10 to 20 in number and receive drainage from the genitalia, perineum, gluteal region and the anterior abdominal wall. More deeply, the subinguinal nodes receive drainage from the lower extremity. One of the deep subinguinal nodes (node of Rosenmüller or Cloquet) lies in the femoral ring.

2) within the pelvis and abdomen, visceral lymph nodes lie close to the organs which they drain. These visceral nodes then channel lymph through chains of parietal nodes which generally are located along the paths of the major arteries and veins. Thus, external iliac, internal iliac (hypogastric) and common iliac nodes are located in proximity to these vessels in the pelvis.

3) along the posterior abdominal wall are found right and left lumbar chains which course along the sides of the abdominal aorta. Other groups of nodes, the preaortic, are arranged along the roots of the major unpaired branches of the aorta, forming the celiac and superior and inferior mesenteric node chains.

4) at about the level of the 2nd lumbar vertebra there is a confluence of lymph channels which forms a dilated sac, the cisterna chyli. This is located somewhat posterior and to the right of the aorta and marks the commencement of the thoracic duct.

Fig. 341   **III**

Fig. 342: An Iliac Arteriogram in a Female

NOTE that the bifurcation of the aorta (*1*) into the two common iliac arteries (*2*) occurs at the lower border of the body of the L 4 vertebra. The common iliac vessels branch into external (*3*) and internal (*4*) iliac arteries. The internal iliac artery (*4*) on each side serves a number of branches to the pelvis, perineum, and gluteal region, while the external iliac artery (*3*), after giving off the inferior epigastric (*15*) and deep circumflex iliac (*16*) arteries, becomes the femoral artery below the inguinal ligament. (From Wicke, L., *Atlas of Radiologic Anatomy*, 3rd Edition, Urban and Schwarzenberg, Baltimore, 1982.)

1. Abdominal aorta	5. Femoral artery	9. Uterine artery	13. Internal pudendal artery	17. Deep femoral artery
2. Common iliac artery	6. Lumbar arteries	10. Uterus	14. Superior gluteal artery	L 4 - 4 th lumbar vertebra
3. External iliac artery	7. Iliolumbar artery	11. Lateral sacral artery	15. Inferior epigastric artery	SP - Symphysis pubis
4. Internal iliac artery	8. Median sacral artery	12. Obturator artery	16. Deep circumflex iliac artery	

Fig. 342

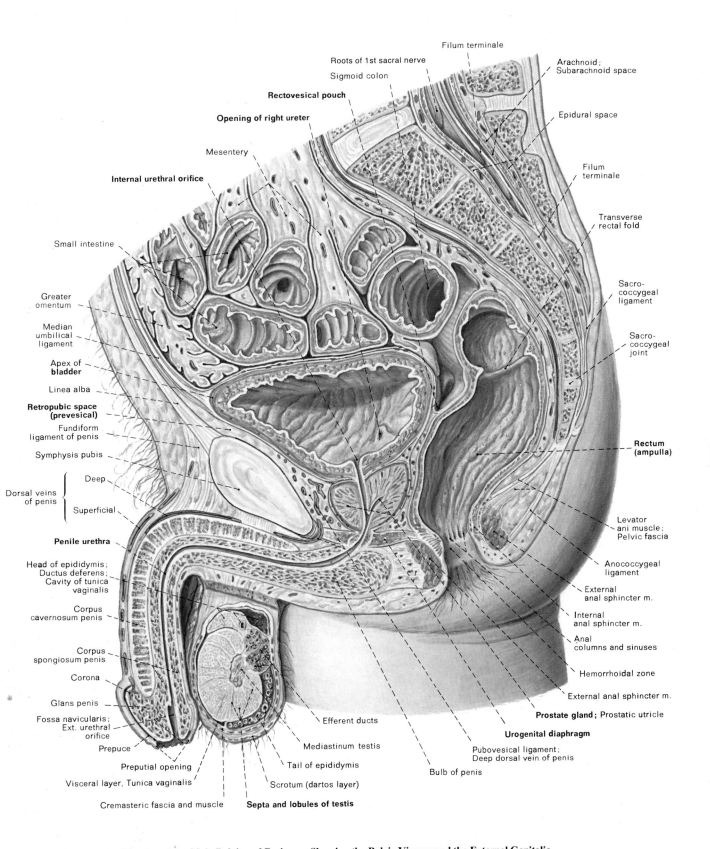

Fig. 343: Median Sagittal Section of the Male Pelvis and Perineum Showing the Pelvic Viscera and the External Genitalia

Fig. 343   IV

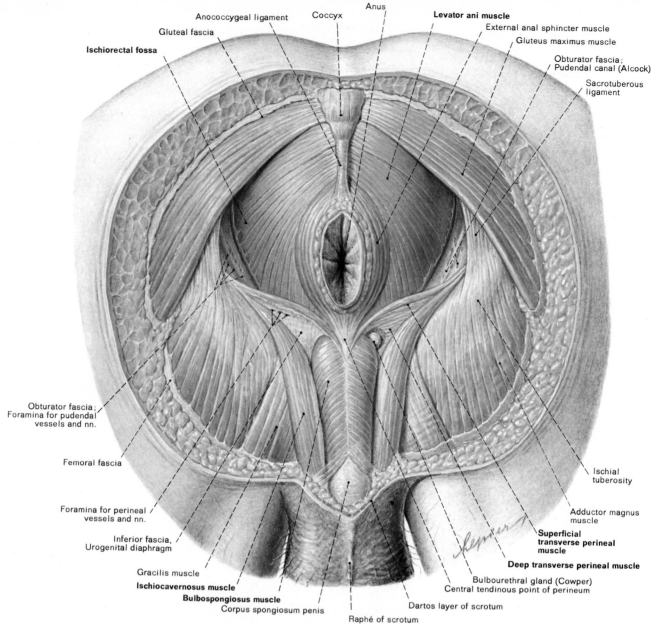

Ischiorectal fossa
Gluteal fascia
Anococcygeal ligament
Coccyx
Anus
Levator ani muscle
External anal sphincter muscle
Gluteus maximus muscle
Obturator fascia;
Pudendal canal (Alcock)
Sacrotuberous ligament

Obturator fascia;
Foramina for pudendal vessels and nn.

Femoral fascia

Foramina for perineal vessels and nn.

Inferior fascia, Urogenital diaphragm

Gracilis muscle
Ischiocavernosus muscle
Bulbospongiosus muscle
Corpus spongiosum penis
Raphé of scrotum
Dartos layer of scrotum
Bulbourethral gland (Cowper)
Central tendinous point of perineum
Superficial transverse perineal muscle
Deep transverse perineal muscle
Adductor magnus muscle
Ischial tuberosity

Fig. 344: The Superficial Muscles of the Male Perineum

Fig. 345: Diagram of Frontal Section Through Male Pelvis and Perineum

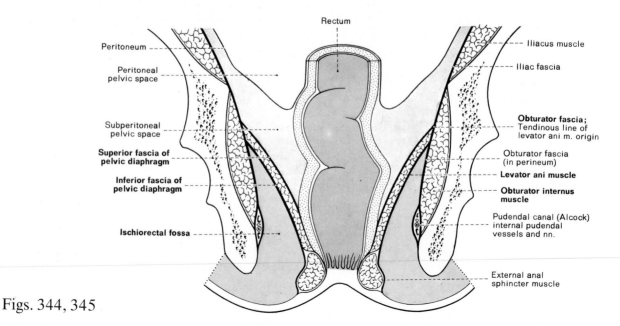

Rectum
Peritoneum
Peritoneal pelvic space
Subperitoneal pelvic space
Superior fascia of pelvic diaphragm
Inferior fascia of pelvic diaphragm
Ischiorectal fossa

Iliacus muscle
Iliac fascia
Obturator fascia; Tendinous line of levator ani m. origin
Obturator fascia (in perineum)
Levator ani muscle
Obturator internus muscle
Pudendal canal (Alcock) internal pudendal vessels and nn.
External anal sphincter muscle

Figs. 344, 345

Posterior

Anococcygeal nn. and aa.

Levator ani muscle

Anococcygeal ligament

Gluteus maximus muscle

Sacrotuberous ligament

Inferior cluneal nerve

Internal pudendal artery

Inferior rectal arteries (hemorrhoidal aa.)

Pudendal nerve

Sacrospinous ligament

Internal pudendal artery and vein

Inferior rectal nerves; Perineal nerves

Pudendal nerve

Superficial verse perineal muscle

Inferior cluneal nerve

Perineal artery

Perineal branch of posterior femoral cutaneous nerve

External anal sphincter muscle

Dorsal nerve of penis

Ischiocavernosus muscle

Artery to bulb of penis

Bulbospongiosus muscle

Perineal artery

Posterior scrotal arteries

Posterior scrotal nerves

Anterior

Fig. 346: Nerves and Blood Vessels of the Male Perineum

NOTE: 1) the skin of the male perineum as well as the fat of the ischiorectal fossae have been removed in order to expose the muscles, vessels and nerves of both the anal and urogenital regions of the perineum.

2) emerging from the pelvis through the lesser sciatic foramen by way of the pudendal canal (Alcock) are the internal pudendal vessels and the pudendal nerve. These structures enter the perineum at the lateral border of the ischiorectal fossa. There is an immediate branching of the inferior rectal (hemorrhoidal) vessels and nerves which course transversely across the ischiorectal fossa to supply the levator ani and external anal sphincter muscles.

3) the internal pudendal structures then continue anteriorly, pierce the urogenital diaphragm, and become the perineal vessels and nerve and the dorsal vessels and nerve of the penis. The muscles of the urogenital triangle are innervated by the perineal nerve, while the dorsal nerve of the penis is the principal sensory nerve of that organ.

Fig. 346   IV

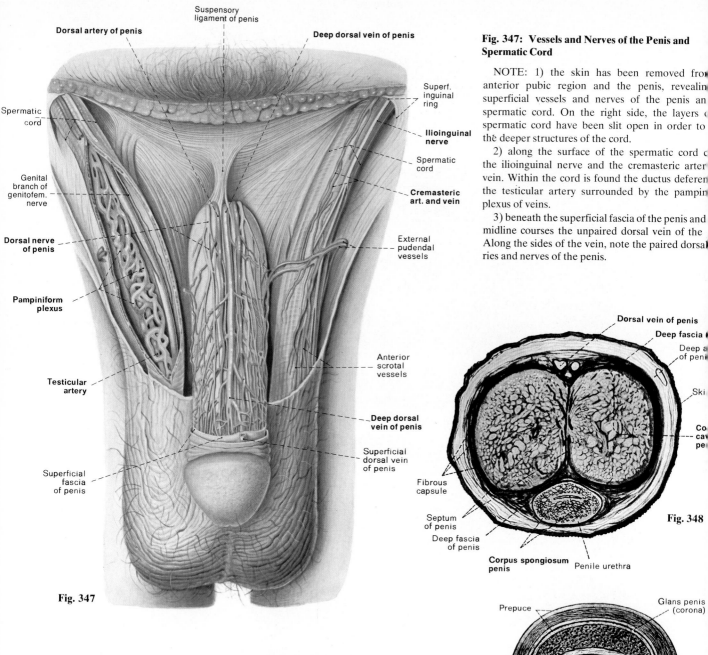

Fig. 347 Vessels and Nerves of the Penis and Spermatic Cord — labels: Dorsal artery of penis, Suspensory ligament of penis, Deep dorsal vein of penis, Spermatic cord, Superf. inguinal ring, Ilioinguinal nerve, Spermatic cord, Cremasteric art. and vein, Genital branch of genitofem. nerve, Dorsal nerve of penis, External pudendal vessels, Pampiniform plexus, Testicular artery, Anterior scrotal vessels, Deep dorsal vein of penis, Superficial dorsal vein of penis, Superficial fascia of penis

Fig. 348 labels: Dorsal vein of penis, Deep fascia, Deep a. of penis, Skin, Corpora cavernosa penis, Fibrous capsule, Septum of penis, Deep fascia of penis, Corpus spongiosum penis, Penile urethra

Fig. 349 labels: Prepuce, Glans penis (corona), Septum penis, Urethra

Fig. 350 labels: Urethra (navicular fossa), Frenulum, Septum of glans penis

Fig. 347: Vessels and Nerves of the Penis and Spermatic Cord

NOTE: 1) the skin has been removed from anterior pubic region and the penis, revealing superficial vessels and nerves of the penis and spermatic cord. On the right side, the layers of spermatic cord have been slit open in order to the deeper structures of the cord.

2) along the surface of the spermatic cord the ilioinguinal nerve and the cremasteric artery vein. Within the cord is found the ductus deferen the testicular artery surrounded by the pampin plexus of veins.

3) beneath the superficial fascia of the penis and midline courses the unpaired dorsal vein of the Along the sides of the vein, note the paired dorsal ries and nerves of the penis.

Cross Sections of Penis

Fig. 348: Section Through Middle of Penis

NOTE that the penis is composed principally of two laterally situated corpora cavernosa penis containing erectile tissue and one corpus spongiosum penis placed ventrally and in the midline containing the penile portion of the urethra. These are surrounded by a closely investing layer of deep fascia. During erection, blood fills the erectile tissue (as is seen in this cross section), causing them to become rigid. This engorgement exerts pressure on the veins and maintains the erection by preventing the blood from draining back into the general circulation.

Fig. 349: Section at Neck of Glans Penis

This section is taken from the proximal part of the glans penis. Note that the corpora cavernosa penis becomes smaller distally, while the corona of the glans penis is formed by the spongy tissue of the corpus spongiosum penis.

Fig. 350: Section Through Glans Penis

The expanded distal extremity of the corpus spongiosum penis is called the glans penis. At its distal end is the opening of the urethra. In the uncircumcised male, the glans penis is covered by a duplication of thin skin, the prepuce, which is attached to the glans penis ventrally by the frenulum.

Figs. 347–350

Apex and body of bladder

Medial umbilical fold
(umbilical artery)

Peritoneum

Inferior epigastric
a. and v.

Median umbilical fold (urachus)

External iliac
artery and vein

Inguinal
ligament

Ductus deferens

Right ureter

Superior
ramus of pubis

Left ureter

Rectovesical pouch

Ampulla of ductus deferens

Seminal vesicle

Seminal vesicle

Duct of seminal
vesicle

Fundus of bladder

Ejaculatory duct

Prostate gland

Inferior ramus of pubis

Crus penis

Membranous urethra

Bulbourethral glands

Deep fascia (Buck's)

Bulb of penis

Corona

Corpora cavernosa penis

Glans penis

Corpus spongiosum penis

Frenulum

Fig. 352

Prepuce

Urethral
orifice

Sulcus for corpus
spongiosum penis

Corona

Glans penis

Fig. 351

Fig. 351: Distal End of Penis

NOTE: 1) this surface view of the distal end of the penis shows the glans penis as it is attached by the frenulum to the duplicated fold of skin, the prepuce, which, more or less, covers the glans penis.

2) the skin of the penis is thin and delicate and is loosely attached to the underlying closely investing deep fascia. This accounts for the freely moveable nature of the skin of the penis over the more deeply located bodies of cavernous tissue.

Fig. 352: The Erectile Bodies of the Penis Attached to the Bladder and Other Organs by the Membranous Urethra

NOTE: 1) the firmly investing deep fascia which surrounds the erectile bodies of the penis has been removed, and the distal portion of the corpus spongiosum penis (which contains the penile urethra) has been displaced from its position between the two corpora cavernosa penis.

2) the posterior surface of the bladder and prostate and the associated seminal vesicles, vasa deferens, and bulbourethral glands are also demonstrated. These structures all communicate with the urethra, the membranous portion of which is in continuity with the penile urethra.

3) the tapered crura of the corpora cavernosa penis diverge laterally at their base to become adherent to the ischial and pubic rami. They are surrounded by the fibers of the ischiocavernosus muscles. The base of the corpus spongiosum penis is also expanded and is called the bulb. It is enclosed by the bulbocavernosus muscle.

Figs. 351, 352   **IV**

Fig. 353: The Inferior Reflection of Peritoneum over the Pelvic Organs

NOTE: 1) the inferior extent of the peritoneum anteriorly when the bladder is empty is to the level of the symphysis pubis, whereas when the bladder is full the peritoneum is elevated as much as 3 or 4 inches superior to the symphysis pubis. Between the rectum and the bladder the peritoneum forms the rectovesical pouch.

2) in the scrotum, the visceral and parietal layers of the tunica vaginalis testis also enclose a cavity lined by peritoneum.

3) that the prostate and bladder may be reached anteriorly by means of a suprapubic approach, and inferiorly by ascending through the perineum, in front of the rectum. By either route, these organs may be achieved without entering the peritoneal cavity.

Median umbilical ligament
Urinary bladder
Retropubic space
Symphysis pubis
Cavity of tunica vaginalis testis

Tunica vaginalis testis { Parietal layer / Visceral layer }

Rectum
Rectovesical pouch
Seminal vesicle and prostate gland
Testis and epididymis

Red = Peritoneum

Fig. 354: The Male Pelvic Organs Viewed from the Left Side ▶

NOTE that the peritoneum has been removed from the left side of the bladder and rectum.

Ventral ramus, S-2 nerve; Spinal br., lat. sacral a., v.
Ventral ramus, S-1 nerve; Spinal br., lat. sacral a., v.
Sacrum
Peritoneum
Lumbar art. and vein; L-5 nerve (ant. ramus)
Piriformis m.
Ext. and int. iliac veins
Gluteus maximus m.
Common iliac a.
Sigmoid mesocolon
Left ureter
Rectum, sacral flexu
Ductus deferens
Rectove pouch
Sigmoid colon; Appendices epiploicae
Sacr cocc joint
Peritoneum over bladder
Urinary bladder
Rectus abdominis m.
Pubis
Puboprostatic lig. (Pubovesical lig.)
Spermatic cord
Ductus deferens
Cremaster m.
Anococcygea
Dartos layer (scrotum)
Levator ani m. (pelvic diaphragm)
Crus penis; Deep artery of penis
Ischiocavernosus m.
Deep transverse perineal m.; Urogenital diaphragm
Seminal vesicle
Urethral sphincter m.
External anal sphincter m.
Prostate gland
Rectum, perineal flexure
Bulbourethral gland and duct
Deep transverse perineal m.
Bulbospongiosus m.

Figs. 353, 354

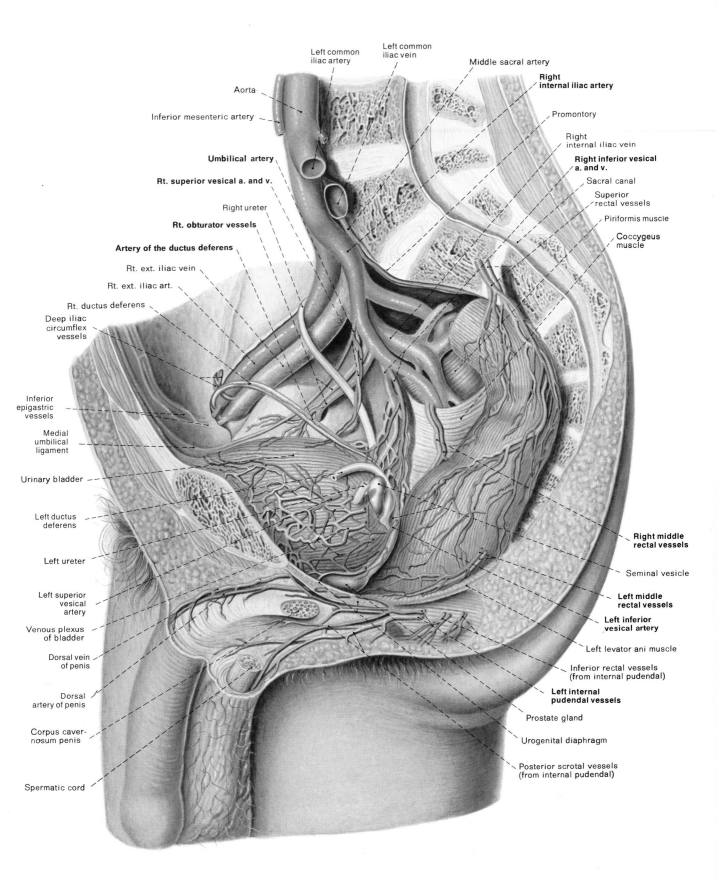

Fig. 355: Blood Vessels of the Male Pelvis, Perineum and External Genitalia

NOTE: 1) the aorta bifurcates into the common iliac arteries which then divide into the external and internal iliac arteries. The external iliac becomes the chief arterial trunk of the lower extremity, while the internal iliac artery supplies the organs of the pelvis and perineum.

2) the branches of the internal iliac artery include visceral and parietal vessels. The *visceral* branches are (a) the umbilical (from which is derived the superior vesical artery), (b) the inferior vesical, (c) the artery of the vas deferens (uterine in the female) and, (d) the middle rectal. The *parietal* branches include (a) the iliolumbar, (b) lateral sacral, (c) superior gluteal, (d) inferior gluteal, (e) obturator, and (f) internal pudendal.

Fig. 355   **IV**

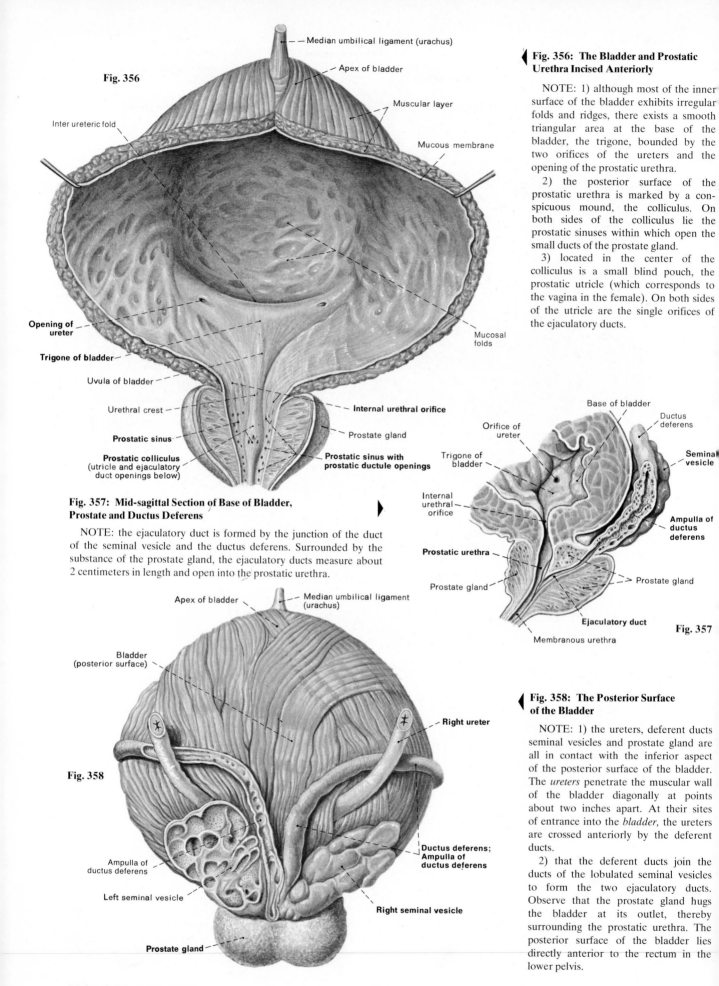

Median umbilical ligament (urachus)

Fig. 356

Apex of bladder

Muscular layer

Inter ureteric fold

Mucous membrane

Opening of ureter

Mucosal folds

Trigone of bladder

Uvula of bladder

Internal urethral orifice

Urethral crest

Prostate gland

Prostatic sinus

Prostatic colliculus
(utricle and ejaculatory duct openings below)

Prostatic sinus with prostatic ductule openings

Fig. 357: Mid-sagittal Section of Base of Bladder, Prostate and Ductus Deferens

NOTE: the ejaculatory duct is formed by the junction of the duct of the seminal vesicle and the ductus deferens. Surrounded by the substance of the prostate gland, the ejaculatory ducts measure about 2 centimeters in length and open into the prostatic urethra.

Base of bladder

Ductus deferens

Orifice of ureter

Seminal vesicle

Trigone of bladder

Internal urethral orifice

Ampulla of ductus deferens

Prostatic urethra

Prostate gland

Prostate gland

Ejaculatory duct

Fig. 357

Membranous urethra

Apex of bladder

Median umbilical ligament (urachus)

Bladder (posterior surface)

Right ureter

Fig. 358

Ductus deferens; Ampulla of ductus deferens

Ampulla of ductus deferens

Left seminal vesicle

Right seminal vesicle

Prostate gland

Fig. 356: The Bladder and Prostatic Urethra Incised Anteriorly

NOTE: 1) although most of the inner surface of the bladder exhibits irregular folds and ridges, there exists a smooth triangular area at the base of the bladder, the trigone, bounded by the two orifices of the ureters and the opening of the prostatic urethra.

2) the posterior surface of the prostatic urethra is marked by a conspicuous mound, the colliculus. On both sides of the colliculus lie the prostatic sinuses within which open the small ducts of the prostate gland.

3) located in the center of the colliculus is a small blind pouch, the prostatic utricle (which corresponds to the vagina in the female). On both sides of the utricle are the single orifices of the ejaculatory ducts.

Fig. 358: The Posterior Surface of the Bladder

NOTE: 1) the ureters, deferent ducts seminal vesicles and prostate gland are all in contact with the inferior aspect of the posterior surface of the bladder. The *ureters* penetrate the muscular wall of the bladder diagonally at points about two inches apart. At their sites of entrance into the *bladder,* the ureters are crossed anteriorly by the deferent ducts.

2) that the deferent ducts join the ducts of the lobulated seminal vesicles to form the two ejaculatory ducts. Observe that the prostate gland hugs the bladder at its outlet, thereby surrounding the prostatic urethra. The posterior surface of the bladder lies directly anterior to the rectum in the lower pelvis.

Figs. 356, 357, 358

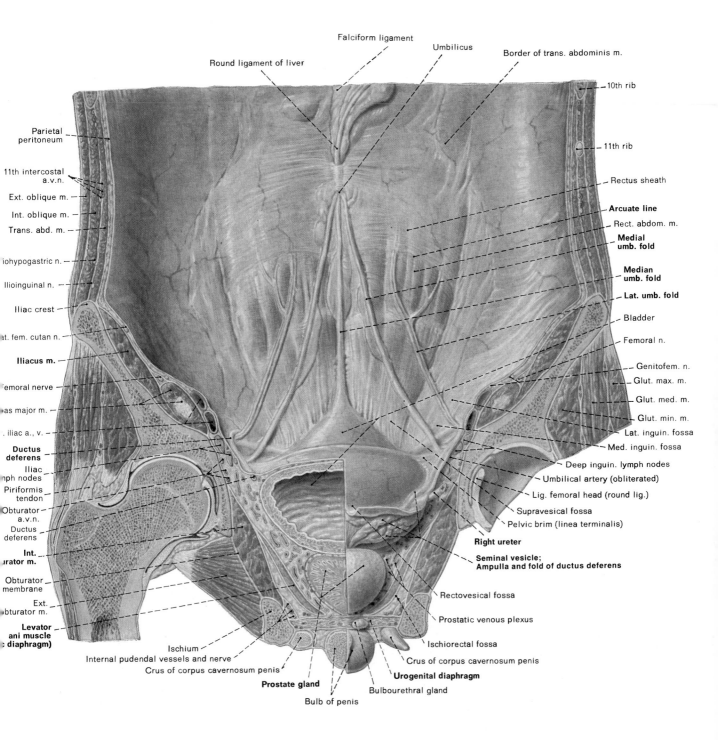

Fig. 359: The Posterior Aspect of the Ventral Abdominal Wall and the Male Pelvic Organs

Labels on image:

Falciform ligament
Umbilicus
Border of trans. abdominis m.
Round ligament of liver
10th rib
Parietal peritoneum
11th rib
11th intercostal a.v.n.
Rectus sheath
Ext. oblique m.
Arcuate line
Int. oblique m.
Rect. abdom. m.
Trans. abd. m.
Medial umb. fold
iohypogastric n.
Median umb. fold
Ilioinguinal n.
Lat. umb. fold
Iliac crest
Bladder
at. fem. cutan n.
Femoral n.
Iliacus m.
Genitofem. n.
emoral nerve
Glut. max. m.
as major m.
Glut. med. m.
. iliac a., v.
Glut. min. m.
Ductus deferens
Lat. inguin. fossa
Iliac nph nodes
Med. inguin. fossa
Piriformis tendon
Deep inguin. lymph nodes
Obturator a.v.n.
Umbilical artery (obliterated)
Ductus deferens
Lig. femoral head (round lig.)
Int. urator m.
Supravesical fossa
Obturator membrane
Pelvic brim (linea terminalis)
Ext. bturator m.
Right ureter
Levator ani muscle (: diaphragm)
Seminal vesicle; Ampulla and fold of ductus deferens
Ischium
Rectovesical fossa
Internal pudendal vessels and nerve
Prostatic venous plexus
Crus of corpus cavernosum penis
Ischiorectal fossa
Prostate gland
Crus of corpus cavernosum penis
Bulb of penis
Urogenital diaphragm
Bulbourethral gland

NOTE: 1) the inner aspect of the anterior abdominal wall shows the courses of the umbilical ligaments and the round ligament of the liver, as well as the smooth contours of the rectus abdominis muscle and the arcuate line, which marks the inferior limit of the posterior layer of the rectus sheath.

2) the frontal section through the bones of the pelvis and the femur. Observe the expanded wings (alae) of each ilium which extend laterally to reach the skin as the iliac crest. The wings of the ilia bound the greater (or false) pelvis. On their internal or pelvic surface lie the iliacus and psoas muscles along with the iliac vessels and the various nerves of the lumbar plexus. Their external surface is directed toward the gluteal region.

3) that the lesser (or true) pelvis lies below the pelvic brim. It is restricted by bone and bounds more snugly the pelvic organs (bladder, prostate, seminal vesicle, etc.). Inferiorly the pelvic organs are separated from the perineum by the pelvic diaphragm (levator ani muscles) and, to a lesser extent, the urogenital diaphragm (deep transverse perineal muscles).

4) the reflection of peritoneum as it invests the inner surface of the anterior abdominal wall, curves over the superior surface of the bladder and dips somewhat posterior to the bladder (rectovesical pouch) to come into contact with the seminal vesicles and deferent ducts.

5) the obturator internus muscle which covers much of the inner surface of the lateral wall of the true pelvis. Extending into the perineum, this muscle also forms the lateral boundary of the ischiorectal fossa.

Fig. 359   **IV**

Mucosal folds
of bladder

Urinary
bladder

Orifice of
ureter

Trigone

Uvula (of bladder)

**Internal
urethral orifice**

* **I**

Urethral crest

Colliculus;
Prostatic utricle

Orifices of
ejaculatory ducts

Prostatic ducts
which open into the
prostatic sinus

* **II**

Bulbourethral gland and duct

Urethral crest

Bulb of penis

— Crus of penis

**Opening
of bulbourethral
gland**

* Parts of Urethra
  I = Prostatic Part
  II = Membranous Part
  III = Penile Part

Tunica
albuginea
(of corpus
cavernosum penis)

Cavernous spaces
(of corpus
spongiosum penis)

Trabeculae
(of corpus
cavernosum penis)

Deep
artery of penis

Cavernous
spaces
(filled with
spongy tissue)

Helicine
arteries

* **III**

Urethral lacunae

Fig. 361

Corona
(of glans penis)

Valve of
navicular
fossa

Glans penis

Navicular
fossa

Prepuce

External urethral orifice

Fig. 360: Radiograph of Bladder, Seminal Vesicles, Deferent Ducts and Ejaculatory Ducts

NOTE: 1) this figure is a positive print of an X-ray. The bladder has been filled with air and appears light, whereas the images of the seminal vesicles, deferent ducts and ejaculatory ducts stand out as dark.

2) that the convoluted seminal vesicles, which secrete the seminal fluid, consist of coiled tubes 4−5 mm in diameter and 2 to 3 inches in length.

3) the shadows of the deferent ducts. These cross the bladder surface toward the midline to join the seminal vesicles forming the ejaculatory ducts.

Figs. 360, 361

Fig. 361: The Male Urethra and its Associated Orifices

NOTE: 1) the male urethra is a canal that extends from its internal urethral orifice at the bladder to its external urethral orifice at the end of the glans penis. Since the male urethra transverses the prostate gland, the urogenital diaphragm (membrane) and the penis, it is divided into three parts: prostatic, membranous and penile.

2) urine passes through the urethra from the bladder. The urethra also transports the seminal fluid which is composed of a mixture of sperm from the testis and the secretions of the seminal vesicles and prostate. Just prior to ejaculation, the urethra is lubricated by a viscous fluid secreted by the bulbourethral glands (of Cowper). These glands are located in the urogenital diaphragm, but their ducts open about one inch or more distally into the penile urethra.

3) the total urethra measures between 7 and 8 inches in length. The prostatic urethra is about 1½ inches long, the membranous urethra about ½ inch and the penile urethra 5 to 6 inches. On its posterior wall, the *prostatic urethra* is marked by a ridge, the urethral crest and a mound, the colliculus. It receives the secretions of the ejaculatory ducts along with those of the prostate. Enlargement of the prostate, often occurring in older men, tends to constrict the urethra at this site and frequently results in difficulty in urination.

4) the *membranous urethra* is short and narrow. In its course through the urogenital diaphragm, it is completely surrounded by the circular fibers of the urethral sphincter muscle (see Figure 366). Since this important sphincter is under voluntary control, its relaxation initiates urination while its tonic contraction constricts the urethra and maintains urinary continence.

5) the penile (or spongy) portion of the urethra at once is surrounded by the bulb of the penis and, thus, the bulbospongiosus muscle. It traverses the penile shaft embedded within the corpus spongiosum penis. In its course, it receives the ducts of the bulbourethral glands. The internal surface of its distal half is marked by a number of small recesses, the urethral lacunae. The distal portion of the penile urethra is somewhat narrowed and its external urethral orifice simply a vertical slit.

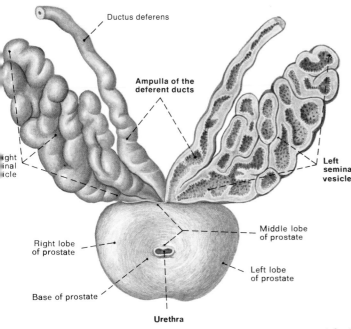

Ductus deferens

Ampulla of the
deferent ducts

Right
[seminal]
[ves]icle

Left
seminal
vesicle

Right lobe
of prostate

Middle lobe
of prostate

Left lobe
of prostate

Base of prostate

Urethra

Fig. 362

Fig. 362: The Prostate Gland, Seminal Vesicles and Ampullae of the Deferent Ducts (Superior View)

NOTE: the left seminal vesicle and ductus deferens were cut longitudinally, while the urethra was cut transversely just distal to the bladder. The prostate gland is conical in shape and normally measures just over 1½ inches across, 1 inch in thickness and slightly longer than 1 inch vertically. In the young adult male it weighs about 25 grams and is formed by two lateral lobes surrounding a middle lobe.

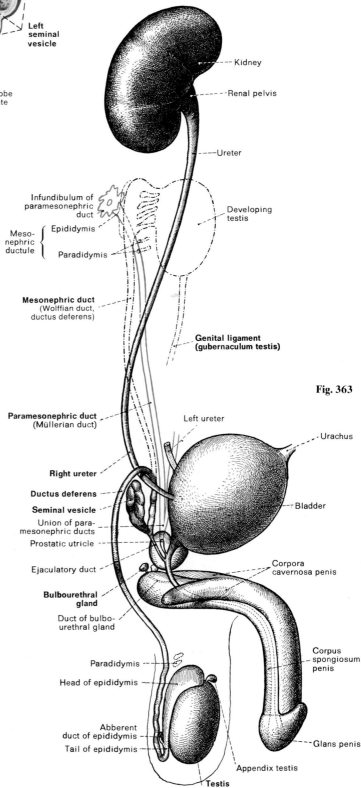

Kidney

Renal pelvis

Ureter

Developing
testis

Infundibulum of
paramesonephric
duct

Meso-
nephric
ductule

Epididymis

Paradidymis

Mesonephric duct
(Wolffian duct,
ductus deferens)

**Genital ligament
(gubernaculum testis)**

Fig. 363

Paramesonephric duct
(Müllerian duct)

Left ureter

Urachus

Right ureter

Ductus deferens

Seminal vesicle

Union of para-
mesonephric ducts

Prostatic utricle

Bladder

Corpora
cavernosa penis

Ejaculatory duct

**Bulbourethral
gland**

Duct of bulbo-
urethral gland

Corpus
spongiosum
penis

Paradidymis

Head of epididymis

Abberent
duct of epididymis

Tail of epididymis

Glans penis

Appendix testis

Testis

Fig. 363: Diagram of the Male Genitourinary System

NOTE: 1) this figure shows:

a) the organs of the adult male genitourinary system;

b) the structures of the genital system prior to the descent of the testis (interrupted black lines);

c) those structures which partially or entirely became atrophic and disappeared during development (red lines).

2) the urinary system includes the *kidneys* which produce urine by filtration of the blood, the *ureters* which convey the urine to the *bladder,* where it is stored, and the *urethra* through which urine is discharged.

3) the adult male genital system includes the *testis* where sperm are generated, the *epididymis* and *ductus deferens* which transport the sperm to the *ejaculatory duct* where the *seminal vesicle* joins the genital system. The *prostate* and *bulbourethral glands* along with the ejaculatory ducts join the *urethra,* which then courses through the male copulatory organ, the *penis.*

4) embryologically, structures capable of developing into both male and female genital systems exist in all individuals. In the male, the Wolffian or mesonephric duct (which becomes the epididymis, vas deferens ejaculatory duct and seminal vesicle) and the penis, develop, while the paramesonephric or Müllerian duct becomes vestigial.

5) the testes are developed on the posterior abdominal wall and are attached by a fibrous genital ligament called the gubernaculum testis to the abdominal wall. As development continues, each testis gradually "migrates" from its site of formation, so that by the 5th month it comes to lie adjacent to the abdominal inguinal ring. The gubernaculum testis is still attached to anterior abdominal wall tissue, which by this time has evaginated as the developing scrotum. The testes then commence their descent through the inguinal canal, so that by the 8th month they usually lie in the scrotum. During this "migration", the testes pass behind the peritoneum but are attached to it by its peritoneal reflection, the processus vaginalis testis. This becomes the *tunica vaginalis testis.*

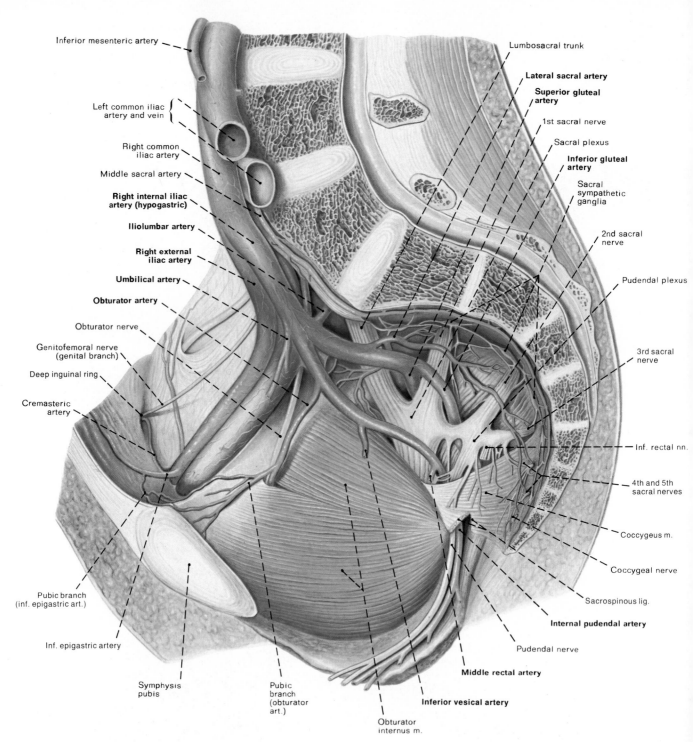

Inferior mesenteric artery

Left common iliac
artery and vein

Right common
iliac artery

Middle sacral artery

**Right internal iliac
artery (hypogastric)**

Iliolumbar artery

**Right external
iliac artery**

Umbilical artery

Obturator artery

Obturator nerve

Genitofemoral nerve
(genital branch)

Deep inguinal ring

Cremasteric
artery

Pubic branch
(inf. epigastric art.)

Inf. epigastric artery

Symphysis
pubis

Pubic
branch
(obturator
art.)

Obturator
internus m.

Inferior vesical artery

Middle rectal artery

Pudendal nerve

Internal pudendal artery

Sacrospinous lig.

Coccygeal nerve

Coccygeus m.

4th and 5th
sacral nerves

Inf. rectal nn.

3rd sacral
nerve

Pudendal plexus

2nd sacral
nerve

Sacral
sympathetic
ganglia

**Inferior gluteal
artery**

Sacral plexus

1st sacral nerve

**Superior gluteal
artery**

Lateral sacral artery

Lumbosacral trunk

Fig. 364: Blood Vessels and Nerves of the Pelvic Wall

NOTE: 1) this is a mid-sagittal view of the right pelvic wall viewed from the left side. The pelvic viscera have been removed and the parietal blood vessels and nerves demonstrated.

2) the principal arteries of the pelvic wall are derived from the internal iliac artery. Although the branches of this vessel are quite variable, in at least 50% of cadavers it courses about 1½ inches toward the greater sciatic foramen before branching into a posterior division of 4 vessels and an anterior division of 6 vessels.

3) the four posterior division vessels include a) the *iliolumbar* which courses superiorly toward the iliac fossa, b) the *lateral sacral* which courses inferiorly, anastomoses with the middle sacral artery and supplies branches to the upper sacral foramina, c) the *superior gluteal* which is the largest of the branches of the internal iliac and which leaves the pelvis above the border of the piriformis muscle, and d) the *inferior gluteal* which leaves the pelvis below the piriformis muscle.

4) the anterior division of the internal iliac artery gives rise to four visceral arteries (umbilical, inferior vesical, middle rectal and uterine or deferential; see in Fig. 355). These are simply indicated by cut stumps in the figure. The two parietal vessels of this anterior division are the *obturator* artery which courses through the obturator canal to the medial thigh, and the long *internal pudendal* artery which leaves the pelvis through the greater sciatic foramen, crosses the ischial spine to reenter the pelvis by way of the lesser sciatic foramen. It then courses toward the perineum by way of the pudendal canal to supply the anal and urogenital triangles.

Fig. 364

Fig. 365: The Muscular Floor of the Pelvis: Pelvic Diaphragm

NOTE: 1) with the pelvic organs removed, this superior view of the floor of the pelvis emphasizes the muscular nature of the pelvic outlet. The *pelvic diaphragm* consists of the levator ani and coccygeus muscles along with two fascial layers which cover the pelvic (supra-anal fascia) and perineal (infraanal fascia) surfaces of these muscles.

2) the muscles and fascial layers composing the pelvic diaphragm stretch across the pelvic floor in a concave sling-like manner, thereby forming a separation between the structures of the pelvis and those of the perineum below.

3) the more caudal part of this "sling" is formed by the two coccygeus muscles. Since these muscles stretch from the ischial spines to the sacrum and coccyx, they are sometimes referred to as the ischiococcygeus muscles. The mid and anterior portions of the "sling" are formed by the iliococcygeus and pubococcygeus muscles. These latter combine to form the levator ani muscle. The levator ani arises from the tendinous arc along the pelvic surface of the obturator internus and inserts into the anococcygeal raphé, the central point of the perineum, the external spincter and the lower segments of the coccyx.

4) in the male, the pelvic diaphragm is perforated by the anal canal and urethra.

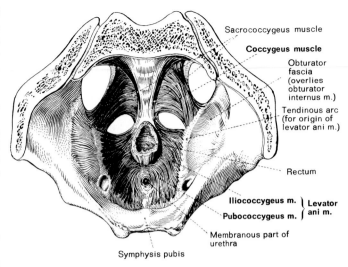

Sacrococcygeus muscle

Coccygeus muscle

Obturator fascia (overlies obturator internus m.)

Tendinous arc (for origin of levator ani m.)

Rectum

Iliococcygeus m. } **Levator ani m.**
Pubococcygeus m. }

Membranous part of urethra

Symphysis pubis

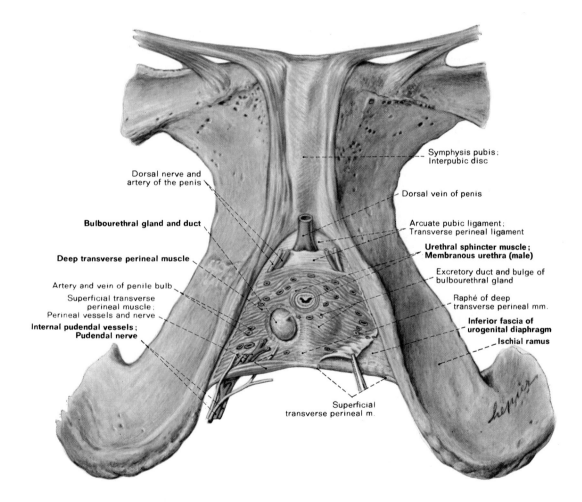

Dorsal nerve and artery of the penis

Bulbourethral gland and duct

Deep transverse perineal muscle

Artery and vein of penile bulb
Superficial transverse perineal muscle;
Perineal vessels and nerve
Internal pudendal vessels; Pudendal nerve

Symphysis pubis; Interpubic disc

Dorsal vein of penis

Arcuate pubic ligament; Transverse perineal ligament

Urethral sphincter muscle; Membranous urethra (male)

Excretory duct and bulge of bulbourethral gland

Raphé of deep transverse perineal mm.

Inferior fascia of urogenital diaphragm

Ischial ramus

Superficial transverse perineal m.

Fig. 366: The Urogenital Diaphragm; Deep Transverse Perineal Muscle (Male)

NOTE: 1) the deep transverse perineal muscle, which stretches between the rami of the ischium, is covered by fascia on both its internal (pelvic or superior) surface and its external (perineal or inferior) surface. As such, this muscle and these two fascial sheaths constitute the urogenital diaphragm.

2) the region between the superior and inferior fascial planes is frequently referred to as the deep perineal compartment (pouch, cleft or space). In the male it contains a) the deep transverse perineal muscle, b) the membranous sphincter of the urethra, c) the bulbourethral glands and ducts, d) the membranous urethra and e) the various branches of the internal pudendal vessels and nerves.

3) the urogenital diaphragm assists somewhat in strengthening the anterior portion of the levator ani muscle where, in the midline at the so-called genital hiatus, it is penetrated by the urethra in the male and the urethra and vagina in the female.

Figs. 365, 366   **IV**

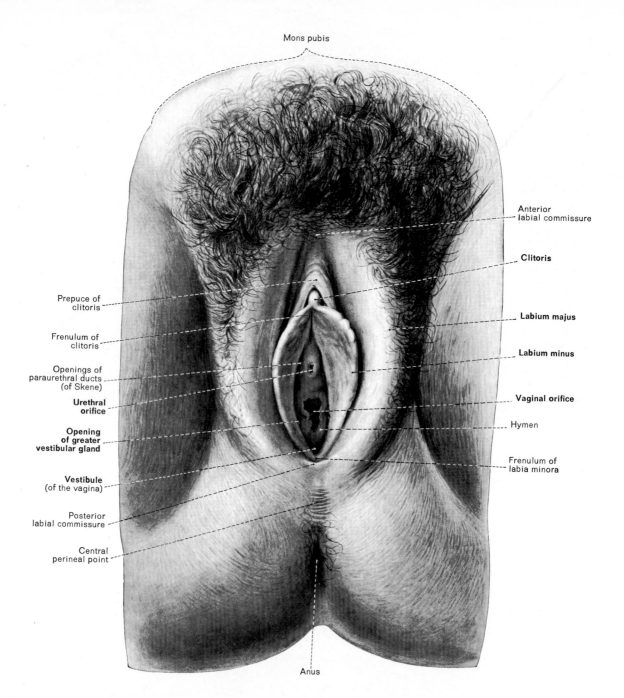

Labels on figure:

Mons pubis

Anterior labial commissure

Clitoris

Prepuce of clitoris

Frenulum of clitoris

Openings of paraurethral ducts (of Skene)

Urethral orifice

Opening of greater vestibular gland

Vestibule (of the vagina)

Posterior labial commissure

Central perineal point

Labium majus

Labium minus

Vaginal orifice

Hymen

Frenulum of labia minora

Anus

Fig. 367: The External Genitalia of an 18 Years Old Virgin

NOTE: 1) the female external genitalia include a) the labia majora, b) the labia minora, c) the clitoris and d) the vestibule of the vagina. The mons pubis, a rounded mound of adipose tissue anterior to the symphysis pubis and covered with hair in the adult, might also be considered an external genital structure. The orifices of the female perineum include the urethral orifice, the vaginal orifice, the two openings of the ducts of the greater vestibular glands, the orifices of the small paraurethral ducts (of Skene) and the anus.

2) the labia majora are two elongated folds of skin which form natural extensions from the mons pubis toward the anus. Although there is some variation in size and thickness dependent on age and obesity, the labia majora are in contact laterally with the thighs, unite both anteriorly and posteriorly to form integumentary commissures and represent the female homologous structures to the male scrotum. The anterior end of each labium majus receives the fibrous round ligament of the uterus as it leaves the superficial inguinal ring.

3) the labia minora are two thin folds of skin situated between the labia majora. Anteriorly, the labia minora commence at the glans clitoris, although small extensions of the labia pass over the dorsum of the clitoris to unite and form the prepuce. Posteriorly, the labia minora meet at the midline to form the frenulum of the labia.

4) the clitoris, homologous to the male penis, is an erectile organ and measures one inch or less in length. It is composed of two corpora cavernosa which are bound by dense connective tissue and which are attached by crura to the pubic rami; the crura are covered by small ischiocavernosus muscles. The clitoris is maintained by a suspensory ligament and capped by the glans.

5) the vestibule (of the vagina) is the region between the two labia minora. Into it open the urethra ventrally, the ducts of the greater vestibular glands bilaterally and the vagina. The vaginal orifice is partially closed in the virgin by a thin mucous membrane, the hymen, which separates the vestibule from the vagina proper. Generally, the hymen is ruptured at first copulation, however since its form and extent are quite variable, the establishment of virginity in this manner cannot be absolutely ascertained.

Fig. 367

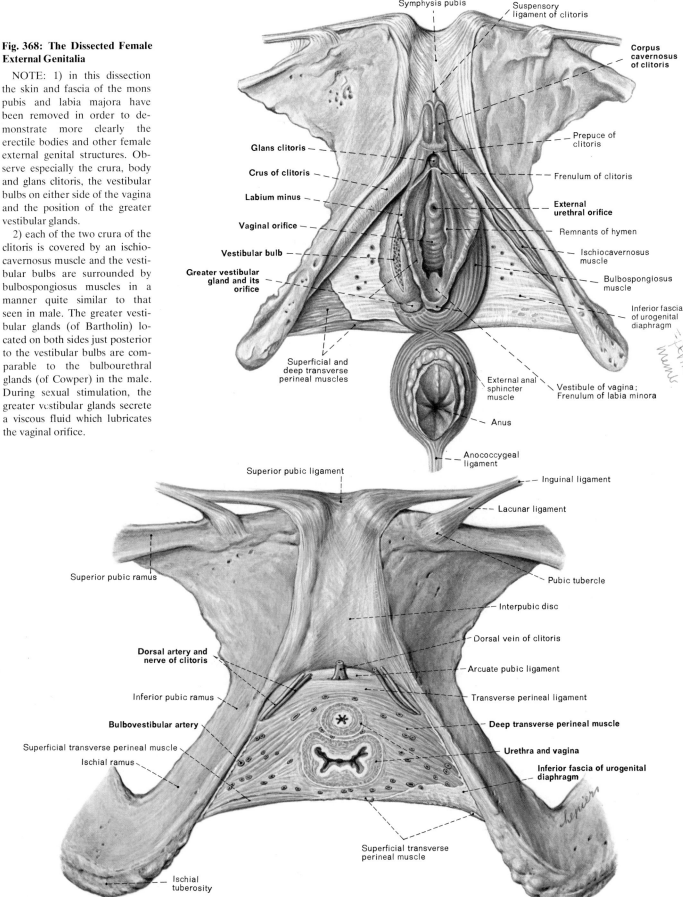

Fig. 368: The Dissected Female External Genitalia

NOTE: 1) in this dissection the skin and fascia of the mons pubis and labia majora have been removed in order to demonstrate more clearly the erectile bodies and other female external genital structures. Observe especially the crura, body and glans clitoris, the vestibular bulbs on either side of the vagina and the position of the greater vestibular glands.

2) each of the two crura of the clitoris is covered by an ischiocavernosus muscle and the vestibular bulbs are surrounded by bulbospongiosus muscles in a manner quite similar to that seen in male. The greater vestibular glands (of Bartholin) located on both sides just posterior to the vestibular bulbs are comparable to the bulbourethral glands (of Cowper) in the male. During sexual stimulation, the greater vestibular glands secrete a viscous fluid which lubricates the vaginal orifice.

Symphysis pubis

Suspensory ligament of clitoris

Corpus cavernosus of clitoris

Glans clitoris

Crus of clitoris

Labium minus

Vaginal orifice

Vestibular bulb

Greater vestibular gland and its orifice

Prepuce of clitoris

Frenulum of clitoris

External urethral orifice

Remnants of hymen

Ischiocavernosus muscle

Bulbospongiosus muscle

Inferior fascia of urogenital diaphragm

Superficial and deep transverse perineal muscles

External anal sphincter muscle

Vestibule of vagina; Frenulum of labia minora

Anus

Anococcygeal ligament

Superior pubic ligament

Inguinal ligament

Lacunar ligament

Superior pubic ramus

Pubic tubercle

Interpubic disc

Dorsal vein of clitoris

Dorsal artery and nerve of clitoris

Arcuate pubic ligament

Inferior pubic ramus

Transverse perineal ligament

Bulbovestibular artery

Deep transverse perineal muscle

Superficial transverse perineal muscle

Urethra and vagina

Ischial ramus

Inferior fascia of urogenital diaphragm

Superficial transverse perineal muscle

Ischial tuberosity

Fig. 369: The Urogenital Diaphragm in the Female

NOTE that in the female both the urethra and the vagina pass through the urogenital diaphragm. As in the male, the female urogenital diaphragm consists of the deep transverse perineal muscles and a layer of deep fascia on each of their superior and inferior surfaces. Observe the circular sphincter surrounding the membranous urethra.

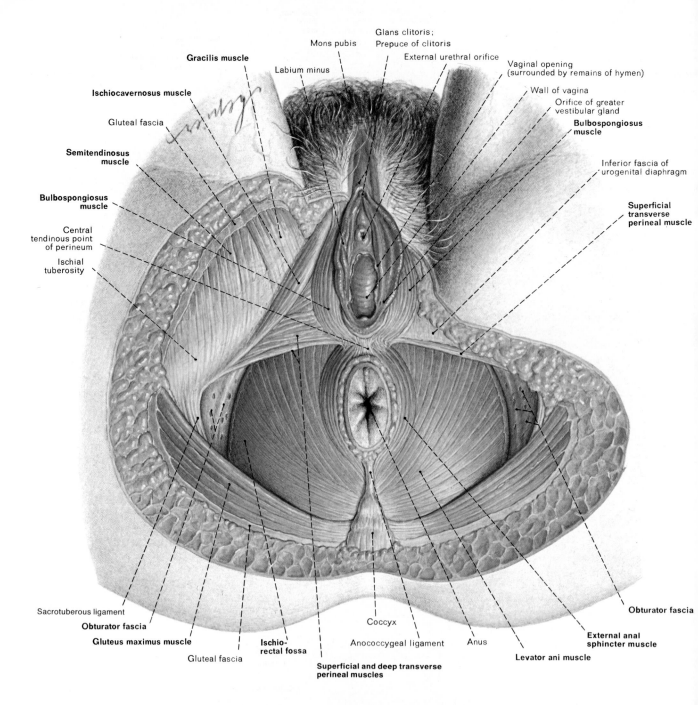

Gracilis muscle

Ischiocavernosus muscle

Gluteal fascia

Semitendinosus muscle

Bulbospongiosus muscle

Central tendinous point of perineum

Ischial tuberosity

Mons pubis

Labium minus

Glans clitoris; Prepuce of clitoris

External urethral orifice

Vaginal opening (surrounded by remains of hymen)

Wall of vagina

Orifice of greater vestibular gland

Bulbospongiosus muscle

Inferior fascia of urogenital diaphragm

Superficial transverse perineal muscle

Sacrotuberous ligament

Obturator fascia

Gluteus maximus muscle

Gluteal fascia

Ischio-rectal fossa

Superficial and deep transverse perineal muscles

Coccyx

Anococcygeal ligament

Anus

Levator ani muscle

External anal sphincter muscle

Obturator fascia

Fig. 370: Superficial Muscles of the Female Perineum

NOTE: 1) the perineum is a diamond-shaped region which is located inferior to the pelvis and separated from it by the muscular pelvic diaphragm. Four points limit the perineum: the symphysis pubis anteriorly; the tip of the coccyx posteriorly; and the two ischial tuberosities laterally. A line drawn transversely across the perineum between the two ischial tuberosities, passing anterior to the anus through the central point of the perineum, divides the diamond-shaped region into an anterior urogenital region and a posterior anal region.

2) the urogenital region contains the external genital organs and the associated muscles and glands. A description of this region frequently refers to a superficial and deep perineal compartment (space, pouch). Simply stated, the superficial perineal compartment lies superficial to the inferior layer of fascia of the urogenital diaphragm and contains the ischiocavernosus, bulbocavernosus and superficial transverse perineal muscle, plus a number of other structures related to the external genitalia. It is traversed by the perineal vessels and nerves and is limited superficially by a layer of deep fascia, the external perineal fascia which stretches just deep to Colles' fascia. The deep perineal compartment is that space enclosed between the superior and inferior layers of fascia of the urogenital diaphragm. Thus, it contains the deep transverse perineal und urethral sphincter muscles (plus the bulbourethral glands in the male) and is traversed by the urethra and vagina in the female and the urethra in the male.

3) the anal region is situated posterior to the urogenital region. The anus, surrounded by the external anal sphincter muscle is located about 1½ inches anterior to the tip of the coccyx. A large portion of the anal region of the perineum is occupied on each side by the fat-filled ischiorectal fossae. Each fossa is wedge-shaped with the base of the wedge directed inferiorly toward the skin. The medial wall of the ischiorectal fossa is formed by the levator ani muscle, the lateral wall being the fascia over the obturator internus muscle. Recesses of each ischiorectal fossa extend anteriorly, adjacent (superior) to the urogenital diaphragm.

Fig. 370

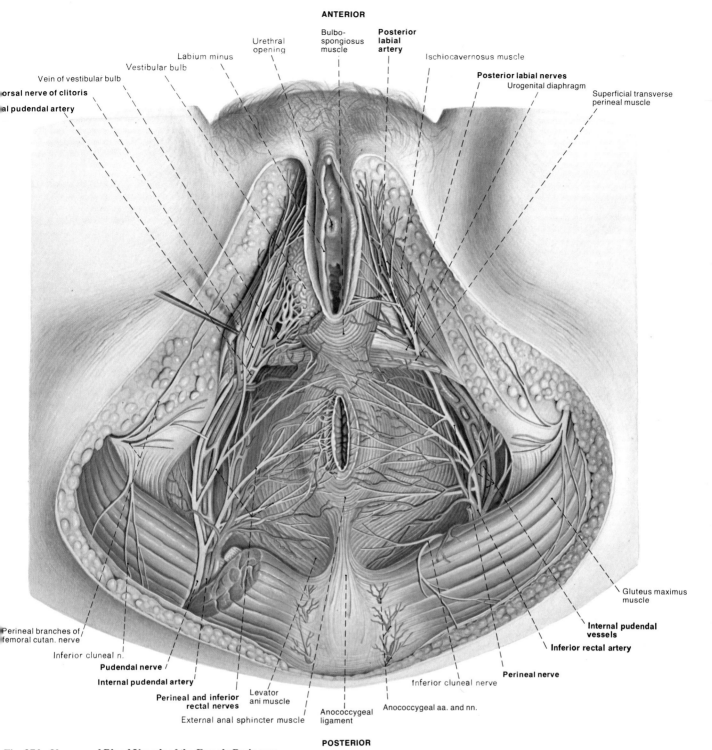

ANTERIOR

Urethral opening
Labium minus
Vestibular bulb
Bulbo-spongiosus muscle
Posterior labial artery
Ischiocavernosus muscle
Posterior labial nerves
Urogenital diaphragm
Superficial transverse perineal muscle

Vein of vestibular bulb
orsal nerve of clitoris
al pudendal artery

Gluteus maximus muscle

Perineal branches of femoral cutan. nerve
Inferior cluneal n.
Pudendal nerve
Internal pudendal artery
Perineal and inferior rectal nerves
Levator ani muscle
External anal sphincter muscle
Anococcygeal ligament
Anococcygeal aa. and nn.
Inferior cluneal nerve
Perineal nerve
Inferior rectal artery
Internal pudendal vessels

POSTERIOR

Fig. 371: Nerves and Blood Vessels of the Female Perineum

NOTE: 1) in this dissection the skin and superficial fascia have been removed from both the urogenital and anal regions of the female perineum. The ischiorectal fossae have been cleared of fat as well.

2) the principal nerve from which most of the branches which innervate the perineum are derived is the *pudendal nerve*. It originates in the sacral cord and contains fibers of the S_2, S_3 and S_4 segments. In its course within the pelvis, it is joined by the *internal pudendal artery* and *vein* at the lower border of the piriformis muscle at the greater sciatic foramen. Together the vessels and nerve leave the pelvis through the greater sciatic foramen, cross the ischial spine (sacrospinous ligament) to enter the pelvis once again through the lesser sciatic foramen.

3) the pudendal structures achieve the perineum from the pelvis by way of the pudendal canal (of Alcock) which courses beneath the fascia of the obturator internus muscle. Within the perineum, the pudendal structures are first seen at the lateral wall of the ischiorectal fossa. At this point the *inferior rectal vessels* and nerves branch and cross the ischiorectal fossa toward the midline, thereby supplying the levator ani and external anal sphincter muscles along with the other structures in the anal region.

4) continuing anteriorly the pudendal nerve and internal pudendal vessels approach the urogenital diaphragm to become the perineal vessels and nerve. Upon entering the urogenital region, superficial and deep branches supply the structures of the superficial and deep perineal compartments.

5) the superficial perineal branches in the female supply the labia majora and the external genital structures, while the deep branches supply the muscles of the urogenital region, the vestibular bulb and the clitoris.

Fig. 371   **IV**

Fig. 372: Diagram of the Female Genitourinary System

NOTE: 1) this figure shows:

a) all the organs of the adult female genitourinary system;

b) the structures and relevant positions of the female genital organs (gonad and ovarian ligament and uterine tube) prior to their descent into the pelvis (interrupted black lines); and

c) the structures which became atrophic during development (red lines).

2) as in the male, the urinary system of the female includes the kidney which produces urine from the blood, the ureter which conveys the urine to the bladder where it is stored. Leading from the bladder is the urethra through which urine passes to the external urethral orifice during micturition.

3) the adult female genital system includes the *ovary, uterine tube, uterus* and *vagina,* plus the associated glands and external genital organs.

4) at one time during development, structures capable of developing into both male and female genital systems existed. In the female, the Müllerian or paramesonephric duct forms the uterine tube, the uterus and vagina, while the Wolffian or mesonephric duct becomes vestigial. Also the developing gonads become ovaries, while their attachments become the ovarian ligaments.

5) the ovaries produce ova which are discharged periodically between adolescence and the menopause. The ova are captured by the uterine tube where fertilization may occur. If this happens, the fertilized ovum is transported to the uterus and about a week after fertilization, implantation occurs in the wall of the uterus. The endometrium nourishes the embryo in this early period of development.

Labels (Fig. 372)

Kidney
Renal pelvis
Ureter
Cranial mesonephric ductules
Developing ovary
Caudal mesonephric ductules
Para-mesonephric duct (Müllerian) (developing uterine tube)
Mesonephric duct (Wolffian)
Genital ligament (developing ovarian ligament)
Uterine tube
Uterus
Bladder
Urachus
Infundibulum of uterine tube
Epoophoron
Appendix vesiculosa
Paraoophoron
Ovary
Ovarian ligament
Round ligament of uterus
Mesonephric duct (Wolffian)
Ureter
Vagina
Urethra
Glans clitoris
Crus of clitoris
External urethral orifice
Vestibular bulb
Vaginal orifice
Greater vestibular glands

Fig. 373: Diagram of Peritoneal Reflections Over Female Pelvic Organs (Mid-Sagittal Section)

Peritoneum in red

NOTE: 1) that the parietal peritoneum is reflected over the free abdominal surfaces of the pelvic organs. Observe that as the uterus and vagina are interposed between the bladder and rectum, that peritoneal pouches are formed between the bladder and the uterus (vesicouterine) and between the rectum and the uterus (rectouterine pouch of Douglas).

2) the vesicouterine pouch is relatively shallow. The forward tilt or inclination of the uterus (anteversion) toward the superior surface of the bladder reduces the potential size of the vesicouterine pouch. This fossa does not extend as far inferiorly as the vagina, whereas the deeper rectouterine pouch dips to the posterior surface of the fornix of the vagina. This important anatomical relationship stresses the fact that the fornix of the vagina is separated from the peritoneal cavity only by the thin vaginal wall and the peritoneum.

Labels (Fig. 373)

Uterus
Rectum
Vesicouterine pouch
Rectouterine pouch (of Douglas)
Bladder
Retropubic space
Symphysis pubis
Fornix of vagina

Figs. 372, 373

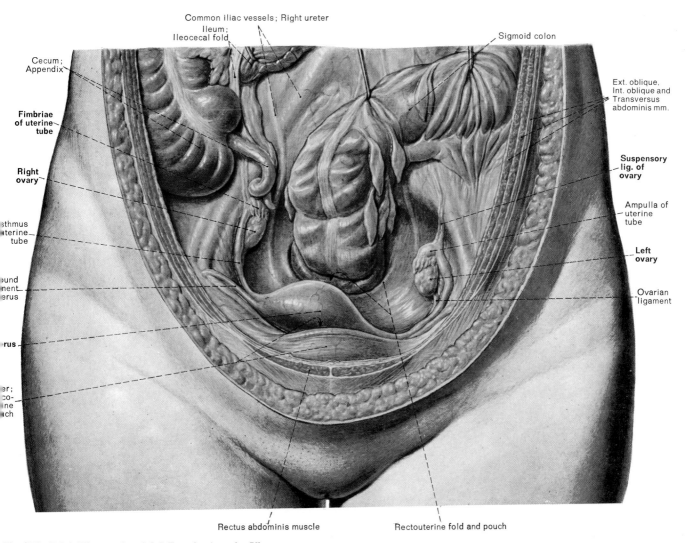

Common iliac vessels; Right ureter
Ileum;
Ileocecal fold
Sigmoid colon
Cecum;
Appendix
Ext. oblique,
Int. oblique and
Transversus
abdominis mm.
Fimbriae
of uterine
tube
Suspensory
lig. of
ovary
Right
ovary
Ampulla of
uterine
tube
isthmus
uterine
tube
Left
ovary
und
ment
erus
Ovarian
ligament
rus

er;
co-
ne
ch

Rectus abdominis muscle   Rectouterine fold and pouch

Fig. 374: Pelvic Viscera of an Adult Female: Anterior View

NOTE: 1) that the ovaries are situated on the posterolateral aspect of the true pelvis on each side. Having descended from the posterior abdominal wall to their location just below the pelvic brim, the ovaries are held in position by ligamentous attachments. The suspensory ligament transmits the ovarian vessels and nerves.

2) the position of the uterus interposed between the bladder and rectum. Observe that the uterus is frequently located somewhat to one or the other side of the midline.

3) the fimbriae of the uterine tubes as they extend from the ampullae of the tubes to encircle the upper medial surfaces of the ovaries. These tubes vary from 3 to 6 inches in length and, as extensions of the uterus, they convey the ova to the uterus. It is within the uterine tube that fertilization of the ovum usually occurs.

Fig. 375: Utero-Salpingogram

By means of a cannula (K) placed in the vagina, radiopaque material has been injected into the uterus and uterine tubes (salpinx). Observe the narrow lumen of the isthmus of the uterine tubes and note how the tubes enlarge at the ampullae. On the specimen's left side (reader's right side), even the fimbriated end of the tube is discernible, while on the specimen's right side (reader's left side) a small portion of the radiopaque material has been forced into the pelvis through the opening of the uterine tube.

Uterine
opening
of tube

Isthmus of
uterine tube

Uterus

Ampulla of
uterine tube

Isthmus of
uterus

K

Figs. 374, 375   IV

Obturator nerve

Internal iliac vessels

Left ureter

Left common iliac artery and vein

Transversus abdominis muscle
Internal oblique muscle
External oblique muscle

Piriformis muscle

Levator ani (pubic part)

Left coccygeus muscle

Iliacus muscle

External iliac a. and v.

Terminal line of pelvis

Deep circumflex iliac a. and v.

Inf. epigastric a. and v.

Obturator art., vein and nerve

Obturator internus muscle

Tendinous arc (origin of levator ani m.)

Urogenital diaphragm;
Int. pudendal vessels

Dorsal vein of clitoris;
Arcuate lig. of pubis; Clitoris

Urethral sphincter;
Urogenital diaphragm

External urethral orifice

Ventral sacrococcygeal ligament
Ventral sacrococcygeal muscle
Anococcygeal ligament

Vagina

Labium minus

Labium majus

Levator ani (ischial part)

Rectococcygeus muscle

Ext. anal sphincter m.
Hemorrhoidal zone
Int. anal sphincter m.
Ext. anal sphincter m.

Central tendinous point (of perineum)

Levator ani muscle

Rectum

Fig. 376: Muscles of the Lateral Wall and Floor of the Female Pelvis (Left Side)

NOTE: 1) the lateral wall of the true pelvis is covered principally by the piriformis and obturator internus muscles while the floor of the pelvis is formed by both the pubic and ischial portions of the levator ani muscle and, more posteriorly, by the coccygeus muscle.

2) although the *piriformis muscle* arises from the ventral surface of the 2nd, 3rd and 4th sacral vertebrae, it is frequently studied with the gluteal muscles because its fibers converge and leave the pelvis through the greater sciatic foramen. The *obturator internus muscle*, covered by its fascia, has an extensive origin on the inner surface of the lateral and anterior wall of the true bony pelvis. It surrounds the obturator foramen (note the obturator vessels and nerve) and its fibers converge to form a tendon which passes out of the pelvis to enter the gluteal region through the lesser sciatic foramen.

3) both the pubic and ischial portions of the *levator ani* muscle arise principally from the tendinous arc of the obturator internus fascia. Observe the *internal* and *external* anal sphincters surrounding the anal orifice.

Fig. 376

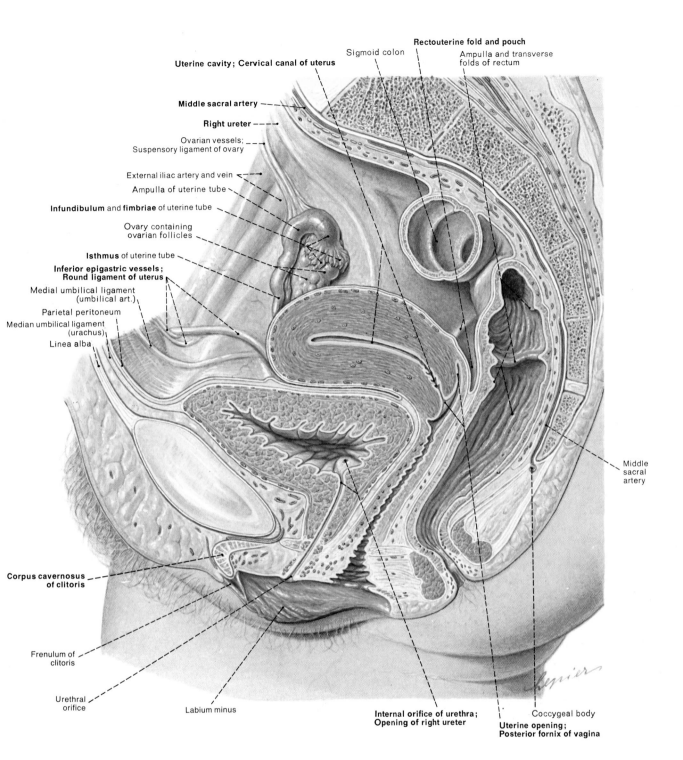

Uterine cavity; Cervical canal of uterus

Sigmoid colon

Rectouterine fold and pouch

Ampulla and transverse
folds of rectum

Middle sacral artery

Right ureter

Ovarian vessels;
Suspensory ligament of ovary

External iliac artery and vein

Ampulla of uterine tube

Infundibulum and **fimbriae** of uterine tube

Ovary containing
ovarian follicles

Isthmus of uterine tube

**Inferior epigastric vessels;
Round ligament of uterus**

Medial umbilical ligament
(umbilical art.)

Parietal peritoneum

Median umbilical ligament
(urachus)

Linea alba

Middle
sacral
artery

**Corpus cavernosus
of clitoris**

Frenulum of
clitoris

Urethral
orifice

Labium minus

Internal orifice of urethra;
Opening of right ureter

Coccygeal body

Uterine opening;
Posterior fornix of vagina

Fig. 377: The Adult Female Pelvis. Median Sagittal Section

NOTE: 1) this medial view of the right half of the female pelvis illustrates the relationships among the bladder, uterus and vagina, rectum, ovary and uterine tube. Observe the immediate retropubic position of the empty *bladder* and the relatively short course of the female *urethra*, which leads from the bladder through the urogenital diaphragm to open in the midline, anterior to the vagina and between the labia minora.

2) the opening between the vagina and the uterus. An extension of the vagina, the posterior fornix, reaches enough superiorly to lie just in front of the rectouterine pouch (of Douglas) and separated from it only by the vaginal wall. Note the interposition of the vagina and uterus between the bladder and rectum. The pear-shaped uterus is so positioned over the superior surface of the empty bladder that when the woman is standing erect, the uterus is horizontal.

3) that the round ligament is directed laterally and anteriorly to enter the abdominal inguinal ring and the course of the inferior epigastric vessels in relation to this ligament. Likewise observe the course of the ovarian vessels within the suspensory ligament of the ovary and their important relationship to the descending ureter on the posterolateral wall of the pelvis.

4) the sigmoid flexure of the large bowel and the relatively direct course of the rectum toward the anal canal. The peritoneum is reflected over the anterior surface of the rectum, thereby lining the rectouterine pouch.

Fig. 377 **IV**

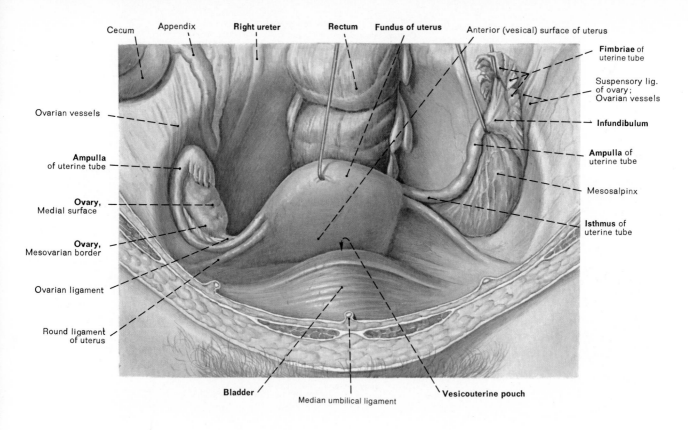

Cecum • Appendix • **Right ureter** • Rectum • Fundus of uterus • Anterior (vesical) surface of uterus

Fimbriae of uterine tube

Suspensory lig. of ovary; Ovarian vessels

Ovarian vessels

→ **Infundibulum**

Ampulla of uterine tube

Ampulla of uterine tube

Mesosalpinx

Ovary, Medial surface

Ovary, Mesovarian border

Isthmus of uterine tube

Ovarian ligament

Round ligament of uterus

Bladder • Median umbilical ligament • **Vesicouterine pouch**

Fig. 378: The Female Pelvic Organs: Anterosuperior View

Observe that the body of the uterus has been elevated, thereby exposing the vesicouterine pouch and demonstrating the broad ligaments.

Fig. 379: The Internal Genital Organs of an Immature Girl

Ovarian vessels • Suspensory ligament of ovary • **Ampulla** of uterine tube • Ovarian fimbria • **Ampulla** of uterine tube

Ampulla of uterine tube

Longitudinal duct of epoophoron

Infundibulum and fimbriae of uterine tube

Transverse ducts of epoophoron

Uterine tube • Uterus

Isthmus of uterine tube

Infundibulum of tube

Fimbriae of tube

Ovary

Ovarian vessels

Suspensory lig. of ovary; Vesicular appendix

Left ureter

Mesosalpinx

Medial surface and meso-varian border of **ovary**

Mesosalpinx

Right ureter

Ovarian ligament

Body of uterus (intestinal surface)

Broad ligament of uterus

Isthmus of uterus

Rectouterine fold

Cervix of uterus (supravaginal portion)

Rectouterine muscle

Rectouterine pouch

Peritoneum

Vagina (posterior surface)

Figs. 378, 379

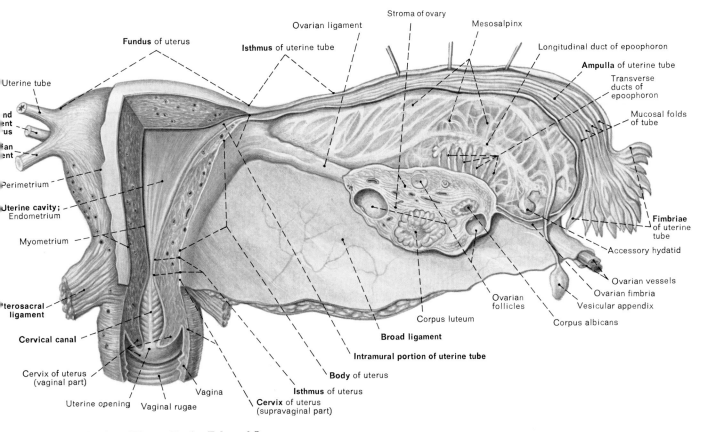

Fundus of uterus
Isthmus of uterine tube
Ovarian ligament
Stroma of ovary
Mesosalpinx
Longitudinal duct of epoophoron
Ampulla of uterine tube
Transverse ducts of epoophoron
Mucosal folds of tube
Uterine tube
nd ent us
an ent
Perimetrium
Uterine cavity; Endometrium
Myometrium
Fimbriae of uterine tube
Accessory hydatid
Ovarian vessels
Ovarian fimbria
Vesicular appendix
Corpus albicans
Ovarian follicles
Corpus luteum
Ovarian follicles
terosacral ligament
Cervical canal
Broad ligament
Intramural portion of uterine tube
Cervix of uterus (vaginal part)
Body of uterus
Uterine opening
Vagina
Vaginal rugae
Isthmus of uterus
Cervix of uterus (supravaginal part)

Fig. 380: Frontal Section of Uterus, Uterine Tube and Ovary

NOTE: 1) the vagina communicates with the pelvic cavity through the uterus and the uterine tube. The lumen of this pathway varies in diameter, and its most narrow sites are the isthmus of the uterus and the intrauterine (intramural) portion of the uterine tube.

2) the uterus consists of the cervix (vaginal and supravaginal portions) and the body of the uterus. These are interconnected by the isthmus. The attachments of the uterus include a) the broad ligaments which are mesentery-like attachments to the lateral margins of the uterus, b) the fibrous round ligament of the uterus and the ligament of the ovary attached just below the uterine tube, c) the uterosacral ligaments and d) the lateral cervical or cardinal ligaments (not shown in this figure). The cardinal ligaments are generally regarded as the principal ligamentous support of the uterus and upper vagina.

Fig. 381: Arterial Supply to Female Pelvic Genital Organs

NOTE: 1) the principal vessels supplying the female pelvic genital organs are the uterine arteries from the internal iliac vessels and the ovarian arteries which stem directly from the aorta. The uterine and ovarian arteries anastomose freely along both lateral borders of the uterus.

2) inferiorly, the uterine artery also anastomoses with the arterial supply to the vagina. Frequently, the vaginal arteries branch directly from the uterine, however, they may branch from the inferior vesical artery or even directly from the internal iliac artery.

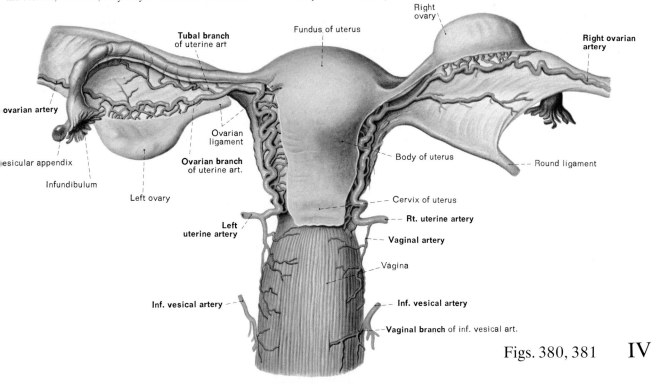

Tubal branch of uterine art
Fundus of uterus
Right ovary
Right ovarian artery
ovarian artery
Ovarian ligament
Ovarian branch of uterine art.
esicular appendix
Infundibulum
Left ovary
Body of uterus
Round ligament
Cervix of uterus
Left uterine artery
Rt. uterine artery
Vaginal artery
Vagina
Inf. vesical artery
Inf. vesical artery
Vaginal branch of inf. vesical art.

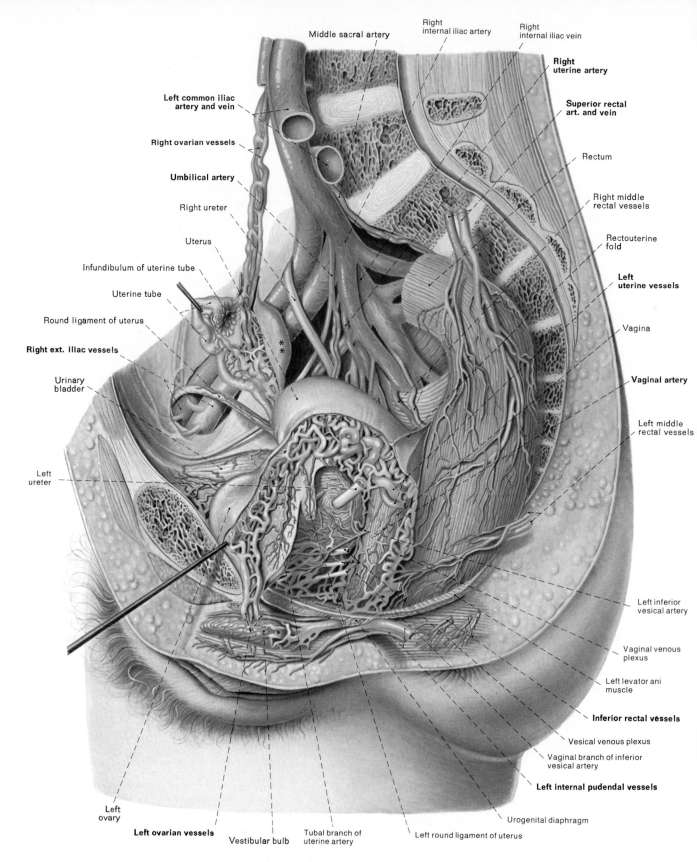

Middle sacral artery

Right internal iliac artery

Right internal iliac vein

Right uterine artery

Left common iliac artery and vein

Superior rectal art. and vein

Right ovarian vessels

Rectum

Umbilical artery

Right middle rectal vessels

Right ureter

Rectouterine fold

Uterus

Left uterine vessels

Infundibulum of uterine tube

Uterine tube

Vagina

Round ligament of uterus

Right ext. iliac vessels

Vaginal artery

Urinary bladder

Left ureter

Left middle rectal vessels

Left inferior vesical artery

Vaginal venous plexus

Left levator ani muscle

Inferior rectal vessels

Vesical venous plexus

Vaginal branch of inferior vesical artery

Left internal pudendal vessels

Left ovary

Urogenital diaphragm

Left ovarian vessels

Vestibular bulb

Tubal branch of uterine artery

Left round ligament of uterus

Fig. 382: Blood Vessels of the Female Pelvis and Genital System

NOTE: 1) the left half of the pelvis has been removed while most of the female pelvic organs are still in place. Observe the dense plexuses of veins. These include the ovarian, uterine, vaginal and vesical plexuses which accompany their respective arteries and which drain the pelvic organs.

2) with the exception of the *ovarian artery* which is derived from the aorta and the *superior rectal artery* (hemorrhoidal) which branches from the inferior mesenteric, all the other arteries supplying blood to the pelvic organs, perineum and genital tract are derived from the *internal iliac artery* or its branches. Observe the anastomosis among the superior, middle and inferior rectal vessels.

3) the descending course of the ureter over the pelvic brim from the posterior abdominal wall. In its path it crosses the external iliac artery and vein, as does the round ligament of the uterus more inferiorly.

Fig. 382

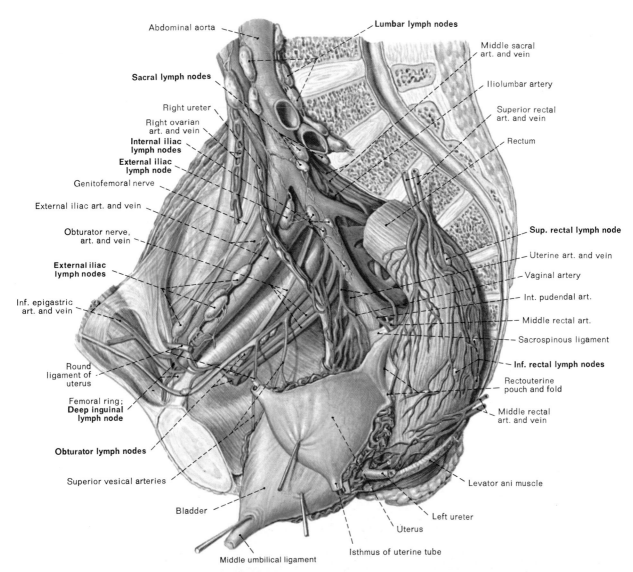

Fig. 383: Lymph Vessels and Nodes of the Female Pelvis

Abdominal aorta

Lumbar lymph nodes

Middle sacral art. and vein

Sacral lymph nodes

Iliolumbar artery

Right ureter

Superior rectal art. and vein

Right ovarian art. and vein

Rectum

Internal iliac lymph nodes

External iliac lymph node

Genitofemoral nerve

External iliac art. and vein

Sup. rectal lymph node

Obturator nerve, art. and vein

Uterine art. and vein

Vaginal artery

External iliac lymph nodes

Int. pudendal art.

Inf. epigastric art. and vein

Middle rectal art.

Sacrospinous ligament

Round ligament of uterus

Inf. rectal lymph nodes

Femoral ring; Deep inguinal lymph node

Rectouterine pouch and fold

Middle rectal art. and vein

Obturator lymph nodes

Levator ani muscle

Superior vesical arteries

Bladder

Left ureter

Uterus

Isthmus of uterine tube

Middle umbilical ligament

Fig. 383: Lymph Vessels and Nodes of the Female Pelvis ▲

NOTE: 1) as a rule, the lymph nodes of the pelvis lie along the course of the major vessels. Generally, the lymphatics drain superiorly and posteriorly to achieve the right und left lumbar lymphatic chains of nodes which lie upon the psoas major muscles on both sides of the aorta.

2) the lymphatics of the bladder drain laterally to the external iliac nodes and posteriorly to the internal iliac nodes. These latter lymphatic channels and nodes also receive lymph from the fundus and body of the uterus in the female and the prostate and seminal vesicles in the male. Lymphatics of the cervix and vagina drain into both the external and internal iliac nodes.

Fig. 384: Lymphograph of Pelvis and Lumbar Region ▶

This lymphograph displays the lymphatic channels from the deeper femoral vessels and nodes, which course superiorly through to the lumbar and aortic nodes. Observe the profuse network along the iliac vessels and the concentration of nodes in the deep inguinal region.

Lumbar and aortic nodes and trunks

Iliac trunks

Deep inguinal lymph nodes

Femoral trunk

Fig. 385: Diagrammatic Section Through the Lesser or True Pelvis in the Female

NOTE: 1) that the lesser pelvis (also called the minor, or true, pelvis) lies below the pelvic brim and inferior to an arbitrary plane that passes from the promontory of the sacrum posteriorly, the linea terminals laterally (see Fig. 386), and the pubic crest anteriorly. Its inferior limit is the muscular floor of the pelvis, as shown in Figure 386.

2) that extending laterally on both sides from the uterine cervix and from the upper vagina to the fascia over the levator ani muscles, and located at the base of the broad ligament below the uterine vessels are the *transverse cervical ligaments* (also called lateral cervical, cardinal, or Mackenrodt's ligaments). Observe that the *uterosacral ligaments* also attach to the cervix and upper vagina, but course posteriorly around the rectum to the front of the sacrum.

3) that the uterus is supported in position by its attachments to the bladder and rectum, by the transverse cervical and uterosacral ligaments, and by the musculature that forms the pelvic floor and urogenital diaphragm.

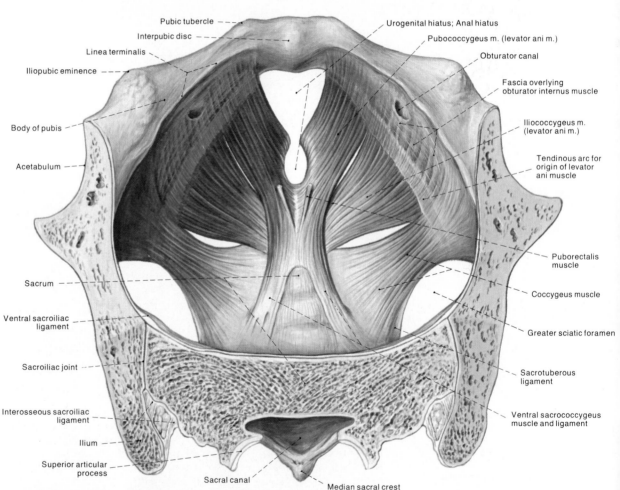

Fig. 386: The Muscular Floor of the Female Pelvis, Viewed from Above

NOTE that the muscular floor of the female pelvis closely resembles that of the male pelvis (see Fig. 365 and Notes) *exept* anteriorly at the urogenital hiatus. Realize that at this site the structure of the urogenital diaphragm (deep transverse perineal muscle and the membranous sphincter of the ureth which lie between two fascial layers) and the organs that must penetrate it (the urethra in the male and the urethra and vagina in the female) account this morphologic difference in the two genders (see Fig. 343, 365, and 366 for the male and Figs. 368-371, 377, and 387 for the femal

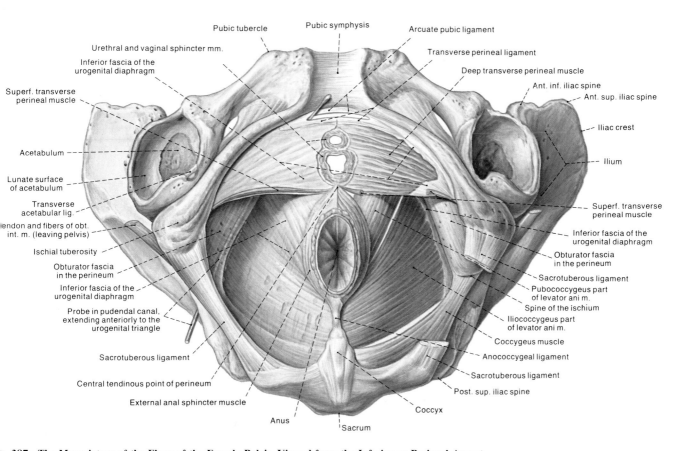

Pubic tubercle
Pubic symphysis
Arcuate pubic ligament
Urethral and vaginal sphincter mm.
Transverse perineal ligament
Inferior fascia of the urogenital diaphragm
Deep transverse perineal muscle
Superf. transverse perineal muscle
Ant. inf. iliac spine
Ant. sup. iliac spine
Acetabulum
Iliac crest
Lunate surface of acetabulum
Ilium
Transverse acetabular lig.
Superf. transverse perineal muscle
endon and fibers of obt. int. m. (leaving pelvis)
Inferior fascia of the urogenital diaphragm
Ischial tuberosity
Obturator fascia in the perineum
Obturator fascia in the perineum
Sacrotuberous ligament
Inferior fascia of the urogenital diaphragm
Pubococcygeus part of levator ani m.
Probe in pudendal canal, extending anteriorly to the urogenital triangle
Spine of the ischium
Iliococcygeus part of levator ani m.
Sacrotuberous ligament
Coccygeus muscle
Central tendinous point of perineum
Anococcygeal ligament
Sacrotuberous ligament
External anal sphincter muscle
Post. sup. iliac spine
Anus
Coccyx
Sacrum

3. 387: The Musculature of the Floor of the Female Pelvis, Viewed from the Inferior or Perineal Aspect

NOTE: 1) that on the specimen's left side (reader's right) the inferior fasciae of the pelvic and urogenital diaphragms have been removed.
2) the manner in which the musculature of the urogenital diaphragm completes the anterior part of the female pelvic floor, still allowing the urethra and gina to pass through the urogenital hiatus (see Fig. 386). Observe also the central tendinous point of the perineum interposed in the midline between the ogenital diaphragm and the anterior limit of the raphé formed by the two external anal sphincters.
3) that the anal hiatus is surrounded in the midline by fibers of the pubococcygeus portions of the two levator ani muscles (see also Fig. 386). These are inforced superiorly by the puborectalis muscle and inferiorly by the external anal sphincters. Observe also that the iliococcygeus parts of the levator ani uscles sweep medially to the coccyx, but some fibers also insert into a short midline anococcygeal raphé and ligament.

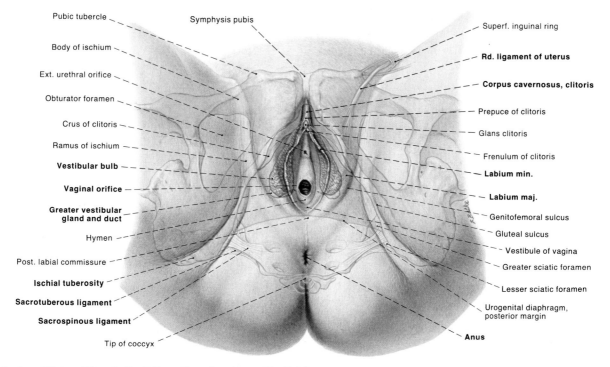

Pubic tubercle
Symphysis pubis
Superf. inguinal ring
Body of ischium
Rd. ligament of uterus
Ext. urethral orifice
Corpus cavernosus, clitoris
Obturator foramen
Prepuce of clitoris
Crus of clitoris
Glans clitoris
Ramus of ischium
Frenulum of clitoris
Vestibular bulb
Labium min.
Vaginal orifice
Labium maj.
Greater vestibular gland and duct
Genitofemoral sulcus
Hymen
Gluteal sulcus
Post. labial commissure
Vestibule of vagina
Ischial tuberosity
Greater sciatic foramen
Sacrotuberous ligament
Lesser sciatic foramen
Sacrospinous ligament
Urogenital diaphragm, posterior margin
Tip of coccyx
Anus

388: Projection of External Female Genitalia on Bony Structures of the Pelvis

mpare the locations of the external genitalia (located in the superficial perineal pouch) with the urogenital diaphragm as seen in Figure 387. Observe external urethral, vaginal, and anal orifices within their locations in the urogenital and anal hiatuses (Fig. 387).

Figs. 387, 388   **IV**

Fig. 389 labels:
Ala of ilium
Anterior gluteal line
Inferior gluteal line
Tuberosity of gluteus max. muscle
Post. sup. iliac spine
Posterior gluteal line
Post. inferior iliac spine
Greater sciatic notch
Acetabulum
Ischial spine
Lesser sciatic notch
Body of ischium
Ischial tuberosity
Posterior obturator tubercle
Ramus of ischium
Obturator foramen
Acetabular notch
Anterior obturator tubercle
Inferior ramus of pubis
Pubic tubercle
Obturator crest
Pecten pubis
Acetabular fossa
Lunate surface (articular surface)
Ant. inferior iliac spine
Body of ilium
Ant. superior iliac spine
Ala of ilium (thin translucent area)
Internal lip
Intermed. line
External lip
Iliac crest

Fig. 389: Lateral View of the Adult Right Hip Bone

Fig. 391 labels:
Iliac crest (cartilaginous)
Ala of ilium
Body of ilium
Iliopubic eminence
Body of pubis
Superior pubic ramus
Body of ischium
Ischial tuberosity
Ischial ramus
Inferior pubic ramus

Fig. 391: Hip Bone of 5 Year Old Child: Lateral View

NOTE that the hip bone is formed by a fusion of the ilium (yellow), ischium (green) and pubis (blue). Although ossification of the inferior pubic ramus occurs during the 7th or 8th year, complete fusion of the three bones at the acetabulum occurs sometime between the 15th and 20th year.

Fig. 390 labels:
Iliac crest
Intermediate line (of iliac crest)
Internal lip (of iliac crest)
Ant. sup. iliac spine
Iliac fossa
Ant. inf. iliac spine
Arcuate line
Obturator groove
Superior ramus of pubis
Post. obturator tubercle
Articular surface (symphysis pubis)
Inferior ramus of pubis
Obturator foramen
Ischial tuberosity
Ramus of ischium
Lesser sciatic notch
Ischial spine
Body of ischium
Greater sciatic notch
Paraglenoid sulcus
Post. inf. iliac spine
Post. sup. iliac spine
Tuberosity of ilium
Articular surface (with sacrum)
Ala of ilium (thin translucent area)

Fig. 390: Medial View of the Adult Right Hip Bone

Fig. 392 labels:
Iliac crest (cartilaginous)
Ant. sup. iliac spine
Body of ilium
Iliopubic surface
Body of pubis
Sup. ramus of pubis
Articular surface (symphysis pubis)
Inf. ramus of pubis
Articular surface (with sacrum)
Body of ischium
Spine of ischium
Body of ischium
Ramus of ischium

Fig. 392: Hip Bone of 5 Year Old Child: Medial View

NOTE the lines of fusion of the three bones above the obturator foramen and the fusion of the inferior pubic ramus and the ischial ramus below that foramen.

Figs. 389–392

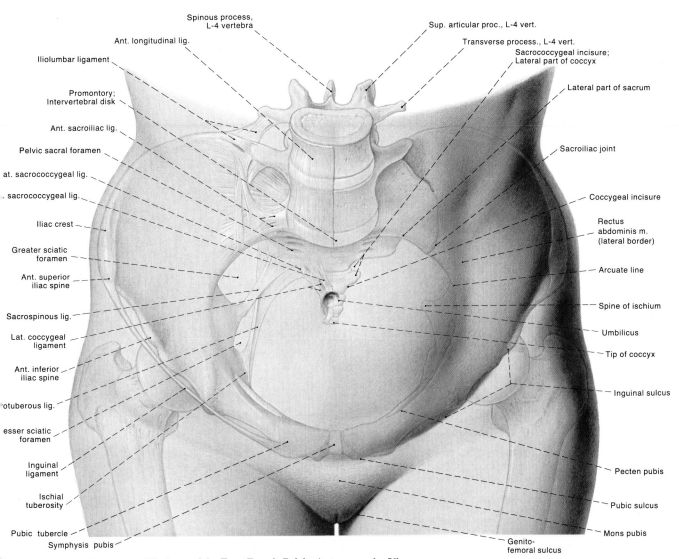

Spinous process,
L-4 vertebra

Sup. articular proc., L-4 vert.

Ant. longitudinal lig.

Transverse process., L-4 vert.

Sacrococcygeal incisure;
Lateral part of coccyx

Iliolumbar ligament

Lateral part of sacrum

Promontory;
Intervertebral disk

Sacroiliac joint

Ant. sacroiliac lig.

Pelvic sacral foramen

Coccygeal incisure

at. sacrococcygeal lig.

Rectus
abdominis m.
(lateral border)

sacrococcygeal lig.

Iliac crest

Arcuate line

Greater sciatic
foramen

Spine of ischium

Ant. superior
iliac spine

Umbilicus

Sacrospinous lig.

Tip of coccyx

Lat. coccygeal
ligament

Inguinal sulcus

Ant. inferior
iliac spine

otuberous lig.

Pecten pubis

esser sciatic
foramen

Inguinal
ligament

Pubic sulcus

Ischial
tuberosity

Mons pubis

Pubic tubercle

Genito-
femoral sulcus

Symphysis pubis

Fig. 393: External Features and Skeleton of the Erect Female Pelvis: Anterosuperior View

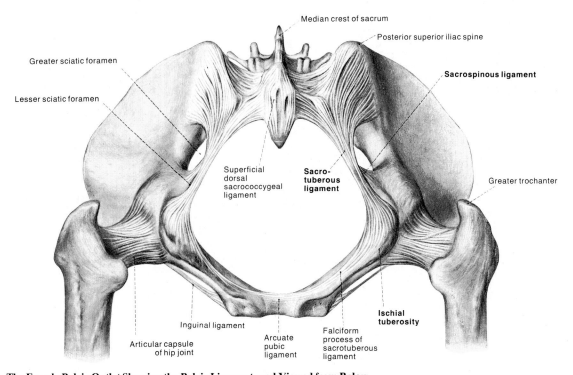

Median crest of sacrum

Posterior superior iliac spine

Greater sciatic foramen

Sacrospinous ligament

Lesser sciatic foramen

Greater trochanter

Superficial
dorsal
sacrococcygeal
ligament

**Sacro-
tuberous
ligament**

**Ischial
tuberosity**

Inguinal ligament

Articular capsule
of hip joint

Arcuate
pubic
ligament

Falciform
process of
sacrotuberous
ligament

Fig. 394: The Female Pelvic Outlet Showing the Pelvic Ligaments and Viewed from Below

NOTE the sacrotuberous, sacrospinous, and arcuate pubic ligaments in this inferior view of the pelvic outlet.

Figs. 393, 394   **IV**

Fig. 395: The Male Pelvis and Associated Ligaments: Anterior Aspect

NOTE that the pelvis is formed by the articulation of the left and right hip bones anteriorly at the symphysis pubis and posteriorly with the sacrum and coccyx of the vertebral column. The articulations inferiorly of the pelvis with the two femora allow the weight of the head, trunk and upper extremities to be transmitted to the lower limbs, thereby maintaining the upright posture characteristic of the human being.

Fig. 396: The Female Pelvis with Joints and Ligaments: Posterior Aspect

NOTE that broad ligamentous bands articulate the two hip bones posteriorly with the sacrum and coccyx. This sacroiliac joint is bound by the extremely strong dorsal sacroiliac ligament. Attaching the sacrum to the ischial tuberosity is the broad sacrotuberous ligament. Additionally, the sacrospinous ligament stretches between the sacrum and the ischium (ischial spine).

Figs. 395, 396

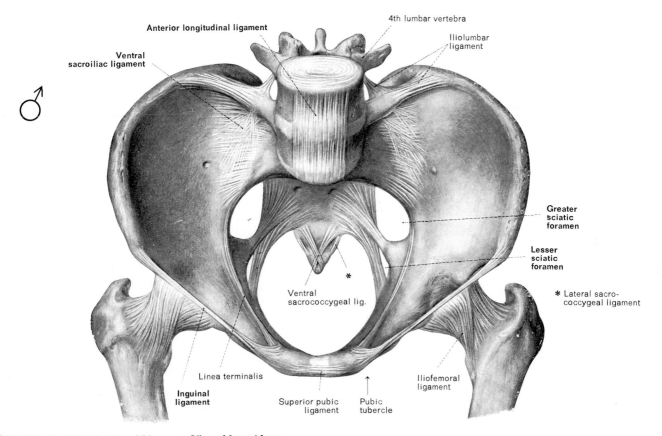

Fig. 397: The Male Pelvis and Ligaments Viewed from Above

NOTE that the size of both the pelvic inlet (superior aperture of the minor pelvis) and inferior outlet of the male pelvis is smaller than that in the female (see Figure 398 below). Thus, the minor pelvis is deeper and narrower in the male and its cavity has a smaller capacity than a female. In the male, however, the pelvic bones are thicker and heavier and generally the major pelvis (above the pelvic brim) is larger than in the female.

Fig. 398: The Female Pelvis and Ligaments Viewed from Above

NOTE that in addition to having wider diameters, both the pelvic inlet and outlet of the female pelvis minor are more circular in shape than in the male. The female pelvic bones are more delicate and the sacrum less curved. The larger capacity of the true pelvis in the female, and the fact that the female hormones of pregnancy tend to relax the pelvic ligaments serve to facilitate the function of child bearing.

Figs. 397, 398   IV

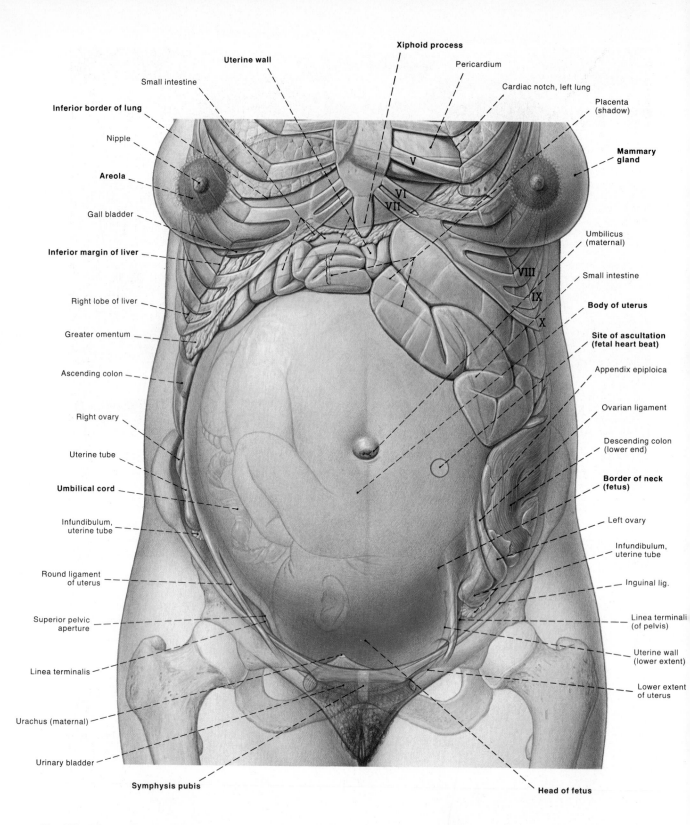

Small intestine
Inferior border of lung
Nipple
Areola
Gall bladder
Inferior margin of liver
Right lobe of liver
Greater omentum
Ascending colon
Right ovary
Uterine tube
Umbilical cord
Infundibulum, uterine tube
Round ligament of uterus
Superior pelvic aperture
Linea terminalis
Urachus (maternal)
Urinary bladder
Symphysis pubis

Uterine wall
Xiphoid process
Pericardium
Cardiac notch, left lung
Placenta (shadow)
Mammary gland

V
VI
VII
VIII
IX
X

Umbilicus (maternal)
Small intestine
Body of uterus
Site of ascultation (fetal heart beat)
Appendix epiploica
Ovarian ligament
Descending colon (lower end)
Border of neck (fetus)
Left ovary
Infundibulum, uterine tube
Inguinal lig.
Linea terminali (of pelvis)
Uterine wall (lower extent)
Lower extent of uterus
Head of fetus

Fig. 399: Diagrammatic Projection of Abdominal and Pelvic Organs in a Pregnant Woman Shortly Before Giving Birth: Anterior View

NOTE that: 1) in the maternal abdomen, the full-term fetus is in a characteristically longitudinal posture, with the dorsum of the fetal head and back oriented toward the mother's anterior abdominal wall. This type of cephalic longitudinal presentation occurs in 95% of births, while longitudinal pelvic presentation (breech) occurs in about 3% of births. In about 1% of births, a transverse presentation of the fetus occurs, with one of the shoulders as the presenting part *(Reid, 1962, A Textbook of Obstetrics, W. B. Saunders Co. Publ.)*;

2) as the fetus grows, the maternal uterus enlarges. By the end of the 3rd month, the uterus occupies most of the pelvis, extending as gestation continues, higher and higher within the abdomen. Near the end of pregnancy, it occupies most of the abdomen, reaching above the costal margin, nearly to the xiphoid process;

3) the maternal liver, stomach and intestines are displaced upward, while the diaphragm is elevated and the dimensions of the thoracic cavity broadened. The breasts enlarge considerably through a proliferation of its glandular tissue in advance of lactation, and the areolar region around the nipple becomes more darkly pigmented.

Fig. 399

Fig. 400: Fetal Roentgenogram

NOTE the body contours of this near-term fetus *in utero* and a number of the ossifying fetal bones. Observe that the uterus extends to the maternal T-12 vertebral body level. This figure is from Wicke, L., *Atlas of Radiologic Anatomy,* 3rd Edition, Urban and Schwarzenberg, Baltimore, 1982.

1. Right fibula	6. Left femur	11. Left ulna	16. External ear
2. Left fibula	7. L-5 vertebra	12. Left radius	17. Fetal head
3. Right tibia	8. Small intestine (fetal)	13. Left humerus	
4. Left tibia	9. L-1 vertebra	14. Right humerus	
5. Right femur	10. Ribs	15. Right scapula	

Fig. 400   IV

1. Iliac crest
2. Gas bubble in colon
3. Ala of ilium
4. Lateral part of sacrum
5. Sacroiliac joint
6. Post. inf. iliac spine
7. Ant. sup. iliac spine
8. Ant. inf. iliac spine
9. Lunate surface of acetabulum
10. Spine of ischium
11. Greater trochanter
12. Intertrochanteric crest
13. Lesser trochanter
14. Ischial tuberosity
15. Superior ramus of pubis
16. Symphysis pubis
17. Inferior ramus of pubis
18. Obturator foramen
19. Neck of femur
20. Head of femur
21. Fovea on head of femur
22. Acetabular fossa
23. Iliopubic eminence
24. Greater sciatic notch
25. Transverse process L-5 vertebra
26. Gas bubble in colon
27. Urinary bladder

Fig. 401: Radiograph of the Pelvis and the Sacroiliac and Hip Joints

This radiograph is taken from Wicke, L., *Atlas of Radiologic Anatomy*, 3rd Edition, Urban and Schwarzenberg, Baltimore, 1982.

Fig. 401

PART V: THE LOWER EXTREMITY

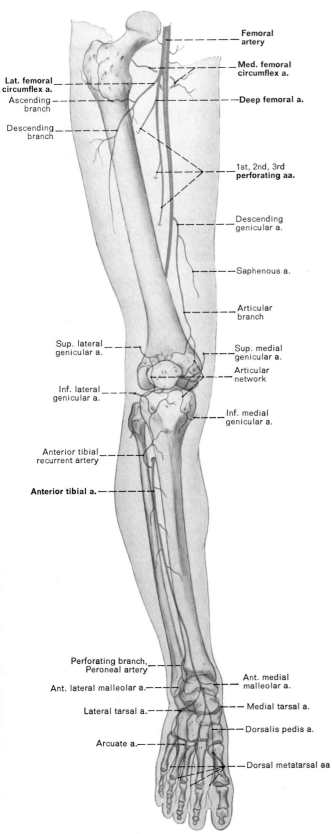

Femoral artery

Med. femoral circumflex a.

Lat. femoral circumflex a.

Ascending branch

Deep femoral a.

Descending branch

1st, 2nd, 3rd perforating aa.

Descending genicular a.

Saphenous a.

Articular branch

Sup. lateral genicular a.

Sup. medial genicular a.

Articular network

Inf. lateral genicular a.

Inf. medial genicular a.

Anterior tibial recurrent artery

Anterior tibial a.

Perforating branch, Peroneal artery

Ant. lateral malleolar a.

Ant. medial malleolar a.

Lateral tarsal a.

Medial tarsal a.

Dorsalis pedis a.

Arcuate a.

Dorsal metatarsal aa

Fig. 402: Arteries and Bones of the Lower Limb (Anterior View)

NOTE the anastomoses in the hip and knee regions, and the perforating branches of the deep femoral artery. In the anterior leg, the anterior tibial artery descends between the tibia and fibula to achieve the malleolar region and dorsum of the foot.

Inferior gluteal a.

1st, 2nd, 3rd perforating aa.

Popliteal a.

Sup. medial genicular a.

Sup. lateral Genicular a.

Sural a.

Middle genicular a.

Sural a.

Inf. lateral genicular a.

Inf. medial genicular a.

Posterior tibial recurrent a.

Post. tibial a.

Anterior tibial a.

Peroneal a.

Communicating branch

Med. malleolar a.

Lat. malleolar a.

Med. plantar a.

Lat. plantar a.

Plantar arch.

Fig. 403: Arteries and Bones of the Lower Limb (Posterior View)

NOTE the branches of the popliteal artery at the knee, and the artery's continuation as the posterior tibial. In the foot this vessel becomes the medial and lateral plantar arteries, which join the plantar arch.

Fig. 404

Fig. 405

Fig. 404: Dermatomes of the Anterior Aspect of the Lower Extremity

NOTE that as a rule the lumbar segments of the spinal cord supply the cutaneous innervation to the anterior aspect of the lower extremity, and that the dermatomes are segmentally arranged in order from L-1 to S-1. Observe that the genital region is supplied by the sacral segments.

Fig. 405: The Distribution of Cutaneous Nerves: Anterior Aspect of the Lower Extremity

The segmental distribution of the cutaneous nerves supplying the anterior aspect of the lower extremity is as follows:

iliohypogastric nerve:	(T_{12}), L_1
genitofemoral nerve:	L_1, L_2
lateral femoral cutaneous nerve:	L_2, L_3
femoral nerve:	L_2, L_3, L_4
obturator nerve:	L_2, L_3, L_4
saphenous nerve (femoral):	L_2, L_3, L_4
deep peroneal (cutaneous br.):	L_4, L_5
superficial peroneal:	L_4, L_5, S_1
lateral sural cutaneous n.:	L_5, S_1, S_2
(common peroneal n.)	
sural nerve (tibial):	S_1, S_2

Fig. 406

Fig. 407

Fig. 406: Dermatomes of the Posterior Aspect of the Lower Extremity

NOTE that the skin on the posterior aspect of the lower extremity receives its sensory innervation principally from L5, S1 and S2. Observe, however, how the posterior medial border of the limb consecutively has the L1, L2, L3 and L4 segments represented. Segments S3, S4 and S5 are more limited to the perineal and anal regions.

Fig. 407: The Distribution of Cutaneous Nerves: Posterior Aspect of the Lower Extremity

NOTE: 1) the principal nerve supplying cutaneous innervation to the posterior aspect of the thigh is the posterior femoral cutaneous nerve (S1, S2, S3). The skin of the medial calf is supplied by the saphenous (femoral) nerve (L2, L3, L4), while the lateral calf receives the sural nerve (S1, S2).

2) the heel of the foot is innervated by the tibial nerve through S1 and S2 segments, and the plantar surface of the foot receives L4 and L5 fibers medially (medial plantar nerve) and S1 and S2 laterally (lateral plantar nerve).

Figs. 404–407

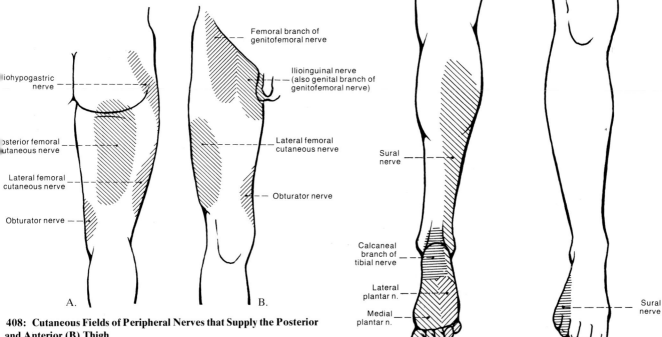

408: Cutaneous Fields of Peripheral Nerves that Supply the Posterior and Anterior (B) Thigh

NOTE that *except* for the posterior femoral cutaneous nerve (S1, 2, 3), all the cutaneous nerves of the thigh are derived from lumbar segments L1
–4. Observe that the obturator nerve supplies a field on the lower medial aspect of the thigh just above the knee.

409: Cutaneous Fields Supplied by the Femoral Nerve and Its Saphenous Branch

NOTE that the femoral nerve, by way of its intermediate (anterior) and medial cutaneous branches, supplies the anteromedial aspect of the thigh below the fields of the ilioinguinal and genitofemoral nerves. The saphenous nerve is the largest cutaneous branch of the femoral, and it supplies the anteromedial (B) and posteromedial aspects of the leg (A).

Fig. 410: The Cutaneous Fields of the Sural Nerve in the Calf and Foot and the Fields of the Calcaneal and Plantar Branches of the Tibial Nerve

NOTE that the sural nerve supplies much of the posterolateral aspect of the calf (A) and that its field extends beyond the lateral malleolus into the lateral heel and lateral part of the dorsum of the foot (B). Observe that the tibial nerve through its medial calcaneal branch supplies the skin over most of the heel, while the lateral and medial plantar branches of the tibial nerve supply the plantar surface of the foot.

Fig. 411: Cutaneous Fields of the Peroneal and Sural Nerves on the Posterolateral and Anterolateral Aspects of the Leg and the Dorsum of the Foot

NOTE that on the posterolateral aspect of the leg (A), above the cutaneous field of the sural nerve, are areas of skin supplied by the lateral cutaneous nerve of the calf (from common peroneal nerve; also called lateral sural nerve) and the sural communicating branch (often from the superficial peroneal nerve), which joins the sural nerve, a branch of the tibial nerve. Observe the large field supplied by the superficial peroneal nerve on the anterior leg and foot dorsum, and the small field supplied by the deep peroneal nerve (B).

Figs. 408–411   V

Anterior superior iliac spine

Tensor fasciae latae muscle

Pectineus muscle

Sartorius muscle

Adductor longus muscle

Rectus femoris muscle

Vastus lateralis muscle

Vastus medialis muscle

Patella

Lateral epicondyle of femur

Patellar ligament

Peroneus longus muscle

Medial head of gastrocnemius muscle

Tibialis anterior muscle

Soleus muscle

Lateral malleolus

Medial malleolus

Great saphenous vein

Tensor fasciae latae muscle

Gluteus maximus muscle

Gluteal sulcus

Adductor magnus muscle

Semimembranos muscle

Long head of the biceps femoris m.

Short head of the biceps femoris m.

Popliteal fossa

Medial head of the gastrocnemius muscle

Lateral head of the gastrocnemius muscle

Calcaneal tendon

Medial malleolus

Lateral malleolus

Calcaneal tuberosity

Abductor hallucis muscle

Abductor digiti minimi muscle

Fig. 412: Surface Anatomy of the Right Lower Limb, Anterior View

NOTE: 1) the muscular features of the anterior thigh. Observe the pectineus and adductor longus muscles which form the floor of the femoral triangle, the sartorius muscle which courses obliquely inferomedially, three of the four components of the quadriceps muscle (vastus lateralis and medialis and the rectus femoris), and the tensor fasciae latae which forms the rounded upper lateral contour of the thigh.

2) that laterally the leg is shaped by the peroneus longus (and brevis) and anteriorly by the tibialis anterior. The medial contour of the leg consists of the gastrocnemius and soleus muscles.

3) the prominent osseous features: the anterior superior iliac spine, the patella and femoral condyles, the tibia (just medial to the tibialis anterior muscle), and the medial and lateral malleoli.

Fig. 413: Surface Anatomy of the Right Lower Limb, Posterior View

NOTE: 1) that the rounded contour of the buttock is formed by the gluteus maximus muscle and an overlying layer of fatty tissue.

2) that the outline of the hamstring muscles (semitendinosus, semimembranosus, and biceps femoris) is visible in the mid-portion of the posterior thigh between the adductor region medially and the quadriceps (not labelled) laterally.

3) the popliteal fossa behind the knee joint, below which are the prominent heads of the gastrocnemius muscle. This muscle helps to form the calcaneal tendon which inserts between the two malleoli into the calcaneal bone. Observe also the muscular contours formed medially by the abductor hallucis muscle and laterally by the abductor digiti minimi muscle on the plantar surface of the foot.

Figs. 412, 413

Femoral
artery

Femoral
vein

Iliohypogastric
nerve

Ant. cutan.
branches
of T-12

Ilioinguinal
nerve

...ficial
...stric
...d vein

...moral
nerve

...moral
...nch of
...ofem.
nerve

...erf.
...cum.
...liac
...sels

External
pudendal
a. and v.

Ant. femoral
vein

Great
saphenous vein

Anterior
cutan.
branches of
femoral n.

Cutan.
branches
of obtu-
rator n.

Descend.
genicular
art.

Patellar
network of
vessels

Infrapatellar
br. of sa-
phenous n.

Fig. 415: The Superficial Inguinal Lymph Nodes and Channels

NOTE that the superficial tissues of the genitalia, lower anterior abdominal wall, inguinal region and anterior thigh drain into the superficial inguinal lymph nodes. These are located around the femoral vessels just below the inguinal ligament and usually number between 10 and 15. In turn these nodes drain into the external iliac nodes within the pelvis.

Fig. 414: Superficial Nerves and Blood Vessels of the Anterior Thigh

NOTE: 1) the great saphenous vein as it ascends on the anterior and medial aspect of the thigh. Just below ($1^{1}/_{2}$ inches) the inguinal ligament, it penetrates the deep fascia (through the saphenous opening) to enter the femoral vein.

2) superficial branches of the femoral artery. These include the superficial epigastric, the external pudendal and the superficial circumflex iliac arteries. Other unnamed inguinal branches complete the radial configuration of the superficial vascular branches in this region.

3) the principal cutaneous nerves of the anterior thigh are: a) the anterior femoral cutaneous branches of the femoral nerve (L2, L3, L4), b) the lateral femoral cutaneous nerve (L2, L3), c) the terminal branches of the ilioinguinal and iliohypogastric nerves derived from the 1st lumbar nerve, and d) the femoral branch of the genitofemoral nerve (L1, L2).

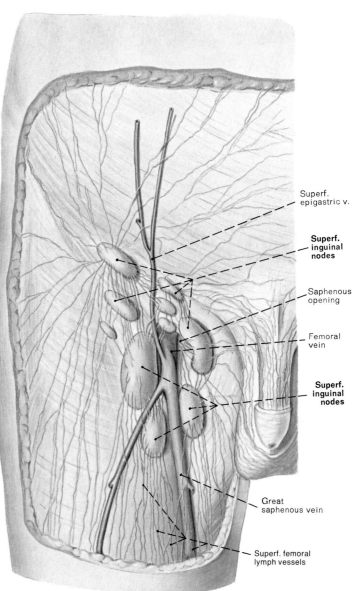

Superf.
epigastric v.

**Superf.
inguinal
nodes**

Saphenous
opening

Femoral
vein

**Superf.
inguinal
nodes**

Great
saphenous vein

Superf. femoral
lymph vessels

Fig. 416: The Fascia of the Anterior Thigh, the Fascia Lata (right)

NOTE: 1) the dense fascia which invests the muscles of the hip and thigh is called the fascia lata. It is attached above to the ischial and pubic rami and inguinal ligament anteriorly, the crest of the ilium laterally and the ischial tuberosity, sacrotuberous ligament, sacrum and coccyx posteriorly.

2) in the inguinal region the fascia lata is pierced by the greater saphenous vein, and inferiorly it extends to the investing fascia below the knee.

Fig. 417: The Anterior Muscles of the Thigh: Superficial View (right)

NOTE: 1) the long narrow sartorius muscle which arises on the anterior superior iliac spine and passes obliquely across the anterior femoral muscles to insert on the medial aspect of the body of the tibia. The sartorius flexes the thigh and rotates it laterally. It also flexes the knee and rotates it medially.

2) the quadriceps muscle forms the bulk of the anterior femoral muscles, and both the sartorius and quadriceps are innervated by the femoral nerve.

Figs. 416, 417

Fig. 418: The Femoral Triangle

NOTE: the boundaries of the femoral triangle are the inguinal ligament, the sartorius muscle and the medial border of the adductor longus. The floor is formed by the iliopsoas and pectineus muscles. The femoral nerve, artery and vein descend beneath the inguinal ligament and traverse the femoral triangle.

Fig. 419: The Quadriceps Femoris, Iliopsoas, and Pectineus Muscles

NOTE: 1) the quadriceps femoris (rectus femoris and vastus lateralis, intermedius and medialis) as it converges inferiorly to form a powerful tendon which encases the patella and which is inserted onto the tuberosity of the tibia. The entire quadriceps extends the leg, while the rectus femoris also flexes the thigh.

2) the iliopsoas muscle is a powerful flexor of the thigh and inserts on the lesser trochanter.

Fig. 420: The Intermediate Layer of Anterior and Medial Thigh Muscles

NOTE: 1) that the rectus femoris and iliopsoas muscles are cut to reveal the underlying vastus intermedius situated between the vastus medialis and lateralis.

2) the adductor longus has been reflected. This displays the pectineus, adductors brevis and magnus and the long gracilis muscles.

▼

Anterior superior iliac spine

Sartorius m.

Rectus femoris m.

Iliopectineal bursa

Gluteus medius m.

Iliofemoral ligament

Iliopsoas m.

Vastus lateralis m.

Fascia lata

Vastus intermedius m.

Iliopsoas m.

Piriformis m.

Pecten of pubis

Adductor longus m.

Pectineus m.

Adductor brevis m.

Gracilis m.

Adductor longus m.

Adductor magnus m.

Adductor hiatus

Vastus medialis m.

Tendon of rectus femoris

Patella

Patellar ligament

Tendon of sartorius m.

Medial condyle of femur

Pes anserinus

Obturator nerve

Femoral artery

Pectineus m

Acetabular Obturator a

Anterior b Obturator

Obturato nerve

Med. fem. circumfl. a

Trans. br. of med. fem. ci cumfl. art.

Femoral vein

Femoral artery

Cutaneous br. of obturator n

Saphenous n.

Adductor canal

Gracilis m.

Saphenous nerve

Sartorius m.

Iliopsoas m.

Femoral nerve

Sartorius m.

Lat. fem. circumfl. art.

Deep femoral art.

Descend. br. of lat. fem. circumfl. a.

Rectus femoris m.

Muscular branch of femoral nerve

Vastus medialis m.

Descend. genicular art. (articular branch)

Fig. 421: The Femoral Vessels and Nerves

NOTE that the femoral vessels and the saphenous branch of the femoral nerve descend in the thigh and enter the adductor canal (of Hunter). Whereas the saphenous nerve then penetrates the overlying fascia to reach the superficial leg region, the vessels continue through the adductor magnus to reach the popliteal fossa on the posterior aspect.

Figs. 420, 421

Fig. 422: The Femoral and Obturator Nerves and the Deep Femoral Artery

Left figure labels:
- moral vein
- moral artery
- moral nerve
- iopsoas m.
- femoral artery
- ircum. artery end. br.
- at. circum. liac artery escend. br.
- Muscular ranches (femoral nerve)
- Rectus femoris m.
- scular branch, **deep femoral artery**
- Perforating arteries
- Vastus lateralis m.
- Muscular branch (femoral nerve)
- Rectus femoris m.
- Saphenous n.
- Descending genicular art.
- Articular branch, Descend. genic. art
- Network of vessels at knee joint
- Obturator nerve
- Great saphenous vein
- **Med. fem. circum. art.**
- **Obturator nerve**
- Obturator artery
- **Obturator nerve branches**
- **Femoral vein**
- **Deep femoral v.**
- Adductor brevis m.
- Adductor longus m.
- Perforating art.
- Cutan. br. obturator n.
- Adductor longus m.
- **Femoral v.**
- Gracilis m.
- Adductor magnus m.
- **Femoral a.**
- Adductor hiatus
- Sartorius m.
- Articular br., Descend. genic. a.
- Superior medial genicular art.
- Inferior medial genicular art.

NOTE that the obturator nerve supplies the adductor muscles, the gracilis and the obturator externus (not shown), while the femoral nerve innervates all the other anterior thigh muscles. The largest branch of the femoral artery is the deep femoral artery from which generally both the medial and lateral femoral circumflex arteries arise. Observe the femoral vessels disappearing in the femoral canal.

Fig. 423: The Deep Layer of Anterior and Medial Thigh Muscles (Right)

NOTE: 1) the rectus femoris and vastus medialis have been removed, thereby revealing the shaft of the femur. Likewise the adductors longus and brevis and the pectineus muscles have been reflected, exposing the obturator externus, the adductor magnus and the adductor minimus (which usually is just the upper portion of the adductor magnus).

2) the common insertion of the tendons of the sartorius, gracilis and semitendinosus muscles on the medial aspect of the knee. The diverging nature of this insertion resembles a goose's foot (pes anserinus). ▼

Right figure labels:
- Sartorius m.
- Rectus femoris m.
- Gluteus medius m.
- Iliopectineal bursa
- Iliopsoas m.
- Pectineus m.
- Adductor brevis m.
- Vastus lateralis m.
- Adductor longus m.
- **Vastus medialis m.**
- Vastus intermedius m.
- Femur
- Tendons form **pes anserinus**
  - Sartorius
  - Gracilis
  - Semitend.
- Iliopsoas m.
- Piriformis muscle
- Pectineus muscle
- Adductor longus m.
- Adductor brevis m.
- Obturator canal
- **Obturator externus m.**
- Lesser trochanter
- **Adductor minimus** (part of adductor magnus)
- **Adductor magnus**
- Gracilis m.
- **Adductor hiatus**
- Tendon of adductor magnus m.
- Tendon of gracilis m.
- Subsartorial bursa
- Subanserina bursa

Figs. 422, 423   **V**

Labels on Fig. 424 (left):
Thoracolumbar fascia
External oblique m.
Gluteal fascia
Iliac crest
Gluteus maximus m.
Sartorius muscle
Tensor of fascia lata
Rectus femoris muscle
Iliotibial tract
Biceps femoris m. (long head)
Vastus lateralis muscle
Semimembranosus m.
Iliotibial tract
Biceps femoris m. (short head)
Plantaris m.
Patella
Gastrocnemius m. (lateral head)
Patellar ligament

Labels on Fig. 425 (right):
S cl n
Ili ga
Medial cluneal nerves
Inferior cluneal nerves
La fe cu
Obturator nerve (cutaneous branch)
Posterior f cutaneous
Great saphenous vein
Communicating vein
Small saphenous

Fig. 424: Superficial Thigh and Gluteal Muscles (Lateral View)

NOTE the massive nature of the vastus lateralis and gluteus maximus muscles. Superficially, the iliotibial tract (band) stretches the length of the thigh, and its muscle, the tensor of the fascia lata, helps to keep the dense fascial sheet taut, thereby assisting in the maintenance of an erect posture.

Fig. 425: Superficial Veins and Nerves of the Gluteal Region and Posterior Thigh

NOTE that the principal cutaneous nerves of the gluteal region are the a) superior cluneal (L1, L2, L3, posterior rami), b) medial cluneal (S1, S2, S3, posterior rami), and c) inferior cluneal (S1, S2, S3 from posterior femoral cutaneous nerve). The skin of the posterior aspect of the thigh is innervated primarily by the posterior femoral cutaneous nerve (S1, S2, S3).

Figs. 424, 425

Fig. 426: Nerves and Vessels of the Posterior Thigh

NOTE: 1) the emergence of the posterior femoral cutaneous nerve below the inferior border of the gluteus maximus muscle and the inferior cluneal nerves reflecting superiorly at that point.

2) the appearance of the major vessels (popliteal artery and vein) and the sciatic nerve (tibial and common peroneal nerves) in the popliteal fossa.

Fig. 427: Gluteal and Posterior Thigh Muscles

NOTE: 1) with the gluteus maximus and medius reflected, observe the underlying gluteus minimus, piriformis, superior gemellus, obturator internus, inferior gemellus and quadratus femoris muscles.

2) the three hamstring muscles: the biceps femoris (long head) and semitendinosus overlying the semimembranosus muscle. These muscles arise from the ischial tuberosity.

Figs. 426, 427 **V**

Fig. 428: Deep Nerves and Vessels of the Gluteal Region and Posterior Thigh

NOTE: 1) the course of the sciatic nerve as it passes through the greater sciatic foramen in the gluteal region, inferior to the piriformis muscle, lateral to the ischial tuberosity and under cover of the gluteus maximus muscle.

2) the superior and inferior gluteal arteries and the posterior femoral cutaneous nerve. In the thigh, observe the perforating arteries and the fact that the sciatic nerve splits to become the tibial and common peroneal nerves.

Fig. 429: Deep Muscles of the Gluteal Region and Posterior Thigh

NOTE: 1) in the gluteal region, the quadratus femoris has been reflected, revealing the obturator externus muscle. Also the tendon of the obturator internus muscle (between the gemelli) has been severed.

2) in the thigh, the common tendon of the long head of the biceps femoris and semitendinosus has been cut, thereby exposing the origin of the semimembranosus, the breadth of the adductor magnus, and the short head of the biceps femoris.

Figs. 428, 429

Iliac crest

Gluteal fascia

Subcutaneous synovial bursa
(over the post. superior
iliac spine)

Gluteus medius muscle

**Superior gluteal
artery and nerve**

Gluteus minimus muscle

**Inferior gluteal artery;
Sciatic nerve**

Subcutaneous synovial bursa
(over the sacrum)

Ischiofemoral
ligament

**Inferior
gluteal nerve**

Piriformis muscle

Trochanteric
bursa
(beneath
gluteus max. m.)

Gluteus maximus muscle

**Greater
trochanter**

Internal pudendal artery

Ischiofemoral
ligament

Sacrospinous ligament;
Superior gemellus muscle

**Inferior
gemellus muscle**

Obturator internus muscle

Obturator
externus muscle

Inferior ramus of pubis;
Sacrotuberous ligament

Intermuscular bursa
(beneath glut. max. m.)

Semimembranosus tendon

Gluteus maximus muscle

Common tendon of origin
(long head of biceps femoris muscle
and semitendinosus muscle)

Lesser trochanter;
Tendon of iliopsoas m.

Quadratus femoris muscle

Adductor magnus muscle

Adductor brevis muscle

Gracilis muscle

1st perforating artery;
Adductor magnus muscle

Semimembranosus muscle

Adductor magnus muscle

Linea aspera of femur

Semitendinosus muscle

Iliotibial tract (fascia lata)

**Biceps femoris muscle
(long head)**

Biceps femoris muscle
(short head)

Fig. 430: The Middle and Deep Gluteal Muscles and the Sciatic Nerve

NOTE: 1) with the gluteal muscles exposed by the reflection of the gluteus maximus muscle, one can appreciate that the centrally located piriformis muscle is the key structure in understanding the anatomy of this region. This muscle, as do most of the other structures which leave the pelvis to enter the gluteal region, passes through the greater sciatic foramen. The nerves and vessels which enter the gluteal region from the pelvis are situated either above the piriformis or below it. The important sciatic nerve enters the gluteal region below the piriformis muscle.

2) through their insertions on or around the greater trochanter, many of the gluteal muscles laterally rotate the femur. The most powerful lateral rotator is the gluteus maximus which is also the most powerful extensor of the thigh at the hip joint.

3) the origin of the hamstring muscles from the ischial tuberosity. The semitendinosus and long head of the biceps femoris have a common tendon of origin deep to which arises the semimembranosus muscle.

Fig. 430   **V**

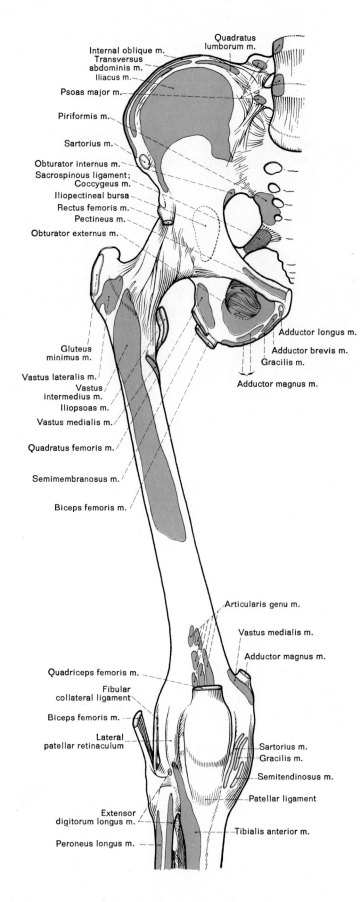

Internal oblique m.
Transversus abdominis m.
Iliacus m.
Quadratus lumborum m.
Psoas major m.
Piriformis m.
Sartorius m.
Obturator internus m.
Sacrospinous ligament;
Coccygeus m.
Iliopectineal bursa
Rectus femoris m.
Pectineus m.
Obturator externus m.
Adductor longus m.
Adductor brevis m.
Gracilis m.
Gluteus minimus m.
Adductor magnus m.
Vastus lateralis m.
Vastus intermedius m.
Iliopsoas m.
Vastus medialis m.
Quadratus femoris m.
Semimembranosus m.
Biceps femoris m.
Articularis genu m.
Vastus medialis m.
Adductor magnus m.
Quadriceps femoris m.
Fibular collateral ligament
Biceps femoris m.
Lateral patellar retinaculum
Sartorius m.
Gracilis m.
Semitendinosus m.
Patellar ligament
Extensor digitorum longus m.
Peroneus longus m.
Tibialis anterior m.

Fig. 431: Anterior View of Right Pelvis and Femur Showing Muscle Attachments

Figs. 431, 432

Neck of femur
Greater trochanter
Fovea of head of femur
Neck of femur
Intertrochanteric line
Lesser trochanter
Body of femur
Medial epicondyle
Lateral epicondyle
Patellar surface

Fig. 432: Right Femur: Anterior View

NOTE: 1) the femur is the longest and largest bone in the body and serves to transmit to the tibia and feet the weight of the trunk, upper extremity and head. It consists of a proximal extremity or head, the body or shaft and a distal extremity which is enlarged by two condyles.

2) the spherical head of the femur fits into the acetabulum of the pelvis. This articulation is protected by the capsule of the hip joint which is further strengthened by several ligaments. Below the head of the femur is the somewhat narrowed femoral neck. The superior aspect of the shaft is marked by two prominent tubercles, the greater and lesser trochanters.

3) the anterior surface of the body of the femur is smooth and its proximal 2/3rds gives origin to the vastus intermedius muscle.

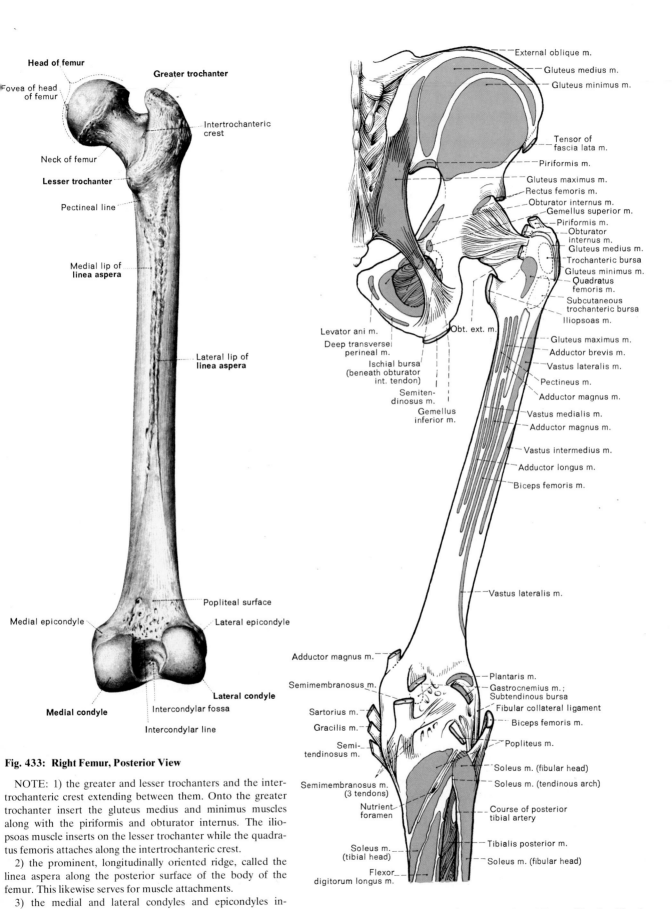

Fig. 433: Right Femur, Posterior View

NOTE: 1) the greater and lesser trochanters and the intertrochanteric crest extending between them. Onto the greater trochanter insert the gluteus medius and minimus muscles along with the piriformis and obturator internus. The iliopsoas muscle inserts on the lesser trochanter while the quadratus femoris attaches along the intertrochanteric crest.

2) the prominent, longitudinally oriented ridge, called the linea aspera along the posterior surface of the body of the femur. This likewise serves for muscle attachments.

3) the medial and lateral condyles and epicondyles inferiorly. The condyles articulate with the tibia and the intercondyloid fossa affords attachment to the cruciate ligaments.

Fig. 434: Posterior View of Right Pelvis and Femur Showing Muscle Attachments

Figs. 433, 434   **V**

Labels for Fig. 433:
- Head of femur
- Fovea of head of femur
- Greater trochanter
- Intertrochanteric crest
- Neck of femur
- Lesser trochanter
- Pectineal line
- Medial lip of linea aspera
- Lateral lip of linea aspera
- Popliteal surface
- Medial epicondyle
- Lateral epicondyle
- Medial condyle
- Lateral condyle
- Intercondylar fossa
- Intercondylar line

Labels for Fig. 434:
- External oblique m.
- Gluteus medius m.
- Gluteus minimus m.
- Tensor of fascia lata m.
- Piriformis m.
- Gluteus maximus m.
- Rectus femoris m.
- Obturator internus m.
- Gemellus superior m.
- Piriformis m.
- Obturator internus m.
- Gluteus medius m.
- Trochanteric bursa
- Gluteus minimus m.
- Quadratus femoris m.
- Subcutaneous trochanteric bursa
- Iliopsoas m.
- Gluteus maximus m.
- Adductor brevis m.
- Vastus lateralis m.
- Pectineus m.
- Adductor magnus m.
- Vastus medialis m.
- Adductor magnus m.
- Vastus intermedius m.
- Adductor longus m.
- Biceps femoris m.
- Vastus lateralis m.
- Levator ani m.
- Deep transverse perineal m.
- Ischial bursa (beneath obturator int. tendon)
- Semitendinosus m.
- Gemellus inferior m.
- Obt. ext. m.
- Adductor magnus m.
- Semimembranosus m.
- Sartorius m.
- Gracilis m.
- Semitendinosus m.
- Semimembranosus m. (3 tendons)
- Nutrient foramen
- Soleus m. (tibial head)
- Flexor digitorum longus m.
- Plantaris m.
- Gastrocnemius m.; Subtendinous bursa
- Fibular collateral ligament
- Biceps femoris m.
- Popliteus m.
- Soleus m. (fibular head)
- Soleus m. (tendinous arch)
- Course of posterior tibial artery
- Tibialis posterior m.
- Soleus m. (fibular head)

Fig. 435: The Right Hip Joint: Anterior View

NOTE: 1) the hip joint is a typical ball and socket joint and consists of the head of the femur which fits snugly into a deepened cavity called the acetabular fossa. The bones are held into position by a series of extremely strong ligaments.

2) the ligaments of the hip joint are the articular capsule, which is reinforced by the iliofemoral, pubofemoral and ischiofemoral ligaments, the acetabular labrum, the transverse acetabular ligament, and the ligament of the head of the femur (formerly called the round ligament of the femur).

3) the longitudinally oriented fibers on the anterior aspect of the articular capsule. Although composed of strong, dense connective tissue, the capsular attachment is loose and portions of it tend to relax during movement.

Tendon of rectus femoris muscle

Pubofemoral ligament

Iliofemoral ligament

Greater trochanter

Obturator membrane

Lesser trochanter

Fig. 436: The Right Hip Joint: Posterior View

NOTE that the fibers of the ischiofemoral ligament are directed almost horizontally across the capsule of the hip joint. Whereas anteriorly (Fig. 439) the capsule attaches along the intertrochanteric line of the femur, posteriorly it encircles the femoral neck. The capsule is thinnest and weaker posteriorly.

Tendon of rectus femoris muscle

Iliofemoral ligament

Ischiofemoral ligament

Neck of femur

Sacrotuberous ligament

Lesser trochanter

Greater trochanter

Gluteal tuberosity

Tendon of rectus femoris muscle

Iliofemoral ligament

Acetabular fossa

Ligament of head of femur

Acetabular labrum

Lunate surface

Articular capsule

Transverse acetabular ligament

Fig. 437: The Socket of the Right Hip Joint

NOTE: 1) the acetabulum is surrounded by a fibrocartilaginous rim called the acetabular labrum. This deepens the joint cavity and accommodates enough of the enlarged distal head of the femur so that it cannot be pulled from its socket without injuring the acetabular labrum.

2) the bony acetabulum is incomplete inferiorly. Here the prominent acetabular notch is partially covered by the transverse acetabular ligament. Through the remaining free portion of the acetabular notch course the vessels and nerves which supply the hip joint.

3) the ligament of the head of the femur attaches the femoral head by two bands to either side of the acetabular notch.

Figs. 435, 436, 437

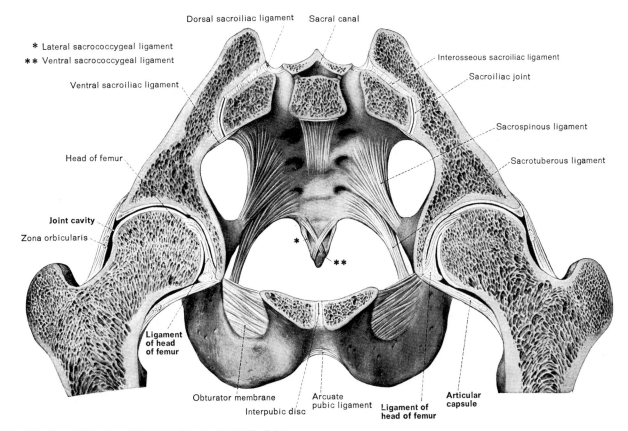

Fig. 438: **Frontal Section of the Pelvis Showing Both Hip Joints**

Fig. 439: **Anterior Exposure of the Right Hip Joint**

NOTE that the anterior aspect of the articular capsule of the hip joint has been opened close to the rounded acetabular labrum. This exposes the cartilage covered head of the femur within the joint cavity. Observe the ligament of the femoral head which is attached to the femur at a site where the cartilage is lacking. This depression is called the fovea of the femoral head.

Adductor magnus m.

Gracilis m.

MEDIAL

Tendinous cover of adductor canal

Opening of adductor canal

Vastus medialis m.

Tendon of adductor magnus m.

Semimem- branosus m.

Sartorius m.

Tendon of semimem- branosus m.

Tendon of semiten- dinosus m.

Gastrocnemius m. (medial head.)

Vastus lateralis m.

Biceps femoris m. (short head)

LATERAL

Linea aspera of femur

Biceps femoris (long head)

Popliteal surface of the femur

Plantaris m.

Gracilis m.

Tendon of biceps femoris m.

Semimem- branosus m.

Gastrocnemius m. (lateral head.)

Semitendinosus m.

Bice femc muse

Tibial nerve

Common peroneal nerve

Popliteal artery

Lat. superio genicular ar

Popliteal vein

Lat. sural cutaneous

Small saphenous vein

Sural arteries

Muscular branches, Tibial n.

Med. sural cutaneous r

Common peroneal n

Tendon of biceps femoris m.

MEDIAL

Medial head of gastrocnemius m.

Lateral head of gastrocnemius m.

LATERAL

Fig. 440: The Deep Muscles of the Popliteal Fossa

NOTE: 1) the popliteal fossa is a diamond-shaped space behind the knee joint. The superior boundaries of this space are the long head of the biceps femoris muscle laterally, and the semi-membranosus and semitendinosus muscles medially. All three of these muscles have been cut in this dissection, thereby exposing the more deeply located adductor magnus and vastus medialis medially and the short head of the biceps femoris laterally.

2) the inferior boundaries of the popliteal fossa are the medial and lateral heads of the gastrocnemius muscle which arise from the medial and lateral condyles of the femur.

3) the inferior opening of the adductor canal which transmits the popliteal artery and vein to the popliteal fossa from the anterior aspect of the thigh.

4) that deep or anterior to the popliteal fossa is the popliteal surface of the femur. This portion of the femur, located just above the epicondyles, can be seen as a flattened area on the lower posterior surface of the femur (see Fig. 433).

Fig. 441: Nerves and Vessels of the Popliteal Fossa

NOTE: 1) the relationships of the popliteal vessels and nerve within the diamond-shaped popliteal fossa. Observe that the sciatic nerve has already divided into the laterally directed common peroneal nerve and the tibial nerve which continues directly into the calf. Both the tibial and common peroneal nerves lie superficial to the vessels in the popliteal fossa.

2) the popliteal vein is located between the tibial nerve and popliteal artery while the artery is the deepest (most anterior) of the three structures and the most medially located.

3) the two muscular branches from the tibial nerve innervating the two heads of the gastrocnemius muscle and a sensory branch (medial sural cutaneous nerve) descending to the calf. Also note the lateral sural cutaneous nerve branching from the common peroneal nerve.

4) that the popliteal fossa is about 2.5 cm (1 inch) wide at its maximum, and realize that in the undissected specimen the fossa is filled with fat and most of the vessels and nerves shown in this figure cannot be seen.

Figs. 440, 441

Fig. 442: Arteriogram of Lower Femoral and Popliteal Arteries

NOTE: 1) this arteriogram shows the arterial tree of the lower third of the thigh and the upper third of the calf. Note the course of the femoral artery as it becomes the popliteal artery just above the intercondylar fossa in the popliteal space. The genicular arteries supplying the knee joint, and the sural arteries descending to supply both superficial and muscular tissues in the calf can be seen arising from the popliteal artery.

2) below the popliteal fossa the popliteal artery becomes the posterior tibial artery. Soon, the anterior tibial artery branches from the posterior tibial to course toward the anterior compartment in the leg, while the posterior tibial continues to descend in the posterior compartment. About 3 inches below the knee the peroneal artery arises from the posterior tibial artery and descends in the lateral portion of the deep calf.

Patella

Patellar surface of femur

Med. and lat. intercondylar tubercles

Tuberosity of tibia

Femoral artery

3rd perforating art.

Popliteal art.

Post. intercondylar fossa

Sup. genicular art.

Medial and lateral condyles of femur

Middle genicular art.

Popliteal art.

Medial and lateral tibial condyles

Sural arteries

Head of fibula

Anterior tibial art.

Ant. tibial recurrent art.

Post. tibial art. and peroneal art.

ANTERIOR

POSTERIOR

Perforating artery

Biceps femoris muscle

Popliteal surface of femur

Biceps femoris m.

Lat. superior genicular art.

Popliteal artery

Sural arteries

Lateral head of gastrocnemius m.

Plantaris m.

Lat. inferior genicular art.

Popliteus muscle

Posterior tibial recurrent art.

Anterior tibial artery

Soleus muscle

Peroneal artery

imem-sus m.

mitend-osus m.

Gracilis muscle

Descending genicular art.

Semimem-ranusus m.

d. superior genicular art.

Middle genicular art.

dial head of gastrocnemius muscle

Med. inferior genicular art.

Soleus muscle

Posterior tibial artery

Fig. 443: The Branches of the Popliteal Artery

NOTE: 1) within the popliteal fossa, the popliteal artery most frequently gives rise to five genicular arteries. There are usually two superior (lateral and medial), one middle and two inferior (lateral and medial) genicular arteries.

2) the genicular vessels course around the bones comprising the knee joint and supply the joint itself. Further, they form an anastomosis with each other and with descending branches from the femoral artery as well as recurrent vessels from the posterior and anterior tibial arteries.

3) the sural arteries branching from the popliteal to supply the two heads of the gastrocnemius muscle.

4) the anterior tibial artery branching from the posterior tibial and, penetrating an aperture above the interosseous membrane, achieves the anterior compartment. Somewhat lower, the peroneal artery also branches from the posterior tibial.

Figs. 442, 443   V

Iliotibial
tract

Tendon,
quadriceps
femoris
muscle

Vastus
lateralis m.

Iliotib.
tract;
Lateral
patellar
retinac.

Patellar
ligament

Head of
fibula

Crural
fascia

Vastus
medialis m.

Subcutaneous
prepatellar bursa;
Patella

Medial
patellar
retinaculum

Tuberosity
of tibia

Pes
anserinus

Tibia

Schratt

Fig. 444: The Region of the Knee Joint, Anterior View (Undissected, Right Lower Limb)

NOTE: 1) that only the skin and superficial fascia have been cut and reflected in this dissection, leaving the lower thigh, upper leg, and the intervening structures of the knee joint covered by the closely investing deep fascia of the lower extremity.

2) that a small longitudinal incision has been made in the deep fascia anterior to the patella, thereby opening the large *subcutaneous prepatellar bursa*. Several other bursae associated with the anterior aspect of the knee joint also may be dissected from this position. These include: the *subcutaneous infrapatellar bursa*, which lies between the lower portion of the tuberosity of the tibia and the overlying deep fascia; the *deep infrapatellar bursa*, which lies below the patella and between the ligamentum patellae and the upper surface of the tibia; and the large *suprapatellar bursa*, which is located above the patella, between the anterior surface of the lower femur and the tendon of the quadriceps femoris muscle (see also Figs. 445, 455, 458).

3) that these bursae may become inflamed, resulting in the painful condition called bursitis. Although the actual cause of bursitis is not known, it is frequently associated with consistent pressure or trauma over a bursa. Prepatellar bursitis (often called "housemaid's knee") usually involves the subcutaneous prepatellar and subcutaneous infrapatellar bursae and is sometimes observed in individuals who kneel frequently and for prolonged periods of time.

Femur

Articularis
genu muscle

Suprapatellar bursa

Quadriceps
tendon

Vastus
medialis m.

Patella

Lateral
patellar
retinaculum

Medial
patellar
retina...

Fibular
collateral
ligament

Tibial
collate...
ligame...

Deep infra-
patellar bursa

Patellar
ligament

Head of
fibula

Tibial
tuberosity

Fig. 445: Right Knee Joint (Anterior View)

NOTE: 1) that the deep fascia has been removed and the bellies of the components of the quadriceps femoris muscle have been cut to reveal the quadriceps tendon, the patella, and the patellar ligament. The latter structure inserts onto the tibial tuberosity located on the proximal aspect of the anterior tibial surface.

2) the medial and lateral patellar retinacula. These structures reinforce the anteromedial and anterolateral parts of the fibrous capsule of the knee joint and often (although not shown in this figure) they are attached to the borders of the patellar ligament and the patella.

3) the tibial and fibular collateral ligaments and the location of the deep infrapatellar bursa.

Figs. 444 and 445

Body of the femur

Patellar surface of the femur

Lateral condylopatellar line

Articular capsule

Lateral intercondylar tubercle

Lateral condyle of the femur

Lateral epicondyle of the femur

Anterior margin of the lateral meniscus

Femoral surface of the lateral meniscus

Lateral meniscus

Fibular collateral ligament

Lateral meniscus

Lateral condyle of tibia

Articular capsule

Anterior border of the lateral condyle of the tibia

Anterior ligament of the head of the fibula

Head of fibula

Lateral meniscus

Lateral patellar retinaculum (longitudinal part)

Lateral patellar retinaculum (transverse part)

Ligamentum patellae

Apex of patella

Patella (lateral articular facet)

Vertical ridge on the posterior surface of patella

Vastus lateralis muscle

Articular capsule

Medial condylopatellar line

Posterior cruciate ligament

Anterior cruciate ligament

Medial condyle of the femur

Medial epicondyle of the femur

Medial intercondylar tubercle

Transverse ligament of the knee

Medial condyle of the tibia

Articular capsule

Tibial collateral ligament

Medial meniscus

Site of attachment of medial meniscus on the tibial plateau

Articular capsule

Medial meniscus (anterior end)

Tibial collateral ligament

Tibia (anterior margin of articular surface)

Deep infrapatellar bursa

Medial patellar retinaculum (longitudinal part)

Patella (medial articular facet)

Medial patellar retinaculum (transverse part)

Base of patella

Tendon of rectus femoris and vastus intermedius muscles

Vastus medialis muscle

Fig. 446: Anterior View of the Right Knee Joint, Opened from the Front to Expose the Ligaments and Menisci

NOTE: 1) that the bellies and tendons of the quadriceps muscle have been severed and reflected downward to expose the inner (posterior) surface of the patella which is attached (a) to the joined tendons of the rectus femoris and vastus medialis superiorly and (b) to the patellar ligament inferiorly.

2) that the knee joint is a bicondylar synovial joint with a single joint cavity between the condyles of the femur and the condyles of the tibia.

3) within the notch between the femoral condyles are attached the posterior and anterior cruciate ligaments. The *posterior cruciate ligament* can be seen to be fixed to the medial condyle of the femur, while the *anterior cruciate ligament* is attached to the lateral condyle of the femur deep in the intercondylar notch. The attachment of the anterior cruciate ligament onto the anterior part of the tibial plateau is well shown in this figure, and the tibial attachment of the posterior cruciate ligament can be seen in Figures 448 and 453. These ligaments are essential for anterior-posterior stability of the knee joint.

4) that the anterior cruciate ligament is best dissected from this frontal approach. Although this ligament helps to prevent posterior displacement of the femur on the upper tibial surface, more importantly, as the ligament becomes tense, it serves to limit the extension (produced by the quadriceps muscle) of the lateral femoral condyle. Further extension beyond this limit places the knee joint in a locked position. This additional extension can be achieved at the knee joint because (a) the medial femoral condyle has a longer articular surface and a greater curvature than the lateral condyle and (b) after the anterior cruciate ligament becomes taut, the lateral condyle can rotate around „the radius of the ligament. This forces the medial condyle to glide backwards into its own full extension" (Last, R. J., *Anatomy, Regional and Applied*, Churchill Livingstone, Edinburgh, 1978, p. 164).

Fig. 446   V

◀ **Fig. 447: Right Knee Joint (Posterior View)**

NOTE that the posterior aspect of the articular capsule is reinforced by the oblique and arcuate popliteal ligaments and to some extent by the tendons of origin and insertion of muscles.

Fig. 448: Posterior View of the Right Knee Joint, Opened from Behind to Expose the Ligaments and Menisci

NOTE: 1) that the posterior part of the articular capsule has been opened, thereby exposing from behind the femoral condyles, the intercondylar fossa, the anterior and posterior cruciate ligaments, and the medial and lateral menisci.

2) the attachment of the anterior cruciate ligament quite far posteriorly onto the medial aspect of the lateral condyle of the femur and the attachment of the posterior cruciate ligament onto the posterior intercondylar surface of the tibia.

3) that when the knee joint is flexed and the lower limb is bearing weight, the *posterior cruciate ligament* prevents the femur from sliding forward along the surface of the tibial plateau. This is especially the case when one is walking downhill or descending stairs.

4) the *posterior meniscofemoral ligament*. It courses upward and medially from the posterior part of the lateral meniscus to attach onto the medial condyle of the femur. Observe that in this specimen it appears to split and to penetrate the fibers of the posterior cruciate ligament.

5) that the tendon of the semimembranosus muscle inserts onto the posterior surface of the medial condyle of the tibia and from its insertion it expands upward and laterally across the posterior surface of the articular capsule of the knee joint as the oblique popliteal ligament (see Fig. 447).

Figs. 447, 448

Fig. 449: The Distal End of the Right Femur, Lateral View

Labels: Lateral epicondyle, Lateral condyle, Notch for attachment of popliteus muscle

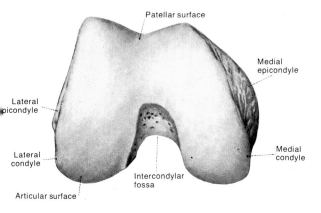

Fig. 450: The Distal End of the Right Femur, Viewed from Below

Labels: Patellar surface, Medial epicondyle, Lateral epicondyle, Lateral condyle, Intercondylar fossa, Medial condyle, Articular surface

Fig. 451 Flexed Right Knee Joint (Anterior View) Showing Cruciate Ligaments

Labels: Patellar surface of femur, Post. cruciate ligament, Medial condyle, Lateral condyle, Medial meniscus, Lateral meniscus, t. cruciate ligament, gament of d of fibula, Transverse nicular lig., Fibula, Tibia

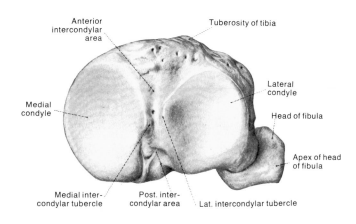

Fig. 452: The Proximal Ends of the Right Tibia and Fibula, Viewed from Above

Labels: Anterior intercondylar area, Tuberosity of tibia, Medial condyle, Lateral condyle, Head of fibula, Apex of head of fibula, Medial intercondylar tubercle, Post. intercondylar area, Lat. intercondylar tubercle

NOTE that the tibial plateau consists of two concave surfaces, the lateral and medial tibial condyles, on which rest the menisci and the femoral condyles. Between the tibial condyles is the intercondylar area onto which attach the cruciate ligaments and the menisci.

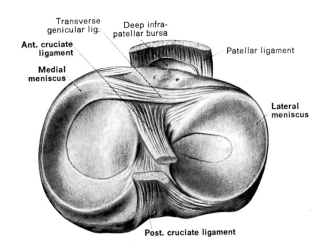

Fig. 453: The Condyles of the Right Tibia (from Above), Showing the Menisci and the Origins of the Cruciate Ligaments

Labels: Transverse genicular lig., Deep infra-patellar bursa, Ant. cruciate ligament, Medial meniscus, Patellar ligament, Lateral meniscus, Post. cruciate ligament

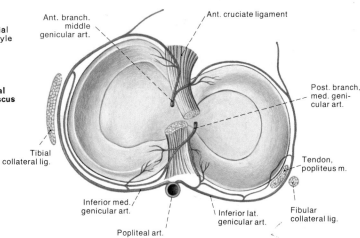

Fig. 454: The Arterial Supply of the Menisci, Right Knee

Labels: Ant. branch. middle genicular art., Ant. cruciate ligament, Post. branch, med. genicular art., Tibial collateral lig., Tendon, popliteus m., Inferior med. genicular art., Inferior lat. genicular art., Fibular collateral lig., Popliteal art.

NOTE that the medial and lateral *inferior* genicular arteries encircle the tibia and supply the menisci. The *middle* genicular (not shown in this figure) supplies the cruciate ligaments. (From Sick, H. and Kortiké, J. G., Z. Anat. Entwickl.-Gesch., *129*: 359–379, 1969.)

Fig. 455: Cast of Knee Joint (Distended) Showing Bursae and Joint Cavity

NOTE: 1) that this lateral view of the distended synovial cavity of the right knee joint demonstrates well that the synovial membrane of this joint is the most extensive of any in the body.

2) that the synovial membrane extends superiorly several centimeters above the patella to form a large pouch called the suprapatellar bursa. Laterally it courses deep to the popliteus tendon and fibular collateral ligament, while posteriorly it extends above the menisci as high as the origins of the heads of the gastrocnemius muscle. Inferiorly, the joint cavity is seen to descend below the lateral meniscus (and medial meniscus, see Fig. 456).

Fig. 456: Cast of Knee Joint Showing Bursae and Joint Cavity (Posterior View)

NOTE that in this posterior dissection of the right knee joint, the fibrous articular capsule has been removed to expose the joint cavity. The synovial membrane extends above the menisci deep to the heads of the gastrocnemius muscle, and below the menisci deep to the popliteus muscle laterally and the semimembranosus medially.

Figs. 455, 456, 457

Fig. 457: Radiograph of the Right Knee (Ant.-Post. Projection)

NOTE the following bony structures on the femur, tibia, and fibula in the region of the knee.

1. Body of femur
2. Margin of patella
3. Adductor tubercle
4. Medial epicondyle
5. Lateral epicondyle
6. Medial condyle of femur
7. Intercondylar fossa
8. Lateral condyle of femur
9. Med. intercondylar tubercle
10. Ant. intercondylar area
11. Lat. intercondylar tubercle
12. Med. condyle of tibia
13. Lat. condyle of tibia
14. Apex of head of fibula
15. Head of fibula
16. Body of tibia
17. Body of fibula

This radiograph comes from Wicke, L., *Atlas of Radiologic Anatomy*, 3rd Edition, Urban and Schwarzenberg, Baltimore, 1982.

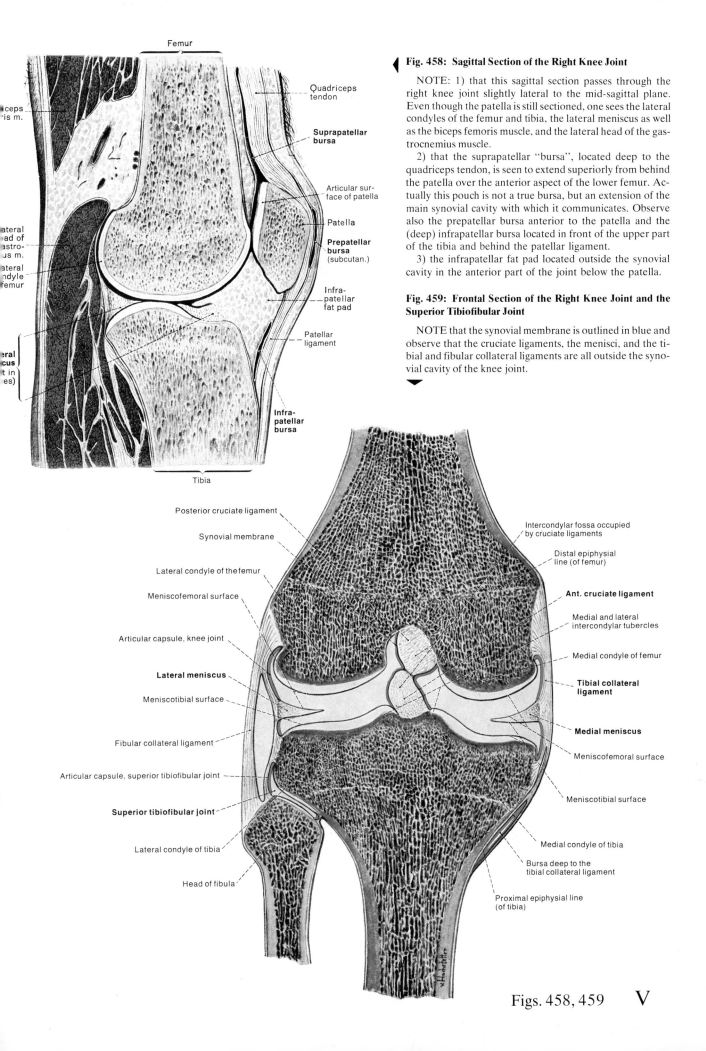

Femur

Quadriceps tendon

ceps is m.

Suprapatellar bursa

Articular surface of patella

lateral head of astro- us m.

Patella

lateral ndyle femur

Prepatellar bursa (subcutan.)

Infra-patellar fat pad

eral cus t in es)

Patellar ligament

Infra-patellar bursa

Tibia

Fig. 458: Sagittal Section of the Right Knee Joint

NOTE: 1) that this sagittal section passes through the right knee joint slightly lateral to the mid-sagittal plane. Even though the patella is still sectioned, one sees the lateral condyles of the femur and tibia, the lateral meniscus as well as the biceps femoris muscle, and the lateral head of the gastrocnemius muscle.

2) that the suprapatellar "bursa", located deep to the quadriceps tendon, is seen to extend superiorly from behind the patella over the anterior aspect of the lower femur. Actually this pouch is not a true bursa, but an extension of the main synovial cavity with which it communicates. Observe also the prepatellar bursa anterior to the patella and the (deep) infrapatellar bursa located in front of the upper part of the tibia and behind the patellar ligament.

3) the infrapatellar fat pad located outside the synovial cavity in the anterior part of the joint below the patella.

Fig. 459: Frontal Section of the Right Knee Joint and the Superior Tibiofibular Joint

NOTE that the synovial membrane is outlined in blue and observe that the cruciate ligaments, the menisci, and the tibial and fibular collateral ligaments are all outside the synovial cavity of the knee joint.

Posterior cruciate ligament

Synovial membrane

Lateral condyle of the femur

Meniscofemoral surface

Articular capsule, knee joint

Lateral meniscus

Meniscotibial surface

Fibular collateral ligament

Articular capsule, superior tibiofibular joint

Superior tibiofibular joint

Lateral condyle of tibia

Head of fibula

Intercondylar fossa occupied by cruciate ligaments

Distal epiphysial line (of femur)

Ant. cruciate ligament

Medial and lateral intercondylar tubercles

Medial condyle of femur

Tibial collateral ligament

Medial meniscus

Meniscofemoral surface

Meniscotibial surface

Medial condyle of tibia

Bursa deep to the tibial collateral ligament

Proximal epiphysial line (of tibia)

Figs. 458, 459   V

Genicular vein

Post. femoral cutaneous n.

Communicating vein

Saphenous nerve

Great saphenous vein

Post. femoral cutaneous n.

Small saphenous vein

Branches of lateral sural cutaneous n.

Communicating vein (betw. great and small saphenous vv.)

Communicating vein

Medial crural cutaneous nerve

Communicating nerve (from lat. sural cutan. n.)

Communicating vein

Small saphenous v.

Medial sural cutaneous n.

Sural nerve

Medial crural cutaneous br. (saphenous nerve)

Venous network on dorsal foot

Lat. dorsal cutan. n.

Small saphenous vein

Great saphenous v

Patella

Infrapatellar branch of saphenous ne

Saphenous nerv

Commun vein

Medial crural cutaneous branches of saphenous nerve

Communic vein to sm saphenous

Medial crural cutaneous branches of saphenous nerve

Superficial peroneal nerve

Medial dorsal cutan. n.

Intermed. dorsal cutaneous n.

Great saphenous vein

Fig. 460: Superficial Veins and Nerves of the Posterior Leg and Foot

NOTE the small saphenous vein which forms on the dorsolateral aspect of the foot and ascends to the popliteal fossa, and the sural nerve which is formed by the junction of the medial sural cutaneous nerve and a communicating branch from the lateral sural cutaneous nerve.

Fig. 461: Superficial Veins and Nerves on the Medial Aspect of the Leg and Foot

NOTE the formation of the great saphenous vein on the medial aspect of the foot and its course anterior to the medial malleolus and up the medial aspect of the leg. Branches of the saphenous nerve accompany the great saphenous vein below the knee. The saphenous nerve is the largest branch of the femoral nerve.

Figs. 460, 461

Gracilis m.

Semi-tendinosus m.

Vastus medialis m.

Semi-membranosus m.

Sartorius m.

Tendon of gracilis m.

Patella

Tendon of semimembranosus m.

Medial patellar retinaculum

Tendon of semitendinosus m.

Fat body

Patellar ligament

Gastrocnemius m., medial head

Pes anserinus

Tibia

Tibialis anterior m.

Soleus m.

Tendon of gastrocnemius m.

Flexor digitorum longus m.

Flex. hallucis long. m

Inferior extensor retinaculum

Tibialis post. tendon (synovial sheath)

Tibialis ant. m. (synovial sheath)

Ext. hallucis long. m. (synovial sheath)

Calcaneal tendon (Achilles)

Ext. digitorum long. m. (synovial sheath)

Flex. digitorum longus tendon (synovial sheath)

edial cuneiform bone

Flex. hallucis longus tendon (synovial sheath)

etatarsal

Bursa deep to calcaneal tendon

Abductor hallucis m.

Flexor retinaculum

Flex. hallucis longus m.

Flex. digitorum longus tendon (synovial sheath)

Deltoid lig.

Abductor hallucis m.

Fig. 462: Superficial Muscles and Tendons of the Right Lower Thigh and Leg, Medial View

NOTE: 1) the tendons of the sartorius, gracilis and semitendinosus (pes anserinus) protecting the medial aspect of the knee (see also Fig. 423). The tendon of the semimembranosus helps reinforce the capsule of the knee joint posteriorly (see also Fig. 447);

2) how the tendons of the muscles in the posterior compartment of the leg course beneath the medial malleolus, surrounded by synovial sheaths (in blue), to enter the foot;

3) the superficial location of most of the tibia in the leg.

Fig. 463: Superficial Muscles and Tendons of the Right Lower Thigh and Leg, Lateral View

NOTE: 1) the disposition of the anterior and lateral compartment muscles of the leg, and how their tendons, surrounded by tendon sheaths (in blue), enter the foot. Observe that the anterior compartment tendons enter the dorsum, while the lateral compartment tendons descend behind the lateral malleolus.

2) the superficial location of the head of the fibula and its relationship to the common peroneal nerve.

Biceps femoris m. (long head)

Iliotibial tract

Biceps femoris m. (short head)

Vastus lateralis m.

Tendon of rectus femoris m.

Fibular collateral lig.

Plantaris m.

Patella

Gastrocnemius m., lateral head

Lat. patellar retinaculum

Common peroneal n.

Deep infrapatellar bursa

Patellar lig.

Ant. ligament of head of fibula

Head of fibula

Soleus m.

Tibialis anterior m.

Peroneus longus m.

Ext. digitorum longus m.

Peroneus brevis m.

Ext. hallucis longus m.

Tibialis ant. tendon (synovial sheath)

Calcaneal tendon

Ext. digit. long. tendon (synovial sheath)

Inf. extensor retinaculum

Ext. hall. long. (synovial sheath)

Lat. malleolus

Ext. digit. brev. m.

Peroneus tert. tendon

Ext. hallucis long. tendon

Subcalcaneal tendon bursa

Sup. peroneal retinaculum

Calcaneofib. lig.

Ext. digit. longus tendons

Inf. peroneal retinac.

Opp. digiti minimi m.

Peroneal tendons (synovial sheath)

Abd. digiti minimi m.

* Tuberosity of 5th metatarsal

Figs. 462, 463   V

Fig. 464: Muscles of the Anterior Compartment of the Leg

NOTE: 1) the four anterior compartment muscles are the tibialis anterior, extensor hallucis longus, extensor digitorum longus and peroneus tertius.

2) the tibialis anterior dorsally flexes and supinates the foot. The other muscles extend the toes as well as dorsiflex the foot. Additionally, the extensor hallucis longus assists in supination, while the extensor digitorum longus and peroneus tertius are pronators.

Fig. 465: Nerves and Arteries of the Anterior and Lateral Compartments of the Leg

NOTE: 1) as the common peroneal nerve courses laterally around the head of the fibula, it divides into the superficial and deep peroneal nerves which innervate the muscles of the lateral and anterior compartments.

2) the deep peroneal nerve is joined by the anterior tibial artery which descends toward the foot.

Figs. 464, 465

Head of fibula

Tuberosity of tibia

...eus ...s m.

...rior ...bial ...ode

...eep ...mph ...els

...rior ...bial ...els

Tibialis anterior muscle

Medial surface of tibia

Gastrocnemius muscle

...nterior ...veins

Anterior tibial artery

Tendon of tibialis anterior muscle

Ext. digitorum longus m.

Inferior extensor retinaculum

Lateral malleolus

Vastus lateralis m.

Biceps femoris m.

Tendon of biceps femoris m.

Head of fibula

Patella

Patellar ligament

Tuberosity of tibia

Peroneus longus muscle

Tibialis anterior muscle

Soleus muscle

Groove for anterior intermuscular septum

Peroneus brevis muscle

Extensor digitorum and peroneus tertius muscles

Tendon of tibialis anterior muscle

Calcaneus tendon

Extensor hallucis longus m.

Lateral malleolus

Inferior extensor retinaculum

Ext. digitorum brevis m.

Sup. peroneal retinaculum

Tendon of peroneus tertius muscle
Tendons of ext. digitorum long. m.

Tendon of peroneus longus m.

Tendon of ext. hallucis brevis m.

Calcaneal tuberosity

Inferior peroneal retinaculum

Tendon of peroneus brevis m.

Fig. 466: Deep Lymphatic Channels and Nodes of the Anterior Leg

NOTE that lymphatic channels from the dorsum of the foot course superiorly and collect along the path of the more deeply situated anterior tibial vessels and nerve. At times a lymph node can be found just ventral to the anterior tibial artery below the knee.

Fig. 467: Muscles of the Lateral Compartment of the Leg

NOTE that the peroneus longus and brevis occupy the lateral compartment of the leg. Their tendons descend into the foot behind the lateral malleolus. The peroneus longus tendon crosses the sole of the foot to insert on the base of the 1st metatarsal bone, while the peroneus brevis inserts directly onto the 5th metatarsal bone.

Figs. 466, 467   **V**

Fig. 468: Superficial Nerves and Veins of the Dorsal Right Foot

NOTE: 1) cutaneous innervation of the dorsal foot is supplied principally by the superficial peroneal nerve (L 4, L 5, S 1). Additionally, the deep peroneal nerve (L 4, L 5) supplies the adjacent sides of the 1st and 2nd toes, while the lateral dorsal cutaneous nerve (S 1, S 2; terminal branch of the sural nerve in the foot) supplies the lateral and dorsal aspect of the 5th digit.

2) the digital and metatarsal veins drain back from the toes to form the dorsal venous arch of the foot. From this arch, the great saphenous vein ascends medially and the small saphenous vein laterally on the foot dorsum.

Fig. 469: Muscles and Tendons of the Dorsal Right Foot (Superficial View)

NOTE: 1) the tendons of the tibialis anterior, extensor hallucis longus and extensor digitorum longus are bound by the Y-shaped inferior extensor retinaculum as they enter the dorsum of the foot at the level of the ankle joint.

2) the long extensor tendons insert onto the dorsal aspect of the distal phalanx of each toe. In addition, the tendons of the extensor digitorum longus also insert onto the dorsum of the middle phalanx of the lateral four toes.

3) the tendon of the peroneus tertius insert on the base of the 5th metatarsal bone (and at times the 4th also).

Figs. 468, 469

Tendon, Tibialis anterior m.

Extensor hallucis longus muscle

Inferior extensor retinaculum

Extensor digitorum longus muscle

Lateral malleolus

don of peroneus brevis muscle

Extensor digitorum evis muscle

Extensor hallucis brevis muscle

ndon of roneus tertius muscle

Dorsal interosseous muscle

on eus vis lon

Tendons of extensor digitorum brevis m.

dons of extensor itorum longus m.

Ext. digitor.long. m.

Extensor hallucis longus m.

Perforating branch of peroneal artery

Ant. tibial artery

Ant. lat. malleolar art.

Lat. malleolar network

Ext. digitor. long. m.

Ext. digitor. brevis m.

Lateral tarsal artery

Arcuate artery

Dorsal metatarsal aa.

Dorsal digital aa.

Dorsal digital nn. (deep peroneal n.)

Tendon, Tibialis anterior m.

Tibia

Anterior medial malleolar art.

Deep peroneal nerve

Medial malleolar network

Ant. medial malleolar art.

Tarsal branch of deep peroneal nerve

Medial tarsal aa.

Articular branches of peroneal nerve

Dorsalis pedis a.

Deep plantar a.

Tendon, Extensor hallucis brevis m.

Tendon, Extensor hallucis longus m.

Fig. 470: The Intrinsic Muscles of the Dorsal Foot (right)

NOTE: 1) the inferior extensor retinaculum has been opened and the tendons of the extensor digitorum longus and peroneus tertius have been severed.

2) the extensor hallucis brevis and the three small bellies of the extensor digitorum brevis. The delicate tendons of these muscles insert on the proximal phalanx of the medial four toes.

3) the four dorsal interosseous muscles. These muscles abduct the toes from the longitudinal axis of the foot (down the middle of the 2nd toe). The first dorsal interosseous muscle inserts on the medial side of the 2nd toe, while the remaining three insert on the lateral side of the 2nd, 3rd, and 4th toes.

Fig. 471: Deep Nerves and Arteries of the Dorsal Foot

NOTE: 1) the deep coursing anterior tibial artery and deep peroneal nerve and their branches have been exposed. They enter the foot between the tendons of the extensor hallucis longus and extensor digitorum.

2) the anterior tibial artery becomes the dorsalis pedis artery below the ankle joint. Observe the malleolar, tarsal, arcuate, dorsal metatarsal and digital arteries.

3) the deep peroneal nerve supplies the extensor brevis muscle in the foot and continues distally to terminate as two dorsal digital nerves supplying the adjacent sides of the 1st and 2nd toes.

Figs. 470, 471   V

Fig. 472: The Deep Fascia of the Leg (the Crural Fascia), Posterior View

NOTE that the deep fascia of the leg closely invests all of the muscles between the knee and ankle and forms the fascial covering over the popliteal fossa. It is continuous above with the fascia lata of the thigh and inferiorly with the retinacula which bind the tendons close to the bones.

Fig. 473: Muscles of the Posterior Leg: Superficial Calf Muscles

NOTE: 1) the gastrocnemius muscle arises by two heads from the condyles and posterior popliteal surface of the femur and its fibers are oriented inferomedially toward a central tendinous raphe. It inserts by means of the strong calcaneal tendon onto the calcaneal tuberosity.

2) the gastrocnemius is a powerful plantar flexor of the foot and its continued action also tends to flex the leg at the knee joint.

Figs. 472, 473

Medial head of
Grocnemius m.

branosus m.

Sub-gastro-
emius bursa

-semimem-
osus bursa

ue popliteal
ligament

dial condyle
of tibia

Posterior
tibial vessels

leus muscle

Tendon of
antaris m.

Tendon of
strocnemius m.

Flexor
gitorum longus m.

Tendon of
ialis posterior m.

dial malleolus

lcaneal tendon

Flexor
retinaculum

Calcaneal
tuberosity

Biceps femoris m.

Lateral head of
gastrocnemius m.

Arcuate popliteal
ligament

Plantaris m.

Gastrocnemius m.

Peroneus
longus m.

Flexor hallucis
longus m.

Cleavage for posterior
intermuscular septum

Peroneus
brevis m.

Superior
peroneal
retinaculum

Semimembranosus m.

Semitendinosus m.

Sural vessels

Medial head of
gastrocnemius m.

Medial inferior
genicular artery

**Posterior
tibial vein**

Tendinous arch
of soleus muscle

Tendon of
plantaris m.

Tibial nerve

**Posterior
tibial vessels**

Tendon of tibialis
posterior m.

Flexor retinaculum

Calcaneal tendon

Biceps femoris m.

Tibial nerve

Popliteal vein

Small saphenous v.

Lateral head of
gastrocnemius m.

Sural vessels

**Common
peroneal n.**

**Muscular branches
of tibial nerve**

Soleus muscle

Gastrocnemius
muscle

Peroneus longus m.

Peroneus brevis m.

Lateral malleolus

Superior peroneal
retinaculum

Fig. 474: Muscles of the Posterior Leg, Second Layer of Calf Muscles

NOTE: 1) both heads of the gastrocnemius have been severed to
uncover the underlying soleus and plantaris muscles. The soleus is
broad and thick, arising from the posterior surface of the fibula,
the intermuscular septum and the dorsal aspect of the tibia. Its
fibers join the calcaneal tendon.

2) the plantaris courses between the gastrocnemius and soleus.
Both muscles are plantar flexors of the foot.

Fig. 475: Nerves and Vessels of the Posterior Leg: Superficial Layer

NOTE that the popliteal vessels and tibial nerve, descending from
the popliteal fossa into the posterior compartment of the leg,
commence in the middle of the leg and course medially in a gradual
fashion so that at the ankle they lie behind the medial malleolus.

Figs. 474, 475 **V**

Common peroneal nerve

Tibial nerve

Popliteal vein

Popliteal artery

Plantaris muscle

Inferior medial genicular artery

Soleus muscle

Popliteal artery

Peroneal artery

Soleus muscle

Posterior tibial artery

Tibial nerve

Tibialis posterior m.

Flexor digitorum longus muscle

Posterior tibial artery

Flexor hallucis longus muscle

Tibial nerve

Tendon of tibialis posterior muscle

Lateral malleolus

Medial malleolus

Superior peroneal retinaculum

Flexor retinaculum

Calcaneal tendon

Fig. 476: Nerves and Vessels of the Right Posterior Leg, Intermediate Layer

NOTE: 1) the soleus muscle has been severed and reflected laterally, exposing the course of the tibial artery and posterior tibial nerve as far as the medial malleolus.

2) that this vessel and nerve descend in the leg between the flexor hallucis longus and the flexor digitorum longus and dorsal to the tibialis posterior muscle.

Figs. 476, 477

Popliteal s(of femur

Med. head of gastro-cnemius m. { Muscle

Biceps fem(

Bursa

Lateral head gastrocnemiu(

Semimem-branosus m. { Tendon

Plantaris m.

Popliteus m.

Bursa

Oblique popliteal ligament

Tibialis posterior m.

Soleus

Medial crest of fibula

Flexor digitorum longus m.

Tibialis posterior muscle

Peroneus longus m.

Flexor hallucis longus muscle

Tibia

Tendon of **flexor digitorum longus m.**

Tendon of **flexor hallucis longus**

Medial malleolus

Tendon of tibialis posterior m.

Superior peroneal retinaculum

Flexor retinaculum

Calcaneal tendon

Calcaneal tuberosity

Fig. 477: Muscles of the Posterior Compartment of the Leg: Deep Group: Four Muscles

NOTE: 1) the four deep posterior compartment muscles are: a) the popliteus, b) the flexor digitorum longus, c) the tibialis posterior and d) the flexor hallucis longus.

2) the popliteus is a femorotibial muscle and tends to rotate the leg medially and flex the leg at the knee joint. The other three muscles are cruropedal muscles and, as a group, they invert the foot, flex the toes and assist in plantarflexion at the ankle joint.

Fig. 478: The Tibialis Posterior and Flexor Hallucis Longus Muscles

NOTE: 1) the tendon of the flexor digitorum longus and the popliteus muscle have been severed. The tendon of the tibialis posterior crosses beneath that of the flexor digitorum longus just before entering the foot.

2) the flexor hallucis longus muscle arises from the distal 2/3rds of the fibula and the intermuscular septa. Its tendon lies in a groove on the posterior surface of the talus.

Fig. 479: Nerves and Muscles of the Deep Posterior Leg

NOTE: 1) the soleus muscle was resected and the tibial nerve pulled aside. Observe the branching of the peroneal artery from the posterior tibial, and its descending course toward the lateral malleolus.

2) in the popliteal fossa, the tibial nerve courses superficial to the popliteal artery, whereas at the ankle, the posterior tibial artery is superficial to the tibial nerve.

Figs. 478, 479   **V**

Anterior ligament of head of fibula
(proximal tibiofibular joint)

Lateral condyle

Head of fibula

Tibial tuberosity

Tuberosity of tibia

Anterior border (crest)

Lateral surface (of tibial shaft)

Interosseous membrane

Tibia

Fibular notch

Inferior articular surface

Fig. 480

Medial malleolus

Lateral malleolus

Anterior tibiofibular ligament
(distal tibiofibular syndesmosis)

Superior articular surface of medial condyle

Medial condyle

Medial surface (of tibial shaft)

Medial malleolus

Fig. 481

Iliotibial tract

Ext. digitorum longus muscle

Biceps femoris m.

Sartorius m.

Gracilis m.

Quadriceps femoris m.

Semitendinosus m.

Peroneus longus m.

Tibialis anterior m.

Extensor digitorum longus muscle

Peroneus brevis m.

Extensor hallucis longus muscle

Fig. 482

Fig. 480: The Tibiofibular Union and Interosseous Membrane (Right Leg)

NOTE: 1) from this anterior view that the shafts of the fibula and the tibia are connected from the knee to the ankle by the interosseous membrane. Additionally, the two bones are joined proximally (the tibiofibular joint) and distally (the tibiofibular syndesmosis).

2) proximally, the head of the fibula articulates with the inferolateral aspect of the lateral condyle of the tibia. This is a gliding joint, surrounded by an articular capsule and strengthened by the anterior and posterior ligaments of the head of the fibula.

3) the ligamentous union between the distal ends of the fibula and tibia is formed by the anterior and posterior tibiofibular ligaments.

Fig. 481: The Right Tibia, Anterior View

Note that the proximal extremity is marked by the two tibial condyles and the tibial tuberosity. The medial aspect of the distal extremity forms the medial malleolus.

Fig. 482: Muscle Attachments on the Right Tibia and Fibula (Anterior Surface)

NOTE: 1) that most of the upper 3/4ths of the anterior fibular surface affords attachment to muscles, while much of the anterior aspect of the tibia is free of muscle attachments. The only muscle of the anterior and lateral compartments which does *not* arise from the fibula is the tibialis anterior. The only muscle of the thigh which attaches to the fibula is the biceps femoris.

2) portions of the anterior surface of the interosseous membrane is used by all three muscles of the anterior compartment (tibialis anterior, extensor hallucis longus, extensor digitorum longus) for their *origin*, whereas neither of the lateral compartment muscles (peroneus longus and brevis) extend that far medially.

3) onto the medial condyle of the tibia insert the sartorius, gracilis and semitendinosus muscles forming a tendinous expansion sometimes called the pes anserinus (goose's foot), while onto the tibial tuberosity inserts the massive quadriceps femoris muscle.

Figs. 480, 481, 482

Fig. 483: Muscle Attachments on the Right Tibia and Fibula (Posterior Surface)

NOTE: 1) that of the posterior compartment muscles, only the gastrocnemius and plantaris muscles do not attach to the posterior surface of the tibia, fibula or interosseous membrane.

2) that virtually the entire posterior surface of the fibula serves for the origin of muscles. The soleus arises from the upper one-third of the posterior fibular surface and along the soleal line of the tibia. Inferior to the origin of the soleus which spans across both bones, the flexor hallucis longus arises principally from the fibula, while the flexor digitorum longus arises primarily from the tibia.

3) the tibialis posterior is interposed between the flexors hallucis longus and digitorum longus, thereby arising from the posterior surface of the interosseous membrane.

4) the arrows indicating the course of the tendons into the foot from the posterior surface. Observe that the tendon of the tibialis posterior crosses from lateral to medial beneath the tendon of the flexor digitorum longus and enters the foot immediately behind the medial malleolus.

Fig. 483

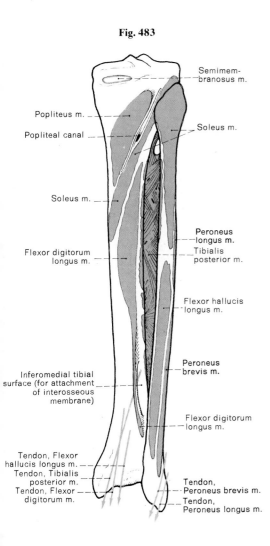

Semimem-branosus m.

Popliteus m.

Popliteal canal

Soleus m.

Soleus m.

Flexor digitorum longus m.

Peroneus longus m.

Tibialis posterior m.

Flexor hallucis longus m.

Peroneus brevis m.

Inferomedial tibial surface (for attachment of interosseous membrane)

Flexor digitorum longus m.

Tendon, Flexor hallucis longus m.
Tendon, Tibialis posterior m.
Tendon, Flexor digitorum m.

Tendon, Peroneus brevis m.
Tendon, Peroneus longus m.

Intercondylar eminence

Medial condyle

Lateral condyle

Fibular articular surface

Apex (styloid process)

Head of fibula

Soleal line

Nutrient foramen

Posterior border

Anterior border

Lateral surface

Medial margin

Posterior surface

Interosseous margin

Lateral surface

Malleolar groove

Distal extremity

Lateral malleolar groove

Lateral malleolus

Malleolar articular surface

Inferior articular surface

Fig. 484

Fig. 485

Fig. 484: The Right Tibia, Posterior View

NOTE: 1) the smooth posterior surface of the shaft of the tibia is marked by a prominent ridge (the soleal line) and a large oblong foramen (the nutrient foramen). The tibial shaft tapers toward a larger proximal extremity and somewhat less pronounced distal extremity.

2) at the proximal extremity the rounded medial and lateral condyles are separated by the intercondylar eminence, anterior and posterior to which attach the cruciate ligaments. At its distal extremity, the tibia articulates with the talus and, on this posterior surface, presents grooves for the passage of the tendons of the tibialis posterior, flexor digitorum longus and flexor hallucis longus.

Fig. 485: The Right Fibula, Lateral View

NOTE: 1) the fibula is a long slender bone situated lateral to the tibia to which it articulates proximally (see Figure 480). Distally, the fibula expands to form the lateral malleolus. The medial aspect of its inferior articular surface participates with the tibia in forming the talocrural or ankle joint.

2) although the fibula does not bear any weight of the trunk (since it does not participate in the knee joint articulation), it is important because of the numerous muscles wich attach to its surface (see Figures 482 and 483) and because it assists in the formation of the ankle joint.

LATERAL   **MEDIAL**

Medial femoral intermuscular septum

Rectus femoris muscle

Vastus intermedius muscle

Anterior cutaneous branches of femoral nerve

Perforating artery (from femoral artery)

Muscular branch of femoral nerve
(to vastus medialis muscle)

Muscular branches of femoral nerve

Anterior cutaneous branch of femoral nerve

Vastus lateralis muscle

Fascia lata

Iliotibial tract

Vastus medialis muscle

Femur

Fascia between vastus medialis and adductor canal

Skin

Medial femoral intermuscular septum

Superficial fascia

Great saphenous vein

Sartorius muscle

Saphenous nerve

Linea aspera

Subsartorial fascia

Lateral femoral intermuscular
septum

Adductor longus muscle

Accessory saphenous vein

Biceps femoris muscle
(short head)

Cutaneous branch of obturator nerve

Perforating artery and vein

Femoral artery and vein

Gracilis muscle

Sciatic nerve (tibial and common peroneal nn.)

Adductor canal

Fascia lata

Biceps femoris muscle (long head)

Adductor magnus muscle

Posterior portion of fascia lata

Semimembranosus muscle

Semitendinosus
muscle

Fascia between adductor muscles
and hamstring muscles

Posterior femoral cutaneous nerve

Fig. 486: Cross Section Through Middle Third of Right Thigh (Distal Surface)

Fig. 487: Cross Section of Right Thigh Just Above Patella (Distal Surface)

LATERAL   **MEDIAL**

Suprapatellar bursa

Ant. cutaneous branch of femoral nerve

Vastus medialis muscle

Fascia lata (anterior part)

Tendon of quadriceps femoris m.
Articularis genu muscle

Ant. cutaneous branch of femoral nerve

Femur

Saphenous branch of descend. genicular a.

Vastus lateralis muscle

Cutaneous branch of obturator n.

Iliotibial tract

Fascia lata

Lateral femoral
intermuscular septum

Tendon, adductor magnus m.

Popliteal fossa

Infrapatellar branch
of saphenous nerve

Biceps femoris muscle

Med. sup. genicular a.;
Saphenous nerve

Tibial nerve

Great saphenous vein

Common peroneal nerve

Popliteal lymph node

Lateral sural cutan. nerve

Sartorius muscle

Medial sural cutan. nerve;
Small saphenous vein

Fascia deep to
sartorius muscle

Gracilis muscle

Popliteal fascia
(posterior part of fascia lata)

Popliteal artery and vein

Tendon of semitendinosus muscle

Semimembranosus muscle

Fig. 486

Fig. 487

Fig. 489

Fig. 490

Fig. 491

Fig. 515

Fig. 516

**Fig. 488: Cross Sectional Planes of Lower
Extremity Shown in Seven Figures of This Atlas**

Figs. 486, 487, 488

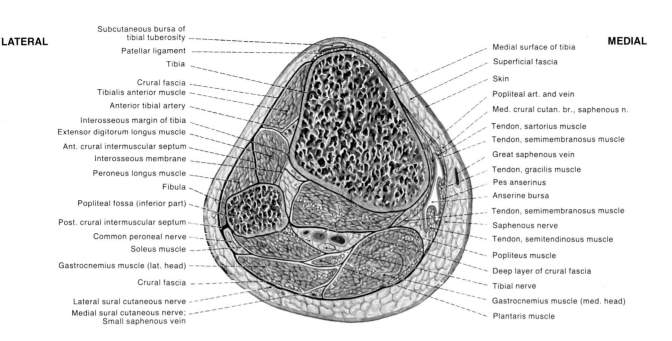

LATERAL

Subcutaneous bursa of tibial tuberosity
Patellar ligament
Tibia
Crural fascia
Tibialis anterior muscle
Anterior tibial artery
Interosseous margin of tibia
Extensor digitorum longus muscle
Ant. crural intermuscular septum
Interosseous membrane
Peroneus longus muscle
Fibula
Popliteal fossa (inferior part)
Post. crural intermuscular septum
Common peroneal nerve
Soleus muscle
Gastrocnemius muscle (lat. head)
Crural fascia
Lateral sural cutaneous nerve
Medial sural cutaneous nerve; Small saphenous vein

MEDIAL

Medial surface of tibia
Superficial fascia
Skin
Popliteal art. and vein
Med. crural cutan. br., saphenous n.
Tendon, sartorius muscle
Tendon, semimembranosus muscle
Great saphenous vein
Tendon, gracilis muscle
Pes anserinus
Anserine bursa
Tendon, semimembranosus muscle
Saphenous nerve
Tendon, semitendinosus muscle
Popliteus muscle
Deep layer of crural fascia
Tibial nerve
Gastrocnemius muscle (med. head)
Plantaris muscle

Fig. 489: Cross Section Through Upper Third of Right Leg (Distal Surface)

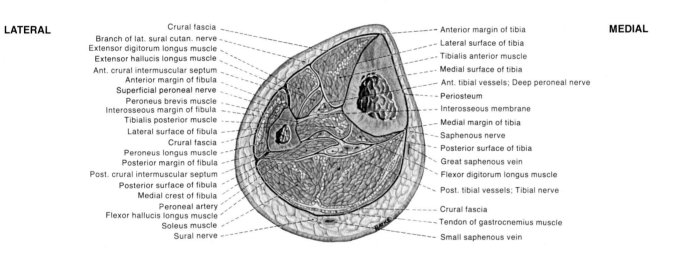

LATERAL

Crural fascia
Branch of lat. sural cutan. nerve
Extensor digitorum longus muscle
Extensor hallucis longus muscle
Ant. crural intermuscular septum
Anterior margin of fibula
Superficial peroneal nerve
Peroneus brevis muscle
Interosseous margin of fibula
Tibialis posterior muscle
Lateral surface of fibula
Crural fascia
Peroneus longus muscle
Posterior margin of fibula
Post. crural intermuscular septum
Posterior surface of fibula
Medial crest of fibula
Peroneal artery
Flexor hallucis longus muscle
Soleus muscle
Sural nerve

MEDIAL

Anterior margin of tibia
Lateral surface of tibia
Tibialis anterior muscle
Medial surface of tibia
Ant. tibial vessels; Deep peroneal nerve
Periosteum
Interosseous membrane
Medial margin of tibia
Saphenous nerve
Posterior surface of tibia
Great saphenous vein
Flexor digitorum longus muscle
Post. tibial vessels; Tibial nerve
Crural fascia
Tendon of gastrocnemius muscle
Small saphenous vein

Fig. 490: Cross Section Through the Middle of Right Leg (Distal Surface)

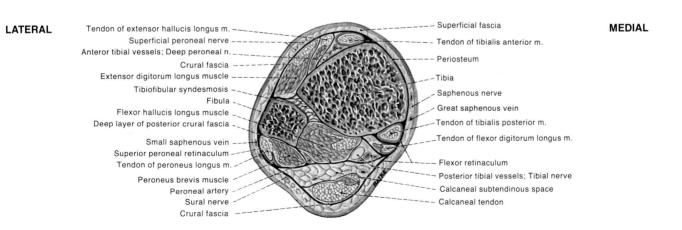

LATERAL

Tendon of extensor hallucis longus m.
Superficial peroneal nerve
Anterior tibial vessels; Deep peroneal n.
Crural fascia
Extensor digitorum longus muscle
Tibiofibular syndesmosis
Fibula
Flexor hallucis longus muscle
Deep layer of posterior crural fascia
Small saphenous vein
Superior peroneal retinaculum
Tendon of peroneus longus m.
Peroneus brevis muscle
Peroneal artery
Sural nerve
Crural fascia

MEDIAL

Superficial fascia
Tendon of tibialis anterior m.
Periosteum
Tibia
Saphenous nerve
Great saphenous vein
Tendon of tibialis posterior m.
Tendon of flexor digitorum longus m.
Flexor retinaculum
Posterior tibial vessels; Tibial nerve
Calcaneal subtendinous space
Calcaneal tendon

Fig. 491: Cross Section Through the Right Leg Just Above the Malleoli (Distal Surface)

Figs. 489, 490, 491   **V**

Proper
digital aa.

Proper plantar
digital nn.

Common
plantar
digital
nerves

Plantar
metatarsal aa.

Tendon
sheath of
flex. hallu-
cis long m.

Lateral
plantar nerve
(superficial branch)

Cutaneous branches
(med. plantar nerve)

Proper
digital
plantar
nerve

Cutaneous
branches
(lat. plan-
tar nerve)

Lateral
plantar
eminence

Plantar
aponeurosis

Medial
plantar
eminence

Plantar
aponeurosis

Flexo
retina

Medial p

Post. tibial a

Lateral plantar n

Plantar
aponeurosis

Calcaneal tuberosity

Medial calcaneal nerve

Fig. 492: The Sole of the Right Foot: Plantar Aponeurosis

NOTE: 1) the plantar aponeurosis which stretches across the sole of the foot. Similar to the palmar aponeurosis in the hand, the plantar aponeurosis is a thickened layer of deep fascia which serves both a protective and supportive function to the underlying muscles, vessels and nerves.

2) the longitudinal orientation of the fibers of the plantar aponeurosis and their attachment to the calcaneal tuberosity. Distally, the aponeurosis divides into five digital slips, one of which courses to each toe. Fibers extend from the margins of the aponeurosis to cover partially both the medial and lateral plantar eminences.

Fig. 493: The Sole of the Right Foot: Superficial Nerves and Arteries

NOTE: 1) the medial and lateral plantar nerves and posterior tibial artery as they enter the foot behind the medial malleolus and immediately course beneath the plantar aponeurosis toward the digits. Sensory branches of the nerves penetrate the aponeurosis to innervate the overlying skin and superficial fascia.

2) between the digital slips of the plantar aponeurosis, the vessels and the nerves course superficially toward the toes. Metatarsal arteries and common plantar digital nerves divide to supply adjacent portions of the toes as proper plantar digital arteries and nerves.

Figs. 492, 493

Fibrous sheaths
of the digits

Tendon,
Flexor
hallucis
longus m.

Flexor
hallucis
brevis
muscle

Lumbrical
mm.

exor
digiti
nimi
s m.

ntar
eous
scle

bductor
digiti
nimi m.

Flexor
digitorum
brevis m.

Abductor
hallucis m.

Plantar
aponeurosis

Calcaneal tuberosity

Opened digital
tendon sheaths

Tendons,
Flexor
digitorum
brevis m.

Adductor
hallucis m.
(transverse
head)

Flexor digiti
minimi brevis m.

Abductor digiti
minimi m.

Plantar
interosseous
muscles

Peroneus
longus
muscle

Tendon
sheath

Tendon

Tendon,
Flexor
hallucis
longus m.

Tendons,
Flexor
digitor.
long. m.

Flexor
hallucis
brevis m.

Tendon,
Flexor
digitorum
longus m.

Tendon,
Flexor
hallucis
longus m.

Abductor
hallucis m.

Quadratus plantae m.

Abductor digiti
minimi muscle

Abductor digiti
minimi muscle
(deep head)

Flexor digitorum
brevis m.

Calcaneal
tuberosity

Fig. 495: The Sole of the Right Foot: Second Layer of Plantar Muscles

NOTE: 1) the tendons of the flexor digitorum brevis muscle were severed and removed, thereby exposing the underlying tendons of the flexor digitorum longus muscle.

2) the muscles of the second layer in the plantar foot include the quadratus plantae muscle and the four lumbrical muscles. The quadratus plantae arises by two heads from the calcaneus and inserts into the tendon of the flexor digitorum longus.

3) the four lumbrical muscles arising from the tendons of the flexor digitorum longus muscle. They insert on the medial aspect of the first phalanx of the lateral four toes as well as on the dorsal extensor hoods.

Fig. 494: The Sole of the Right Foot: First Layer of Plantar Muscles

NOTE: 1) with most of the plantar aponeurosis removed, three muscles comprising the first layer of the sole are exposed. These are the abductor hallucis, the flexor digitorum brevis, and the abductor digiti minimi.

2) all three muscles arise from the tuberosity of the calcaneus. The abductor hallucis inserts on the proximal phalanx of the large toe. The flexor digitorum brevis separates into four tendons which insert onto the middle phalanges of the lateral four toes. The abductor digiti minimi inserts onto the proximal phalanx of the little toe.

Figs. 494, 495   V

Proper digital aa.

Tendons, Flexor
digitorum brevis m.

**Proper digital
plantar nerves**

**Plantar
metatarsal
arteries**

**Common
plantar
digital
nerves**

Flexor
hallucis
brevis m.

**Lateral
plantar n.**

Quadratus
plantae m.

**Lateral
plantar a.**

Abductor
digiti
minimi m.

Flexor
digitorum
brevis m.

Calcaneal network

Tendon,
Flexor
hallucis
longus m.

Flexor
digiti
minimi
brevis m.

Adductor hallucis m.
(oblique head)

Plantar arch

**Deep branch,
Lateral plantar n.**

Cutaneous
branch,
Med. plantar n.

**Lateral
plantar nerve**

Abductor
digiti minimi m.

**Medial
plantar art.**

Abductor
hallucis m.

Flexor
retinaculum

**Medial
plantar nerve**

**Posterior
tibial artery**

Lateral plantar nerve

Opened synovial
tendon sheath

Tendon,
Flexor
hallucis
longus m.

**Plantar
metatarsal
arteries**

Tend
Flexor
halluc
longus

Adducto
hallucis
(transve
head)

Flexor
hallucis
brevis m

**Deep pla
artery**

**Medial
plantar
artery**

Tendon, F
hallucis lo

Quadrat
plantae

**Medial
plantar
nerve**

**Lateral
plantar a**

Abducto
hallucis

**Medial
plantar ne**

Post. tibial a

Lateral plantar ne

**Fig. 497: The Sole of the Right Foot: the Plantar Arch
and Deep Vessels and Nerves**

Fig. 496: The Sole of the Right Foot: the Plantar Nerves and Arteries

NOTE: 1) whereas the tibial nerve divides into medial and lateral plantar nerves just inferior to the medial malleolus, the posterior tibial artery enters the plantar surface of the foot as a single vessel and divides into medial and lateral plantar arteries beneath or at the medial border of the abductor hallucis muscle.

2) the lateral plantar nerve supplies the lateral 1−1/2 digits while the medial plantar nerve supplies the medial 3−1/2 digits. Observe the formation of the common digital plantar nerves which then divide into the proper digital plantar nerves.

3) that the main trunks of the plantar vessels and nerves cross the sole of the foot from medial to lateral deep to the flexor digitorum brevis and abductor hallucis muscles (first layer), but superficial to the quadratus plantae and lumbrical muscles (second layer).

NOTE: 1) the formation of the deep plantar arch principally from the lateral plantar artery, and the junction of the deep plantar arch with the deep plantar artery from the foot dorsum (see Fig. 471). From the plantar arch branch plantar metatarsal arteries which then divide into proper digital arteries.

2) the muscles of the foot are innervated in the following manner:

	medial plantar nerve	*lateral plantar nerve*
1st layer	abductor hallucis	abductor digiti minimi
	flexor digitorum brevis	
2nd layer	1st lumbrical	quadratus plantae
		2nd, 3rd and 4th lumbrical
3rd layer	flexor hallucis brevis	adductor hallucis
		flexor digiti minimi brevis
4th layer	———	plantar interossei
		dorsal interossei

Figs. 496, 497

Tendons, Flexor digitorum longus m.

Tendon, Flexor hallucis longus m.

Tendons, Flexor digitorum brevis m.

Adductor hallucis (transverse head)

Adductor hallucis (oblique head)

Flexor hallucis brevis m.

...ons of ...al mm.

...lantar ...seous ...nuscle

...pponens digiti ...inimi m.

...exor digiti minimi m.

...luctor digiti minimi m.

...don, Peroneus longus muscle

Quadratus plantae m.

Long plantar ligament

Abductor digiti minimi m.

Tendon, Flexor hallucis longus m.

Abductor hallucis m.

Tendon, Flexor hallucis longus m.

Tendon, Flexor digit. longus m.

Tendon, Tibialis posterior m.

Flexor retinaculum

Abductor hallucis m.

Flexor digitorum brevis m.

Fig. 499

Fig. 500

Fig. 498: The Sole of the Right Foot: the Third Layer of Plantar Muscles

NOTE: 1) the third layer of plantar muscles consists of two flexors and an adductor, in contrast to the first layer which contains one flexor and two abductors. Thus, the flexor hallucis brevis, flexor digiti minimi brevis and the two heads (oblique and transverse) of the adductor hallucis form the third layer of plantar muscles.

2) at times those fibers of the flexor digiti minimi brevis muscle which insert on the lateral side of the first phalanx of the 5th toe are referred to as a separate muscle, the opponens digiti minimi.

3) the tendon of the peroneus longus muscle which crosses the plantar aspect of the foot obliquely to insert on the lateral side of the base of the first metatarsal and the first (medial) cuneiform bone.

Fig. 499: The Plantar Interossei

NOTE that there are three plantar interossei. These muscles adduct the 3rd, 4th and 5th toes toward the 2nd toe which acts as the longitudinal axis of the foot.

Fig. 500: The Dorsal Interossei

NOTE that there are four dorsal interossei. These muscles abduct the toes from the reference axis. Both plantar and dorsal interossei flex the metatarsophalangeal joints and extend the interphalangeal joints.

Distal phalanx ⎫
Middle phalanx ⎬ 2nd digit
Proximal phalanx ⎭

Phalanges of large toe

Heads of metatarsal bones

1st (medial) cuneiform bone

2nd (intermediate) cuneiform bone

Navicular bone

Tuberosity of 5th metatarsal bone

3rd (lateral) cuneiform bone

Cuboid bone

Head of talus
Calcaneus
Trochlea of talus (articulates with tibia)
Lateral (malleolar) process of talus

Calcaneus

Fig. 502: Dorsal Aspect of the Bones of the Right Foot Showing the Attachments of Muscles

Red = origin; Blue = insertion

NOTE: 1) the insertion of the calcaneal tendon (of Achilles) on the posterior surface of the calcaneus. This tendon is the strongest in the body and a bursa is interposed between the bone and the tendon proximal to this insertion. The only other muscle which attaches to the tarsal bones on this dorsal aspect is the extensor digitorum brevis, which arises from the dorsolateral surface of the calcaneus, distal to its articulation with the talus. The medial portion of this muscle (extensor hallucis brevis) inserts on the proximal phalanx of the large toe, while three other tendons insert onto the middle phalanx of the 2nd, 3rd and 4th toes.

2) the insertions of the peroneus brevis and tertius onto the base of the 5th metatarsal.

3) the 1st and 2nd dorsal interosseus muscles inserting onto the 2nd toe, while the 3rd and 4th insert onto the dorsolateral aspect of the 3rd and 4th digits. These muscles serve as abductors.

Figs. 501, 502

Fig. 501: The Bones of the Right Foot, Dorsal View

NOTE: 1) the skeleton of the foot consists of 7 tarsal bones, 5 metatarsal bones and 14 phalanges. The toes are numbered in order from medial to lateral so that the large toe is the 1st digit while the small toe is the 5th digit.

2) the weight of the body is transmitted by the tibia to the talus, which then redistributes this weight to the calcaneus inferiorly (the "heel" of the foot) and the navicular bone distally (toward the heads of the metatarsals and the "ball" of the foot).

3) distal to the navicular and calcaneus are the three cuneiform bones and the cuboid; these then articulate with the individual metatarsal bones of the digits. Observe the similarity of the anatomy of the skeleton of the human foot and the hand, but appreciate their marked differences in function.

Extensor hallucis longus

Extensor hallucis brevis

Dorsal interossei

Cuneiform bones

Exte digi lon

Extenso digitoru brevis

Peroneus tertiu

Peroneus brevis

Extensor digitorum brevis

Calcaneal tendon

NAVICULAR

CUBOID

TALUS

CALCANEUS

Fig. 503 (illustration, left)

Pha-
langes

anges

Sesamoid
bones

arsal
ones

of
ta-
sal
es

Tuberosity
of the 1st meta-
tarsal bone

erosity
the 5th
atarsal

1st (medial)
cuneiform bone

2nd (intermediate)
cuneiform bone

Cuboid
sulcus

Cuboid
bone

Navicular bone

d (lateral)
cuneiform
bone

**Tarsal
bones**

Head of talus

Sustentaculum tali

Calcaneal tuberosity
(medial process)

Calcaneal tuberosity
(lateral process)

Fig. 503: The Bones of the Right Foot: Plantar View

NOTE: 1) the largest bone in the foot is the calcaneus. From this surface can be seen the prominent calcaneal tuberosity which projects posteriorly and inferiorly (forming the heel) and the sustentaculum tali, the dorsal surface of which contains articular facets for the talus.

2) the cuboid bone and the sulcus on its plantar surface for the passage of the peroneus longus tendon across the sole of the foot.

3) the long, slender metatarsal bones which are curved, such as to be concave on their plantar surface and convex dorsally. Observe the large tuberosity on the lateral side of the base of the 5th metatarsal.

Fig. 504 (illustration, right)

Flexor digitorum longus

Flexor digitorum
brevis

Flexor hallucis
longus

Flexor hallucis
brevis and
Adductor hallucis

Flexor hallucis
brevis and
Abductor hallucis

Plantar
interossei

Abductor
digiti minimi

Flexor digiti
minimi brevis

Plantar
interossei

Tibialis anterior

Adductor
hallucis
(oblique head)

Peroneus longus

Flexor digiti
minimi brevis

3 Cuneiform bones

Flexor
hallucis
brevis

Tibialis
posterior

CUBOID   NAVICULAR

TALUS

Quadratus
plantae

Abductor
digiti
minimi

Abductor hallucis

Flexor digitorum brevis

CALCANEUS

J. Pensheus

Fig. 504: Plantar Aspect of the Bones of the Right Foot Showing the Attachments of Muscles

NOTE: 1) that the muscles comprising the 1st and 2nd plantar layers (except the lumbricals) all arise from the plantar surface of the calcaneal bone. These four muscles include the abductors hallucis and digiti minimi, the flexor digitorum brevis and the quadratus plantae.

2) the tendons of five extrinsic muscles of the foot (arising in the leg) insert on the plantar aspect. These are the peroneus longus, the tibialis anterior and tibialis posterior and the flexors hallucis longus and digitorum longus. The tendon of the tibialis posterior sends some fibers of insertion onto the plantar surface of six of the seven tarsal bones (only the talus is omitted in its insertion).

3) the three plantar interossei arise from the 3rd, 4th and 5th metatarsals and insert on the proximal phalanges of these same digits. These muscles act as adductors of these three digits, capable of moving them toward the 2nd digit, the center of which is the longitudinal axis of the foot.

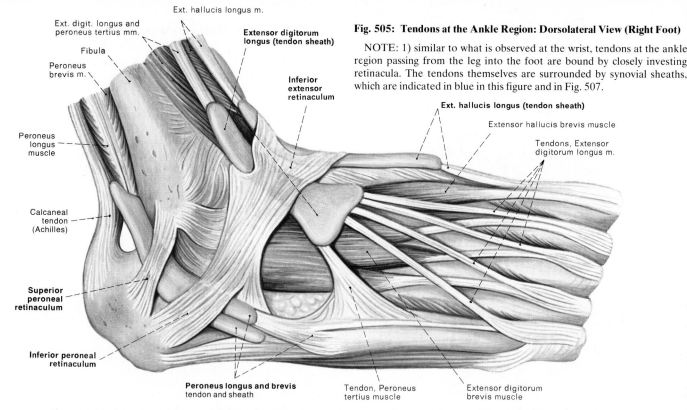

Ext. digit. longus and peroneus tertius mm.

Ext. hallucis longus m.

Extensor digitorum longus (tendon sheath)

Fibula

Peroneus brevis m.

Inferior extensor retinaculum

Fig. 505: Tendons at the Ankle Region: Dorsolateral View (Right Foot)

NOTE: 1) similar to what is observed at the wrist, tendons at the ankle region passing from the leg into the foot are bound by closely investing retinacula. The tendons themselves are surrounded by synovial sheaths, which are indicated in blue in this figure and in Fig. 507.

Ext. hallucis longus (tendon sheath)

Extensor hallucis brevis muscle

Tendons, Extensor digitorum longus m.

Peroneus longus muscle

Calcaneal tendon (Achilles)

Superior peroneal retinaculum

Inferior peroneal retinaculum

Peroneus longus and brevis tendon and sheath

Tendon, Peroneus tertius muscle

Extensor digitorum brevis muscle

2) anterior to the ankle joint and on the dorsum of the foot are three separate synovial sheaths. One is for the extensor digitorum longus and peroneus tertius, a second is for the extensor hallucis longus and the third surrounds the tibialis anterior (see Fig. 507). Behind the lateral malleolus is a single tendon sheath for the peroneus longus and brevis which then splits distally to continue along each individual tendon for some distance.

3) the inferior extensor retinaculum and the superior and inferior peroneal retinacula which bind the tendons and their sheaths close to bone.

Fig. 506: The Tendons of the Peroneus Longus and Tibialis Anterior Muscle

NOTE that the tendons of the tibialis anterior and peroneus longus muscles insert on the medial aspect of the plantar surface of the foot. The peroneus longus muscle achieves this insertion by traversing the sole of the foot from lateral to medial. In this manner, the two muscles form a tendinous sling under the foot which serves to support the transverse arch. Also assisting in this support is the tendon of the tibialis posterior muscle.

Fig. 507: Tendons at the Ankle Region: Medial View (Right Foot)

NOTE: 1) from this medial view can be seen the synovial sheaths and tendons of the tibialis anterior and extensor hallucis longus on the dorsum of the foot, as well as the three tendons which course beneath the medial malleolus from the posterior compartment of the leg into the plantar foot: tibialis posterior, flexor digitorum longus and flexor hallucis longus.

2) the bifurcating nature of the inferior extensor retinaculum, and the manner in which the flexor retinaculum secures the structures beneath the medial malleolus.

Fig. 507

Tibialis anterior (tendon sheath)

Tibialis posterior (tendon shea...

Flex. digitor... longus (tendon she...

Flex. halluc... longus (tendon she...

Inf. extensor retinaculum

Ext. hallucis longus (tendon sheath)

Calcanea... tendon (Achilles...

Flexor retinac...

Fig. 506

Peroneus longus m.

Tibialis anterior m.

Flex. hallucis longus (tendon sheath)

Abductor hallucis tendon

Tibialis posterior m.

Abdu... hallu... musc...

Flexor digit... brevis musc...

Figs. 505, 506, 507

Flex. digitorum longus (tendon sheath)

Tibialis posterior (tendon sheath)

Tibia

Fibula

Anterior (inferior)
tibiofibular ligament

Ant. talofibular lig.

Lat. **talocalcaneal** lig.

Interosseous
talocalcaneal lig.

Ant. talofibular
ligament

Calcaneonavicular lig.
(part of **bifurcate** lig.)

Dorsal cuboideonavicular lig.

Dorsal
cuneonavicular ligs.

Dorsal metatarsal ligs.

Metatarsal bone

Lateral
malleolus

Calcaneofibular
ligament

Deep transverse
metatarsal ligs.

alcaneus →

Long
plantar lig.

Bifurcate
ligament

Dorsal calcaneo-
cuboid ligament

Tendon,
peroneus
brevis m.

Dorsal tarsometatarsal ligs.

**Fig. 508: Ligaments of the Ankle and Foot: Dorsolateral View
(Right Foot)**

NOTE: 1) the fibula is attached to the tibia distally by the anterior (inferior) tibiofibular ligament. Additionally, the lateral malleolus of the fibula is attached to the talus by the relatively weak anterior and posterior (Fig. 512) talofibular ligaments, and to the calcaneus by the calcaneofibular ligament.

2) the joint between the talus and calcaneus (subtalar joint) is principally strenghtened by the interosseous talocalcaneal ligament. The talocalcaneonavicular joint more anteriorly is of important clinical significance since the weight of the body tends to push the head of the talus down between the navicular and calcaneus. The stability of this joint is assisted dorsolaterally by the calcaneonavicular ligament (a part of the bifurcate ligament); however, the thick plantar calcaneonavicular or spring ligament (Figs. 509, 511, 513, 514) is the principal support for this joint in the maintenance of the longitudinal arch of the foot.

3) the bifurcate ligament consists of the calcaneonavicular ligament and the calcaneocuboid ligament.

Fig. 509: Ligaments of the Ankle and Foot: Medial View (Right Foot)

NOTE: 1) the medial aspect of the ankle joint is protected by the deltoid ligament, which is triangular in shape and which connects the tibia (medial malleolus) to the navicular, calcaneus and talus. The deltoid ligament consists of 4 parts: a) an anterior part which attaches the medial malleolus to the navicular (tibionavicular part), b) a superficial part attaching the malleolus to the sustentaculum tali of the calcaneus (tibiocalcaneal part), and c) and d) the anterior and posterior tibiotalar parts which lie more deeply and attach the malleolus to the adjacent talus.

2) the insertions of the tendons of the tibialis anterior and tibialis posterior muscles which attach on this medial aspect of the foot. Observe also the long plantar and plantar calcaneonavicular ligaments on the plantar surface. These are shown more clearly in Figures 511, 513 and 514.

Tibia

Ant. tibiotalar
part

Deltoid ligament

Tibionavicular
part

Tendon, **Tibialis anterior m.**

Dorsal tarsometatarsal ligament

Tibiocalcaneal
part

**Deltoid
ligament**

Post. tibiotalar
part

Tendon, **Tibialis posterior** m.

Sustentaculum tali

Metatarsal
bones

Calcaneus

Calcaneal tendon

Plantar calcaneocuboid
ligament

Long
plantar ligament

Tuberosity of calcaneus

Figs. 508, 509   **V**

Fig. 510 labels (left illustration):

1st metatarsal (of large toe)
2nd metatarsal
3rd metatarsal
4th metatarsal
5th metatarsal
Interosseous metatarsal lig.
Tarsometatarsal joint of large toe
Tarsometatarsal joint
1st (med.) cuneiform
2nd (intermed.) cuneiform
Cuneonavicular joint
Navicular bone
Talonavicular joint
Talus
Interosseous talocalcaneal lig.
Subtalar joint
Calcaneus
Tarsometatarsal joint
Tuberosity of 5th metatarsal
Interosseous tarsal lig.
3rd (lat.) cuneiform
Cuboid bone
Calcaneocuboid joint

Fig. 511: The Talocalcaneonavicular Joint (Viewed from Above), Right

NOTE that the talus has been removed. This reveals the three articulations it makes with the calcaneus and the anterior articulation it makes with the navicular bone. Observe the plantar calcaneonavicular ("spring") ligament stretching across the plantar aspect of the talocalcaneonavicular joint.

Fig. 511 labels (bottom left illustration):

Tibia
Fibula
Posterior tibio-fibular ligament
Medial malleolus
Posterior talo-fibular ligament
Post. tibiotalar part of **deltoid ligament**
← Lateral malleolus
Posterior talo-calcaneal ligament
Calcaneofibular ligament
Talus bone →
Tibiocalcaneal part of **deltoid ligament**
Medial talo-calcaneal lig.
Calcaneus
Tuberosity of calcaneus
Calcaneal tendon

Fig. 510: The Intertarsal and Tarsometatarsal Joints (Horizontal Section of the Right Foot)

NOTE: 1) a transverse intertarsal joint, extending across the foot and formed by two separate joint cavities, the calcaneocuboid joint and the talonavicular portion of the talocalcaneonavicular joint. These two joints allow some dorsi and plantarflexion of the anterior part of the foot with respect to the posterior foot.

2) that the joints in the foot form a natural division of the bones into a medial group (talus, navicular, the 3 cuneiform and the medial three metatarsals and phalanges) and a lateral group (calcaneus, cuboid and the lateral two metatarsals and phalanges).

Fig. 510 labels (right illustration):

Dorsal tarsometatarsal ligaments
1st metatarsal (for large toe)
5th metatarsal
Dorsal cuneo-cuboid ligament
Dorsal inter-cuneiform ligs.
Tuberosity of 5th metatarsal
Dorsal cuneo-navicular ligs.
Cuboid bone
Dorsal calcaneo-cuboid ligament
Navicular bone →
Posterior navicular facet (with talus)
Tendon, Peroneus brevis muscle
Plantar calcaneo-navicular ligament
Middle calcaneal facet (with talus)
Interosseous talocalcaneal lig.
Anterior calcaneal facet (with talus)
Posterior calcaneal facet (with talus)
Calcaneus
Calcaneal tuberosity

Fig. 512: The Ankle Joint (Talocrural) Viewed from Behind (Right Foot)

NOTE: 1) the ankle joint is a ginglymus or hinge joint. The bony structures participating in this joint superiorly are the distal end of the tibia and its medial malleolus, and the distal fibula and its lateral malleolus. Together these structures form a concave receptacle for the convex proximal surface of the talus.

2) the posterior aspect of the articular capsule is somewhat strengthened by the posterior talofibular and posterior tibiofibular ligaments. Laterally, the calcaneofibular ligament and medially, the strong deltoid ligament assist in protecting this joint.

3) the ligamentous bands which help to stabilize the talocalcaneal articulation posteriorly: the posterior and medial talocalcaneal ligaments.

Figs. 510, 511, 512

NOTE: 1) that the long plantar ligament is the longest and most superficial of the plantar tarsal ligaments. It stretches from the calcaneus posteriorly to an oblique ridge on the plantar surface of the cuboid, where most of its deeper fibers terminate. A number of the more superficial fibers pass over the cuboid to insert on the bases of the lateral three metatarsal bones, thereby forming a tunnel or retinaculum for the peroneus longus tendon.

2) the plantar calcaneocuboid or short plantar ligament is very strong and lies deeper to the long plantar ligament and closer to the bones. More medially, identify the fibroelastic plantar calcaneonavicular (spring) ligament. It is attached to the sustentaculum tali of the calcaneus and extends along the entire inferior surface of the navicular bone.

Labels (left figure):
- Plantar ligaments
- Superficial transverse metatarsal ligaments
- Base of 1st metatarsal
- Plantar tarso-metatarsal lig.
- 1st (med.) cuneiform
- Plantar cuneo-navicular lig.
- Tuberosity of navicular bone
- Plantar cuboideo-navicular lig.
- **Plantar calcaneo-navicular lig.**
- Tuberosity of 5th metatarsal
- Sulcus for peroneus longus tendon
- **Long plantar lig.** (retinaculum for peroneus long. tendon)
- **Plantar calcaneo-cuboid ligament**
- **Long plantar lig.**
- Calcaneofibular lig.
- Sustentaculum tali
- Tibiocalcaneal part of deltoid lig.
- Sulcus for flexor hallucis longus tendon
- Medial process of calcaneal tuberosity
- Tuberosity of calcaneus

Labels (right figure):
- Deep transverse metatarsal ligaments
- Metatarsophalangeal joints
- Sesamoid bone
- **Tendon, Peroneus longus muscle**
- Plantar tarso-metatarsal ligs.
- **Tendon, Tibialis anterior muscle**
- Plantar inter-metatarsal ligaments
- Plantar tarsal ligs.
- Plantar cuboideo-navicular ligament
- **Tendon, Tibialis posterior muscle**
- Tendon of peroneus brevis muscle
- **Sulcus for peroneus longus tendon**
- **Plantar calcaneo-cuboid ligament**
- **Plantar calcaneo-navicular ligament**
- Calcaneal tuberosity

Fig. 514: The Plantar Calcaneonavicular Ligament and the Insertions of Three Tendons (Right Foot) ▶

NOTE: 1) the metatarsal extensions of the long plantar ligament have been cut away to reveal the groove for the tendon of the peroneus longus muscle. This tendon is seen inserting onto the base of the 1st metatarsal bone. It also sends a small slip of insertion to the 1st cuneiform. Two other long tendons inserting on the medial side of the plantar surface are those of the tibialis anterior and tibialis posterior muscles.

2) that the fibers of the calcaneocuboid (short plantar) and calcaneonavicular (spring) ligaments all stem from the calcaneus and then diverge in a radial manner toward the medial side of the foot. Observe that the course and insertion of the tibialis posterior tendon also lends some support to the short tendon and spring ligaments.

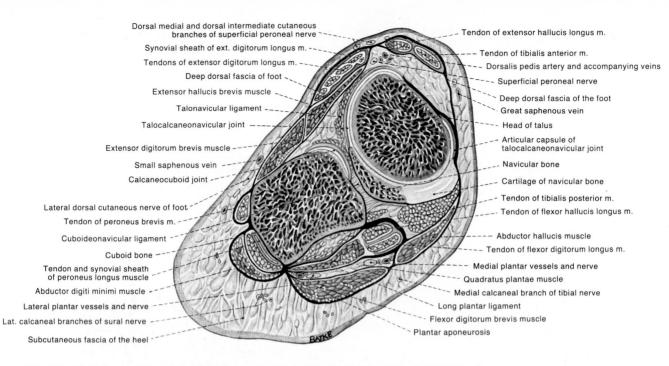

Fig. 515: Cross Section Through the Right Foot at the Level of the Head of the Talus (Distal Surface)

NOTE that the tendon sheaths and synovial membranes are shown in light blue. The level of this cross section is shown in the diagram Figure 488.

The labels in Fig. 515 are:

- Dorsal medial and dorsal intermediate cutaneous branches of superficial peroneal nerve
- Synovial sheath of ext. digitorum longus m.
- Tendons of extensor digitorum longus m.
- Deep dorsal fascia of foot
- Extensor hallucis brevis muscle
- Talonavicular ligament
- Talocalcaneonavicular joint
- Extensor digitorum brevis muscle
- Small saphenous vein
- Calcaneocuboid joint
- Lateral dorsal cutaneous nerve of foot
- Tendon of peroneus brevis m.
- Cuboideonavicular ligament
- Cuboid bone
- Tendon and synovial sheath of peroneus longus muscle
- Abductor digiti minimi muscle
- Lateral plantar vessels and nerve
- Lat. calcaneal branches of sural nerve
- Subcutaneous fascia of the heel
- Tendon of extensor hallucis longus m.
- Tendon of tibialis anterior m.
- Dorsalis pedis artery and accompanying veins
- Superficial peroneal nerve
- Deep dorsal fascia of the foot
- Great saphenous vein
- Head of talus
- Articular capsule of talocalcaneonavicular joint
- Navicular bone
- Cartilage of navicular bone
- Tendon of tibialis posterior m.
- Tendon of flexor hallucis longus m.
- Abductor hallucis muscle
- Tendon of flexor digitorum longus m.
- Medial plantar vessels and nerve
- Quadratus plantae muscle
- Medial calcaneal branch of tibial nerve
- Long plantar ligament
- Flexor digitorum brevis muscle
- Plantar aponeurosis

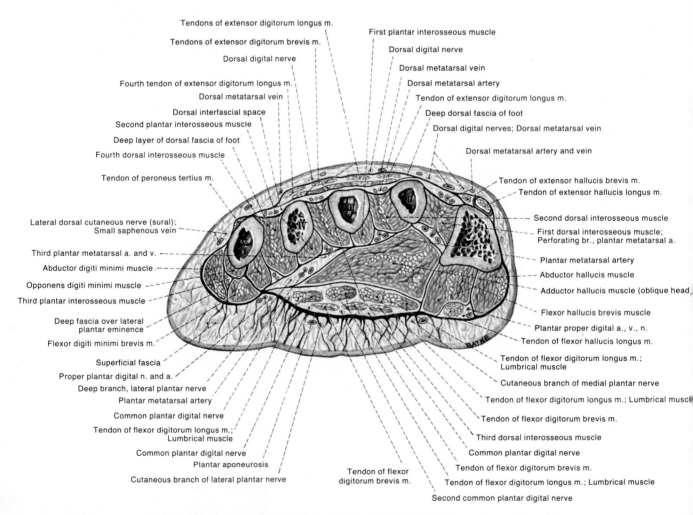

Fig. 516: Cross Section of the Right Foot Through the Metatarsal Bones (Distal Surface)

NOTE that the level of this cross section is shown in the diagram Figure 488.

The labels in Fig. 516 are:

- Tendons of extensor digitorum longus m.
- Tendons of extensor digitorum brevis m.
- Dorsal digital nerve
- Fourth tendon of extensor digitorum longus m.
- Dorsal metatarsal vein
- Dorsal interfascial space
- Second plantar interosseous muscle
- Deep layer of dorsal fascia of foot
- Fourth dorsal interosseous muscle
- Tendon of peroneus tertius m.
- Lateral dorsal cutaneous nerve (sural); Small saphenous vein
- Third plantar metatarsal a. and v.
- Abductor digiti minimi muscle
- Opponens digiti minimi muscle
- Third plantar interosseous muscle
- Deep fascia over lateral plantar eminence
- Flexor digiti minimi brevis m.
- Superficial fascia
- Proper plantar digital n. and a.
- Deep branch, lateral plantar nerve
- Plantar metatarsal artery
- Common plantar digital nerve
- Tendon of flexor digitorum longus m.; Lumbrical muscle
- Common plantar digital nerve
- Plantar aponeurosis
- Cutaneous branch of lateral plantar nerve
- First plantar interosseous muscle
- Dorsal digital nerve
- Dorsal metatarsal vein
- Dorsal metatarsal artery
- Tendon of extensor digitorum longus m.
- Deep dorsal fascia of foot
- Dorsal digital nerves; Dorsal metatarsal vein
- Dorsal metatarsal artery and vein
- Tendon of extensor hallucis brevis m.
- Tendon of extensor hallucis longus m.
- Second dorsal interosseous muscle
- First dorsal interosseous muscle; Perforating br., plantar metatarsal a.
- Plantar metatarsal artery
- Abductor hallucis muscle
- Adductor hallucis muscle (oblique head)
- Flexor hallucis brevis muscle
- Plantar proper digital a., v., n.
- Tendon of flexor hallucis longus m.
- Tendon of flexor digitorum longus m.; Lumbrical muscle
- Cutaneous branch of medial plantar nerve
- Tendon of flexor digitorum longus m.; Lumbrical muscle
- Tendon of flexor digitorum brevis m.
- Third dorsal interosseous muscle
- Common plantar digital nerve
- Tendon of flexor digitorum brevis m.
- Tendon of flexor digitorum longus m.; Lumbrical muscle
- Second common plantar digital nerve
- Tendon of flexor digitorum brevis m.

Figs. 515, 516

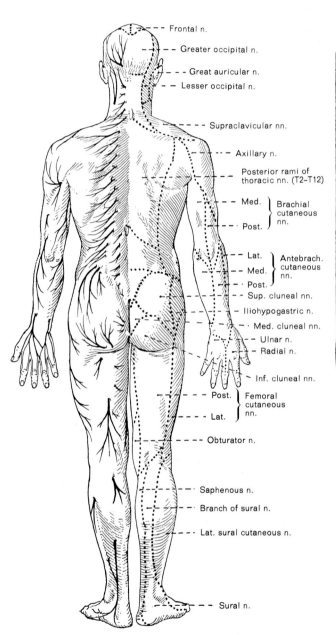

Frontal n.

Greater occipital n.

Great auricular n.

Lesser occipital n.

Supraclavicular nn.

Axillary n.

Posterior rami of thoracic nn. (T2–T12)

Med. } Brachial cutaneous nn.
Post.

Lat. } Antebrach. cutaneous nn.
Med.
Post.

Sup. cluneal nn.

Iliohypogastric n.

Med. cluneal nn.

Ulnar n.

Radial n.

Inf. cluneal nn.

Post. } Femoral cutaneous nn.
Lat.

Obturator n.

Saphenous n.

Branch of sural n.

Lat. sural cutaneous n.

Sural n.

Fig. 517: The Cutaneous Nerve Surface Areas, Posterior Aspect of the Body

NOTE that on the left side the position and course of the spinal cutaneous nerves are shown, while on the right side the surface areas of distribution are indicated. Demonstrated are the posterior surface zones for the cervical, thoracic, lumbar and sacral segmental nerves.

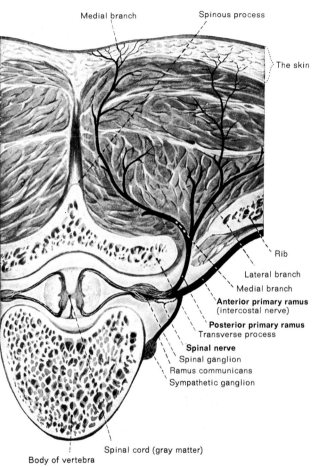

Medial branch

Spinous process

The skin

Rib

Lateral branch

Medial branch

Anterior primary ramus (intercostal nerve)

Posterior primary ramus
Transverse process

Spinal nerve
Spinal ganglion
Ramus communicans
Sympathetic ganglion

Spinal cord (gray matter)

Body of vertebra

Fig. 518: The Branching of a Typical Spinal Nerve

NOTE: 1) fibers from both dorsal and motor roots join to form a spinal nerve which soon divides into a posterior and an anterior primary ramus. The posterior primary ramus courses dorsally to innervate the muscles and skin of the back. The anterior primary ramus courses laterally and anteriorly around the body, to innervate the remainder of the segment.

2) the posterior primary divisions of typical spinal nerves are smaller in diameter than the anterior divisions, and each usually divides into medial and lateral branches which contain both motor and sensory fibers innervating structures in the back.

3) unlike the anterior primary divisions of the spinal nerves which join to form the cervical, brachial and lumbosacral plexuses, the peripheral nerves derived from posterior primary divisions, as a rule, do not intercommunicate and form plexuses. There is, however, some segmental overlap of the peripheral sensory fields, as occurs with anterior primary division nerves.

Figs. 517, 518   **VI**

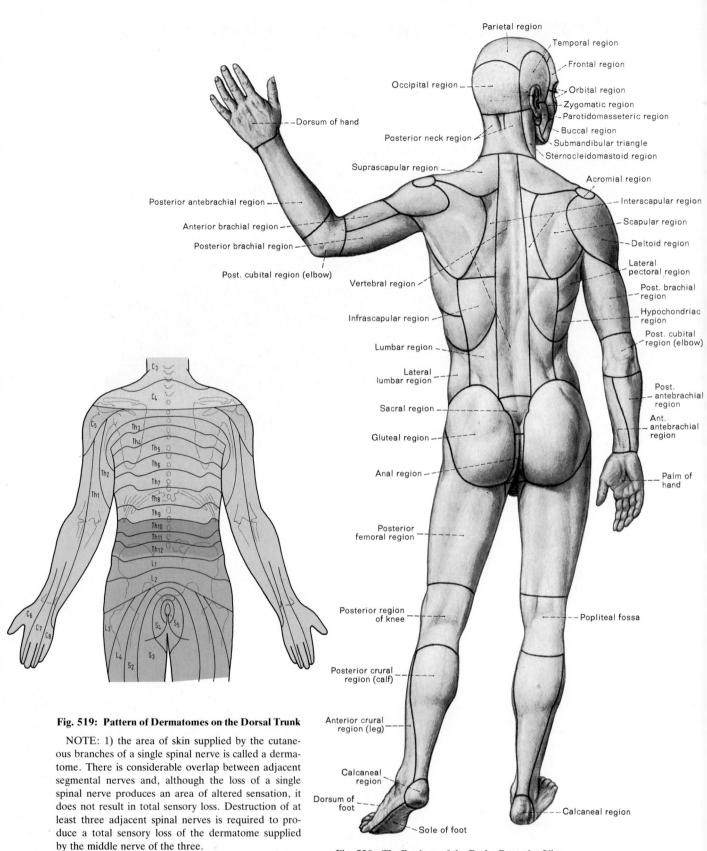

Fig. 519: Pattern of Dermatomes on the Dorsal Trunk

NOTE: 1) the area of skin supplied by the cutaneous branches of a single spinal nerve is called a dermatome. There is considerable overlap between adjacent segmental nerves and, although the loss of a single spinal nerve produces an area of altered sensation, it does not result in total sensory loss. Destruction of at least three adjacent spinal nerves is required to produce a total sensory loss of the dermatome supplied by the middle nerve of the three.

2) mapping of skin areas affected by herpes zoster (shingles) has also allowed the mapping of dermatomes. Another method is the method of "remaining sensibility". In the latter, dermatome areas are established after the destruction of several roots above and below the intact root whose dermatome is being studied.

Fig. 520: The Regions of the Body: Posterior View

NOTE: the posterior aspect of the head, trunk and limbs is subdivided into many topographic regions to allow more exact anatomical localization and communication. Although the boundaries between the regions are somewhat arbitrary, it can be observed that the regions assume the names of bony structures, muscles, organs, joints and orifices comparable to those observed on the anterior aspect of the body (Figure 1).

Figs. 519, 520

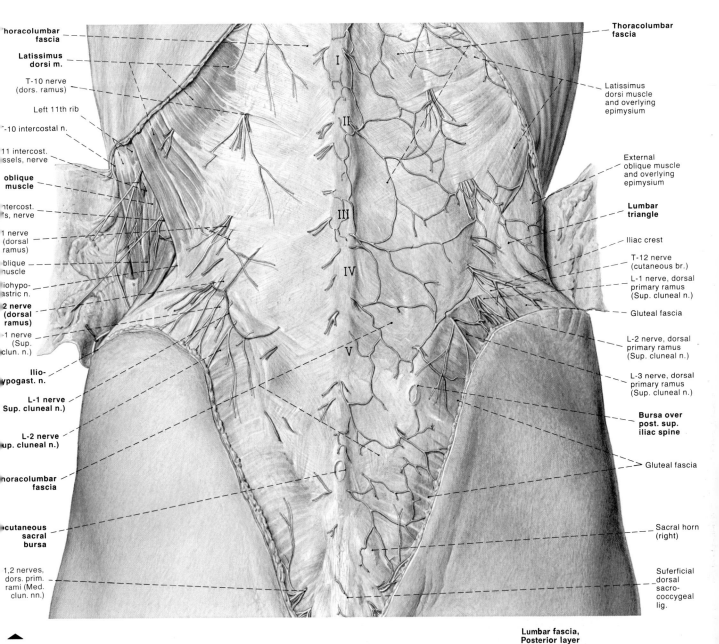

Labels (left side, top to bottom):
- Thoracolumbar fascia
- Latissimus dorsi m.
- T-10 nerve (dors. ramus)
- Left 11th rib
- T-10 intercostal n.
- T-11 intercost. vessels, nerve
- oblique muscle
- intercost. s, nerve
- 1 nerve (dorsal ramus)
- blique muscle
- iliohypo- gastric n.
- 2 nerve (dorsal ramus)
- 1 nerve (Sup. clun. n.)
- Ilio- hypogast. n.
- L-1 nerve (Sup. cluneal n.)
- L-2 nerve (Sup. cluneal n.)
- Thoracolumbar fascia
- cutaneous sacral bursa
- 1,2 nerves, dors. prim. rami (Med. clun. nn.)

Labels (right side, top to bottom):
- Thoracolumbar fascia
- Latissimus dorsi muscle and overlying epimysium
- External oblique muscle and overlying epimysium
- Lumbar triangle
- Iliac crest
- T-12 nerve (cutaneous br.)
- L-1 nerve, dorsal primary ramus (Sup. cluneal n.)
- Gluteal fascia
- L-2 nerve, dorsal primary ramus (Sup. cluneal n.)
- L-3 nerve, dorsal primary ramus (Sup. cluneal n.)
- Bursa over post. sup. iliac spine
- Gluteal fascia
- Sacral horn (right)
- Suferficial dorsal sacro- coccygeal lig.

(Vertebral spinous processes numbered I, II, III, IV, V)

Fig. 521: The Lumbosacral Region of the Back, Superficial View

NOTE that the spinous processes of the five lumbar vertebrae are numbered and that the superficial vessels and nerves penetrate the thoracolumbar fascia. Observe the lumbar triangle (labeled on the right) which is bounded by the crest of the ilium and the external oblique and latissimus dorsi muscles (see also Figure 523).

Fig. 522: Cross Section of Back, Lumbar Region

NOTE: the sacrospinalis muscle is ensheathed by the thick lumbar part of the thoracolumbar fascia which attaches medially to the spinous and transverse processes of the lumbar vertebrae, and which becomes continuous laterally with the aponeuroses and fasciae of the latissimus dorsi and anterior abdominal muscles.

Labels (Fig. 522):
- Lumbar fascia, Posterior layer
- Sacrospinalis muscle
- Spinous process, Lumbar vertebra
- Lumbar fascia, Posterior layer
- Latissimus dorsi muscle
- Lumbar triangle
- Trans- versalis fascia
- Quadratus lumborum m.
- Psoas fascia
- Lumbar fascia, Anterior layer
- Psoas major muscle
- Body of lumbar vertebra
- External oblique muscle
- Internal oblique muscle
- Transversus abdominis muscle

Figs. 521, 522   VI

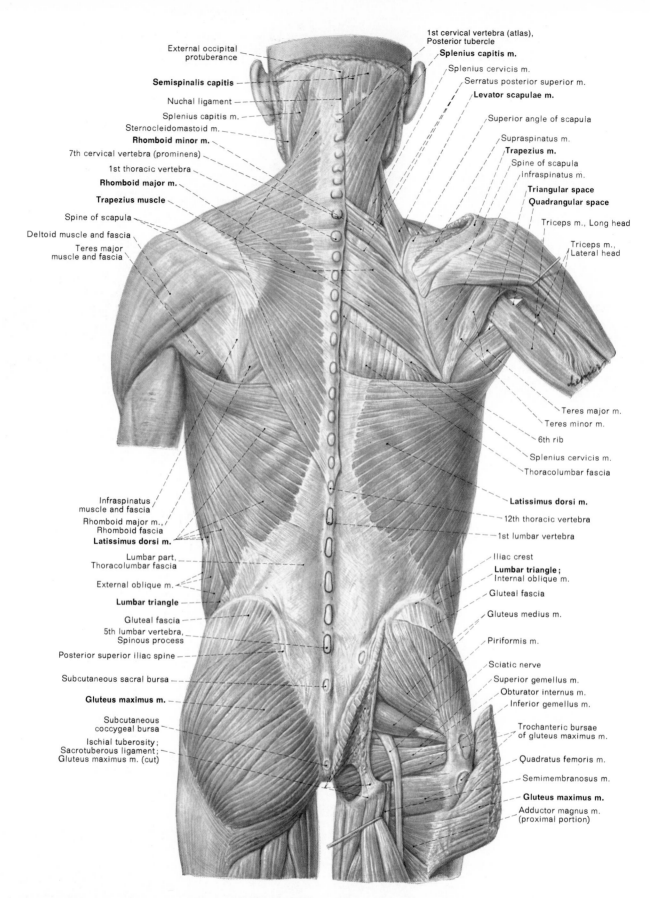

Fig. 523: Muscles of the Posterior Neck, Shoulder, Back and Gluteal Region

NOTE that the most superficial layer of back muscles includes the latissimus dorsi and trapezius. Beneath the trapezius, observe the levator scapulae and rhomboid major and minor muscles attaching along the vertebral border of the scapula. In the neck, the splenius capitis and semispinalis capitis muscles lie directly under the trapezius.

Fig. 523

Labels in figure:

External occipital protuberance
Semispinalis capitis
Nuchal ligament
Splenius capitis m.
Sternocleidomastoid m.
Rhomboid minor m.
7th cervical vertebra (prominens)
1st thoracic vertebra
Rhomboid major m.
Trapezius muscle
Spine of scapula
Deltoid muscle and fascia
Teres major muscle and fascia
Infraspinatus muscle and fascia
Rhomboid major m., Rhomboid fascia
Latissimus dorsi m.
Lumbar part, Thoracolumbar fascia
External oblique m.
Lumbar triangle
Gluteal fascia
5th lumbar vertebra, Spinous process
Posterior superior iliac spine
Subcutaneous sacral bursa
Gluteus maximus m.
Subcutaneous coccygeal bursa
Ischial tuberosity; Sacrotuberous ligament; Gluteus maximus m. (cut)

1st cervical vertebra (atlas), Posterior tubercle
Splenius capitis m.
Splenius cervicis m.
Serratus posterior superior m.
Levator scapulae m.
Superior angle of scapula
Supraspinatus m.
Trapezius m.
Spine of scapula
Infraspinatus m.
Triangular space
Quadrangular space
Triceps m., Long head
Triceps m., Lateral head
Teres major m.
Teres minor m.
6th rib
Splenius cervicis m.
Thoracolumbar fascia
Latissimus dorsi m.
12th thoracic vertebra
1st lumbar vertebra
Iliac crest
Lumbar triangle; Internal oblique m.
Gluteal fascia
Gluteus medius m.
Piriformis m.
Sciatic nerve
Superior gemellus m.
Obturator internus m.
Inferior gemellus m.
Trochanteric bursae of gluteus maximus m.
Quadratus femoris m.
Semimembranosus m.
Gluteus maximus m.
Adductor magnus m. (proximal portion)

Fig. 524: Muscles of the Back: Intermediate Layer (left), Deep Layer (right)

NOTE: 1) *on the left side* the superficial back muscles (trapezius and latissimus dorsi) have been cut, as have the rhomboid major and minor which attach the vertebral border of the scapula to the vertebral column. Observe the underlying serratus posterior superior and serratus posterior inferior muscles.

2) *on the right side* the serratus posterior muscles and the thoracolumbar fascia have been removed, revealing the erector spinae muscle (formerly called the sacrospinalis muscle).

3) *in the neck* the splenius cervicis, splenius capitis and semispinalis capitis underlie the trapezius.

Fig. 524   VI

Splenius capitis m.
Semispinalis capitis m.
Nuchal ligament
Longissimus capitis m.
Splenius cervicis m.
Levator scapulae m.
Longissimus cervicis m.
Iliocostalis cervicis
Scalenus posterior m.
Semispinalis capitis m.
Serratus posterior superior m.
Longissimus cervicis m.
Levator costae m.
Longissimus thoracis m.
External intercostal mm.
Semispinalis thoracis and cervicis mm.
Iliocostalis thoracis
Levatores costarum mm.
Serratus posterior inferior m.
Spinalis thoracis m.
Semispinalis thoracis m.
Longissimus thoracis m.
Latissimus dorsi m.
External oblique m.
Serratus posterior inferior m.
Iliocostalis lumborum m.
Internal oblique m.
Tendon of origin, Latissimus dorsi m.
Gluteal fascia
Lumbar part of thoracolumbar fascia
Erector spinae m.
Gluteus maximus m.

Semispinalis capitis m. (medial fascicle)
Semispinalis capitis m. (lateral fascicle)
Longissimus cervicis m.
Longissimus capitis m.
Spinalis cervicis and capitis m.
Iliocostalis cervicis m.
Iliocostalis thoracis m.
Longissimus thoracis m.
Spinalis thoracis m.
Iliocostalis lumborum m.
Longissimus muscle

Red { Iliocostalis lumborum
      Iliocostalis thoracis
      Iliocostalis cervicis

Black { Longissimus thoracis
        Longissimus cervicis
        Longissimus capitis

Blue { Spinalis thoracis
       Spinalis cervicis
       Spinalis capitis

Green { Semispinalis capitis
        (med. and lat, fasciculi)

Fig. 525: Deep Muscles of the Back and Neck: the Erector Spinae Muscle

NOTE: 1) *on the left,* the erector spinae (sacrospinalis) muscle is separated into its iliocostalis, longissimus and spinalis portions. In the neck observe the semispinalis capitis which has both medial and lateral fascicles. The semispinalis cervicis and thoracis extend inferiorly from above, and lie deep to the sacrospinalis layer of musculature.

2) *on the right,* all of the muscles have been removed and their attachments have been diagrammed by means of colored lines.

Fig. 525

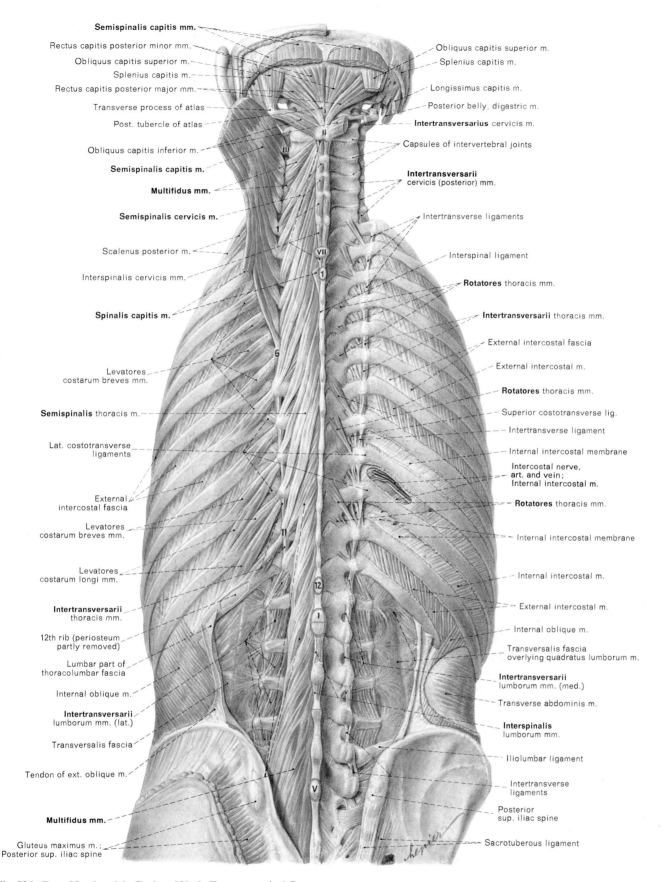

Semispinalis capitis mm.
Rectus capitis posterior minor mm.
Obliquus capitis superior m.
Splenius capitis m.
Rectus capitis posterior major mm.
Transverse process of atlas
Post. tubercle of atlas
Obliquus capitis inferior m.
Semispinalis capitis m.
Multifidus mm.
Semispinalis cervicis m.
Scalenus posterior m.
Interspinalis cervicis mm.
Spinalis capitis m.
Levatores costarum breves mm.
Semispinalis thoracis m.
Lat. costotransverse ligaments
External intercostal fascia
Levatores costarum breves mm.
Levatores costarum longi mm.
Intertransversarii thoracis mm.
12th rib (periosteum partly removed)
Lumbar part of thoracolumbar fascia
Internal oblique m.
Intertransversarii lumborum mm. (lat.)
Transversalis fascia
Tendon of ext. oblique m.
Multifidus mm.
Gluteus maximus m.; Posterior sup. iliac spine

Obliquus capitis superior m.
Splenius capitis m.
Longissimus capitis m.
Posterior belly, digastric m.
Intertransversarius cervicis m.
Capsules of intervertebral joints
Intertransversarii cervicis (posterior) mm.
Intertransverse ligaments
Interspinal ligament
Rotatores thoracis mm.
Intertransversarii thoracis mm.
External intercostal fascia
External intercostal m.
Rotatores thoracis mm.
Superior costotransverse lig.
Intertransverse ligament
Internal intercostal membrane
Intercostal nerve, art. and vein; Internal intercostal m.
Rotatores thoracis mm.
Internal intercostal membrane
Internal intercostal m.
External intercostal m.
Internal oblique m.
Transversalis fascia overlying quadratus lumborum m.
Intertransversarii lumborum mm. (med.)
Transverse abdominis m.
Interspinalis lumborum mm.
Iliolumbar ligament
Intertransverse ligaments
Posterior sup. iliac spine
Sacrotuberous ligament

Fig. 526: Deep Muscles of the Back and Neck: Transversospinal Group

NOTE: 1) the transversospinal groups of muscles lie deep to the erector spinae muscles and generally extend between the transverse processes of the vertebrae to the spinous processes of more superior vertebrae. Their actions extend the vertebral column, or upon acting individually and on one side, they bend and rotate the vertebrae.

2) within this group of muscles are the semispinalis (thoracis, cervicis, and capitis), the multifidus, the rotatores (lumborum, thoracis, cervicis), the interspinales (lumborum, thoracis, cervicis) and the intertransversarii.

Fig. 526   VI

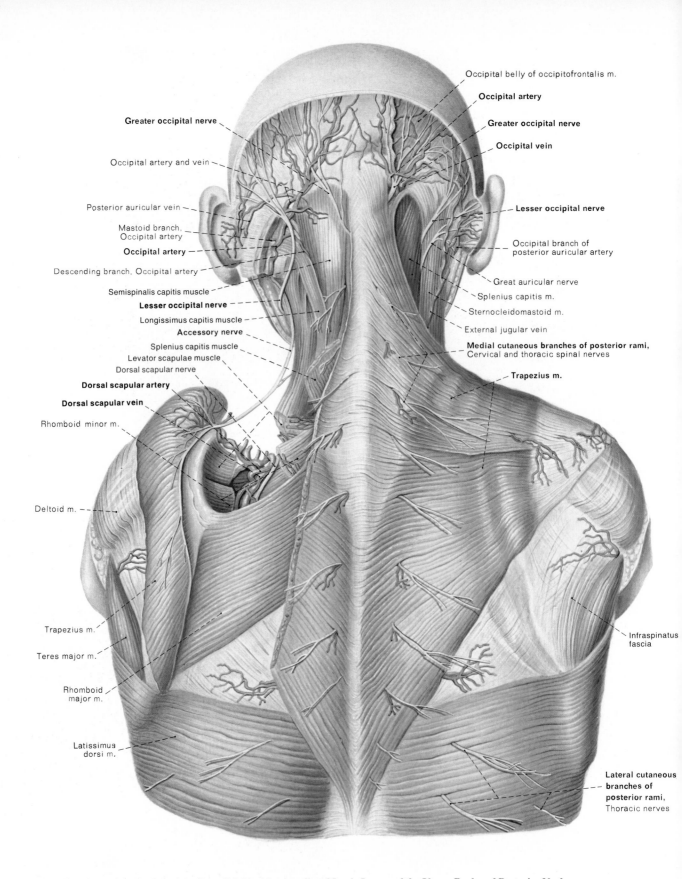

Fig. 527: Nerves and Vessels of the Superficial and Intermediate Muscle Layers of the Upper Back and Posterior Neck

NOTE: 1) the segmental distribution of the cutaneous branches of the posterior primary rami of the cervical and thoracic nerves over the posterior neck and back. Observe the accessory nerve (XI) as it descends to innervate the trapezius and sternocleidomastoid muscles.

2) the greater occipital nerve, which is a sensory nerve, ascending to the posterior scalp. It derives from the posterior primary ramus of the C-2 spinal nerve and is accompanied in its course by the occipital artery and vein. Observe also the lesser occipital nerve which courses to the lateral posterior scalp and which arises from the anterior primary ramus of C-2.

3) the dorsal scapular nerve, artery and vein which course beneath the levator scapulae and the rhomboid muscles.

Fig. 527

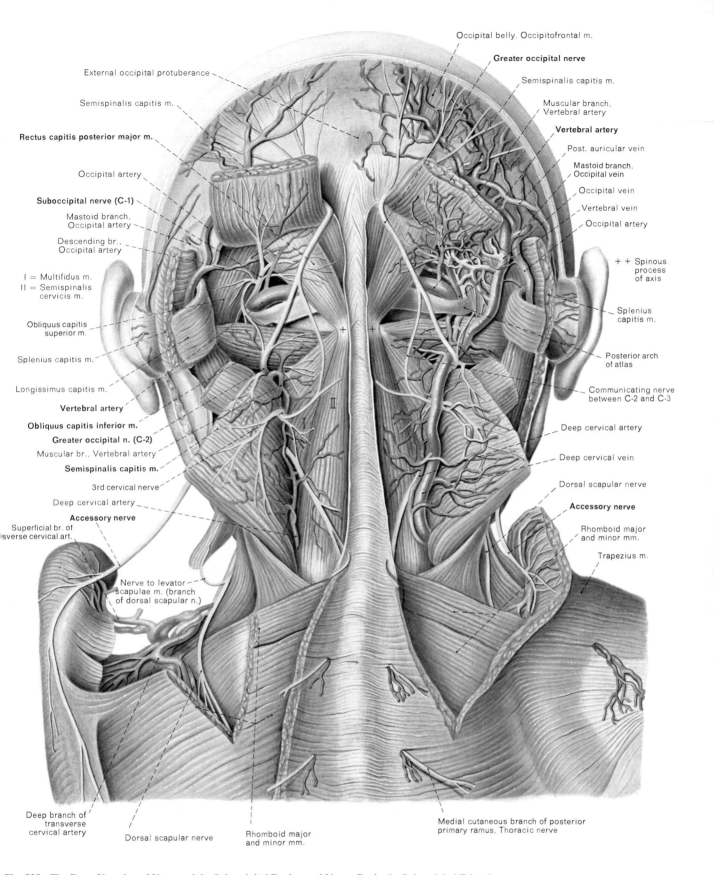

Occipital belly, Occipitofrontal m.

Greater occipital nerve

External occipital protuberance

Semispinalis capitis m.

Semispinalis capitis m.

Muscular branch,
Vertebral artery

Rectus capitis posterior major m.

Vertebral artery

Occipital artery

Post. auricular vein

Suboccipital nerve (C-1)

Mastoid branch,
Occipital vein

Mastoid branch,
Occipital artery

Occipital vein

Descending br.,
Occipital artery

Vertebral vein

Occipital artery

I = Multifidus m.
II = Semispinalis
cervicis m.

+ + Spinous
process
of axis

Obliquus capitis
superior m.

Splenius
capitis m.

Splenius capitis m.

Posterior arch
of atlas

Longissimus capitis m.

Communicating nerve
between C-2 and C-3

Vertebral artery

Obliquus capitis inferior m.

Deep cervical artery

Greater occipital n. (C-2)

Muscular br., Vertebral artery

Deep cervical vein

Semispinalis capitis m.

3rd cervical nerve

Dorsal scapular nerve

Deep cervical artery

Accessory nerve

Accessory nerve

Superficial br. of
sverse cervical art.

Rhomboid major
and minor mm.

Trapezius m.

Nerve to levator
scapulae m. (branch
of dorsal scapular n.)

Deep branch of
transverse
cervical artery

Medial cutaneous branch of posterior
primary ramus, Thoracic nerve

Dorsal scapular nerve

Rhomboid major
and minor mm.

Fig. 528: The Deep Vessels and Nerves of the Suboccipital Region and Upper Back; the Suboccipital Triangle

NOTE: 1) the suboccipital triangle lies directly beneath the semispinalis capitis muscle and is bounded by the rectus capitis posterior major, obliquus capitis superior and the obliquus capitis inferior.

2) the vertebral artery crosses (from lateral to medial) the suboccipital triangle, while the suboccipital nerve (posterior primary ramus of C-1) emerges through the triangle to distribute motor innervation to the three muscles which bound the triangle, as well as the rectus capitis posterior minor and the overlying semispinalis capitis muscle.

3) the greater occipital nerve (posterior primary ramus of C-2) is a sensory nerve which makes its appearance caudal to the obliquus capitis inferior, and then courses medially and superiorly to become subcutaneous just lateral and below the external occipital protuberance.

Fig. 528   VI

Semispinalis capitis m.

Splenius capitis m.

Obliquus capitis sup. m.

Longissimus capitis m.

Digastric m.

Styloid process; Rectus capitis lat. m.

Trans. process of atlas

Obliquus capitis inferior m.

Post. atlantooccip. membr.; **Foramen for vertebral artery**

Intertransversarius cervicis m.

Transverse process of axis

Obliquus capitis inferior m.

Multifidus mm.

Semispinalis cervicis m.

Rectus capitis posterior minor

Rectus capitis posterior major

Vertebral artery

Splenius cervicis m.

Capsule of intervertebral joint

Multifidus mm.

Scalenus medius m.

Intertransversarii mm. (posterior cervical)

Scalenus posterior m.

Interspinales mm. (cervical)

Fig. 529: The Suboccipital Triangle

NOTE: the obliquus capitis superior, obliquus capitis inferior and rectus capitis posterior major outline the suboccipital triangle. Observe the vertebral artery, as it penetrates the atlantooccipital membrane in order to enter the foramen magnum, where the two vertebral arteries join to form the basilar artery on the ventral aspect of the brain stem.

Anterior tubercle

Superior articular facet

Fovea for dens

Vertebral foramen

Transverse process

Lateral mass

Transverse foramen

Groove for vertebral artery

Posterior tubercle

Fig. 530: The Atlas, Viewed from Above

Odontoid process (dens)

Superior articular process

Posterior articular surface

Body of axis

Transverse process

Transverse foramen

Transverse foramen

Inferior articular process

Vertebral foramen

Arch of axis

Spinous process (bifid)

Fig. 532: The Axis, Viewed from Above

Anterior tubercle

Margin of superior articular facet

Anterior arch

Inferior articular facet

Vertebral foramen

Transverse foramen

Lateral mass

Transverse process

Posterior arch

Posterior tubercle

Fig. 531: The Atlas, Caudal View

Odontoid process of axis (dens)

Superior articular facet of atlas

Anterior articular surface of dens

Inferior articular facet of atlas

Posterior arch of atlas

Fovea for dens

Superior process and superior articular surface of axis

Body of axis

Transverse foramen

Spinous process of axis

Arch of axis

Transverse process

Inferior articular process

Fig. 533: Articulated Atlas and Axis, Median Sagittal Section

Figs. 529–533

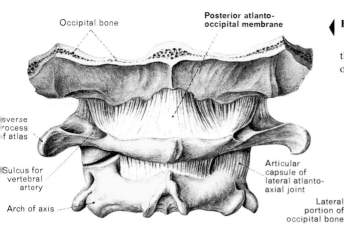

Occipital bone

Posterior atlanto-occipital membrane

sverse rocess f atlas

Sulcus for vertebral artery

Arch of axis

Articular capsule of lateral atlanto-axial joint

Fig. 534: Atlantooccipital and Atlantoaxial Joints (Posterior View)

NOTE: the posterior atlantoccipital membrane extends from the posterior margin of the foramen magnum to the upper border of the posterior arch of the atlas.

Basilar portion of occipital bone

Anterior atlanto-occipital membrane

Lateral portion of occipital bone

Lateral portion of occipital bone

Articular capsule

Atlas →

Anterior longitudinal ligament

Axis →

3rd cervical vertebra

1st inter-vertebral disc

Body of 3rd cervical vertebra

Fig. 535: Articulations of Occipital Bone and First Three Cervical Vertebrae (Anterior View)

NOTE: the anterior atlantooccipital membrane extending between the occipital bone and the anterior arch of the atlas and continuing laterally to join the articular capsules. Also observe the anterior longitudinal ligament.

Cruciform ligament (sup. longitudinal crus)

Alar ligaments

Basilar part of occipital bone

Atlantooccipital articular capsule

Hypoglossal canal

Sulcus for sigmoid sinus

Posterior arches of atlas and axis

Cruciform ligament (transverse part)

Body of axis

Fig. 536: The Atlantooccipital and Atlantoaxial Joints Showing the Cruciform Ligament (Posterior View)

NOTE: the posterior arches of the atlas and axis have been removed and the cruciform ligament is seen from this posterior view. This ligament consists of the transverse ligament (see Figure 537) and the longitudinal fascicles extending superiorly and inferiorly.

Fig. 537: Median Atlantoaxial Joint (from Above)

NOTE: that the odontoid process (dens) of the axis articulates with the anterior arch of the atlas, thereby forming the median atlantoaxial joint, and that the thick strong transverse ligament (part of the cruciform ligament) of the atlas retains the dens on its posterior surface.

Spinous process of axis

Posterior articular surface of dens

Superior articular facet of atlas

Transverse ligament of atlas

Anterior articular surface of dens

Dens of axis

Fovea for dens

Apical ligament of dens

Alar ligaments

Occipital bone

Articular capsules

Dens of axis   **Body of axis**

Fig. 538: The Alar and Apical Ligaments (Posterior View)

NOTE: this figure's orientation is similar to Figure 536. The posterior arches of the atlas and axis have been removed as well as the cruciform ligament (both transverse and longitudinal parts). This reveals the odontoid process of the axis, which is attached superiorly to the occipital bone by the two alar ligaments and the apical ligament of the dens. These ligaments tend to limit lateral rotation of the skull.

Fig. 540: Median section of Atlantooccipital Region

NOTE: the relationships from anterior to posterior of the following structures: the anterior arch of the atlas, the joint between it and the dens, the dens, the "joint" between the dens and the transverse ligament of the atlas, the tectorial membrane and finally, the dura mater covering the spinal cord.

Fig. 539: The Tectorial Membrane, Dorsal View

NOTE: the tectorial membrane is a broadened upward extension of the posterior longitudinal ligament and attaches the axis to the occipital bone (see also Figure 540). This membrane is seen to cover the posterior surface of the odontoid process and lies dorsal to the cruciform ligament, covering it as well.

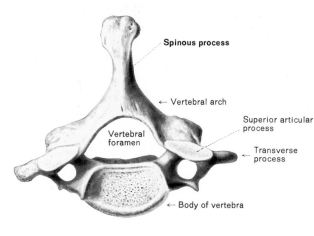

Fig. 541: Fifth Cervical Vertebra (from Above)

Fig. 542: Seventh Cervical Vertebra (from Above)

NOTE: the 7th cervical vertebra, being transitional between the cervical and thoracic vertebrae, has a transverse foramen similar to the cervical and a large spinous process similar to the thoracic. The latter gives it the name vertebra prominens.

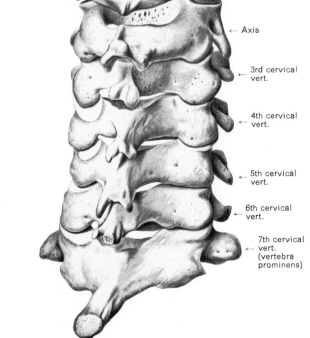

Fig. 543: The Cervical Spinal Column (Dorsal)

NOTE: while flexion and extension of the head are performed at the atlantooccipital joint, rotation of the head is the result of rotation of the atlas on the axis.

Figs. 539–543

Cervical vertebrae

Thoracic vertebrae

Lumbar vertebrae

Sacrum (sacral vertebrae)

Coccyx (coccygeal vertebrae)

Vertebra prominens

Anterior   *Posterior*

Inter-vertebral foramina

Promontory

Sacrum and coccyx

Fig. 544: Anterior View   **Fig. 545: Posterior View**   **Fig. 546: Left Lateral View**

Figs. 544, 545 and 546: The Vertebral Column, Including the Sacrum and Coccyx

NOTE: 1) the vertebral column generally consists of 7 cervical, 12 thoracic and 5 lumbar vertebrae and the sacrum and coccyx, thus, 26 bones in all. Its principal functions are to assist in the maintenance of the erect posture in man, to encase and protect the spinal cord and to allow attachments of the musculature important for movements of the head and trunk.

2) from a dorsal or ventral view, the normal spinal column is straight. When viewed from the side, the spinal column presents two ventrally convex curvatures (cervical and lumbar) and two dorsally convex curvatures (thoracic and sacral).

Fig. 547: Sixth Thoracic Vertebra (from Above)

Fig. 548: Sixth Thoracic Vertebra (from Left Lateral Side)

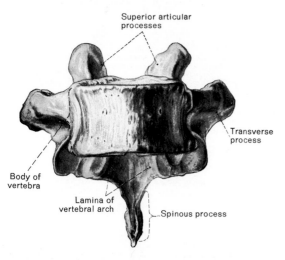

Fig. 549: Tenth Thoracic Vertebra (Ventral View)

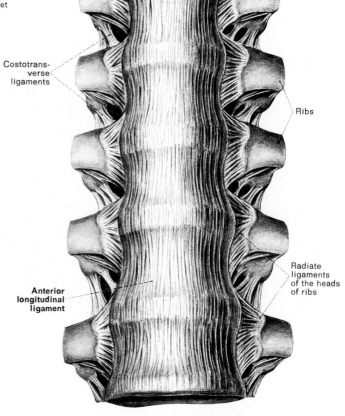

Fig. 550: Anterior Longitudinal Ligament (Ventral View)

NOTE: the anterior longitudinal ligament extends from the axis to the sacrum along the anterior aspect of the bodies of the vertebrae and the intervertebral discs to which it is firmly attached. Its longitudinal fibers are white and glistening.

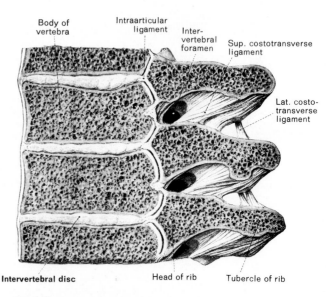

Fig. 551: Sagittal Section (at an Angle) through Spinal Column Showing Costovertebral Articulations

NOTE: the intervertebral discs, the intraarticular and costotransverse ligaments, and the intervertebral foramina which transmit the spinal nerves.

Figs. 547–551

Vertebral arch

Intertransverse ligaments

Costo-ransverse ligaments

Superior costo-transverse ligaments

Lateral costo-transverse ligaments

Left

Right

Ligamentum flavum

Supraspinal ligaments

Vertebral arch

Fig. 552: The Lower Costovertebral Joints (Posterior View)

NOTE: 1) five pairs of costovertebral joints, viewed from behind, show to advantage the articulations between the necks and tubercles of the ribs and the transverse processes of the thoracic vertebrae. The ligaments which connect these gliding joints are the costotransverse, lateral costotransverse and superior costotransverse ligaments.

2) The costotransverse joints (neck of rib with transverse process) are not to be confused with the joints between the heads of the ribs and the vertebral bodies.

Costo-transverse facets (for ribs)

Ligamenta flava

Lat. costo-transverse ligaments

Ribs

Vertebral pedicles (vertebral arch)

Right

Left

Fig. 553: The Ligamenta Flava (Ant. View)

NOTE that the bodies of the thoracic vertebrae have been removed. This reveals from within the vertebral foramen the ligamenta flava interconnecting the laminae of the dorsal vertebral arches. Thus, the pedicles of the vertebrae have been cut longitudinally. On the left side the ribs have been removed. The ligamenta flava are composed of yellow, elastic tissue.

Right rib

Dorsal lamina (of vertebral arch)

Ligamentum flavum

Spinous process

Vertebral foramen

Sup. articular processes

Transverse process

Lat. costotransverse ligament

Costotransverse joint

Costotransverse ligament

Neck and tubercle of left rib

Costotransverse ligament

Head of rib articulation (joint)

Radiate ligament of head of rib

Body of vertebra

Fig. 554: Costovertebral Joints, Transverse Section

NOTE: each rib articulates with the thoracic vertebra at two places: a) the head of the rib articulates with the vertebral body and b) the tubercle on the neck of the rib articulates with the transverse process of the vertebra.

Figs. 552, 553, 554   **VI**

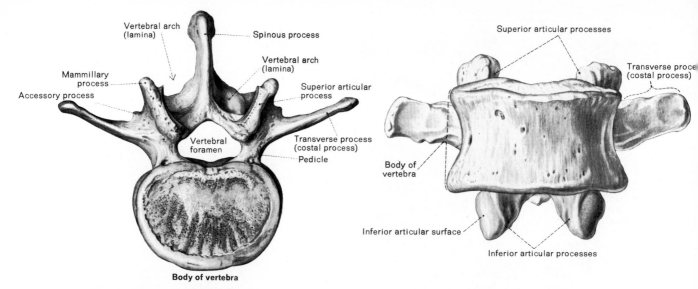

Fig. 555: **Lumbar Vertebra (Cranial View)**

NOTE: the large bodies characteristic of the lumbar vertebrae.

Fig. 556: **Lumbar Vertebra (Anterior View)**

Fig. 557: **Posterior Longitudinal Ligament and Intervertebral Discs, Lumbosacral Region**

NOTE: this dorsal view of the spinal column shows the pedicles of the vertebral arches of the lumbar vertebrae severed to expose the posterior longitudinal ligament coursing along the posterior aspect of the bodies of the lumbar vertebrae within the vertebral canal. This ligament extends from the axis (where it joins the tectorial membrane) to the sacrum, which is shown in this figure.

Fig. 558: **Last Three Thoracic and First Two Lumbar Vertebrae (Lateral View)**

Figs. 555–558

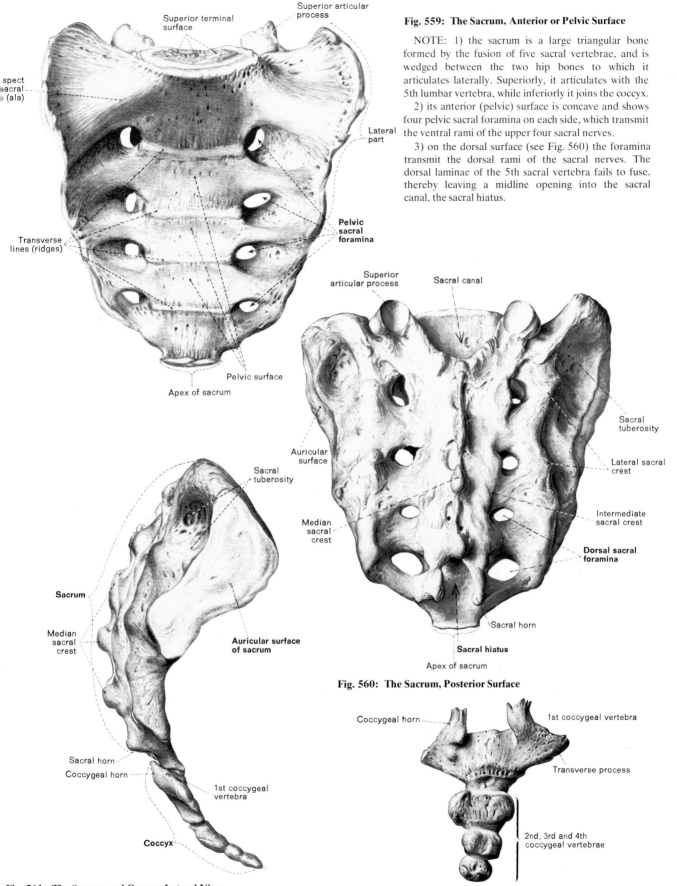

Superior terminal surface

Superior articular process

spect sacral (ala)

Lateral part

Transverse lines (ridges)

Pelvic sacral foramina

Pelvic surface

Apex of sacrum

Fig. 559: The Sacrum, Anterior or Pelvic Surface

NOTE: 1) the sacrum is a large triangular bone formed by the fusion of five sacral vertebrae, and is wedged between the two hip bones to which it articulates laterally. Superiorly, it articulates with the 5th lumbar vertebra, while inferiorly it joins the coccyx.

2) its anterior (pelvic) surface is concave and shows four pelvic sacral foramina on each side, which transmit the ventral rami of the upper four sacral nerves.

3) on the dorsal surface (see Fig. 560) the foramina transmit the dorsal rami of the sacral nerves. The dorsal laminae of the 5th sacral vertebra fails to fuse, thereby leaving a midline opening into the sacral canal, the sacral hiatus.

Superior articular process

Sacral canal

Sacral tuberosity

Lateral sacral crest

Intermediate sacral crest

Dorsal sacral foramina

Auricular surface

Median sacral crest

Sacral horn

Sacral hiatus

Apex of sacrum

Fig. 560: The Sacrum, Posterior Surface

Sacrum

Sacral tuberosity

Median sacral crest

Auricular surface of sacrum

Sacral horn

Coccygeal horn

1st coccygeal vertebra

Coccyx

Coccygeal horn

1st coccygeal vertebra

Transverse process

2nd, 3rd and 4th coccygeal vertebrae

Fig. 561: The Sacrum and Coccyx, Lateral View

NOTE: the auricular (ear-like) surface of the sacrum articulates with the iliac portion of the pelvis. Inferiorly, the sacral apex joins the coccyx.

Fig. 562: The Coccyx, Dorsal View

NOTE: this coccyx has 4 segments, but in many instances there are 3 or 5.

Figs. 559–562   **VI**

Cerebral hemisphere

Cerebellum

Medulla oblongata

Brain

2nd cervical spinal ganglion

Spinal cord, (Cervical enlargement)

Spinal ganglia

Occipital bone

Dorsal roots of thoracic spinal nerves

Intercostal nerves

Dorsal roots

Posterior primary rami

Thoracic spinal cord

Ribs

Lumbar spinal ganglia

Spinal cord, (Lumbar enlargement)

Right kidney

Conus medullaris

Ilium of pelvis

Cauda equina

Sacral spinal ganglia

Yellow: Cervical segments (C1–C8)
Red: Thoracic segments (T1–T12)
Blue: Lumbar segments (L1–L5)
Black: Sacral segments (S1–S5)
White: Coccygeal segments (C1–C2)

Fig. 563: The Spinal Cord and Brain of a Newborn Child (Posterior View)

NOTE: 1) the central nervous system has been exposed by removal of the spinal column and dorsal cranium. The spinal ganglia have been dissected as well as their corresponding spinal nerves.

2) although in this dissection it appears as though the substance of the spinal cord terminates at about L-1, it is more usual in the newborn for the cord to end at about L-3 or L-4, thereby filling the spinal canal more completely than in the adult.

Fig. 564: The Emerging Spinal Nerves and their Segments in the Adult

NOTE: many spinal nerves travel considerable distances before leaving the vertebral canal in the adult.

Figs. 563, 564

Fig. 565: The Spinal Cord Within the Vertebral Canal (Dorsal View)

Brain stem

Glossopharyngeal and vagus nn.

Hypoglossal n.

1st cervical n. — **Atlas**

2nd cervical n.

3rd cervical n.

4th cervical n. — Cervical spinal ganglia

5th cervical n.

6th cervical n.

7th cervical n. — **7th cervical vertebra**

8th cervical n. — **1st thoracic vertebra**

1st thoracic n.

2nd thoracic n.

3rd thoracic n.

4th thoracic n.

5th thoracic n. — Dura mater

6th thoracic n.

7th thoracic n.

8th thoracic n.

9th thoracic n.

10th thoracic n.

11th thoracic n.

12th thoracic n. — 1st lumbar vertebra

1st lumbar n.

2nd lumbar n. — Lumbar spinal ganglion

3rd lumbar n.

— 5th lumbar vertebra

4th lumbar n.

5th lumbar n. — Sacrum

1st sacral n.

2nd sacral n.

rd sacral n.

4th sacral n.

5th sacral n. — Filum of dura mater

Coccygeal nerve — Coccyx

NOTE: 1) the 1st cervical nerve emerges above the first vertebra and the 8th cervical nerve emerges below the 7th vertebra.

2) the cervical spinal cord is continuous above with the medulla oblongata of the brain stem.

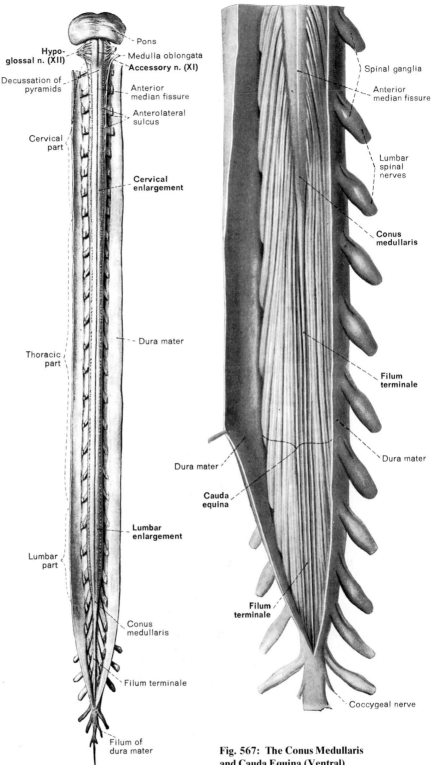

Fig. 566: The Spinal Cord (Ventral View)

Pons

Hypo-glossal n. (XII) — Medulla oblongata

Decussation of pyramids — **Accessory n. (XI)**

Cervical part — Anterior median fissure

— Anterolateral sulcus

Cervical enlargement

Thoracic part — Dura mater

Lumbar part

Lumbar enlargement

Conus medullaris

Filum terminale

Filum of dura mater

NOTE: 1) the origin of the spinal portion of the accessory nerve (Cranial XI) arising from the cervical spinal cord and ascending to join the bulbar portion of that nerve.

2) the alignment of the rootlets of the hypoglossal nerve (Cranial XII) with the ventral roots of the spinal cord.

Spinal ganglia

Anterior median fissure

Lumbar spinal nerves

Conus medullaris

Filum terminale

Dura mater — Dura mater

Cauda equina

Filum terminale

Coccygeal nerve

Fig. 567: The Conus Medullaris and Cauda Equina (Ventral)

NOTE: 1) the termination of the neural portion of the spinal cord at the conus medullaris, but its membranous continuation as the filum terminale which consists principally of pia mater.

2) the long (approx. 8 inches) cauda equina (horse's tail) consisting of the intra-vertebral portions of the lower spinal nerves.

3) prolongations of the dura mater continue to cover the spinal nerves for some distance as they enter the intervertebral foramina.

Figs. 565, 566, 567   **VI**

Anterior median fissure

Anterolateral sulcus

Spinal nerve

Dorsal root filaments

Ventral root filaments

Spinal ganglion

Spinal nerve

Fig. 568

Fig. 568: Spinal Cord with Nerve Roots

NOTE: the many filaments which form the dorsal and ventral roots of a spinal nerve enter into and emerge from the cord in a straight line.

Fig. 569: The Anterior Spinal Artery

NOTE that the anterior spinal artery is formed by vessels derived from the vertebral arteries. It receives important anastomotic branches in the cervical region from the vertebral arteries and the thyrocervical trunk, as well as the 5th and 10th intercostal arteries.

Basilar artery

Anterior spinal artery

Vertebral artery

Spinal branch of vertebral artery

Spinal branches of thyrocervical trunk

Thyrocervical trunk

Subclavian artery

Costocervical trunk

5th intercostal a. (spinal branch)

Fig. 569

Anterior spinal artery

10th intercostal a. (spinal branch)

Renal artery

Common artery

Posterior median sulcus

Anterior median fissure

Denticulate ligaments

Dura mater

Posterolateral sulcus

Dorsal root filaments

Arachnoid

Spinal ganglia

Fig. 570

Dura mater (meningeal)

Fig. 570: Spinal Cord with Dura Mater Dissected Open (Dorsal View)

NOTE that extensions of the pia mater to the meningeal dura mater between the roots of the spinal nerves are called denticulate ligaments. The arachnoid sends fine attachments to both the pia and dura.

Figs. 568, 569, 570

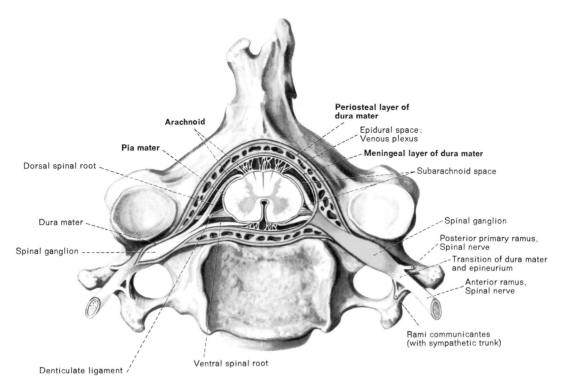

Fig. 571: Meninges of the Spinal Cord Shown at Cervical Level (Transverse Section)

NOTE: 1) the meningeal dura mater (inner layer of yellow) surrounds the spinal cord and continues along the spinal nerve through the intervertebral foramen. Its outer periosteal layer (outer layer of yellow) is formed of connective tissue which closely adheres to the bone of the vertebrae forming the vertebral canal.

2) the delicate, film-like arachnoid which lies between the meningeal layer of dura mater, and the vascularized pia mater which is closely applied to the cord.

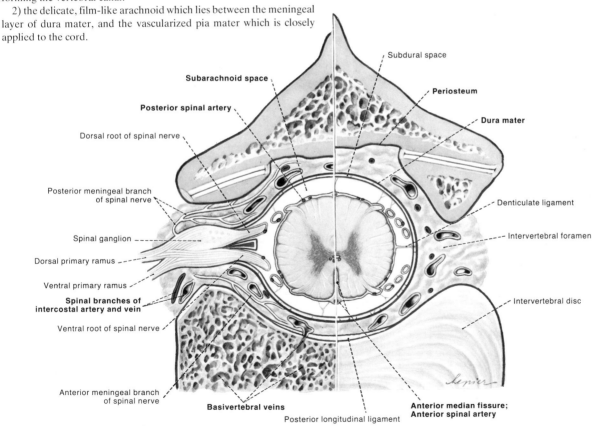

Fig. 572: The Spinal Cord Within the Vertebral Canal of the Spinal Column (Transverse Section)

NOTE: 1) that this transverse section is taken through the thoracic region of the spinal cord and shows one level *on the left* through the body of a vertebra and another level *on the right* through an intervertebral disc;

2) that the arachnoid membrane and the arteries are in red; the pia mater and the veins are in blue; the dura mater and the periosteum are in black;

3) the anterior and posterior spinal arteries as well as the intradurally located spinal veins that drain the cord. Observe also the extensive system of extradurally located vertebral veins within the spinal canal which anastomose with the basivertebral veins draining the bodies of the vertebrae.

Filaments of dorsal and
ventral roots

Superior articular facet of
vertebra

Denticulate ligament

Spinal ganglion and
dural sheath

Pedicle of vertebral arch

Articular facet for neck of rib
(on transverse process of vertebra)

**Sympathetic ganglia;
Rami communicantes**

Articular facet for head of rib
(on body of vertebra)

External intercostal muscle

Body of rib

Intercostal nerve,
artery and vein

Endothoracic fascia;
Internal
intercostal m.

Costal pleura

Sympathetic trunk

Greater splanchnic n.

Diaphragmatic pleura

Pericardiacophrenic
artery and vein;
Phrenic nerve

Dura mater, Meningeal layer
Arachnoid

Anterior spinal artery and vein
and their radicular (root)
branches

Posterior primary ramus \ Spinal
Anterior primary ramus / nerve

Spinal ganglion; Ventral root
of spinal nerve

Subarachnoid space

Subdural space

Posterior meningeal branch of spinal ner

Spinal ganglion ensheathed with dura ma
Anterior meningeal branch
of spinal nerve

**Internal vertebral plexus
of veins and arteries;**
Epidural fat

Posterior longitudinal lig.

Body of thoracic vertebra
(superior surface)

Anterior longitudinal lig.

Hemiazygos vein

Endothoracic fascia
Costal pleura

Thoracic aorta;
Aortic plexus

Posterior
esophageal nn.
(right vagus n.)

Esophageal
aa. and vv.

Esophagus

Anterior
esophageal nn.
(left vagus n.)

Pericardium
(diaphragmatic
portion)

Inferior vena cava;
Hepatic veins joining
inferior vena cava

Azygos vein

Thoracic duct

Fig. 573: Anterior Dissection of Vertebral Column, Spinal Cord and Prevertebral Structures at a Lower Thoracic Level

NOTE: 1) the internal vertebral plexus of veins and arteries which lie in the epidural space, where also is found the epidural fat. These should not be confused with the spinal vessels which are situated in the pia mater and which are seen to be intimately applied to the spinal cord tissue.

2) the ganglionated sympathetic chain observable here in the thoracic region receiving and giving communicating rami with the spinal nerves. Note also the formation of the greater splanchnic nerve and its descent prevertebrally into the abdomen.

3) the aorta, inferior vena cava, azygos and hemiazygos veins, esophagus and thoracic duct all lying anterior or somewhat to the left of the vertebral column and passing through the diaphragm.

Fig. 573

PART VII: THE NECK & HEAD

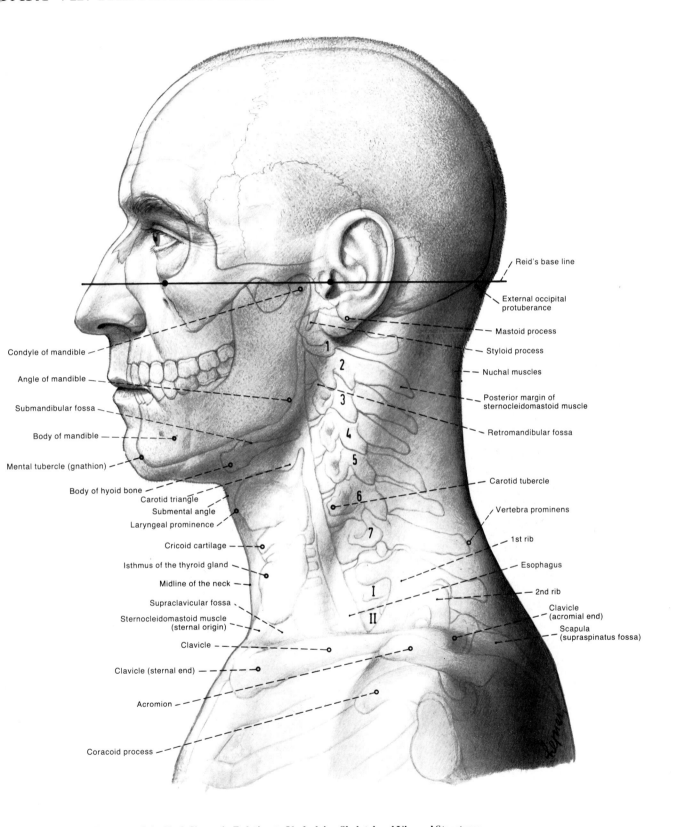

Reid's base line

External occipital protuberance

Mastoid process

Styloid process

Nuchal muscles

Posterior margin of sternocleidomastoid muscle

Retromandibular fossa

Carotid tubercle

Vertebra prominens

1st rib

Esophagus

2nd rib

Clavicle (acromial end)

Scapula (supraspinatus fossa)

Condyle of mandible

Angle of mandible

Submandibular fossa

Body of mandible

Mental tubercle (gnathion)

Body of hyoid bone

Carotid triangle

Submental angle

Laryngeal prominence

Cricoid cartilage

Isthmus of the thyroid gland

Midline of the neck

Supraclavicular fossa

Sternocleidomastoid muscle (sternal origin)

Clavicle

Clavicle (sternal end)

Acromion

Coracoid process

Fig. 574: External Features of the Neck Shown in Relation to Underlying Skeletal and Visceral Structures

NOTE: 1) that the palpable bony points are indicated by open circles at the end of certain leader lines;

2) the seven cervical and two upper thoracic vertebrae as well as the prominent skeletal features of the pectoral girdle. Observe the laryngeal cartilages and hyoid bone in the anterior neck and their respective cervical vertebral planes;

3) that a horizontal line (Reid's base line), drawn from the inferior margin of the orbit through the center of the external auditory canal and continuing backward to the center of the occipital bone, is frequently used for cranial topography and cephalometric studies.

Fig. 574   VII

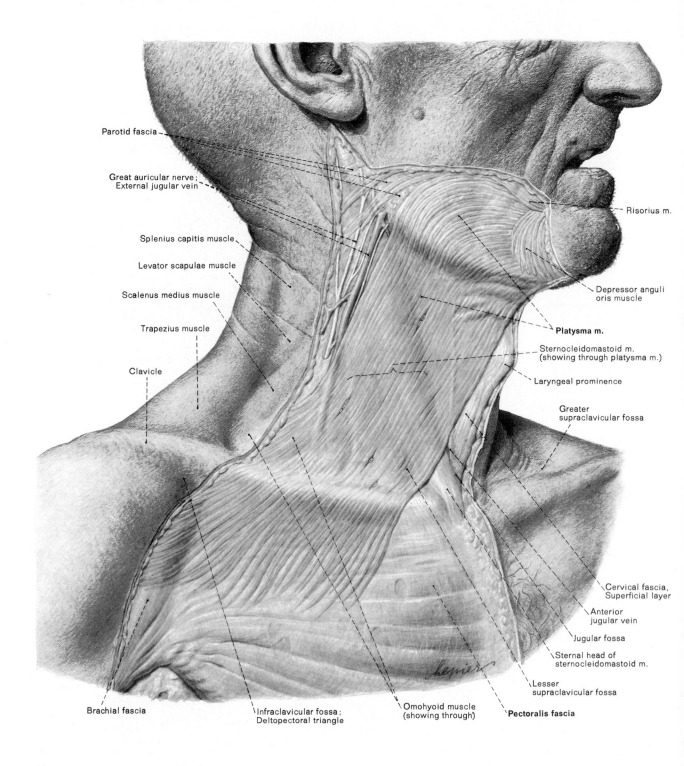

Parotid fascia

Great auricular nerve;
External jugular vein

Splenius capitis muscle

Levator scapulae muscle

Scalenus medius muscle

Trapezius muscle

Clavicle

Risorius m.

Depressor anguli
oris muscle

Platysma m.

Sternocleidomastoid m.
(showing through platysma m.)

Laryngeal prominence

Greater
supraclavicular fossa

Cervical fascia,
Superficial layer

Anterior
jugular vein

Jugular fossa

Sternal head of
sternocleidomastoid m.

Lesser
supraclavicular fossa

Brachial fascia

Infraclavicular fossa;
Deltopectoral triangle

Omohyoid muscle
(showing through)

Pectoralis fascia

Fig. 575: The Right Platysma Muscle and Pectoral Fascia

NOTE: 1) the platysma muscle is a broad, thin quadrangular muscle located in the superficial fascia on the anterolateral aspect of the neck, extending from the angle of the mouth and chin across the clavicle to the upper part of the thorax and anterior shoulder.

2) the platysma muscle can be considered as one of the muscles of facial expression, which characteristically do not arise and insert on bony structures, but within superficial fascia instead. Upon contraction, the platysma tends to depress the angle of the mouth and wrinkle the skin of the neck, thereby participating in the formation of facial expressions of anxiety, sadness, dissatisfaction and suffering.

3) similar to the other muscles of facial expression, the platysma is innervated by the cervical branch of the facial or VIIth cranial nerve.

4) overlying the pectoralis major is the well developed pectoralis fascia which extends from the midline in the thorax laterally to the axilla. Observe the external jugular vein and great auricular nerve exposed in the upper lateral aspect of the neck.

Fig. 575

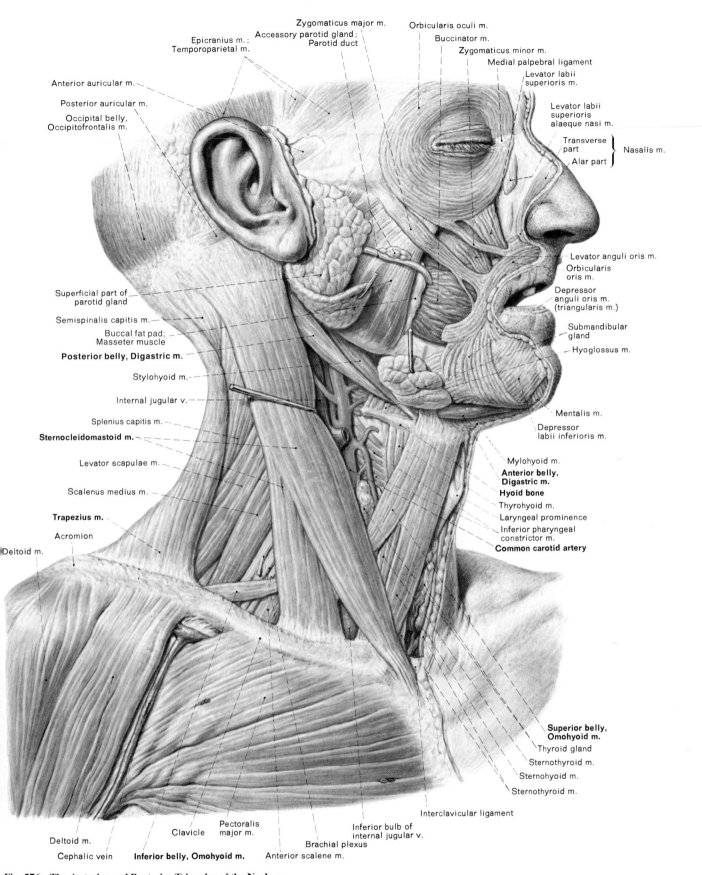

Zygomaticus major m.
Accessory parotid gland;
Parotid duct
Epicranius m.;
Temporoparietal m.
Orbicularis oculi m.
Buccinator m.
Zygomaticus minor m.
Medial palpebral ligament
Levator labii
superioris m.
Anterior auricular m.
Posterior auricular m.
Occipital belly,
Occipitofrontalis m.
Levator labii
superioris
alaeque nasi m.
Transverse
part
Alar part
Nasalis m.
Levator anguli oris m.
Orbicularis
oris m.
Depressor
anguli oris m.
(triangularis m.)
Submandibular
gland
Hyoglossus m.
Superficial part of
parotid gland
Semispinalis capitis m.
Buccal fat pad;
Masseter muscle
Posterior belly, Digastric m.
Stylohyoid m.
Internal jugular v.
Mentalis m.
Depressor
labii inferioris m.
Splenius capitis m.
Sternocleidomastoid m.
Levator scapulae m.
Scalenus medius m.
Mylohyoid m.
**Anterior belly,
Digastric m.**
Hyoid bone
Thyrohyoid m.
Laryngeal prominence
Inferior pharyngeal
constrictor m.
Common carotid artery
Trapezius m.
Acromion
Deltoid m.
**Superior belly,
Omohyoid m.**
Thyroid gland
Sternothyroid m.
Sternohyoid m.
Sternothyroid m.
Interclavicular ligament
Deltoid m.
Cephalic vein
Clavicle
Pectoralis
major m.
Inferior belly, Omohyoid m.
Anterior scalene m.
Inferior bulb of
internal jugular v.
Brachial plexus

Fig. 576: The Anterior and Posterior Triangles of the Neck

NOTE: 1) the *anterior triangle* of the neck is bounded by the midline of the neck, the anterior border of the sternocleidomastoid and the mandible. This area is further subdivided by the superior belly of the omohyoid and the two bellies of the digastric into the following: a) *muscular triangle* (midline, superior belly of omohyoid, sternocleidomastoid), b) *carotid triangle* (superior belly of omohyoid, sternocleidomastoid and posterior belly of digastric), c) *submandibular triangle* (anterior and posterior bellies of digastric and the inferior margin of the mandible), and d) *suprahyoid triangle* (midline, anterior belly of digastric and hyoid bone).

2) the *posteror triangle* of the neck is bounded by the posterior border of the sternocleidomastoid, the trapezius and the clavicle. This area is subdivided into the *occipital triangle* above, and *subclavian triangle* below, by the inferior belly of the omohyoid muscle.

Fig. 576   VII

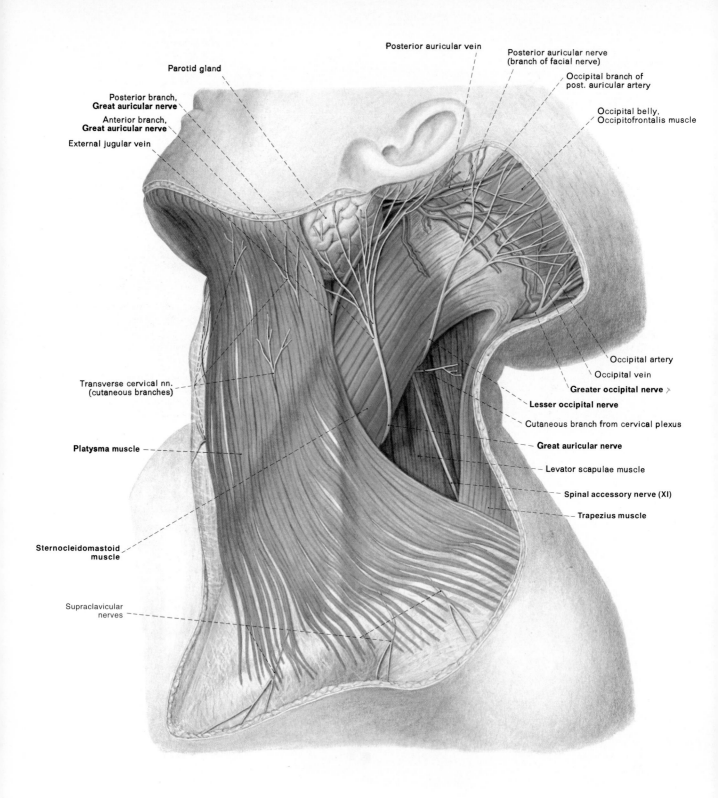

Posterior auricular vein

Posterior auricular nerve
(branch of facial nerve)

Occipital branch of
post. auricular artery

Parotid gland

Occipital belly,
Occipitofrontalis muscle

Posterior branch,
Great auricular nerve

Anterior branch,
Great auricular nerve

External jugular vein

Occipital artery

Occipital vein

Greater occipital nerve >

Lesser occipital nerve

Cutaneous branch from cervical plexus

Great auricular nerve

Levator scapulae muscle

Spinal accessory nerve (XI)

Trapezius muscle

Transverse cervical nn.
(cutaneous branches)

Platysma muscle

**Sternocleidomastoid
muscle**

Supraclavicular
nerves

Fig. 577: Nerves and Blood Vessels of the Neck, Stage 1: Platysma Layer

NOTE: 1) the skin has been removed from both anterior and posterior triangles of the neck to reveal the platysma muscle. Observe the cutaneous branches of the transverse cervical nerves emanating from the cervical plexus and penetrating through the platysma (and superficial fascia) to reach the skin of the anterolateral aspect of the neck.

2) four other nerves: a) the great auricular (C-2, C-3), b) the lesser occipital (C-2), c) the greater occipital (C-2) and d) the spinal accessory (XI).

3) after it has supplied the sternocleidomastoid muscle, the spinal accessory nerve (XI) descends in the posterior triangle to reach the trapezius muscle which it also supplies with motor innervation.

4) the supraclavicular nerves, which descend in the lateral part of the neck, under cover of the deep fascia and the superficial fascia and platysma muscle. These nerves become superficial just above the clavicle and they then cross that bone as anterior (medial), middle (intermediate), and posterior (lateral) supraclavicular nerves (see also Fig. 578). They are derived from the 3rd and 4th cervical nerves, and they supply the skin over the clavicle and over the upper trunk (down to the 2nd rib) and shoulder from the acromion laterally to the midline anteriorly.

Fig. 577

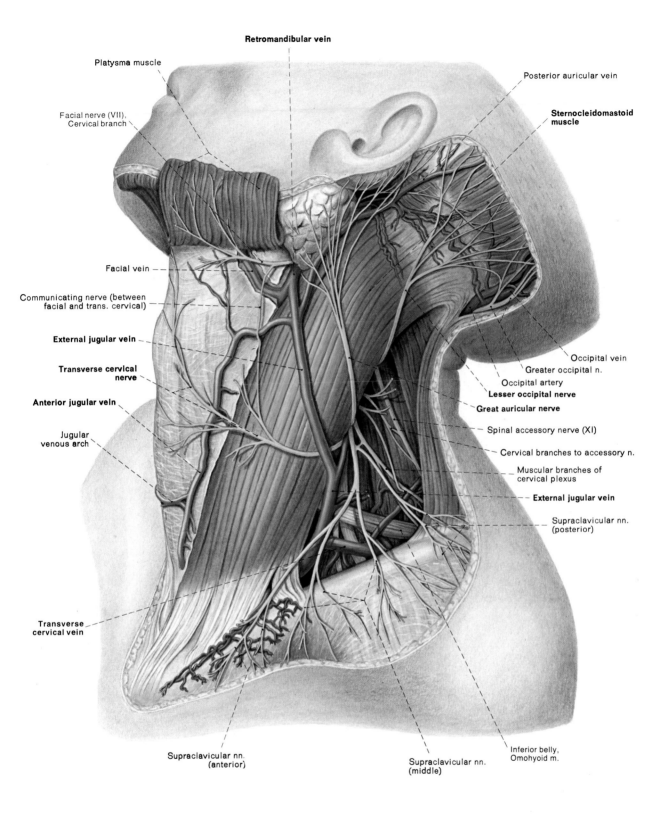

Retromandibular vein

Platysma muscle

Posterior auricular vein

Facial nerve (VII),
Cervical branch

Sternocleidomastoid
muscle

Facial vein

Communicating nerve (between
facial and trans. cervical)

External jugular vein

Transverse cervical
nerve

Anterior jugular vein

Jugular
venous arch

Occipital vein
Greater occipital n.
Occipital artery
Lesser occipital nerve
Great auricular nerve
Spinal accessory nerve (XI)
Cervical branches to accessory n.
Muscular branches of
cervical plexus
External jugular vein
Supraclavicular nn.
(posterior)

Transverse
cervical vein

Supraclavicular nn.
(anterior)

Supraclavicular nn.
(middle)

Inferior belly,
Omohyoid m.

Fig. 578: Nerves and Blood Vessels of the Neck, Stage 2: Sternocleidomastoid Layer

NOTE: 1) with the platysma reflected upward, the full extent of the sternocleidomastoid muscle is exposed. Observe that the nerves of the cervical plexus diverge at the posterior border of the sternocleidomastoid muscle: the great auricular and lesser occipital ascend to the head, the transverse colli course across the neck toward the midline, while the supraclavicular descend over the clavicle.

2) the external jugular vein formed by the junction of the retromandibular and posterior auricular veins. The external jugular crosses the sternocleidomastoid muscle obliquely and receives tributaries from the anterior jugular, posterior external jugular, transverse cervical and suprascapular veins before terminating into the subclavian vein.

3) the cervical branch of the facial (VII) nerve supplying the inner surface of the platysma muscle with motor innervation.

Fig. 578   **VII**

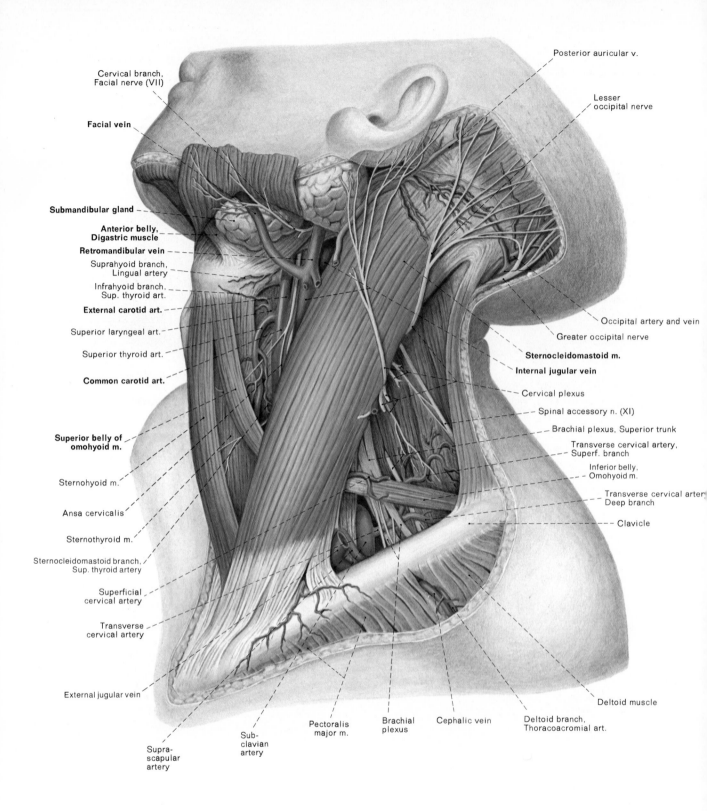

Fig. 579: Nerves and Blood Vessels of the Neck, Stage 3: the Anterior Triangle

NOTE: 1) with the investing fascia removed, the outlines of the muscular, carotid and submandibular triangles, which subdivide the anterior neck region, are revealed.

2) the infrahyoid (strap) muscles which cover the thyroid gland in the *muscular triangle* (bounded by sternocleidomastoid, midline and superior belly of omohyoid).

3) the carotid vessels and jugular vein in the *carotid triangle* (bounded by superior belly of omohyoid, posterior belly of digastric and sternocleidomastoid).

4) the submandibular gland in the *submandibular triangle* (bounded by anterior and posterior bellies of digastric and the inferior border of the mandible).

Fig. 579

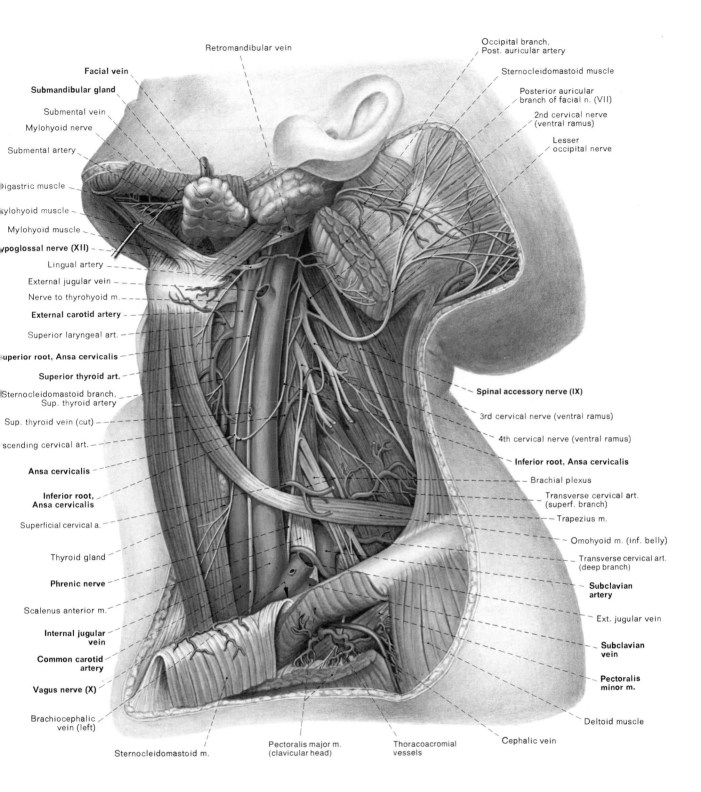

Retromandibular vein

Occipital branch, Post. auricular artery

Sternocleidomastoid muscle

Facial vein

Submandibular gland

Posterior auricular branch of facial n. (VII)

Submental vein

2nd cervical nerve (ventral ramus)

Mylohyoid nerve

Submental artery

Lesser occipital nerve

Digastric muscle

Stylohyoid muscle

Mylohyoid muscle

Hypoglossal nerve (XII)

Lingual artery

External jugular vein

Nerve to thyrohyoid m.

External carotid artery

Superior laryngeal art.

Superior root, Ansa cervicalis

Superior thyroid art.

Sternocleidomastoid branch, Sup. thyroid artery

Sup. thyroid vein (cut)

Ascending cervical art.

Ansa cervicalis

Inferior root, Ansa cervicalis

Superficial cervical a.

Thyroid gland

Phrenic nerve

Scalenus anterior m.

Internal jugular vein

Common carotid artery

Vagus nerve (X)

Brachiocephalic vein (left)

Sternocleidomastoid m.

Pectoralis major m. (clavicular head)

Thoracoacromial vessels

Spinal accessory nerve (IX)

3rd cervical nerve (ventral ramus)

4th cervical nerve (ventral ramus)

Inferior root, Ansa cervicalis

Brachial plexus

Transverse cervical art. (superf. branch)

Trapezius m.

Omohyoid m. (inf. belly)

Transverse cervical art. (deep branch)

Subclavian artery

Ext. jugular vein

Subclavian vein

Pectoralis minor m.

Deltoid muscle

Cephalic vein

Fig. 580: Nerves and Blood Vessels of the Neck, Stage 4: the Large Vessels

NOTE: 1) the sternocleidomastoid muscle and the superficial veins and nerves have been removed to expose the internal and external carotid arteries, the internal jugular vein, both bellies of the omohyoid muscle, the vagus nerve and the ansa cervicalis.

2) superiorly, the facial vein has been cut and the submandibular gland elevated, thereby exposing the hypoglossal nerve (XII). Observe that nerve fibers (originating from C-1 and travelling for a short distance) leave the hypoglossal nerve to descend in the neck. These form the superior root of the ansa cervicalis and are joined by other descending fibers from C-2 and C-3 which are called the inferior root of the ansa cervicalis. These two roots form the ansa cervicalis, from which innervation for a number of the strap muscles is derived.

3) the left phrenic nerve descending toward the thorax, where it and the right phrenic nerve are the only motor nerves that supply the musculature of the diaphragm. This nerve arises principally from the fourth cervical nerve, but it also receives fibers from C-3 and C-5. Observe that it courses deep to the omohyoid muscle and superficial to the anterior scalene muscle.

4) the common carotid artery, internal jugular vein, and vagus nerve, forming a vertically oriented neurovascular bundle in the neck that is normally surrounded by the carotid sheath of deep fascia. Observe that the common carotid artery bifurcates at about the level of the hyoid bone (or a bit lower) to form the external and internal carotid arteries.

Fig. 580   VII

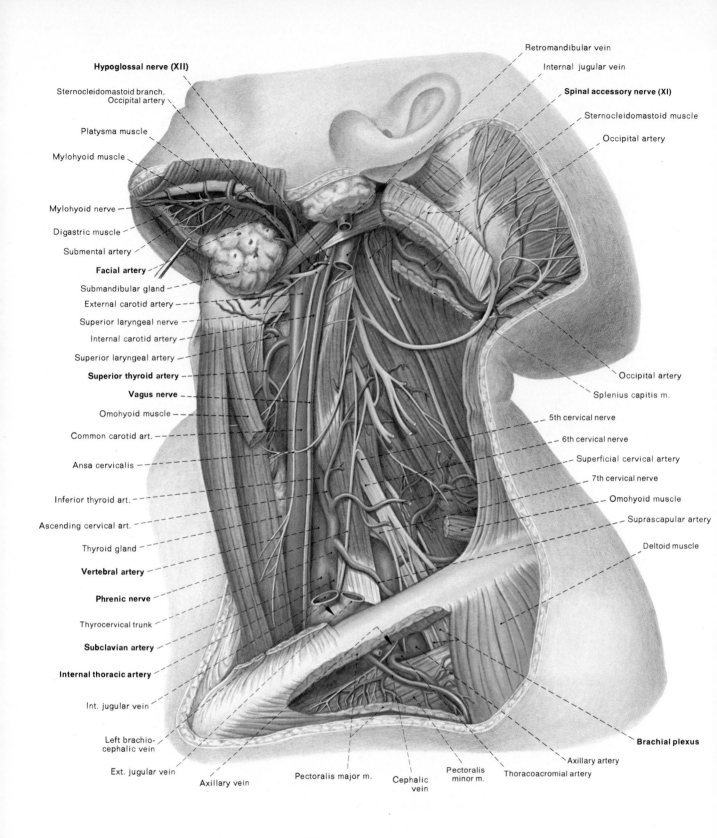

Fig. 581: Nerves and Blood Vessels of the Neck, Stage 5: the Subclavian Artery

NOTE: 1) with the internal and external jugular veins removed, the subclavian artery becomes exposed as it ascends from the thorax and loops in the subclavian triangle of the neck to descend beneath the clavicle into the axilla. Observe the vertebral, thyrocervical and internal thoracic branches and the transverse cervical artery, which comes off separately in this dissection and which divides into an ascending superficial branch and a descending deep branch (not labelled).

2) the vagus nerve coursing with the internal and common carotid arteries and the phrenic nerve descending in the neck along the surface of the anterior scalene muscle toward the thorax.

3) some of the vessels derived from the external carotid artery; well illustrated are the superior thyroid, facial, and occipital arteries. The lingual artery is also shown but is not labelled. The occipital artery courses posteriorly, deep to the sternocleidomastoid and splenius capitis muscle, and it becomes superficial on the posterior aspect of the scalp, just lateral to the superior nuchal line.

Fig. 581

Facial artery
Mylohyoid nerve
Vagus nerve (X)
Internal jugular vein
Communicating rami, Sympathetic trunk
Occipital artery
Mastoid branch, Occipital artery
bmental artery
ypoglossal nerve (XII)
ernal carotid artery
Internal carotid artery
Superior cervical ganglion
Omohyoid muscle
Superior thyroid artery
Sternohyoid muscle
up. cardiac br. of vagus n.
Vagus nerve
Ansa cervicalis
pharyngeal constrictor m.
rior cervical cardiac n.
ernothyroid muscle
Accessory cervical ganglion
or thyroid vein
nf. thyroid artery
Middle ervical ganglion
yrocervical trunk
Vertebral artery
Subclavian artery
ernal thoracic art.
urrent laryngeal n.
Trachea
Inf. thyroid vein
Middle cardiac cervical nerve
Vertebral vein
on carotid art.
nal jugular vein
rnal jugular vein

Lesser occipital nerve
Greater occipital nerve
Spinal accessory nerve (XI)
Ascending cervical artery
Phrenic nerve
Scalenus anterior m.
Superficial cervical artery
Superf. branch, Trans. cervical art.
Brachial plexus
Suprascapular nerve
Suprascapular artery
Clavicle
Axillary artery
Deltoid muscle
Acromial branch, Thoracoacromial artery
Thoracoacromial artery

✱ = 1st rib

Left brachio-cephalic vein
Pectoralis major m.
Cephalic vein
Branches of pectoral nerves
Pectoralis minor m.
Lateral thoracic vessels
Thoracoepigastric vein
Long thoracic nerve
Thoracodorsal nerve
Intercostobrachial nerve
Axillary vein
Brachial plexus
Cephalic vein

Fig. 582: Nerves and Blood Vessels of the Neck, Stage 6: the Brachial Plexus

NOTE: 1) with the carotid arteries, jugular vein and clavicle removed, the roots forming the trunks of the brachial plexus are exposed as they divide and descend into the axilla to surround the axillary artery.

2) the sympathetic trunk lying deep to the carotid arteries and coursing with the vagus nerve and the superior cardiac branch of the vagus nerve.

3) the thyroid gland receiving the superior and inferior thyroid arteries and being drained by the thyroid veins. Observe also the proximity of the recurrent laryngeal nerve to the thyroid gland.

Fig. 582   VII

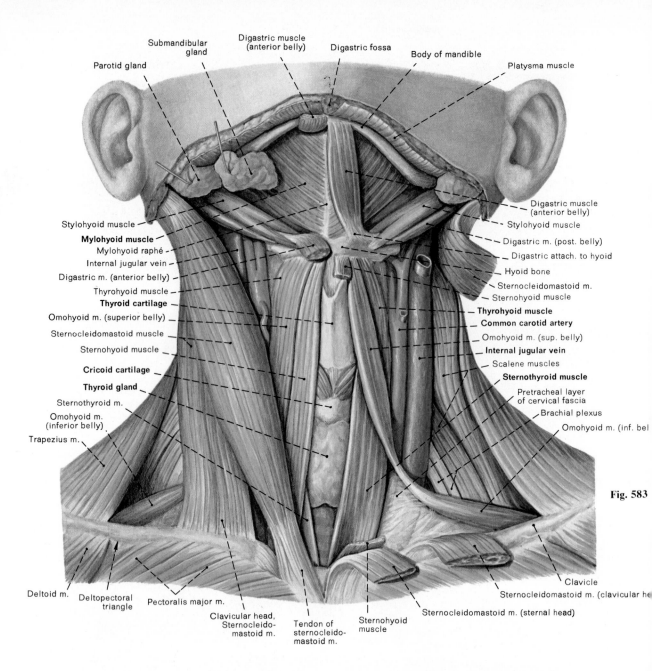

Parotid gland

Submandibular gland

Digastric muscle (anterior belly)

Digastric fossa

Body of mandible

Platysma muscle

Stylohyoid muscle

Mylohyoid muscle

Mylohyoid raphé

Internal jugular vein

Digastric m. (anterior belly)

Thyrohyoid muscle

Thyroid cartilage

Omohyoid m. (superior belly)

Sternocleidomastoid muscle

Sternohyoid muscle

Cricoid cartilage

Thyroid gland

Sternothyroid m.

Omohyoid m. (inferior belly)

Trapezius m.

Deltoid m.

Deltopectoral triangle

Pectoralis major m.

Clavicular head, Sternocleidomastoid m.

Tendon of sternocleidomastoid m.

Sternohyoid muscle

Digastric muscle (anterior belly)

Stylohyoid muscle

Digastric m. (post. belly)

Digastric attach. to hyoid

Hyoid bone

Sternocleidomastoid m.

Sternohyoid muscle

Thyrohyoid muscle

Common carotid artery

Omohyoid m. (sup. belly)

Internal jugular vein

Scalene muscles

Sternothyroid muscle

Pretracheal layer of cervical fascia

Brachial plexus

Omohyoid m. (inf. bel

Fig. 583

Clavicle

Sternocleidomastoid m. (clavicular he

Sternocleidomastoid m. (sternal head)

Fig. 584

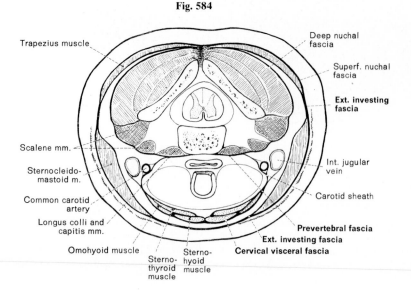

Trapezius muscle

Scalene mm.

Sternocleidomastoid m.

Common carotid artery

Longus colli and capitis mm.

Omohyoid muscle

Sterno-thyroid muscle

Sterno-hyoid muscle

Deep nuchal fascia

Superf. nuchal fascia

Ext. investing fascia

Int. jugular vein

Carotid sheath

Prevertebral fascia

Ext. investing fascia

Cervical visceral fascia

Fig. 583: Anterior View of the Musculature of the Neck

NOTE: 1) the right superior belly of the digastric muscle was removed and submandibular gland elevated in order to show the mylohyoid muscle. On the left side, the sternocleidomastoid and sternohyoid muscles have been transected and the submandibular gland removed.

2) the relationship of the strap muscles to the thyroid gland and realize that inferior to the thyroid gland and above the suprasternal notch, the trachea lies immediately under the skin.

Fig. 584: Fascial Planes of the Neck in a Newborn Child (Cross Section)

NOTE: the external investing fascia splits to encase the sternocleidomastoid and trapezius muscles. The prevertebral fascia encloses the vertebral column and its muscles, while the cervical visceral fascia encloses the esophagus, trachea, thyroid gland and strap muscles.

Digastric muscle (anterior belly)
Anterior jugular vein
Submental vein
Submandibular gland
Facial vein
Retro-
andibular vein
ylohyoid muscle
Occipital branch of
ext. jugular vein
Facial vein
Internal jugular vein
Superior thyroid vein
External jugular vein
Common carotid artery
Sternocleidomastoid muscle
Superficial cervical vein
ransverse cervical vein
hyoid muscle
inferior belly)
phalic vein
Pectoralis major m.
Perforating branches,
Int. thoracic artery
Ant. cutaneous branch,
Intercostal nerve
Perforating branches,
Int. thoracic vessels
Inferior thyroid vein

Mylohyoid muscle
Hyoglossus muscle
Submental vein
Facial artery
Facial vein
Accompanying vein
of hypoglossal nerve
Hypoglossal nerve
Parotid gland
Facial vein
Occipital branch,
Ext. jugular v.
External jugular vein
Laryngeal prominence
Superior thyroid vein
Sternocleidomastoid muscle
Ansa cervicalis
Internal jugular vein
Isthmus of thyroid gland
External jugular vein
Anterior jugular vein
Omohyoid muscle
Trapezius
muscle
Cephalic vein
Pectoralis major m.
Thoracoacromial vein
Axillary vein
Sternocleidomastoid m.
Jugular
venous arch

Fig. 585: Veins of the Neck and Infraclavicular Region

NOTE: 1) the jugular system of veins, although somewhat variable, generally consists of an anterior jugular, external jugular and internal jugular vein, all of which are shown on the left side where the sternocleidomastoid muscle has been removed.

2) the anterior jugular descends close to the midline, is frequently small and drains laterally through several tributaries into the external jugular vein. The external jugular courses along the surface of the sternocleidomastoid muscle. It commences usually within the parotid gland and enlarges through the junction of occipital, retromandibular and facial branches. It flows into the subclavian vein with the internal jugular after it receives branches from the shoulder and clavicular regions.

3) the internal jugular is large and collects blood from the brain, face and neck. At its junction with the subclavian, the brachiocephalic vein is formed.

Fig. 585   VII

Fig. 586:   Deep Arteries and Veins of the Neck and Great Vessels of the Thorax

NOTE: 1) in the neck, the sternocleidomastoid and strap muscles have been removed, thereby exposing the carotid arteries, internal jugular veins and thyroid gland.

2) the middle portion of the anterior thoracic wall has been resected in order to show the aortic arch and its branches, the brachiocephalic veins, the superior vena cava and the vagus nerves.

3) in the submandibular region, the mylohyoid and anterior digastric muscles have been cut, revealing the lingual and hypoglossal nerves.

Fig. 586

Cavernous sinus
Parotid lymph nodes
Superficial temporal vein;
Preauricular lymph nodes
Superior petrosal sinus
Occipital lymph nodes

Nasofrontal vein
Angular vein
Transverse facial vein
Facial vein
Middle submandibular lymph nodes

Transverse sinus

Mastoid foramen;
Retroauricular lymph nodes
Sigmoid sinus; Subauricular
lymph nodes; Posterior auricular vein
Retromandibular vein
Superficial cervical lymph nodes;
Facial vein
Deep superior cervical lymph
nodes (jugular)
Superior laryngeal vein;
Internal jugular vein
Deep inferior cervical lymph
nodes (jugular)
Superficial cervical vein

Transverse cervical vein
Deep inferior cervical lymph
nodes (supraclavicular)
Suprascapular vein

Submental vein;
Ant. submandibular
lymph nodes
Submental lymph nodes
Post. submandibular lymph nodes
Accompanying vein of the
hypoglossal nerve

Anterior jugular vein
External jugular vein;
Right jugular lymphatic trunk
Median cervical vein
Inferior bulb, internal jugular vein;
Opening of right lymphatic duct
Right brachiocephalic vein

Transverse cervical vein

Subclavian lymphatic trunk; Subclavian vein;
Apical lymph nodes

Fig. 587: The Superficial Lymph Nodes, Lymphatic Channels and Veins of the Face, Lower Head and Neck (Right Lateral View)

NOTE that the superficial lymphatic channels of the face and the temporal and occipital regions of the head drain inferiorly and posteriorly to the superficial and deeper cervical nodes accompanying the internal jugular vein. These in turn drain into the right jugular lymphatic trunk.

A = Middle scalene m.
B = Ant. scalene m.
C = Post. scalene m.
D = Omohyoid m.

E = Sternohyoid m.
F = Sternothyroid m.
G = Thyrohyoid m.
Gl. th. = Thyroid gland

H₁ = Digastric m. (ant. belly)
H₂ = Digastric m. (post belly)
J = Mylohyoid m.
K = Stylohyoid m.

L = Hyoglossus m.
M = Styloglossus m.
Ma. st. = Manubrium sterni
1., 2. R = 1st and 2nd ribs

Fig. 587   VII

Hyoid bone

Internal laryngeal artery and nerve; Thyrohyoid membrane

Sup. thyroid art. and vein; Thyrohyoid muscle

Thyroid gland (pyramidal lobe)

Sternohyoid muscle

Thyroid gland (left lobe)

Inf. laryngeal art.; Recurrent laryngeal n.; Esophagus

Left inferior parathyroid gland

Trachea

Thyroid ima vein

Esophageal branches, recurrent laryngeal nerve

Brachiocephalic artery

Left brachiocephalic vein

Aortic arch; Left recurrent laryngeal nerve

Ascending aorta

External carotid artery

Internal carotid artery

Internal jugular vein

Carotid sinus (dilatation at bifurcation of internal carotid artery)

Inferior pharyngeal constrictor muscle

Sternocleidomastoid muscle

Common carotid artery; Left vagus nerve; Internal jugular vein

Inferior thyroid artery

Brachial plexus

Cervical sympathetic cardiac nerves

Inferior cervical ganglion

Thoracic duct Transverse cervical art.

Left subclavian vein; First rib

Left subclavian artery

Left lung

Fig. 588: The Nerves and Vessels in the Deep Part of the Lower Neck, Anterolateral View

NOTE: 1) that this is an anterolateral view of the *left side* of the lower neck, so that the lateral aspect of the left lobe of the thyroid gland and the vessels entering and leaving the gland, the left superior and inferior thyroid arteries and veins and the thyroid ima vein, are clearly seen. Observe a parathyroid gland located behind the thyroid adjacent to the inferior thyroid vessels.

2) that in this dissection the lower part of the left common carotid artery, near its origin from the aortic arch, has been cut away, while the left subclavian artery has been left intact. Additionally, the left brachiocephalic vein has been removed from its point of formation at the junction of the left subclavian and internal jugular veins to the site at which the thyroid ima vein joins it.

3) that with these large vessels removed, the left vagus nerve with its recurrent laryngeal branch is exposed. Observe the surgically important relationship between the two principal terminal branches of the inferior thyroid artery and the recurrent laryngeal nerve near the point of entrance of these vessels into the thyroid gland. On the left side the recurrent nerve courses between these two branches (as shown in this figure) about 33% of the time. The nerve ascends deep to these vessels 50 to 55% of the time and superficial, or in front of them, 11 to 12% of the time (Hollinshead, W. H., Surg. Clin. North Amer., *32*: 1115, 1952). Care must be taken that the recurrent laryngeal nerves are not injured during thyroidectomy, because they are the source of motor innervation to nearly all of the muscles of the larynx.

Fig. 588

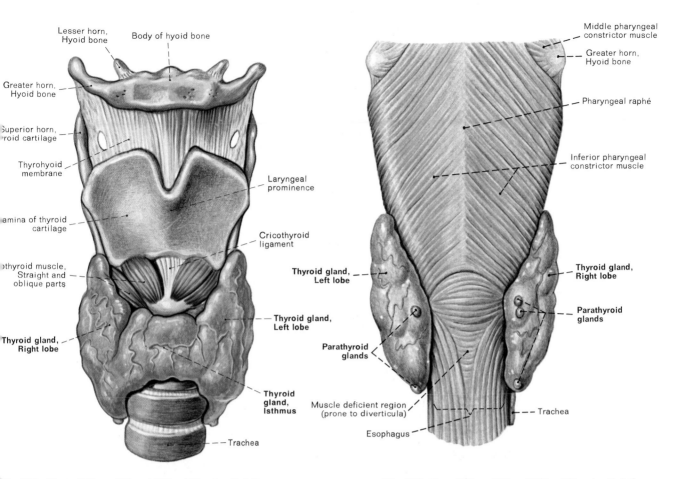

Lesser horn, Hyoid bone

Body of hyoid bone

Greater horn, Hyoid bone

Superior horn, roid cartilage

Thyrohyoid membrane

amina of thyroid cartilage

othyroid muscle, Straight and oblique parts

Thyroid gland, Right lobe

Laryngeal prominence

Cricothyroid ligament

Thyroid gland, Left lobe

Thyroid gland, Isthmus

Trachea

Middle pharyngeal constrictor muscle

Greater horn, Hyoid bone

Pharyngeal raphé

Inferior pharyngeal constrictor muscle

Thyroid gland, Left lobe

Parathyroid glands

Muscle deficient region (prone to diverticula)

Esophagus

Thyroid gland, Right lobe

Parathyroid glands

Trachea

Fig. 589: Ventral View of Thyroid Gland Showing Relation to Larynx and Trachea

Fig. 590: Dorsal View of Thyroid Gland Showing Relation to Pharynx and Parathyroids

Fig. 591: Cross Section of Cervical Viscera Showing Relation of Thyroid Gland to Trachea, Esophagus, Parathyroid Glands and Cervical Vessels and Nerves

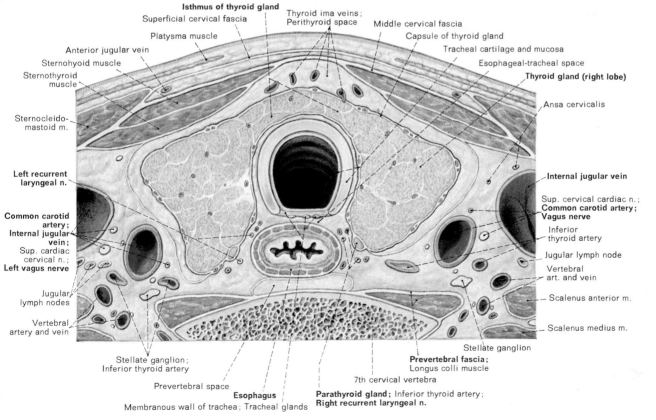

Isthmus of thyroid gland

Superficial cervical fascia

Platysma muscle

Anterior jugular vein

Sternohyoid muscle

Sternothyroid muscle

Sternocleido- mastoid m.

Left recurrent laryngeal n.

Common carotid artery; Internal jugular vein; Sup. cardiac cervical n.; Left vagus nerve

Jugular lymph nodes

Vertebral artery and vein

Thyroid ima veins; Perithyroid space

Middle cervical fascia

Capsule of thyroid gland

Tracheal cartilage and mucosa

Esophageal-tracheal space

Thyroid gland (right lobe)

Ansa cervicalis

Internal jugular vein

Sup. cervical cardiac n.; **Common carotid artery; Vagus nerve**

Inferior thyroid artery

Jugular lymph node

Vertebral art. and vein

Scalenus anterior m.

Scalenus medius m.

Stellate ganglion

Stellate ganglion; Inferior thyroid artery

Prevertebral space

Esophagus

Membranous wall of trachea; Tracheal glands

Prevertebral fascia; Longus colli muscle

7th cervical vertebra

Parathyroid gland; Inferior thyroid artery; **Right recurrent laryngeal n.**

Figs. 589, 590, 591   VII

Fig. 592 labels (within image):

Superior thyroid artery

Fourth cervical nerve (C-4);
Superior laryngeal nerve

Right vagus nerve;
Superior cardiac branch,
right vagus nerve

Phrenic nerve;
Cricothyroid ligament

Anastomotic branch between
sup. and inf. thyroid aa.;
Fifth cervical nerve (C-5)

Ascending cervical branches,
inferior thyroid artery;
Middle thyroid vein

Sup. cardiac br.,
vagus nerve;
Vertebral art.;
Trans. cerv. art.

Ansa subclavia;
Superf. cerv.
art. and vein;
Dors. scapular n.

Suprascapular
art. and vein;
Nerve to
subclavius m.

Sup. cardiac
br., vagus n.;
Thyrocervical
trunk; Jug.
lymph. trunk

Rt. internal
thoracic art.

Ext. jugular v.;
Subclavian
lymph. trunk;
Accessory
phrenic nerve

Rt. brachiocephalic v.;
Artery to sterno-
clavicular joint

Right superior thyroid artery and vein

Ansa cervicalis (superior root)

Nerve to omohyoid muscle

Internal jugular vein;
Ansa cervicalis (inferior root)

Cricothyroid branch,
superior thyroid art.;
Left vagus nerve;
Jugular lymph trunk

Asc. cervical branches,
inf. thyroid artery;
Ansa cervicalis

Ext. jugular vein;
Nerve to omohyoid
(from ansa cervicalis)

Super
cervic
art. an

Inferior
thyroid
artery

Vertebral
art. and v
Thoracic

Lymph no
(Virchow'
Transvers
cerv. art.

Subclavia
art. and ve

Ansa
subclavia;
Subclavian
lymphatic
trunk

Left intern
thoracic a
Phrenic n.
Anterior
bronchom
lymph. tru

Middle cardiac branch,
vagus nerve;
Cervical pleura

Right vagus nerve;
Middle cardiac branch, vagus n.

Inferior cardiac branch, vagus nerve;
Right vert. v.; Supraclav. lymph node

Inferior thyroid veins; Trachea

Sup. thymic
art. and vein

Left recurrent laryngeal nerve;
Paratracheal lymph node

Superior cardiac branch, vagus nerve;
Left brachiocephalic vein

F. Batke 50

Fig. 592: The Superficial Structures at the Root of the Neck and Thoracic Inlet, Anterior View

NOTE: 1) that in this dissection the two clavicles have been removed, thereby exposing both brachiocephalic veins and their principal tributaries: the internal and external jugular veins, the subclavian veins, and the thyroid veins. Compare the venous pattern in this realistic figure with the more graphic pattern of the veins in the anterior neck shown in Figure 586.

2) that the right subclavian artery and its thyrocervical trunk have been exposed by severing the superior and middle thyroid veins and pulling the right internal jugular vein laterally. Observe the right vagus nerve and its cardiac branches and, posterolaterally, the right vagus nerve. Also note the right ansa subclavia, which loops around the subclavian artery. The ansa subclavia consists principally of communicating sympathetic fibers interconnecting the middle cervical ganglion with either the inferior cervical ganglion or the cervicothoracic (stellate) ganglion.

A = Hyoid bone	E = Thyrohyoid muscle	J = Omohyoid muscle	N = Ext. intercostal muscle
B = Omohyoid muscle	F = Sternothyroid muscle	K = Trapezius muscle	O = Pectoralis major muscle
C = Sternohyoid muscle	G = Cricothyroid muscle	L = Subclavius muscle	P = Anterior scalene muscle
D = Thyrohyoid membrane	H = Isthmus, thyroid gland	M = Int. intercostal muscle	Q = Levator scapulae muscle
			R = Middle scalene muscle

Fig. 592

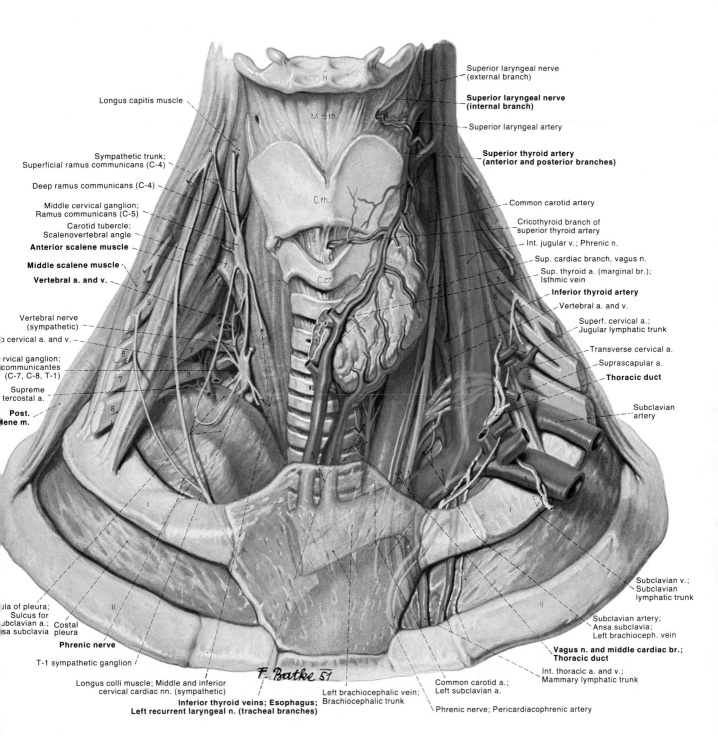

Longus capitis muscle

Sympathetic trunk;
Superficial ramus communicans (C-4)

Deep ramus communicans (C-4)

Middle cervical ganglion;
Ramus communicans (C-5)

Carotid tubercle;
Scalenovertebral angle

Anterior scalene muscle

Middle scalene muscle

Vertebral a. and v.

Vertebral nerve
(sympathetic)

cervical a. and v.

rvical ganglion;
communicantes
(C-7, C-8, T-1)

Supreme
tercostal a.

**Post.
ene m.**

la of pleura;
Sulcus for
ubclavian a.;   Costal
sa subclavia   pleura

Phrenic nerve

T-1 sympathetic ganglion

Longus colli muscle; Middle and inferior
cervical cardiac nn. (sympathetic)

**Inferior thyroid veins; Esophagus;
Left recurrent laryngeal n. (tracheal branches)**

Superior laryngeal nerve
(external branch)

**Superior laryngeal nerve
(internal branch)**

Superior laryngeal artery

**Superior thyroid artery
(anterior and posterior branches)**

Common carotid artery

Cricothyroid branch of
superior thyroid artery

Int. jugular v.; Phrenic n.

Sup. cardiac branch, vagus n.

Sup. thyroid a. (marginal br.);
Isthmic vein

Inferior thyroid artery

Vertebral a. and v.

Superf. cervical a.;
Jugular lymphatic trunk

Transverse cervical a.

Suprascapular a.

Thoracic duct

Subclavian
artery

Subclavian v.;
Subclavian
lymphatic trunk

Subclavian artery;
Ansa subclavia;
Left brachioceph. vein

**Vagus n. and middle cardiac br.;
Thoracic duct**

Int. thoracic a. and v.;
Mammary lymphatic trunk

Phrenic nerve; Pericardiacophrenic artery

Common carotid a.;
Left subclavian a.

Left brachiocephalic vein;
Brachiocephalic trunk

F. Batke 51

Fig. 593: The Root of the Neck and the Thoracic Inlet, Anterior View

NOTE: 1) that the sternocleidomastoid and strap muscles have been removed. Additionally, *on the right side* (reader's left), the large vessels, vagus nerve, and right lobe of the thyroid gland have been resected to reveal the scalene muscles, the roots of the brachial plexus, the inferior and middle cervical ganglia and cupula of the right pleura.

2) *on the left side,* the course of the vagus nerve and its recurrent laryngeal branch. Observe also the thoracic duct as it ascends into the root of the neck to open into the venous system at the angle of junction between the left internal jugular and left subclavian veins.

3) the descending course of the phrenic nerves. These nerves are derived from the 3rd, 4th, and 5th cervical segments, lie along the ventral surface of the anterior scalene muscle, and enter the thorax deep to the sternocostal joints of the first rib.

4) the cupula of the pleura overlying the apex of the lung. On each side these project 3 to 5 cm above the sternal end of the first rib and, therefore, are unprotected by bone.

5) the superior thyroid vessels and their superior laryngeal and cricothyroid branches. Observe the rich vascularity of the thyroid gland and the veins (of considerable size) which course anterior to the trachea at the site where tracheostomy is frequently performed.

C. cr. = Cricoid cartilage
C. th. = Thyroid cartilage
H = Hyoid bone

L. c. = Cricothyroid ligament
M. h. th. = Thyrohyoid membrane
I, II = 1st and 2nd ribs

4–8 = Ventral rami of C-4 to C-8 nerves
I = Ventral ramus of T-1 nerve

Fig. 593   VII

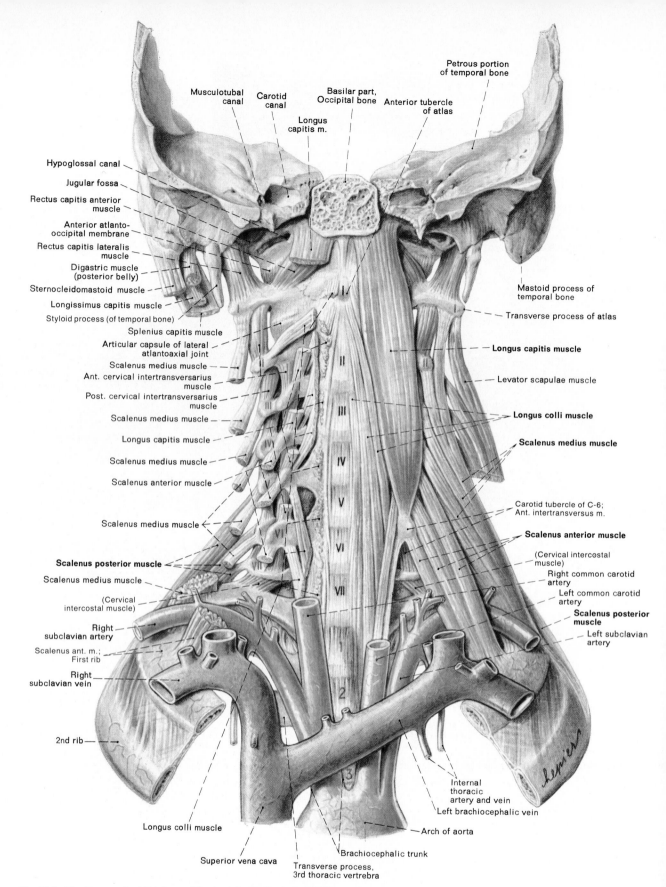

Fig. 594: The Prevertebral Region and Root of the Neck, Anterior View

NOTE: 1) on the specimen's right side, the longus capitis, longus colli and scalene muscles have been removed, exposing the transverse processes of the cervical vertebrae onto which these muscles are seen to attach.

2) the scalenus posterior muscle inserts on the 2nd rib, whereas both the scalenus anterior and medius insert onto the 1st rib. Thus, when these muscles are fixed superiorly, they would act as inspiratory muscles by elevating the first two ribs. Fixed inferiorly, they assist in bending the cervical vertebral column to one or the other side. Between the scalenus anterior and medius emerge the roots which form the trunks of the brachial plexus (see Figs. 593 and 596).

Fig. 594

Ant. communi-
cating art.
Ant. cerebral art.
Int. carotid arteries
Right middle cerebral art.
Post. communicating aa.
Internal carotid artery
Post. cerebral arteries
Superior cerebellar artery
Labyrinthine artery
Inf. anterior cerebellar artery
Basilar artery
Left vertebral artery
Right vertebral artery
Atlantooccipital ligament
Vertebral artery
Internal carotid artery
Transverse process
Vertebral artery
External carotid artery
Common carotid artery
Vertebral artery
Subclavian artery
Arch of aorta

Fig. 595: The Vertebral and Internal Carotid Arteries

NOTE: 1) both the internal carotid and vertebral arteries ascend in the neck to enter the cranial
cavity in order to supply blood to the substance
of the brain. Although the vertebral arteries do
give off certain spinal and muscular branches in
the neck prior to entering the skull, the internal
carotid arteries do not branch until they have
entered the cranial cavity at the base of the brain.

2) the origin of the vertebral artery from the
subclavian, and its ascent in the neck through the
intervertebral foramina of the transverse processes
of the cervical vertebrae. The two vertebral arteries
join to form the basilar artery. This courses along
the ventral aspect of the brainstem to supply the
brainstem and cerebellum, which rest on the floor
of the posterior cranial fossa.

3) the internal carotid artery begins at the bifurcation of the common carotid, and ascends in the
neck to its entrance into the carotid canal in the
petrous portion of the temporal bone (see Fig. 640).
After a somewhat tortuous course, it enters the
cranial cavity to supply the orbit (through its ophthalmic branch) and the cerebral hemispheres. At
the base of the brain, communicating vessels join
with others from the basilar to form the cerebral arterial circle of Willis.

Fig. 596: The Right Subclavian Artery and its Branches

NOTE: 1) the right subclavian artery
arises from the brachiocephalic trunk,
although on the left it branches from
the aorta. It ascends into the root of the
neck, arches laterally and then descends
between the 1st rib and clavicle to
become the axillary artery.

2) the subclavian artery generally has
four major branches and sometimes
five. These are the vertebral artery, the
thyrocervical trunk, the internal thoracic artery and the costocervical
trunk. In about 40% of bodies, there is
also a transverse cervical artery arising
directly from the subclavian. There is
considerable variability in the origin
of vessels such as the suprascapular
artery, the transverse cervical artery and
the superficial and deep cervical
branches.

Deep branch of
ascending cervical a.
Ascending cervical a.
Phrenic nerve
Superficial cervical a.
Thyrocervical trunk
Suprascapular a.
Transverse
cervical a.
Inf. thyroid a.
Vertebral a.
Deep cervical a.
Highest
intercostal a.
**Costocervical
trunk**
Common carotid a.
Brachial
plexus
Subclavian
artery
becoming
axillary a.
**Internal
thoracic a.**
Perforating
branches
Anterior
intercostal a.
Anterior
intercostal a.
Vierling.

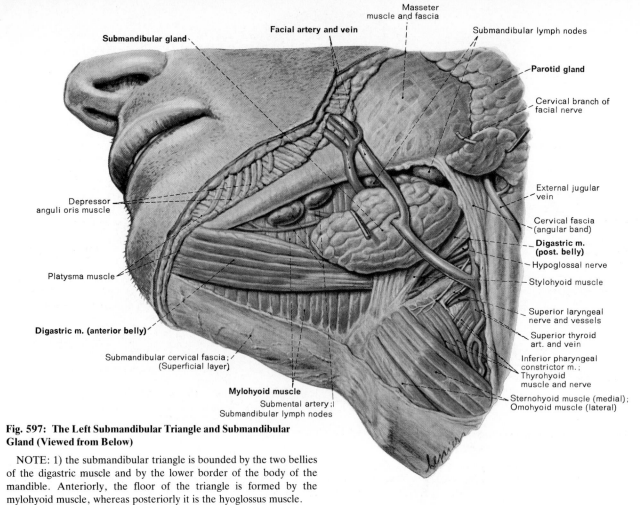

Fig. 597: The Left Submandibular Triangle and Submandibular Gland (Viewed from Below)

NOTE: 1) the submandibular triangle is bounded by the two bellies of the digastric muscle and by the lower border of the body of the mandible. Anteriorly, the floor of the triangle is formed by the mylohyoid muscle, whereas posteriorly it is the hyoglossus muscle.

2) the submandibular gland is situated in the anterior part of the triangle. Crossing obliquely are the anterior facial vein and facial artery. Overlying the posterior part of the triangle is the inferior extension of the parotid gland. Likewise, arranged along the lower border of the body of the mandible are a number of submandibular lymph nodes.

Fig. 598: The Suprahyoid Muscles and Hyoid Bone (Viewed from Below)

NOTE that indicated on the mandible are the inner attachments of the mylohyoid muscle (broken line) and the anterior belly of the digastric muscle (circle). Observe the attachments of the mylohyoid, digastric and stylohyoid muscles as well as the stylohyoid ligament onto the hyoid bone.

Figs. 597, 598

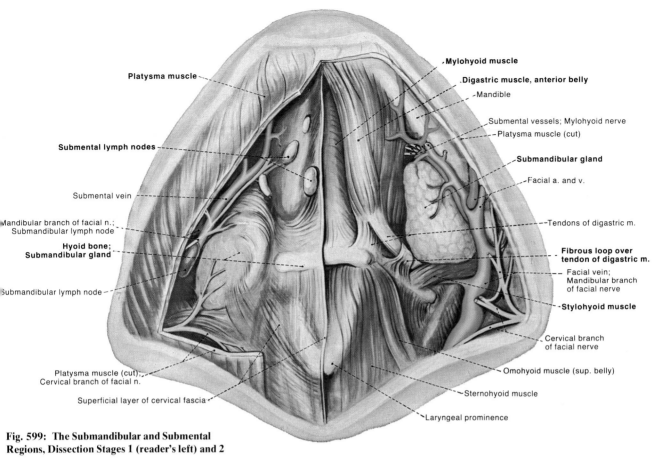

Platysma muscle

Submental lymph nodes

Submental vein

Mandibular branch of facial n.;
Submandibular lymph node

Hyoid bone;
Submandibular gland

Submandibular lymph node

Platysma muscle (cut);
Cervical branch of facial n.

Superficial layer of cervical fascia

Mylohyoid muscle

Digastric muscle, anterior belly

Mandible

Submental vessels; Mylohyoid nerve

Platysma muscle (cut)

Submandibular gland

Facial a. and v.

Tendons of digastric m.

Fibrous loop over
tendon of digastric m.

Facial vein;
Mandibular branch
of facial nerve

Stylohyoid muscle

Cervical branch
of facial nerve

Omohyoid muscle (sup. belly)

Sternohyoid muscle

Laryngeal prominence

**Fig. 599: The Submandibular and Submental
Regions, Dissection Stages 1 (reader's left) and 2**

NOTE that in Dissection Stage 1 the superficial fascia containing the platysma has been opened, revealing the submandibular gland and the superficial lymph nodes. In Stage 2 (reader's right), the superficial layer of cervical fascia has been removed, thereby exposing the substance of the submandibular gland and the digastric (anterior belly), mylohyoid and stylohyoid muscles.

Fig. 600: The Submandibular and Submental Regions, Dissection Stages 3 (reader's left) and 4

NOTE that in Dissection Stage 3 much of the submandibular gland has been removed, revealing the posterior border of the mylohyoid muscle and the submental vessels and mylohyoid nerve. In Stage 4, the anterior belly of the digastric and the mylohyoid muscles have been partially removed, exposing the hypoglossal nerve and its accompanying vein.

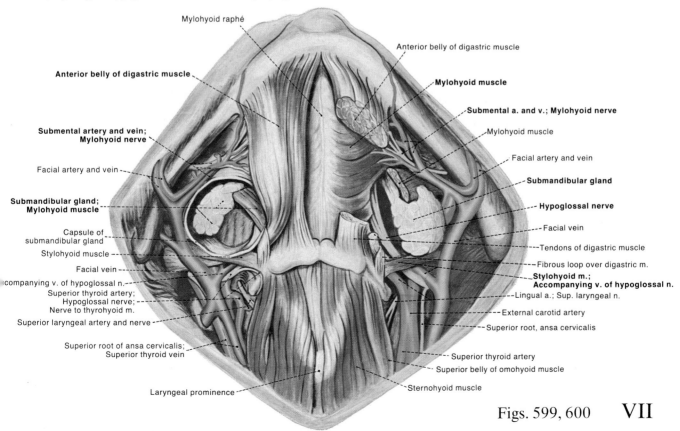

Mylohyoid raphé

Anterior belly of digastric muscle

Anterior belly of digastric muscle

Mylohyoid muscle

Submental a. and v.; Mylohyoid nerve

Submental artery and vein;
Mylohyoid nerve

Mylohyoid muscle

Facial artery and vein

Facial artery and vein

Submandibular gland

Submandibular gland;
Mylohyoid muscle

Hypoglossal nerve

Facial vein

Capsule of
submandibular gland

Tendons of digastric muscle

Stylohyoid muscle

Fibrous loop over digastric m.

Facial vein

Stylohyoid m.;
Accompanying v. of hypoglossal n.

Accompanying v. of hypoglossal n.;

Lingual a.; Sup. laryngeal n.

Superior thyroid artery;
Hypoglossal nerve;
Nerve to thyrohyoid m.

External carotid artery

Superior root, ansa cervicalis

Superior laryngeal artery and nerve

Superior root of ansa cervicalis;
Superior thyroid vein

Superior thyroid artery

Superior belly of omohyoid muscle

Sternohyoid muscle

Laryngeal prominence

Figs. 599, 600   VII

Internasal suture

Nasal bone

Frontal process of
maxilla

Frontolacrimal suture

Sphenofrontal suture

Supraorbital margin

Coronal suture

Parietal bone

Greater wing
(sphenoid)

Orbital surface
of frontal bone

Zygomatic process
of frontal bone

Superior orbital
fissure

Lesser wing
(sphenoid bone)

Greater wing
(sphenoid bone)

Zygomatic bone

Inferior orbital
fissure

Zygomaticomaxillary
suture

Infraorbital margin

Vomer (nasal septum)

Alveolar process
of maxilla

Maxilla

Anterior nasal spine

Mental foramen

Body of mandible

Frontal bone

Frontonasal suture

Frontomaxillary suture

Supraorbital foramen

Sphenoparietal suture

Greater wing of sphenoid
(orbital surface)

Lacrimal bone

Sphenozygomatic suture

Nasomaxillary suture

Infraorbital foramen

Middle nasal concha;
Inferior nasal concha

Ramus of mandible

Fig. 601: The Anterior Aspect of the Skull

NOTE: the bones of the skull shown in this view
are:
frontal bone: lavender
nasal bone: white
maxillary bone: yellow
zygomatic bone: orange
sphenoid bone: green
temporal bone: white
parietal bone: brown
mandible: blue
lacrimal bone: red
vomer: pink
middle concha: orange
(ethmoid)
inferior concha: pink

Fig. 602: Regions of the Anterolateral Head and Neck

Frontal region

Zygomatic region

Temporal region

Orbital
region

Parietal
region

Nasal region

Nares
(nostrils)

Infraorbital
region

Oral region

Parotid-
masseteric
region

Mental
region

Buccal region

Submental region

Hyoid region

Auricular
region

Occipital
region

Submandibular
triangle

Carotid triangle

Sternocleidomastoid
region

Lateral neck region

Lateral neck region

Suprascapular
region

Laryngeal region

Anterior
neck region

Figs. 601, 602

Fig. 603: The Muscles of Facial Expression (Anterior View)

NOTE: 1) the muscles of facial expression are superficial muscles located within the layers of subcutaneous fascia. Having developed from the mesoderm of the 2nd branchial arch, they are all innervated by the nerve of that arch, the seventh cranial or facial nerve.

2) the facial muscles may be grouped into: a) the muscles of the scalp, b) the muscles of external ear, c) the muscles of the eyelid, d) the nasal muscles and e) the oral muscles. Frequently, the limits of the facial muscles are not easily defined and there is a tendency for them to merge. The platysma muscle also belongs in the facial group, even though it extends over the neck.

3) the circular muscles surrounding the eyes (orbicularis oculi) and the mouth (orbicularis oris) assist in closure of the orbital and oral apertures, and thus contribute to functions such as blinking of the eyelids and the oral ingestion of liquids and food.

4) since facial muscles can respond to thoughts and emotions, they are of assistance in communicative functions. The buccinator muscles are flat and are situated on the lateral aspects of the oral cavity. They assist in mastication by pressing the cheeks against the teeth, and thus, prevent food from accumulating in the oral vestibule.

Fig. 603   **VII**

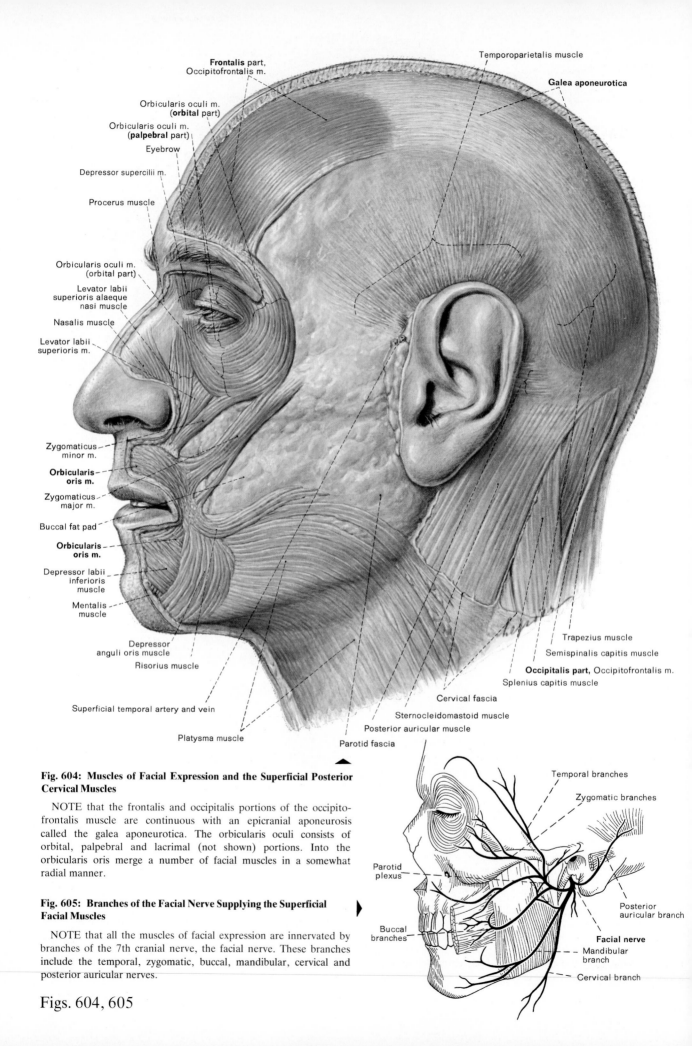

Frontalis part,
Occipitofrontalis m.

Temporoparietalis muscle

Galea aponeurotica

Orbicularis oculi m.
(**orbital** part)

Orbicularis oculi m.
(**palpebral** part)

Eyebrow

Depressor supercilii m.

Procerus muscle

Orbicularis oculi m.
(orbital part)

Levator labii
superioris alaeque
nasi muscle

Nasalis muscle

Levator labii
superioris m.

Zygomaticus
minor m.

**Orbicularis
oris m.**

Zygomaticus
major m.

Buccal fat pad

**Orbicularis
oris m.**

Depressor labii
inferioris
muscle

Mentalis
muscle

Depressor
anguli oris muscle

Risorius muscle

Superficial temporal artery and vein

Platysma muscle

Parotid fascia

Posterior auricular muscle

Sternocleidomastoid muscle

Cervical fascia

Splenius capitis muscle

Occipitalis part, Occipitofrontalis m.

Semispinalis capitis muscle

Trapezius muscle

**Fig. 604: Muscles of Facial Expression and the Superficial Posterior
Cervical Muscles**

NOTE that the frontalis and occipitalis portions of the occipitofrontalis muscle are continuous with an epicranial aponeurosis
called the galea aponeurotica. The orbicularis oculi consists of
orbital, palpebral and lacrimal (not shown) portions. Into the
orbicularis oris merge a number of facial muscles in a somewhat
radial manner.

**Fig. 605: Branches of the Facial Nerve Supplying the Superficial
Facial Muscles**

NOTE that all the muscles of facial expression are innervated by
branches of the 7th cranial nerve, the facial nerve. These branches
include the temporal, zygomatic, buccal, mandibular, cervical and
posterior auricular nerves.

Temporal branches

Zygomatic branches

Parotid
plexus

Buccal
branches

Posterior
auricular branch

Facial nerve

Mandibular
branch

Cervical branch

Figs. 604, 605

Galea aponeurotica

Frontalis muscle
(occipitofrontalis)

Corrugator
supercilii m.

Orbicularis oculi m.
(orbital and
palpebral parts)

Procerus
muscle

Depressor
supercilii m.

Medial pal-
ral ligament

Nasal bone

evator labii
superioris
alaeque
asi muscle

ator labii
erioris m.

Nasalis
muscle

Zygoma-
minor m.

Levator
anguli
oris muscle

Orbicularis
ris muscle

Zygoma-
ticus
major m.

Depressor
labii
inferioris
muscle

Mentalis muscle

Orbicularis
oris muscle

Periosteum

Temporal fascia
(superficial layer)

Temporal fascia
(deep layer)

Adipose layer

Temporo-
parietalis m.

Occipitalis m.

Zygomatic arch

Articular capsule
(lateral ligament)

Parotid gland

Accessory
parotid gland;
Parotid duct

Buccinator muscle

Sternocleido-
mastoid m.

Masseter muscle

Buccal fat pad

Risorius muscle

Depressor
anguli oris m.

Submandibular
gland

Digastric muscle
(anterior belly)

Superficial
cervical fascia

Fig. 606: The Parotid Gland and Duct and the Masseter Muscle ▲

NOTE: 1) the parotid gland extends from the zygomatic arch to
below the angle of the mandible. It lies anterior to the ear and superficial to the masseter muscle. It is enclosed in a tight, dense fascial
sheath, and its duct courses medially across the face to enter the oral
cavity through the fibers of the buccinator muscle.

2) the masseter muscle extends from the zygomatic bone to the
ramus, angle and body of the mandible. It elevates the mandible
(closes the mouth) and is innervated by the mandibular branch of
the trigeminal nerve.

Fig. 607: The Parasympathetic Innervation of the Parotid Gland ▶

NOTE: the preganglionic parasympathetic fibers which innervate the parotid gland emerge from the brainstem in the 9th (glossopharyngeal) cranial nerve. They then travel along the tympanic
nerve to course in the lesser superficial petrosal nerve to the otic
ganglion. Postganglionic fibers then travel by way of the auriculotemporal nerve to reach the parotid gland.

Inferior saliva-
torius nucleus

Lesser (superficial)
petrosal nerve

Tympanic branch
of glosso-
pharyngeal n.

Otic ganglion

Auriculo-
temporal nerve

Figs. 606, 607   **VII**

Periosteum
Temporalis muscle
Galea aponeurotica
Zygomatic arch
Temporomandibular joint capsule

Frontalis portion (occipitofrontalis muscle)
Orbicularis oculi muscle
Corrugator supercilii muscle
Depressor supercilii muscle
Levator labii superioris alaeque nasi muscle
Levator labii superioris m.; Infraorbital nerve
Levator anguli oris m.
Nasalis muscle
Parotid duct; Buccinator muscle

Occipitalis portion (occipito-frontalis m.)
Cartilage of external acoustic mea_
Ramus of mandible
Semispinalis capitis m.
Styloid process
External carotid artery; Styloglossus muscle
Sternocleidomastoid muscle
Posterior belly of digastric muscle
Splenius capitis muscle
Internal jugular vein
Vagus nerve
Trapezius muscle
Levator scapulae muscle
Scalenus medius muscle
Scalenus posterior muscle

Orbicularis oris m.
Masseter m. (deep part)
Orbicularis oris m.
Masseter m. (superficial part)
Mentalis m.

Depressor labii inferioris m.
Depressor anguli oris m.
Anterior belly of digastric m.
Platysma muscle
Hyoid bone
Sternohyoid muscle
Stylohyoid muscle
Hypoglossal nerve
Omohyoid muscle
Thyrohyoid muscle
Inferior pharyngeal constrictor muscle
Sternothyroid muscle
Common carotid artery
Sternocleidomastoid muscle

Brachial plexus
Scalenus anterior muscle

Fig. 608

Fig. 608: The Temporalis and Buccinator Muscles

NOTE: 1) the external ear and zygomatic arch have been removed along with the bulk of the masseter muscle in order to demonstrate the temporalis muscle which arises in the temporal fossa and inserts on the coronoid process of the mandible. Like the masseter, the temporalis is innervated by the mandibular branch of the trigeminal (V).

2) the various fiber bundles of the buccinator muscle as they extend directly into the orbicularis oris at both the upper and lower lips. As the facial muscles, the buccinator is innervated by the facial nerve (VII, buccal branch).

Fig. 609: The Cutaneous Nerve Patterns (Dermatomes) of the Head and Neck

NOTE: The anterior and lateral aspects of the head and face are innervated by the divisions of the trigeminal nerve. The posterior and lateral aspects of the head and neck are supplied by the cervical segments. Small areas of skin around the ear are innervated by the facial (VII), glossopharyngeal (IX) and vagus (X) nerves.

Fig. 609

Figs. 608, 609

Fig. 610: Coronal suture, Sphenofrontal suture, Sphenosquamosal suture, Frontal bone (squama), Sphenozygomatic suture, Frontozygomatic suture, Orbital lamina of ethmoid bone, Lacrimal bone, Nasal bone, Naso-maxillary suture, Lacrimo-maxillary suture, Anterior nasal spine, maxilla, Zygomatico-temporal suture, Mental protuberance, ala major, os zygomaticum, Superior temporal line (parietal bone), os parietale, Inferior temporal line (parietal bone), Squamosal suture, planum temporale, Parietomastoid suture, os temporale (pars squamosa), Lambdoidal suture, fossa temporalis, arcus zygomaticus, processus mastoideus, squama occipitalis, Occipitomastoid suture, External acoustic meatus, Occipital condyle, Styloid process, Condyle of mandible, Coronoid process of mandible, Body of mandible, Base of mandible, Mental foramen

Fig. 610: Lateral Aspect of the Skull

NOTE: the facial bones include the frontal, maxilla, mandible, zygomatic, nasal and lacrimal bones. The frontal, sphenoid, ethmoid, parietal, temporal and occipital bones form the cranial cavity which encloses and protects the brain.

Fig. 611: Schematic Diagram of the Trigeminal Nerve

NOTE: the three major divisions, ophthalmic, maxillary and mandibular, of the trigeminal nerve and their branches are demonstrated. Not shown are: a) the motor branches of the mandibular division which supply the muscles of mastication, b) the mylohyoid motor branch which supplies the mylohyoid and anterior digastric muscles, and c) the branches which supply the tensor tympani and tensor palati muscles.

Lateral branch, Supraorbital nerve; Medial branch, Supraorbital nerve; Supra-trochlear n.; Infra-trochlear n.; External nasal nerve; Infraorbital nerve; Nasociliary nerve; Zygomaticotemporal nerve; Lacrimal nerve; Zygomatic nerve; Pterygo-palatine ganglion; Superior alveolar branches; Auriculo-temporal n.; Inferior alveolar branches (mandibular); Palatine nerve; Submandibular ganglion; Lingual nerve; Buccal nerve; Mental nerve

Figs. 610, 611   **VII**

Fig. 612: The Right Temporomandibular Joint (Lateral View)

NOTE: 1) the articular capsule and the lateral (temporomandibular) ligaments which extend between the zygomatic process of the temporal bone above to the neck of the condylar process of the mandibular ramus below;

2) that the articular capsule is a loose sac which is fused anteriorly and laterally with the lateral (temporomandibular) ligament. Note also the stylomandibular ligament extending from the tip of the styloid process to the angle and posterior border of the mandible.

Fig. 613: The Right Temporomandibular Region (Medial View)

NOTE that medial to the temporomandibular joint the pterygospinous ligament extends from the sphenoidal spine to the posterior margin of the lateral pterygoid plate, while the sphenomandibular ligament descends from the sphenoidal spine to the lingula of the mandible.

Fig. 614: The Medial and Lateral Pterygoid Muscles (Lateral View)

NOTE: 1) the left zygomatic arch has been removed. Posteriorly, the bone has been cut through the temporomandibular joint, revealing the articular disc. The location of the medial pterygoid muscle and part of the lateral pterygoid muscle on the inner aspect of the ramus of the mandible is represented as though the bone were transparent.

2) the lateral pterygoid muscle arises by two heads, a superior from the great wing of the sphenoid bone and an inferior from the lateral surface of the lateral pterygoid plate of the sphenoid. The two heads insert posteriorly on the neck of the condyle of the mandible. The lateral pterygoid muscle opens and protracts the mandible and also moves it from side to side.

3) the medial pterygoid muscle arises from the medial surface of the lateral pterygoid plate of the sphenoid as well as from the palatine bone, and inserts on the medial surface of the ramus and angle of the mandible. It assists the masseter and temporalis in closing the jaw.

Figs. 612, 613, 614

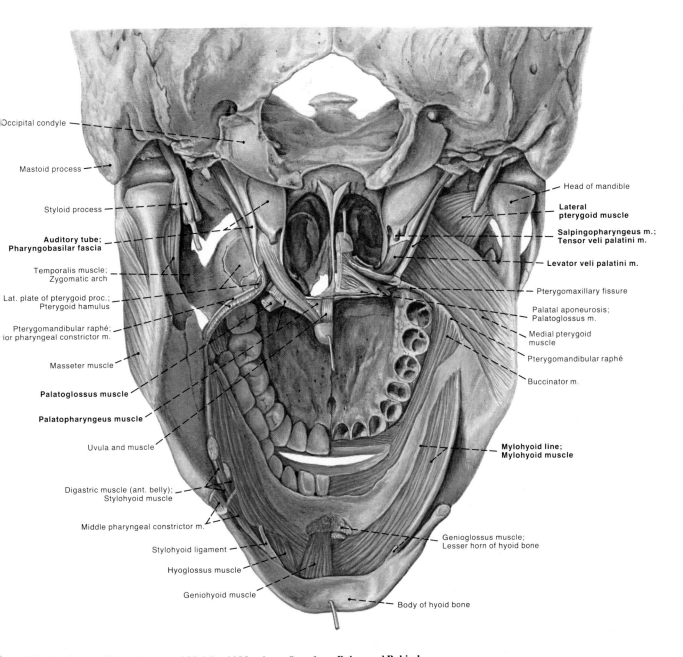

Occipital condyle —

Mastoid process —

Styloid process —

Auditory tube;
Pharyngobasilar fascia —

Temporalis muscle;
Zygomatic arch —

Lat. plate of pterygoid proc.;
Pterygoid hamulus —

Pterygomandibular raphé;
ior pharyngeal constrictor m. —

Masseter muscle —

Palatoglossus muscle —

Palatopharyngeus muscle —

Uvula and muscle —

Digastric muscle (ant. belly);
Stylohyoid muscle —

Middle pharyngeal constrictor m. —

Stylohyoid ligament —

Hyoglossus muscle —

Geniohyoid muscle —

— Head of mandible

— **Lateral**
pterygoid muscle

— **Salpingopharyngeus m.;**
Tensor veli palatini m.

— **Levator veli palatini m.**

— Pterygomaxillary fissure

— Palatal aponeurosis;
Palatoglossus m.

— Medial pterygoid
muscle

— Pterygomandibular raphé

— Buccinator m.

— **Mylohyoid line;**
Mylohyoid muscle

— Genioglossus muscle;
Lesser horn of hyoid bone

— Body of hyoid bone

Fig. 615: The Pterygoid, Buccinator and Mylohyoid Muscles as Seen from Below and Behind

NOTE: 1) that a muscular sling is formed around the posterior border of the ramus of the mandible as far as its angle by the insertions of the medial pterygoid muscle (seen on the right) and the masseter muscle (seen on the left). The medial pterygoid muscle descends to attach along the medial aspect of the mandible, while the fibers of the masseter course downward to insert on the outer aspect of the jaw.

2) that the fibers of the lateral pterygoid muscle (right side) course principally in the horizontal plane. Observe that the mylohyoid and geniohyoid muscles attach the mandible to the hyoid bone. Other muscles shown to advantage in this figure are the tensor and levator veli palatini muscles.

3) the right pterygomandibular raphé extending between the pterygoid hamulus and the mylohyoid line. This raphé gives attachment to the buccinator muscle which forms the soft lateral wall of the oral cavity on each side.

Figs. 616 and 617: Sagittal Sections of Temporomandibular Joint

NOTE: 1) the articular disc (stippled structure) is an oval plate interposed between the mandibular fossa of the temporal bone and the condyle of the mandible. Thus, there exists a joint cavity between the disc and the mandibular fossa and another between the disc and the condyle.

2) with the jaw closed (616), the head of the condyle of the mandible and the articular disc lie totally within the mandibular fossa. When the jaw is opened (617), the condyle turns in a hinge-fashion on the disc, and both bone and disc glide forward within the joint capsule to lie opposite the articular tubercle of the temporal bone.

Fig. 616   **Fig. 617**

Figs. 615, 616, 617   **VII**

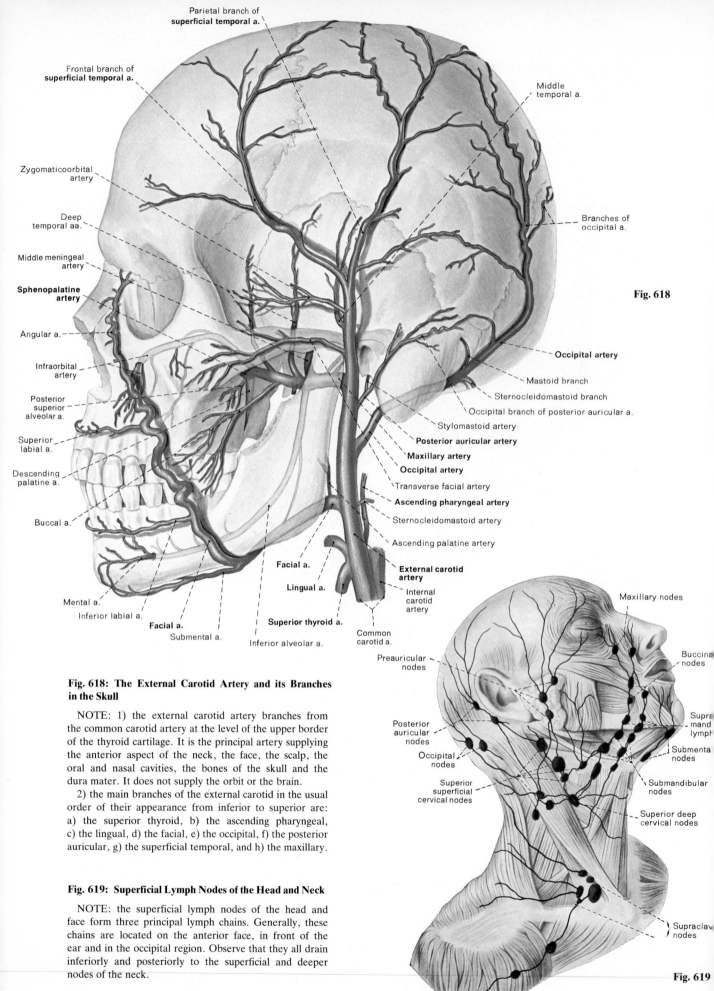

Parietal branch of **superficial temporal a.**

Frontal branch of **superficial temporal a.**

Zygomaticoorbital artery

Deep temporal aa.

Middle meningeal artery

Sphenopalatine artery

Angular a.

Infraorbital artery

Posterior superior alveolar a.

Superior labial a.

Descending palatine a.

Buccal a.

Mental a.

Inferior labial a.

Facial a.

Submental a.

Inferior alveolar a.

Facial a.

Lingual a.

Superior thyroid a.

Middle temporal a.

Branches of occipital a.

Fig. 618

Occipital artery

Mastoid branch

Sternocleidomastoid branch

Occipital branch of posterior auricular a.

Stylomastoid artery

Posterior auricular artery

Maxillary artery

Occipital artery

Transverse facial artery

Ascending pharyngeal artery

Sternocleidomastoid artery

Ascending palatine artery

External carotid artery

Internal carotid artery

Common carotid a.

Preauricular nodes

Posterior auricular nodes

Occipital nodes

Superior superficial cervical nodes

Maxillary nodes

Buccina nodes

Supra mand lymph

Submenta nodes

Submandibular nodes

Superior deep cervical nodes

Supraclav nodes

Fig. 619

Fig. 618: The External Carotid Artery and its Branches in the Skull

NOTE: 1) the external carotid artery branches from the common carotid artery at the level of the upper border of the thyroid cartilage. It is the principal artery supplying the anterior aspect of the neck, the face, the scalp, the oral and nasal cavities, the bones of the skull and the dura mater. It does not supply the orbit or the brain.

2) the main branches of the external carotid in the usual order of their appearance from inferior to superior are: a) the superior thyroid, b) the ascending pharyngeal, c) the lingual, d) the facial, e) the occipital, f) the posterior auricular, g) the superficial temporal, and h) the maxillary.

Fig. 619: Superficial Lymph Nodes of the Head and Neck

NOTE: the superficial lymph nodes of the head and face form three principal lymph chains. Generally, these chains are located on the anterior face, in front of the ear and in the occipital region. Observe that they all drain inferiorly and posteriorly to the superficial and deeper nodes of the neck.

Figs. 618, 619

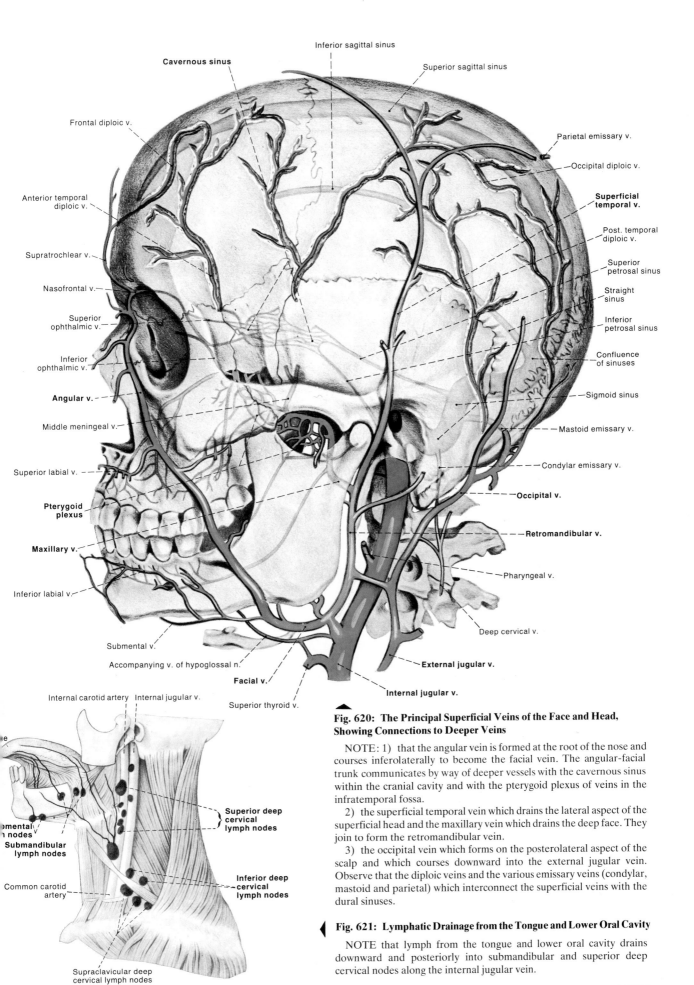

Cavernous sinus

Inferior sagittal sinus

Superior sagittal sinus

Frontal diploic v.

Parietal emissary v.

Occipital diploic v.

Superficial temporal v.

Anterior temporal diploic v.

Post. temporal diploic v.

Supratrochlear v.

Superior petrosal sinus

Nasofrontal v.

Straight sinus

Superior ophthalmic v.

Inferior petrosal sinus

Inferior ophthalmic v.

Confluence of sinuses

Angular v.

Sigmoid sinus

Middle meningeal v.

Mastoid emissary v.

Superior labial v.

Condylar emissary v.

Pterygoid plexus

Occipital v.

Maxillary v.

Retromandibular v.

Inferior labial v.

Pharyngeal v.

Deep cervical v.

Submental v.

External jugular v.

Accompanying v. of hypoglossal n.

Facial v.

Internal jugular v.

Superior thyroid v.

Internal carotid artery   Internal jugular v.

Superior deep cervical lymph nodes

mental nodes

Submandibular lymph nodes

Common carotid artery

Inferior deep cervical lymph nodes

Supraclavicular deep cervical lymph nodes

Fig. 620: The Principal Superficial Veins of the Face and Head, Showing Connections to Deeper Veins

NOTE: 1) that the angular vein is formed at the root of the nose and courses inferolaterally to become the facial vein. The angular-facial trunk communicates by way of deeper vessels with the cavernous sinus within the cranial cavity and with the pterygoid plexus of veins in the infratemporal fossa.

2) the superficial temporal vein which drains the lateral aspect of the superficial head and the maxillary vein which drains the deep face. They join to form the retromandibular vein.

3) the occipital vein which forms on the posterolateral aspect of the scalp and which courses downward into the external jugular vein. Observe that the diploic veins and the various emissary veins (condylar, mastoid and parietal) which interconnect the superficial veins with the dural sinuses.

Fig. 621: Lymphatic Drainage from the Tongue and Lower Oral Cavity

NOTE that lymph from the tongue and lower oral cavity drains downward and posteriorly into submandibular and superior deep cervical nodes along the internal jugular vein.

Figs. 620, 621   **VII**

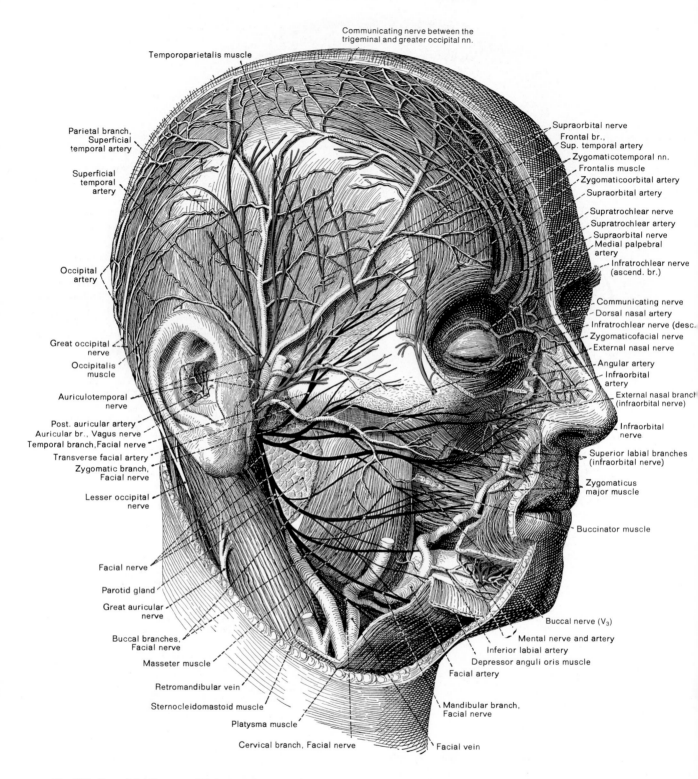

Fig. 622: Superficial Nerves and Vessels of the Face and Head

NOTE: 1) a portion of the parotid gland has been removed in order to reveal the branches of the facial nerve (black) which emerge from within the substance of the gland to supply the superficial muscles of facial expression. Identify the temporal, zygomatic, buccal, mandibular, and cervical branches. The posterior auricular branch is not shown.

2) the superficial branches of the trigeminal nerve are indicated in various colors; ophthlamic (yellow), maxillary (blue) and mandibular (green). The trigeminal nerve serves as the cutaneous nerve of the anterior and lateral face, but is also the motor nerve to the muscles of mastication. The cervical sensory nerves (white, not colored) supply the occipital region and much of the ear and neck.

3) the general distribution of the superficial temporal artery and its branches, the zygomaticoorbital and transverse facial arteries. Follow the course of the facial artery across the face to become the angular artery. Among other structures, the facial supplies the chin and the upper and lower lips and anastomoses with vessels emerging from the orbit.

Fig. 622

Fig. 623: Nerves and Vessels of the Superficial Head and Deeper Face

NOTE: 1) in this dissection, the temporal fascia has been cut and partially reflected. The superficial muscles on the side of the face have been removed along with the parotid gland. The main trunk of the facial nerve has been cut and its branches across the face removed. The masseter muscle has been severed and its upper half reflected upward.

2a) the supraorbital, supratrochlear, infratrochlear and external nasal branches of the ophthalmic division of the trigeminal nerve.

b) zygomaticotemporal, zygomaticofacial and infraorbital branches of the maxillary division of the trigeminal nerve.

c) auriculotemporal, masseteric, buccal, inferior alveolar and mental branches of the mandibular division of the trigeminal nerve.

3) the posterior auricular, digastric and stylohyoid branches of the facial nerve which arise from the main nerve trunk prior to its division within the parotid gland.

4) the anastomosis of arteries above and at the medial aspect of the orbit. The vessels involved include the frontal branch of the superficial temporal, the supraorbital, supratrochlear, dorsal nasal and angular arteries. Observe the palpebral branches (not labelled) supplying the upper and lower eyelids.

Fig. 623   VII

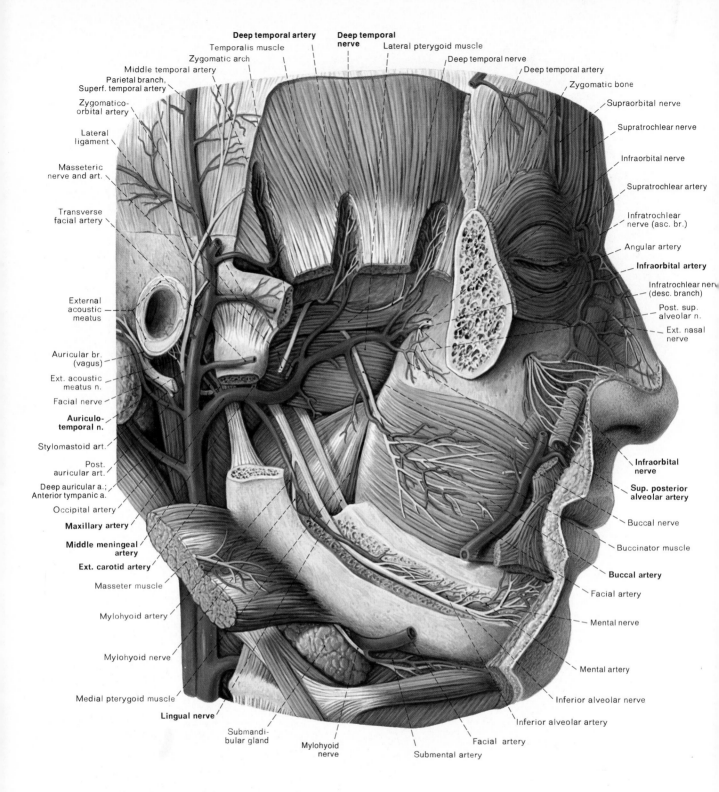

Fig. 624: The Infratemporal Region and the Maxillary Artery

NOTE: 1) the zygomatic arch and a portion of the ramus of the mandible have been removed and the temporalis and masseter muscles have been cut and partially reflected. The pterygoid venous plexus has been removed revealing the maxillary artery and its branches.

2) the infratemporal fossa lies deep to the zygomatic arch and posterior to the maxilla. It contains the medial and lateral pterygoid muscles, the inferior part of the temporalis muscle, the maxillary artery, the pterygoid plexus of veins (not shown) and the mandibular division of the trigeminal nerve.

3) the maxillary artery and a number of its branches. Seen in this dissection are the following branches of the maxillary artery: a) deep auricular, b) anterior tympanic, c) inferior alveolar, d) middle meningeal, e) masseteric (cut), f) deep temporal, g) pterygoid (not labelled), h) buccal, i) posterior superior alveolar, j) infraorbital. Branches of the maxillary artery not seen from this view are the greater palatine, the artery of the pterygoid canal, pharyngeal and the sphenopalatine.

4) the auriculotemporal, lingual, inferior alveolar, mylohyoid, masseteric and deep temporal branches of the mandibular division of the trigeminal nerve. Observe the course of the inferior alveolar nerve, accompanied by the inferior alveolar artery within the mandible.

Fig. 624

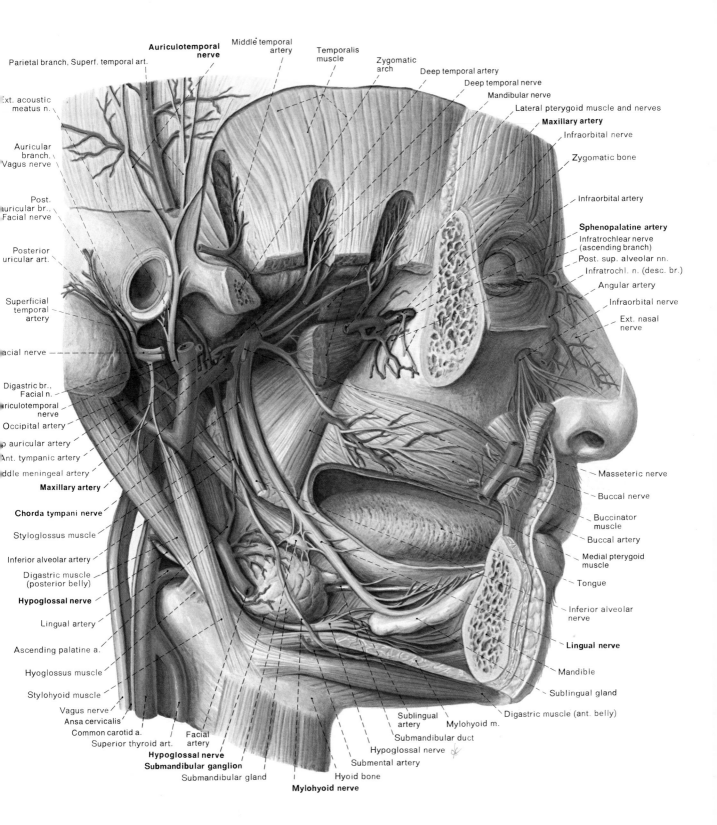

Parietal branch, Superf. temporal art.
Ext. acoustic meatus n.
Auricular branch, Vagus nerve
Post. auricular br., Facial nerve
Posterior auricular art.
Superficial temporal artery
acial nerve
Digastric br., Facial n.
riculotemporal nerve
Occipital artery
p auricular artery
Ant. tympanic artery
ddle meningeal artery
Maxillary artery
Chorda tympani nerve
Styloglossus muscle
Inferior alveolar artery
Digastric muscle (posterior belly)
Hypoglossal nerve
Lingual artery
Ascending palatine a.
Hyoglossus muscle
Stylohyoid muscle
Vagus nerve
Ansa cervicalis
Common carotid a.
Superior thyroid art.
Hypoglossal nerve
Submandibular ganglion
Submandibular gland

Auriculotemporal nerve
Middle temporal artery
Temporalis muscle
Zygomatic arch
Deep temporal artery
Deep temporal nerve
Mandibular nerve
Lateral pterygoid muscle and nerves
Maxillary artery
Infraorbital nerve
Zygomatic bone
Infraorbital artery
Sphenopalatine artery
Infratrochlear nerve (ascending branch)
Post. sup. alveolar nn.
Infratrochl. n. (desc. br.)
Angular artery
Infraorbital nerve
Ext. nasal nerve
Masseteric nerve
Buccal nerve
Buccinator muscle
Buccal artery
Medial pterygoid muscle
Tongue
Inferior alveolar nerve
Lingual nerve
Mandible
Sublingual gland
Digastric muscle (ant. belly)

Facial artery
Sublingual artery
Mylohyoid m.
Submandibular duct
Hypoglossal nerve
Submental artery
Hyoid bone
Mylohyoid nerve

Fig. 625: The Infratemporal Region and the Branches of the Mandibular Nerve

NOTE: 1) this dissection of the deep face has removed the zygomatic arch, much of the right mandible and the lateral pterygoid muscle. A portion of the maxillary artery has been cut away along with the distal part of the inferior alveolar nerve beyond the point where the mylohyoid nerve branches.

2) the lingual nerve as it courses to the tongue. High in the infratemporal fossa, the chorda tympani nerve (which is a branch of the facial) joins the lingual. The chorda tympani not only carries special sensory fibers for taste for the anterior two-thirds of the tongue, but additionally carries the preganglionic parasympathetic fibers from the facial nerve to the submandibular ganglion.

3) the distal portion of the maxillary artery as it courses toward the sphenopalatine foramen. After giving off the infraorbital artery, the vessel passes through the foramen and enters the nasal cavity as the sphenopalatine artery, becoming the principal vessel supplying the mucosa overlying the conchae.

Fig. 625　VII

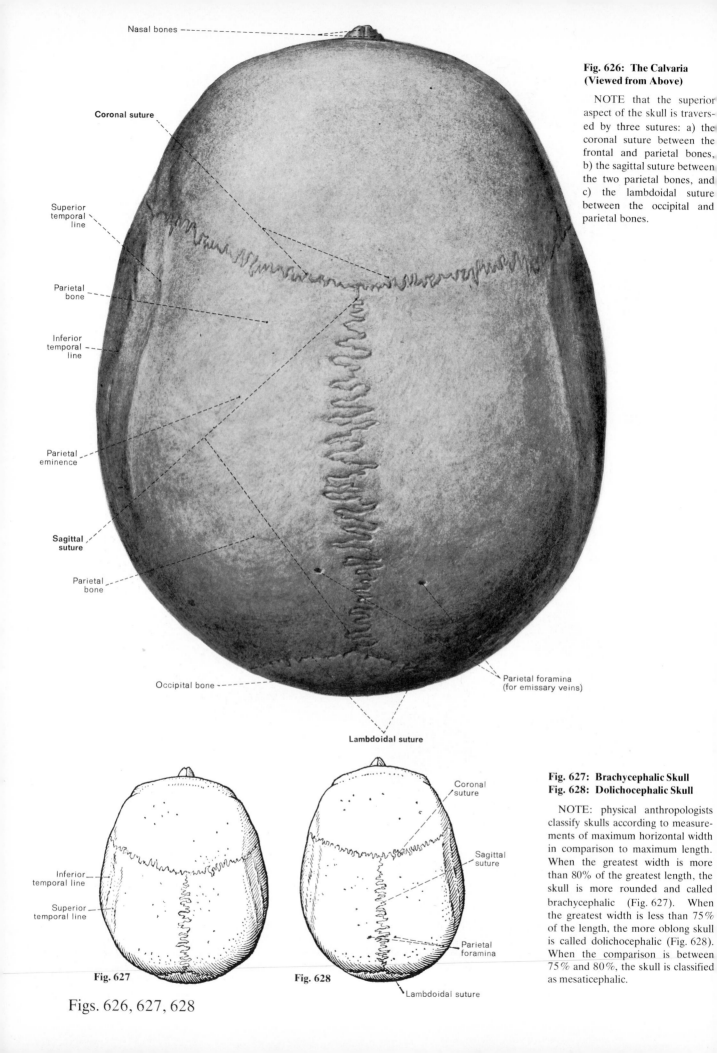

Nasal bones

Coronal suture

Superior temporal line

Parietal bone

Inferior temporal line

Parietal eminence

Sagittal suture

Parietal bone

Occipital bone

Parietal foramina (for emissary veins)

Lambdoidal suture

Fig. 626: The Calvaria (Viewed from Above)

NOTE that the superior aspect of the skull is traversed by three sutures: a) the coronal suture between the frontal and parietal bones, b) the sagittal suture between the two parietal bones, and c) the lambdoidal suture between the occipital and parietal bones.

Fig. 627: Brachycephalic Skull
Fig. 628: Dolichocephalic Skull

NOTE: physical anthropologists classify skulls according to measurements of maximum horizontal width in comparison to maximum length. When the greatest width is more than 80% of the greatest length, the skull is more rounded and called brachycephalic (Fig. 627). When the greatest width is less than 75% of the length, the more oblong skull is called dolichocephalic (Fig. 628). When the comparison is between 75% and 80%, the skull is classified as mesaticephalic.

Coronal suture

Sagittal suture

Parietal foramina

Inferior temporal line

Superior temporal line

Lambdoidal suture

Fig. 627

Fig. 628

Figs. 626, 627, 628

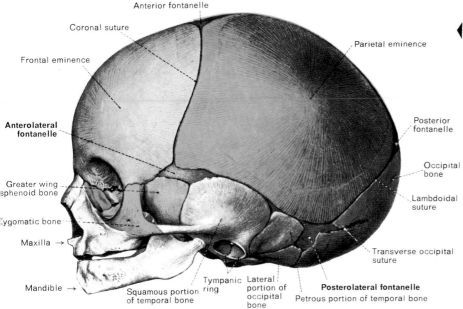

Fig. 629: The Skull at Birth
(Lateral View)

NOTE: 1) ossification of the maturing flat bones of the skull is accomplished by the intramembranous process of bone formation. At birth this process is incomplete, thereby leaving softened membranous sites between the growing bones.

2) the nature of the skull just prior to birth is of some benefit, however, since the mobility of the bones permits some changes in its shape, as might be required during the birth process.

3) the soft sites on the skull of the newborn infant are called fontanelles. From this lateral view can be seen at least two such fontanelles, the antero-lateral (or sphenoid) which is at the pterion, and the posterolateral (or mastoid) at the asterion.

Fig. 630: The Skull at Birth (Seen from Above)

NOTE: 1) the largest of the fontanelles at birth is the anterior fontanelle located at the bregma and interconnecting the frontal and parietal bones. It is approximately diamond-shaped and is situated at the junction of the coronal and sagittal sutures.

2) following the sagittal suture to its junction with the occipital bone will locate the posterior fontanelle (at the lambda). This is generally triangular in shape and is relatively small at birth.

Fig. 631: The Skull at Birth (Posterior-Inferior View)

NOTE: 1) the separate ossification of the petrous and squamous portions of the temporal bone as well as the basilar and squamous portions of the occipital bone. The posterolateral fontanelles are found at the articulation of the occipital, temporal and parietal bones.

2) the skull is large at birth in comparison to the size of the rest of the body, however, the facial bones (see Fig. 629) are still rudimentary and not well developed. The teeth have yet to erupt, and the sinuses and nasal cavity are small.

Figs. 629, 630, 631   VII

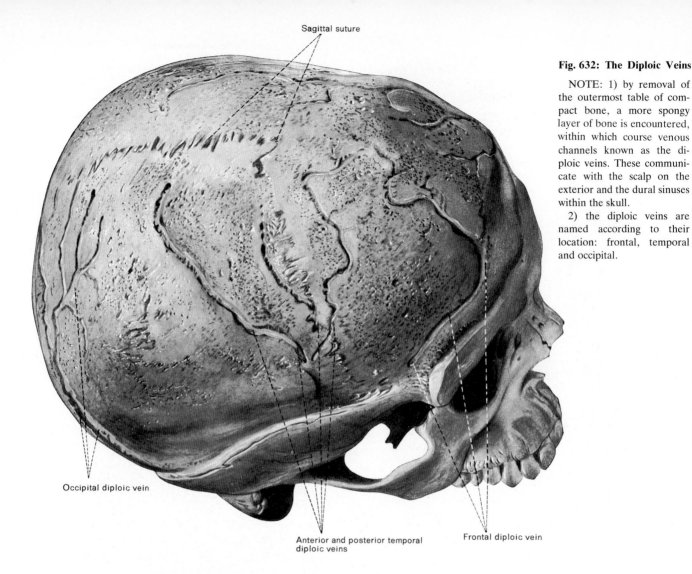

Sagittal suture

NOTE: 1) by removal of the outermost table of compact bone, a more spongy layer of bone is encountered, within which course venous channels known as the diploic veins. These communicate with the scalp on the exterior and the dural sinuses within the skull.

2) the diploic veins are named according to their location: frontal, temporal and occipital.

Occipital diploic vein

Anterior and posterior temporal diploic veins

Frontal diploic vein

Fig. 633: The Scalp, Skull, Meninges and Brain

NOTE: 1) this frontal section through the cranium and upper cerebrum depicts the bony and soft coverings of the brain. The veins and dural sinuses are shown in blue. The layers of the scalp and the bony tissue of the skull lie superficial to the dura mater, arachnoid and pia mater coverings of the neural tissue of the brain.

2) the arachnoid granulations which project into the dural sinuses. These tufts of arachnoid lie next to the endothelium of the sinuses and allow the passage of cerebrospinal fluid from the subarachnoid space into the venous system.

Sagittal suture

Superior sagittal sinus and arachnoid granulation

Arachnoid granulations

Emissary vein

Sebaceous glands

Arrector pili muscles

Epidermis

Dermis

Subcutaneous connective tissue

Galea aponeurotica

Parietal bone and diploic veins

Dura mater
Arachnoid
Pia mater

Dura mater
Arachnoid a
subarachnoid
Pia mater

Gray matter
cerebral cor

Dura mater
(falx cerebri)

White matter of
cerebral cortex

Subarachnoid space

Figs. 632, 633

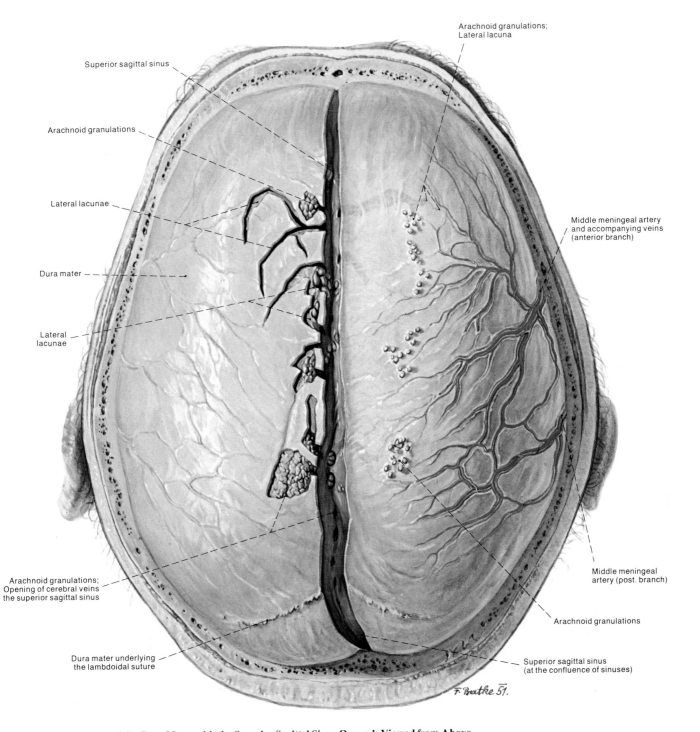

Arachnoid granulations;
Lateral lacuna

Superior sagittal sinus

Arachnoid granulations

Lateral lacunae

Dura mater

Lateral
lacunae

Middle meningeal artery
and accompanying veins
(anterior branch)

Middle meningeal
artery (post. branch)

Arachnoid granulations

Arachnoid granulations;
Opening of cerebral veins
the superior sagittal sinus

Dura mater underlying
the lambdoidal suture

Superior sagittal sinus
(at the confluence of sinuses)

F. Bathe 51.

Fig. 634: The Surface of the Dura Mater with the Superior Sagittal Sinus Opened; Viewed from Above

NOTE: 1) that the skull cap (also called calvaria) has been removed. This was done by making a circular saw cut around the skull, but through the bone only and by carefully separating the dura mater from the internal surface of the skull cap.

2) that although the dura mater is often described as a two layered structure (an internal or *meningeal layer* and an external or *periosteal layer*), the two layers are so closely fused that they are inseparable throughout much of their expanse. After removal of the skull cap, the "two layers" are stripped from the inner surface of the skull as a single membrane.

3) that in some regions the meningeal and periosteal layers are separate, and in this way they form the cavities of the venous sinsus in the dura mater. Observe that in this dissection the longitudinally oriented superior sagittal sinus has been opened, as have a number of lateral venous lacunae that communicate with this venous dural sinus.

4) that the outer or periosteal layer of the dura mater is continuous through foramina in the skull and through the sutures between the bones of the skull with the periosteum that lines the outer surface of the skull and which is called the pericranium (see the dura mater at the lambdoidal suture). Anteriorly, the periosteal layer of dura is continuous through the superior orbital fissure with the periosteum that lines the bones forming the orbital cavity.

5) the *arachnoid granulations*. These are elevated masses that grow in size from infancy through childhood, so that they eventually cause some bone resorption and thereby form visible pits on the inner surface of the skull cap. The arachnoid granulations are collections of small projections of the arachnoid membrane which extend through openings in the dura mater (see Fig. 633). These projections are called the *arachnoid villi*, and they appear as diverticula of the subarachnoid space into the venous sinus. Cerebrospinal fluid appears to pass by osmosis from the subarachnoid space through the arachnoid villi into the venous blood of the dural sinus.

Fig. 634   **VII**

Coronal suture; Scalp

Lateral lacuna; Arachnoid granulation

Dura mater over the frontal lobe

Dura mater over the lateral cerebral sulcus

Dura mater over the frontal pole; Galea aponeurotica

Frontal sinus; Frontal bone

Mid. meningeal art.; Orbital branch, mid. meningeal artery; Lesser wing of sphenoid; Sphenofront. suture

Dura mater over the tip of the temporal pole

Middle meningeal a. and v. (frontal branch)

Temporalis muscle; Infratemporal fat pad; Zygomatic arch

Middle meningeal art. and vein (parietal branch); Dura mater over the temporal lobe

Lateral lacuna communicating with the middle meningeal vein

Arachnoid granulation; Diploë of parietal bone

Dura mater; Parietal bone (internal and external tables)

Lambdo[id] suture

Dura mater; Occipital pol[e] Occipitalis m[uscle]

F. Bratke 1953

Fig. 635: The Dura Mater and the Middle Meningeal Vessels, Viewed Following a Lateral Exposure of the Cranial Cavity

NOTE: 1) that most of the left half of the skull has been removed in order to expose the dura mater covering the left cerebral hemisphere and the middle meningeal artery and veins. The middle meningeal artery arises in the infratemporal fossa from the first part of the maxillary artery (see Figs. 624 and 625), and it ascends between the lateral pterygoid muscle and the sphenomandibular ligament directly to the foramen spinosum at the base of the skull.

2) that the middle meningeal vessels may be located deep to the squamous part of the temporal bone just above the mid-point of the zygomatic arch. A short distance (1 to 2 cm) above this site, the vessels divide into frontal (or anterior) and parietal (or posterior) branches. The dura mater requires only a small amount of blood. Most of the blood in these vessels supplies the bones of the skull, as do meningeal branches from several other arteries.

3) that the cerebral dura is supplied by sensory nerve fibers from all three divisions of the trigeminal nerve and also from the upper three cervical spinal nerves.

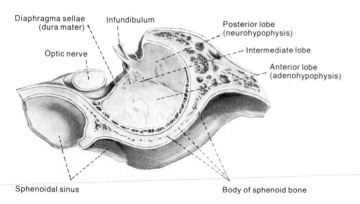

Diaphragma sellae (dura mater)

Infundibulum

Optic nerve

Posterior lobe (neurohypophysis)

Intermediate lobe

Anterior lobe (adenohypophysis)

Sphenoidal sinus

Body of sphenoid bone

Fig. 636: A Median Sagittal Section Through the Pituitary Gland and the Sella Turcica of the Sphenoid Bone

NOTE: 1) that the pituitary gland (or hypophysis cerebri) lies within the cup-shaped sella turcica or pituitary (hypophyseal) fossa of the sphenoid bone and that this fossa is lined by dura mater. Observe that the pituitary gland is covered superiorly by a reflection of dura mater called the diaphragma sellae and that this horizontal sheet of dura separates the sella turcica and the pituitary gland (except for the infundibulum) from the hypothalamus at the base of the brain (see Figs. 637 to 639 and 642).

2) that the three lobes of the pituitary gland (anterior, intermediate, and posterior) form a single organ that lies below and often slightly behind the optic chiasma.

Figs. 635, 636

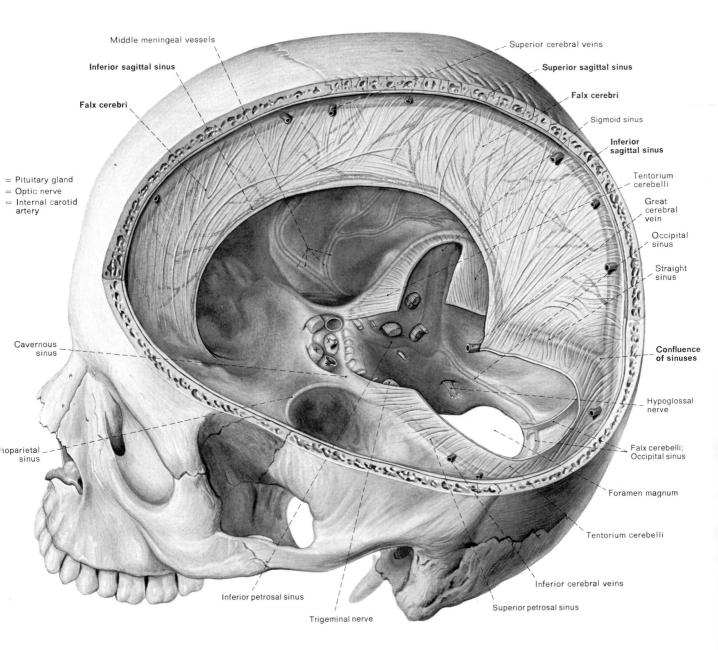

Middle meningeal vessels

Inferior sagittal sinus

Falx cerebri

= Pituitary gland
= Optic nerve
= Internal carotid
  artery

Cavernous
sinus

...oparietal
sinus

Superior cerebral veins

Superior sagittal sinus

Falx cerebri

Sigmoid sinus

Inferior
sagittal sinus

Tentorium
cerebelli

Great
cerebral
vein

Occipital
sinus

Straight
sinus

Confluence
of sinuses

Hypoglossal
nerve

Falx cerebelli;
Occipital sinus

Foramen magnum

Tentorium cerebelli

Inferior cerebral veins

Superior petrosal sinus

Inferior petrosal sinus

Trigeminal nerve

Fig. 637: The Intracranial Dura Mater and the Dural Sinuses

NOTE: 1) with the left skull opened and the brain removed, the reflections of the dura mater and its venous sinuses are exposed. The sinuses are colored blue while the arteries are red. Most of the left tentorium cerebelli and a portion of the right were cut away to open the posterior cranial fossa.

2) the five *unpaired* dural sinuses: the superior sagittal sinus, the inferior sagittal sinus, the straight sinus. Two other unpaired sinuses (not labelled) at the base of the skull include the intercavernous sinus and the basilar sinus. These can be seen in Fig. 638.

3) that the sphenoparietal sinuses course near the posterior margin of the lesser wings of the sphenoid bone and help to form the boundary between the anterior and middle cranial fossae. Similarly, the superior petrosal sinuses course along the superior margins of the petrous portions of the temporal bones at the boundary between the middle and posterior cranial fossae.

4) the seven *paired* dural sinuses: transverse sinus, sigmoid sinus, occipital sinus, superior petrosal sinus, inferior petrosal sinus, cavernous sinus and sphenoparietal sinus. The dural sinuses consist of spaces between the two layers of dura mater which drain the cerebral blood, returning it to the internal jugular veins.

5) the sickle-shaped falx cerebri. This double layer, midline reflection of dura mater extends from the crista galli anteriorly to the tentorium cerebelli posteriorly. It also extends vertically between the two cerebral hemispheres. Within the layers of the falx, observe the superior and inferior sagittal sinuses and the straight sinus which meet at the confluence of sinuses.

6) the tentorium cerebelli is a tent-like reflection of dura mater which forms a partition separating the occipital lobes of the cerebral cortex and the surface of the cerebellum. The falx cerebelli extends vertically between the two cerebellar hemispheres.

Fig. 637   **VII**

Fig. 638: The Base of the Cranial Cavity: Vessels, Nerves and Dura Mater

NOTE: 1) the base of the cranial cavity displays anterior, middle and posterior cranial fossae. The anterior fossa sustains the frontal lobes while the temporal lobes of the brain rest in the middle fossa. Posteriorly, the brain stem and the overlying cerebellum rest in the posterior fossa.

2) the dura mater and the orbital plate of the left frontal bone have been chipped away to expose the structures in the left orbit. The superior ophthalmic vein drains posteriorly and the optic nerve is seen to course from the orbit through the optic canal. Caudal to the optic foramina, observe the pituitary gland within the sella turcica.

3) the medial aspect of the middle cranial fossa shows the internal carotid artery, the 3rd, 4th, 5th and 6th cranial nerves coursing anteriorly or inferiorly toward the orbit or face and the middle meningeal artery traversing the foramen spinosum.

4) the posterior cranial fossa is marked by foramina for the last six pairs of cranial nerves. The 7th and 8th nerves pass through the internal acoustic meatus while the 9th, 10th and 11th nerves emerge through the jugular foramen. The 12th nerve courses through the hypoglossal canal in the occipital bone.

Fig. 638

Frontal pole
Infundibulum
Longitudinal cerebral fissure
Olfactory sulcus
Olfactory bulb
Olfactory tract (I)
Optic nerve (II)

Orbital sulci of frontal pole
Orbital gyri of frontal pole
Pituitary gland
Temporal pole
Anterior perforated substance
Oculomotor nerve (III)
Uncus
Mamillary body
Cerebral peduncle
Pons
Trigeminal nerve (V)
Inferior temporal sulcus
Facial nerve (VII)
Lateral occipito-temporal gyrus
Parahippocampal gyrus
Nervus intermedius
Vestibulocochlear nerve (VIII)
Cerebellar flocculus
Cerebellum
Choroid plexus
Glossopharyngeal nerve (IX)
Vagus nerve (X)
Hypoglossal nerve (XII)
Accessory nerve (XI)

Optic chiasma
Olfactory stria
Tuber cinereum
Maxillary nerve
Ophthalmic nerve
Motor root of **trigeminal (V) nerve**
Mandibular nerve
Semilunar ganglion of trigeminal nerve
Trochlear nerve (IV)
Interpeduncular fossa
Abducens nerve (VI)
Olive
Pyramid
Medulla oblongata
Cerebellar tonsil

I
II
III
IV
V
VI
VII VIII
IX
X
XI
XII

Rootlets of 1st cervical nerve
Decussation of pyramids
Cerebellar vermis
Spinal cord
Occipital pole

Fig. 639: Ventral View of the Brain Showing the Origins of the Cranial Nerves

NOTE: 1) the cranial nerves are numbered sequentially with Roman numerals. The olfactory tracts and optic nerves (I and II) subserve receptors of special sense in the nose and eye and, as cranial nerve trunks, they attach to the base of the forebrain in contrast to all the other cranial nerves which attach at midbrain, pontine or medullary levels.

2) the oculomotor (III), trochlear (IV) and abducens (VI) nerves are motor nerves to the extraocular muscles. While the trigeminal nerve (V) is the largest of all the cranial nerves, the trochlear is the smallest. The abducens nerve emerges from the brainstem at the pontomedullary junction at about the same level, but somewhat more laterally, as the attachments of the facial (VII) and vestibulocochlear (VIII) nerves.

3) the glossopharyngeal (IX) and vagus (X) nerves emerge from the medulla laterally, in a line roughly comparable to the spinal and medullary portions of the accessory nerve (XI). In contrast, the hypoglossal (XII) nerve rootlets emerge from the ventral medulla in a line consistent with the motor ventral rootlets of the cervical segments of the spinal cord.

Fig. 639   VII

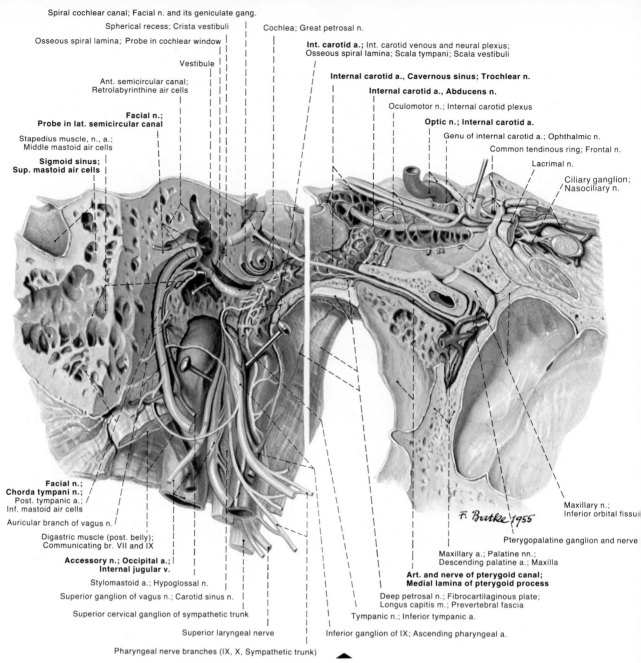

Spiral cochlear canal; Facial n. and its geniculate gang.
Spherical recess; Crista vestibuli
Cochlea; Great petrosal n.
Osseous spiral lamina; Probe in cochlear window
Int. carotid a.; Int. carotid venous and neural plexus;
Osseous spiral lamina; Scala tympani; Scala vestibuli
Vestibule
Internal carotid a., Cavernous sinus; Trochlear n.
Ant. semicircular canal;
Retrolabyrinthine air cells
Internal carotid a., Abducens n.
Oculomotor n.; Internal carotid plexus
Facial n.;
Probe in lat. semicircular canal
Optic n.; Internal carotid a.
Stapedius muscle, n., a.;
Middle mastoid air cells
Genu of internal carotid a.; Ophthalmic n.
Common tendinous ring; Frontal n.
Sigmoid sinus;
Sup. mastoid air cells
Lacrimal n.
Ciliary ganglion;
Nasociliary n.

Facial n.;
Chorda tympani n.;
Post. tympanic a.;
Inf. mastoid air cells
Auricular branch of vagus n.
Maxillary n.;
Inferior orbital fissu
Digastric muscle (post. belly);
Communicating br. VII and IX
Pterygopalatine ganglion and nerve
Accessory n.; Occipital a.;
Internal jugular v.
Maxillary a.; Palatine nn.;
Descending palatine a.; Maxilla
Stylomastoid a.; Hypoglossal n.
Art. and nerve of pterygoid canal;
Medial lamina of pterygoid process
Superior ganglion of vagus n.; Carotid sinus n.
Deep petrosal n.; Fibrocartilaginous plate;
Longus capitis m.; Prevertebral fascia
Superior cervical ganglion of sympathetic trunk
Tympanic n.; Inferior tympanic n.
Superior laryngeal nerve
Inferior ganglion of IX; Ascending pharyngeal a.
Pharyngeal nerve branches (IX, X, Sympathetic trunk)

F. Butke 1955

Fig. 640: The Petrous, Cavernous and Cerebral Portions of the Internal Carotid Artery

NOTE: 1) a vertical section oriented along the superior margin of the petrous portion of the right temporal bone has been made, thereby opening the carotid and facial canals and the inner ear. More anteriorly, the section goes through the sphenoid bone, opening its pterygoid canal and meeting the petrous section in a V-shaped manner.

2) that the *petrous portion* of the internal carotid ascends vertically in the carotid canal and then curves medially and anteriorly. Surrounded by a plexus of small veins and sympathetic nerve fibers, the *cavernous portion* of the artery ascends into the cavernous sinus and curves forward in the carotid sulcus along the side of the body of the sphenoid bone. It then, once again, curves upward to perforate the dura mater just lateral to the optic nerve. This *cerebral portion* immediately passes backward between the optic and oculomotor nerves, where it divides into its terminal branches.

Fig. 641: Frontal Section Through the Left Cavernous Sinus

NOTE that the internal carotid artery (which is seen to have turned back on itself above) and the oculomotor, trochlear, V₁, V₂, and abducens nerves pass through the cavernous sinus.

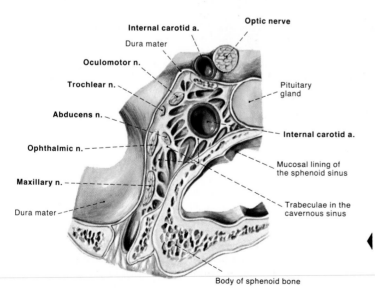

Internal carotid a.
Optic nerve
Dura mater
Oculomotor n.
Trochlear n.
Pituitary gland
Abducens n.
Ophthalmic n.
Internal carotid a.
Maxillary n.
Mucosal lining of the sphenoid sinus
Dura mater
Trabeculae in the cavernous sinus
Body of sphenoid bone

Figs. 640, 641

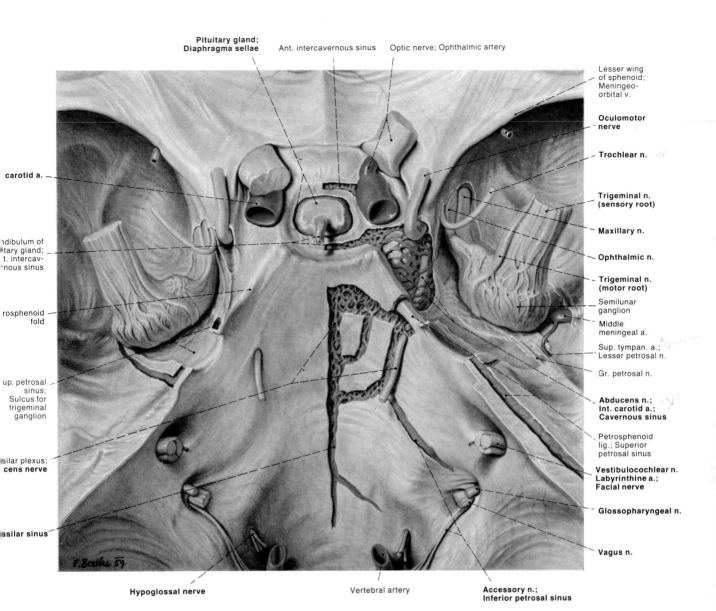

Pituitary gland; Diaphragma sellae — Ant. intercavernous sinus — Optic nerve; Ophthalmic artery

Lesser wing of sphenoid; Meningeo-orbital v.

Oculomotor nerve

Trochlear n.

Trigeminal n. (sensory root)

Maxillary n.

Ophthalmic n.

Trigeminal n. (motor root)

Semilunar ganglion

Middle meningeal a.

Sup. tympan. a.; Lesser petrosal n.

Gr. petrosal n.

Abducens n.; Int. carotid a.; Cavernous sinus

Petrosphenoid lig.; Superior petrosal sinus

Vestibulocochlear n. Labyrinthine a.; Facial nerve

Glossopharyngeal n.

Vagus n.

carotid a.

...dibulum of ...tary gland; ...t. intercav-...nous sinus

...rosphenoid fold

...up. petrosal sinus; Sulcus for trigeminal ganglion

...silar plexus; ...cens nerve

...asilar sinus

F. Bertha 59.

Hypoglossal nerve — Vertebral artery — **Accessory n.; Inferior petrosal sinus**

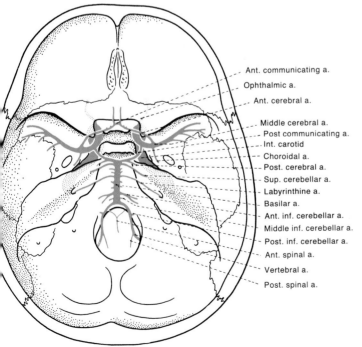

Ant. communicating a.
Ophthalmic a.
Ant. cerebral a.
Middle cerebral a.
Post communicating a.
Int. carotid
Choroidal a.
Post. cerebral a.
Sup. cerebellar a.
Labyrinthine a.
Basilar a.
Ant. inf. cerebellar a.
Middle inf. cerebellar a.
Post. inf. cerebellar a.
Ant. spinal a.
Vertebral a.
Post. spinal a.

Fig. 642: Blood Vessels and Nerves in the Region of the Sella Turcica Viewed from Above

NOTE: 1) that portions of the dura mater have been opened to expose the right cavernous sinus, the anterior and posterior intercavernous sinuses, the basilar plexus of veins and basilar sinus, as well as the right superior and inferior petrosal sinuses.

2) that the stumps of the oculomotor, trochlear and trigeminal nerves have been pulled forward or laterally, and the right optic nerve has been elevated to reveal the origin of the ophthalmic artery from the cerebral portion of the internal carotid artery.

3) the infundibulum, or stalk, of the pituitary gland by which the gland was attached to the hypothalamus of the brain. Also observe the stumps of all the cranial nerves, (except the olfactory tracts), traversing their respective foramina.

Fig. 643: The Relationship of the Arteries Supplying the Brain to the Bones at the Base of the Cranial Cavity

From the two vertebral arteries which form the basilar artery and from the two internal carotid arteries branch all of the named vessels shown in this diagram. For more details, see Figure 644.

Figs. 642, 643   **VII**

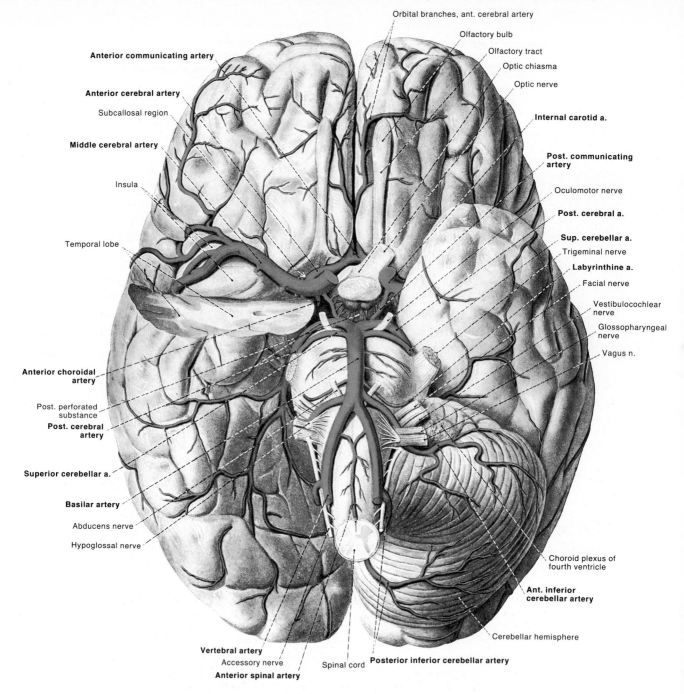

Fig. 644: The Arteries at the Base of the Brain

NOTE: 1) that branches of the vertebral arteries form the anterior spinal artery medially and the posterior inferior cerebellar arteries laterally.

2) the basilar artery is formed near the pontomedullary junction and successively gives off the anterior inferior cerebellar, labyrinthine, pontine (not labelled), superior cerebellar and posterior cerebral arteries.

3) the internal carotid arteries interconnect with the posterior cerebral by way of the posterior communicating arteries, and then give off the middle and anterior cerebral arteries. The anterior cerebral arteries are joined by the anterior communicating artery.

4) the circle of Willis surrounds the optic chiasma and is formed by the posterior cerebral, posterior communicating, internal carotid, anterior cerebral and anterior communicating arteries.

Fig. 645 con't.

Middle Cranial Fossa: a) *optic foramen:* optic nerve and ophthalmic artery. – b) *superior orbital fissure:* oculomotor nerve, trochlear nerve, ophthalmic nerve, abducens nerve, sympathetic fibers, superior ophthalmic vein, orbital branches of the middle meningeal artery and a dural recurrent branch from the lacrimal artery. – c) *foramen rotundum:* maxillary nerve. – d) *foramen ovale:* mandibular nerve, accessory meningeal artery. – e) *foramen spinosum:* middle meningeal artery, recurrent branch from mandibular nerve. – f) *foramen lacerum:* internal carotid artery passes across the superior part of the foramen but does not traverse it; nerve of pterygoid canal and meningeal branch of ascending pharyngeal artery traverse foramen lacerum.

Posterior Cranial Fossa: a) *internal acoustic meatus:* facial nerve, vestibulocochlear nerve, labyrinthine artery. – b) *jugular foramen:* inferior petrosal sinus and transverse sinus which together form the jugular vein; meningeal branches of occipital and ascending pharyngeal arteries; glossopharyngeal, vagus and accessory nerves. – c) *hypoglossal canal:* hypoglossal nerve. – d) *foramen magnum:* spinal cord; accessory nerve; anterior and posterior spinal arteries; vertebral arteries; tectorial membrane.

Fig. 644

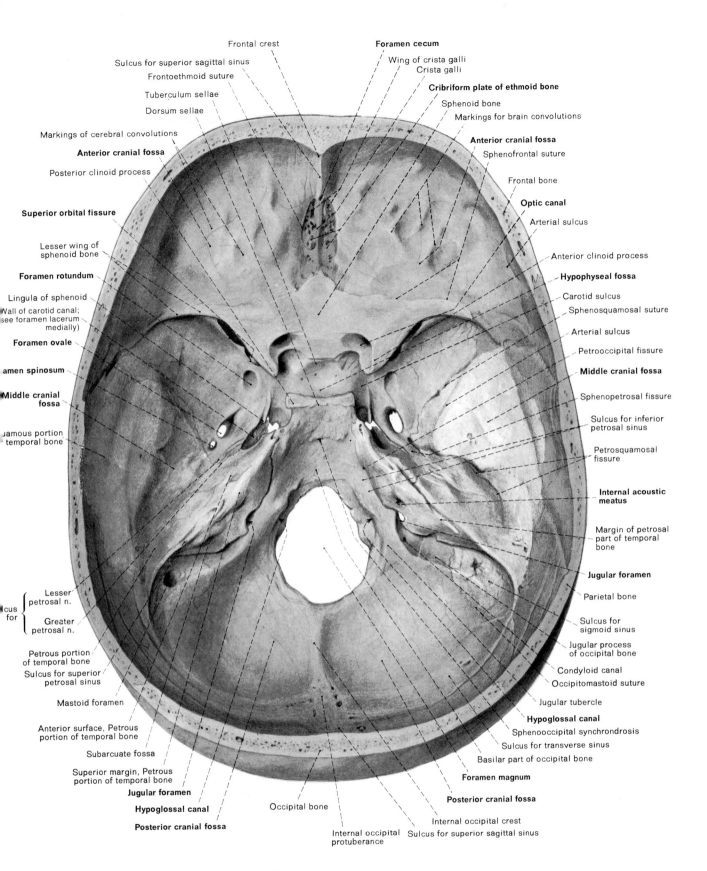

Frontal crest
Sulcus for superior sagittal sinus
Frontoethmoid suture
Tuberculum sellae
Dorsum sellae
Markings of cerebral convolutions
Anterior cranial fossa
Posterior clinoid process
Superior orbital fissure
Lesser wing of sphenoid bone
Foramen rotundum
Lingula of sphenoid
Wall of carotid canal; see foramen lacerum medially)
Foramen ovale
amen spinosum
Middle cranial fossa
quamous portion temporal bone
lcus for
Lesser petrosal n.
Greater petrosal n.
Petrous portion of temporal bone
Sulcus for superior petrosal sinus
Mastoid foramen
Anterior surface, Petrous portion of temporal bone
Subarcuate fossa
Superior margin, Petrous portion of temporal bone
Jugular foramen
Hypoglossal canal
Posterior cranial fossa

Foramen cecum
Wing of crista galli
Crista galli
Cribriform plate of ethmoid bone
Sphenoid bone
Markings for brain convolutions
Anterior cranial fossa
Sphenofrontal suture
Frontal bone
Optic canal
Arterial sulcus
Anterior clinoid process
Hypophyseal fossa
Carotid sulcus
Sphenosquamosal suture
Arterial sulcus
Petrooccipital fissure
Middle cranial fossa
Sphenopetrosal fissure
Sulcus for inferior petrosal sinus
Petrosquamosal fissure
Internal acoustic meatus
Margin of petrosal part of temporal bone
Jugular foramen
Parietal bone
Sulcus for sigmoid sinus
Jugular process of occipital bone
Condyloid canal
Occipitomastoid suture
Jugular tubercle
Hypoglossal canal
Sphenooccipital synchrondrosis
Sulcus for transverse sinus
Basilar part of occipital bone
Foramen magnum
Posterior cranial fossa
Internal occipital crest
Occipital bone
Internal occipital protuberance
Sulcus for superior sagittal sinus

Fig. 645: The Base of the Skull: Internal Aspect (Superior View)

NOTE: 1) the base of the cranial cavity is composed principally of the frontal (lavender) bones, the ethmoid (orange) bone, the sphenoid (green) bone, the temporal (gray) bones and the occipital (blue) bone. Additionally, the sphenoidal angle of each parietal (tan) bone is interposed between the frontal and temporal bones.

2) Important structures traverse the various foramina through the base of the skull:

Anterior Cranial Fossa: a) *foramen cecum:* a small vein. b) *foramina of cribriform plate:* filaments of olfactory receptor neurons to olfactory bulb. c) *anterior ethmoid foramen:* anterior ethmoidal vessels and nasociliary nerve. d) *posterior ethmoid foramen:* posterior ethmoidal vessels and nerve.

Fig. 645   VII

Fig. 646: The Base of the Skull: External Aspect (Inferior View)

NOTE: 1) the base of the skull reveals a posterior region comprised of the occipital and temporal bones which are attached by muscles to the thoracic and vertebral skeleton. More anteriorly are the facial bones consisting of the maxilla, palatine, zygomatic and vomer. Interposed between these two groups of bones is the sphenoid bone.

2) the bony palate and the cruciform suture where the transverse processes of the maxillary bones meet the horizontal plates of the palatine bones. Observe the incisive and greater palatine foramina. The lesser palatine foramina are shown but not labelled.

3) The posterior aspect of the vomer (in red) bounding the posterior nasal apertures, or choanae. Observe the medial and lateral laminae of the pterygoid process of the sphenoid bone (in green), behind which are the foramen ovale and foramen spinosum in the greater wings of that bone.

4) The petrous and mastoid parts of the temporal bone. Identify the foramen lacerum interposed between the sphenoid and temporal bones, as well as the carotid canal and jugular foramen located medial to the styloid process of the temporal bone.

5) That the foramen magnum lies completely within the occipital bone. An arrow has been placed through the hypoglossal canal located just above the occipital condyles.

Fig. 646

Fig. 647: Muscle Origins and Other Structures on the Base of the Skull

NOTE: 1) that the left mandible (reader's right) has been removed while the right muscles of mastication (reader's left), covered by their fascial sheaths, have been retained. Observe the attachments of the superficial and deep parts of the *masseter* muscle, the *temporalis*, the two heads of the *lateral pterygoid* and the *medial pterygoid* muscles.

2) the cartilage of the auditory tube as it opens inferomedially in the lateral wall of the nasopharynx, and the origins of the *tensor* and *levator veli palatini* muscles. The levator arises from the inferior surface of the apex of the petrous temporal bone, anterior to the opening of the carotid canal. The tensor veli palatini lies lateral and anterior to the levator, and it arises from the scaphoid fossa at the base of the medial pterygoid plate, the sphenoidal spine and the lateral aspect of the cartilaginous auditory tube.

3) that the muscles which pass from the skull to cervical and back structures arise from the occipital bone and the mastoid and styloid processes of the temporal bone.

Fig. 648: The Right Eye and Eyelids

NOTE: 1) the eyeball, protected anteriorly by two thin, movable eyelids or palpebrae, is covered by a transparent mucous membrane, the conjunctiva, which is continuous along the inner surface of both eyelids as the palpebral conjunctiva.

2) at the medial angle of the eye is located a small, reddish island of skin called the caruncula lacrimalis. It contains sebaceous and sweat glands which secrete a whitish substance.

3) the pubil is the opening in the iris. Constriction and dilatation of the pupil is controlled autonomically. Parasympathetic fibers in the oculomotor nerve innervate the constrictor muscle of the pupil, while sympathetic fibers from the superior cervical ganglion supply the pupillary dilator muscle.

Fig. 649: The Right Lower Eyelid and Medial Angle

NOTE: 1) that the right lower eyelid has been pulled downward in order to display the inner surface of the lower lid (i. e., the palpebral conjunctiva), and to enlarge the exposure of the medial angle (also called medial canthus). The gaze is oriented superiorly and laterally.

2) that the conjunctiva is highly vascular and its bulbar part (over the eyeball) and inferior palpebral part (on the inner surface of the lower eyelid) are continuous along a line of reflection called the inferior conjunctival fornix. A similar reflection line, the superior conjunctival fornix, lies between the eyeball and the upper eyelid.

3) that when the medial angle is more completely exposed, a pair of small openings, the punctae lacrimali, can be found located above and below the caruncula lacrimalis. These openings lead into the small lacrimal canals, and through them the tear fluid secreted by the lacrimal gland enters the nasolacrimal duct (see Figure 660).

Fig. 650: The Innervation of the Eyelids; Anterior View, Right Eye

NOTE: 1) the rich cutaneous innervation that is found around the anterior aspect of the orbit. These cutaneous nerves are derived from either the ophthalmic or maxillary divisions of the trigeminal nerve and, for the most part, achieve the anterior orbital region through foramina in the frontal, zygomatic, and maxillary bones.

2) that superomedially are found the large medial and lateral rami of the supraorbital branch of the frontal nerve (ophthalmic division of V), which appears above the orbit through the supraorbital foramen or notch. Also observe the supratrochlear branch of the frontal nerve, which becomes superficial through a small foramen above the trochlea of the superior oblique muscle.

3) the infratrochlear nerve, which is the terminal branch of the nasociliary nerve (ophthalmic division of V). It becomes superficial below the trochlea of the superior oblique muscle and, along with the palpebral branches of the infraorbital nerve (maxillary division of V), sends fibers to the lower eyelid.

4) the palpebral branches of the lacrimal nerve (ophthalmic division of V) superolaterally, which helps to supply the upper eyelid. Observe also a cutaneous ramus of the zygomaticofacial branch of the maxillary nerve that helps to supply the lateral aspect of the lower eyelid and the skin over the cheekbone. The temporal branch of the facial nerve is a motor nerve that supplies the orbicularis oculi muscle.

Figs. 648, 649, 650

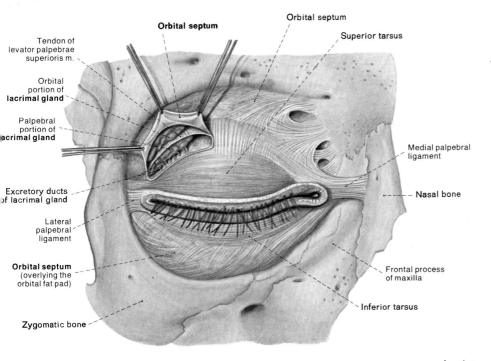

Tendon of
levator palpebrae
superioris m.

Orbital
portion of
lacrimal gland

Palpebral
portion of
lacrimal gland

Excretory ducts
of lacrimal gland

Lateral
palpebral
ligament

Orbital septum
(overlying the
orbital fat pad)

Zygomatic bone

Orbital septum

Orbital septum

Superior tarsus

Medial palpebral
ligament

Nasal bone

Frontal process
of maxilla

Inferior tarsus

Fig. 651: The Orbital Septum, Lacrimal Gland and Tarsi of the Right Eye

NOTE: With the skin, super-ficial fascia and orbicularis oculi muscle removed, the orbital septum is exposed anteriorly. It attaches to the periosteum of the bone peripherally around the orbit and to the tarsi of the eyelids centrally. Observe the lacrimal gland in the upper later-al, aspect of the anterior orbit, lying just beneath the orbital septum.

Fig. 652: The Palpebral Ligaments and Tarsal Plates

NOTE: 1) the superficial structures of the anterior orbit have been removed along with the orbital septum and the tendon of the leva-tor palpebrae superioris muscle.

2) the lateral and medial margins of the tarsal plates are attached to the lateral and medial palpebral ligaments which in turn are attached to bone. Observe that the medial ligament is located just anterior to the lacrimal sac.

3) from this anterior view, both the tendon of the superior oblique muscle and the inferior oblique muscle can be visualized. Note also the location of the orbital portion of the lacri-mal gland. Its secretions course from lateral to medial across the surface of the eye.

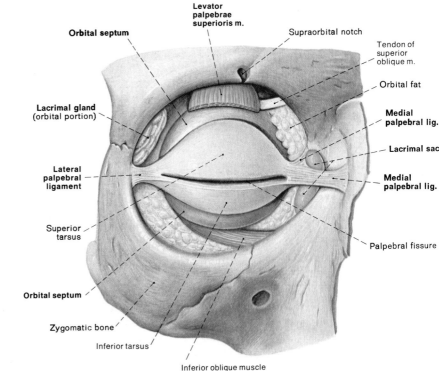

Orbital septum

Lacrimal gland
(orbital portion)

**Lateral
palpebral
ligament**

Superior
tarsus

Orbital septum

Zygomatic bone

Inferior tarsus

Levator
palpebrae
superioris m.

Supraorbital notch

Tendon of
superior
oblique m.

Orbital fat

**Medial
palpebral lig.**

Lacrimal sac

**Medial
palpebral lig.**

Palpebral fissure

Inferior oblique muscle

Upper eyelid

Bulbar fascia

Superficial fascia

Sup. palpebral
conjunctiva

**Inner surface
of upper eyelid**

Post. palpebral
border

Medial angle
of the eye

Superficial
fascia

Palpebral cleft

Punctum lacrimale

**Inner surface of
lower eyelid**

...hes of
...nerve

...crimal artery

Orbital part of
lacrimal gland

Palpebral part of
lacrimal gland

Ducts of lacrimal gland

Lateral angle of the eye

Post. border of upper eyelid

Palpebral cleft

Post. border of lower eyelid

Fig. 653: The Eyelids and Lacrimal Gland, Viewed from Within the Orbit

NOTE: 1) the inner surface of the eyelids and the vessels and nerves that supply the la-crimal gland. Observe that the lacrimal gland within this left orbit is located superior and lateral to the upper eyelid (see also Figs. 651 and 652).

2) the lacrimal artery and nerve. The la-crimal artery is a thin, tortuous branch of the ophthalmic artery. Close to the gland, the la-crimal nerve contains postganglionic fibers from the pterygopalatine ganglion (see Fig. 659 and Note 2, Fig. 659), some sensory fibers that course in the ophthalmic nerve, and a few sympathetic fibers.

Figs. 651, 652, 653   VII

Fig. 654: Anterior Dissection of the Orbit, Stage 1: Superficial Vessels, Nerves and Muscles After Removal of the Skin and the Thin Layer of Superficial Fascia

Labels in Fig. 654:
- Supraorbital nerve (medial branch)
- Supraorbital artery and nerve (lat. branch and sup. palpebral rami)
- Superior palpebral ramus, supraorbital nerve
- Temporal branch, facial nerve; Zygomatico-orbital artery
- Temporal fascia; Zygomaticotemporal nerve
- Supratrochlear n. and art.
- Palpebral branch, lacrimal nerve
- Nasal br., infratroch. n.; Dorsal nasal art.; Comm. br. infratroch. and supratroch. nn.
- Inferior palpebral arterial arch
- Infratrochlear nerve and its inferior palpebral br.; Anastomosis between the angular and ophthal. aa.
- Zygomaticofacial nerve; Branch of zygomatico-orbital artery
- Angular art. and vein
- External nasal artery and nerve
- Zygomatic branches, facial nerve; Transverse facial artery (branch)
- Buccal branch, facial n.; Nasal branch, angular art.
- Branch of infraorbital artery; Communicating ramus between the infraorbital and facial nerves
- Inferior palpebral branches, infraorbital nerve

A = Frontalis part, Occipitofrontalis muscle	B_2 = Palpebral part, Orbicularis oculi m.	E = Levator labii sup. m.	G_2 = Alar part, Nasalis m.
		F = Levator labii sup. alaeque nasi m.	H = Medial palpebral lig.
B_1 = Orbital part, orbicularis oculi m.	C = Zygomaticus major m.		J = Procerus muscle
	D = Zygomaticus minor m.	G_1 = Transverse part, Nasalis muscle	K = Corrugator supercilii m.

Fig. 655: Anterior Dissection of the Orbit, Stage 2: Vessels and Nerves After Removal of the Orbicularis Oculi and Other Superficial Muscles in the Orbital Region

Labels in Fig. 655:
- Supratrochlear nerve
- Supratrochlear art.; Supraorbital nerve (medial branch) and its sup. palpebr. ramus
- Supraorbital artery and nerve; Levator palpebrae sup. m.
- Orbital septum; Superior tarsus; Sup. palpebral arterial arch
- Infratrochlear n.; Corrugator supercilii m.
- Palpebral branch, lacrimal nerve; Zygomatico-orbital art.
- Angular art. and vein; Communicating br. betw. infra. and supratrochlear nn.; Procerus muscle
- Lat. palpebral lig.; Inferior palpebral arterial arch
- Caruncula lacrimalis; Orbicularis oculi m.
- Zygomaticofacial branch of zygomatic nerve
- Med. palpebral lig.; Palpebral branch, infratrochlear nerve
- Ext. nasal art. and n.
- Zygomatic branches of the facial nerve
- Lateral nasal cartilage; Angular art. and vein; Inf. palpebral branch, infraorbital nerve
- Greater alar cartilage of the nose
- Zygomaticus minor muscle
- Zygomaticus major muscle
- Infraorbital art. and nerve
- Levator labii superioris alaeque nasi muscle; Buccal branch, facial n.
- Inferior palpebral br., infraorbital n.; Levator anguli oris muscle

Figs. 654, 655

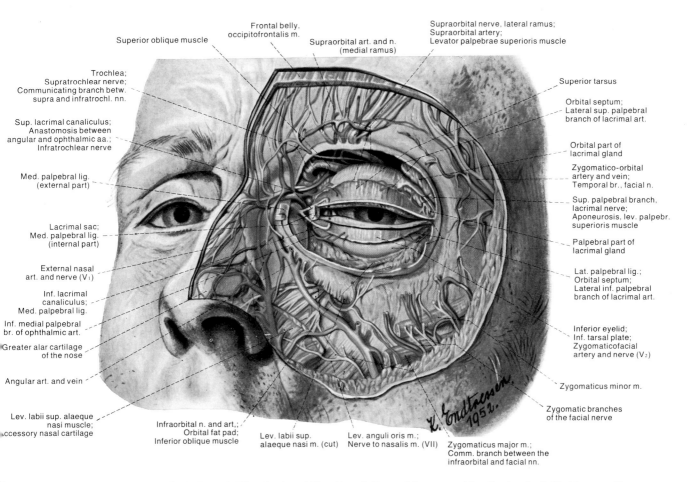

Superior oblique muscle

Trochlea;
Supratrochlear nerve;
Communicating branch betw.
supra and infratrochl. nn.

Sup. lacrimal canaliculus;
Anastomosis between
angular and ophthalmic aa.;
Infratrochlear nerve

Med. palpebral lig.
(external part)

Lacrimal sac;
Med. palpebral lig.
(internal part)

External nasal
art. and nerve (V₁)

Inf. lacrimal
canaliculus;
Med. palpebral lig.

Inf. medial palpebral
br. of ophthalmic art.

Greater alar cartilage
of the nose

Angular art. and vein

Lev. labii sup. alaeque
nasi muscle;
Accessory nasal cartilage

Frontal belly,
occipitofrontalis m.

Supraorbital art. and n.
(medial ramus)

Supraorbital nerve, lateral ramus;
Supraorbital artery;
Levator palpebrae superioris muscle

Superior tarsus

Orbital septum;
Lateral sup. palpebral
branch of lacrimal art.

Orbital part of
lacrimal gland

Zygomatico-orbital
artery and vein;
Temporal br., facial n.

Sup. palpebral branch,
lacrimal nerve;
Aponeurosis, lev. palpebr.
superioris muscle

Palpebral part of
lacrimal gland

Lat. palpebral lig.;
Orbital septum;
Lateral inf. palpebral
branch of lacrimal art.

Inferior eyelid;
Inf. tarsal plate;
Zygomaticofacial
artery and nerve (V₂)

Zygomaticus minor m.

Zygomatic branches
of the facial nerve

Infraorbital n. and art.;
Orbital fat pad;
Inferior oblique muscle

Lev. labii sup.
alaeque nasi m. (cut)

Lev. anguli oris m.;
Nerve to nasalis m. (VII)

Zygomaticus major m.;
Comm. branch between the
infraorbital and facial nn.

Fig. 656: Anterior Dissection of the Orbit, Stage 3: Visualization of More Deeply Located Structures After Cutting the Orbital Septum Circum-ferentially and Severing the Medial Palpebral Ligament

Infratrochlear vessels and n.

Superior oblique m.;
Trochlea;
Supratrochlear n.

Supratrochl. art.;
Supraorb. n. (med. ramus);
Frontal belly,
occipitofrontalis m.

Supraorbital
art. and nerve
(lat. ramus)

Lev. palpebrae sup. m.
(aponeurosis);
Orbital septum

Superior rectus muscle;
Orbital part, lacrimal gland

Medial rectus muscle;
Bulbar fascia;
Superior tarsus

Puncta lacrimalis (sup.)

Caruncula lacrimalis

Orbicularis oculi m.
(lacrimal part);
Lacrimal sac

Ext. nasal art. and n.

Angular art. and vein;
Lateral nasal cartilage

Greater alar cartilage
of the nose

Levator labii sup.
alaeque nasi m.

Aponeurosis, levator
palpebrae superioris m.;
Zygomatico-orbital art.

Bulbar conjunctiva;
Palpebral part,
lacrimal gland

Bulbar conjunctiva;
inferior oblique m.

Orbital fat pad;
Zygomaticofacial
art. and nerve (V₂)

Bulbar conjunctiva;
Inferior oblique m.

Palpebral conjunctiva;
Inferior oblique m.

Levator anguli oris muscle;
Buccal branch, facial nerve

Inferior fornix
of the conjunctiva;
Infraorbital nerve

Zygomaticus
major muscle

Zygomaticus minor muscle;
Zygomatic branches, facial nerve

Fig. 657: Anterior Dissection of the Orbit, Stage 4: Exposure of the Eyeball After Cutting the Lateral Palpebral Ligament and Reflecting the Eyelids Medially

Fig. 658: The Lacrimal Canaliculi and Lacrimal Sac: Left Side, Superficial Dissection

NOTE: 1) that the skin and superficial fascia have been removed from the upper lateral nasal region and over the medial angle of the orbit. Observe that the orbital and lacrimal parts of the orbicularis oculi muscle have been cut and reflected inferolaterally. Observe also that the tarsal attachments of the medial palpebral ligament have been cut, but this ligament remains attached to the frontal process of the maxilla.

2) the inferior oblique muscle, which is located deep to the infraorbital margin of the orbital cavity. In order to visualize better the orientation of the left inferior oblique muscle in this dissection, compare this figure with Figure 671.

3) that severance of the medial palpebral ligament exposes the underlying sac; the relationship of these two structures is more clearly seen in Figure 652. The lacrimal sac is located in a small fossa formed by the maxilla and the lacrimal bone. This bony sulcus is limited by the anterior lacrimal crest of the maxilla and the posterior lacrimal crest of the lacrimal bone (see Figs. 661 and 662). The lacrimal sac receives a lacrimal canaliculus from each eyelid and these two ducts are each about 1 cm in length (see the deeper dissection in Fig. 660).

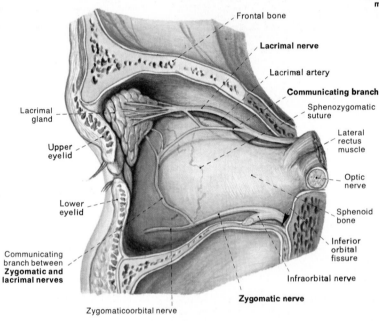

Fig. 660: The Lacrimal Canaliculi, Lacrimal Sac and Nasolacrimal Duct: Left Side, Deep Dissection

NOTE: 1) at the medial edge of both the upper and lower eyelids are found single minute orifices (puncta lacrimalia) of small ducts, the lacrimal canaliculi, which lead from the eyelids to the lacrimal sac. The sac forms the upper dilated end of the nasolacrimal duct, which then extends a distance of about 3½ inches into the inferior meatus of the nasal cavity.

2) secretions from the lacrimal gland pass medially across the surface of the eye toward the canaliculi and then are transported to the nasal cavity by way of the nasolacrimal duct. Excessive secretions (such as during crying) cannot be handled in this manner and, thus, roll over the edge of the lower eyelid as tears.

Fig. 659: The Innervation of the Lacrimal Gland

NOTE: 1) the lacrimal gland receives postganglionic parasympathetic nerve fibers which are secretomotor in nature. The preganglionic fibers are generally said to emerge from the brain with the facial nerve (VII). The synapse between pre and postganglionic fibers occurs in the pterygopalatine ganglion.

2) the preganglionic parasympathetic fibers reach the pterygopalatine ganglion by way of the greater petrosal nerve which becomes the nerve of the pterygoid canal. The postganglionic fibers leave the ganglion and travel for a short distance with the zygomatic branch of the infraorbital nerve. From this point in the inferior aspect of the orbit, the parasympathetic fibers travel by way of a communicating branch to the lacrimal nerve by which they achieve the lacrimal gland.

Figs. 658, 659, 660

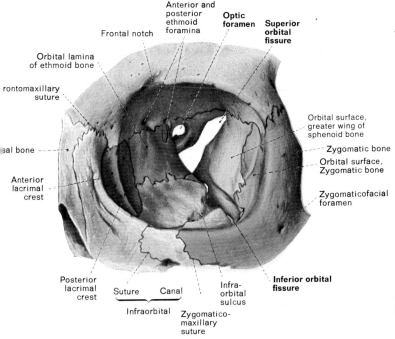

Anterior and
posterior
ethmoid
foramina

Optic
foramen

Superior
orbital
fissure

Frontal notch

Orbital lamina
of ethmoid bone

rontomaxillary
suture

sal bone

Anterior
lacrimal
crest

Orbital surface,
greater wing of
sphenoid bone

Zygomatic bone

Orbital surface,
Zygomatic bone

Zygomaticofacial
foramen

Posterior
lacrimal
crest

Suture   Canal

Infra-
orbital
sulcus

Inferior orbital
fissure

Infraorbital

Zygomatico-
maxillary
suture

◀ Fig. 661: **The Left Bony Orbital Cavity (Anterior View)**

   NOTE: 1) the bony structure of the orbit is composed of parts of seven bones: the maxilla, zygomatic, frontal, lacrimal, palatine, ethmoid and sphenoid.

   2) the *roof* of the orbit is formed by the orbital plate of the frontal bone; the *floor* consists of the orbital plate of the maxilla, the palatine (blue, not labelled) and zygomatic bones; the *medial wall* is thin and delicate and is formed by the frontal process of the maxilla, the orbital lamina of the ethmoid and the lacrimal bone; the strong *lateral wall* consists of the orbital processes of the sphenoid and zygomatic bones.

   3) the optic foramen and the superior and inferior orbital fissures.

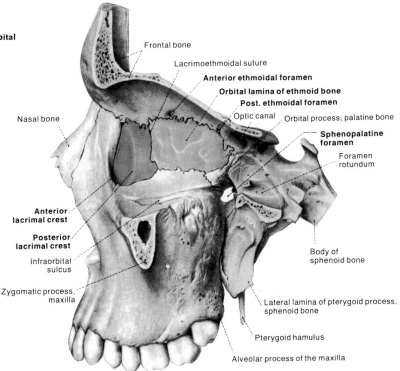

Frontal bone

Lacrimoethmoidal suture

Anterior ethmoidal foramen

Orbital lamina of ethmoid bone

Post. ethmoidal foramen

Optic canal   Orbital process, palatine bone

Nasal bone

**Sphenopalatine
foramen**

Foramen
rotundum

**Anterior
lacrimal crest**

**Posterior
lacrimal crest**

Infraorbital
sulcus

Zygomatic process,
maxilla

Body of
sphenoid bone

Lateral lamina of pterygoid process,
sphenoid bone

Pterygoid hamulus

Alveolar process of the maxilla

Fig. 662: The Medial Wall of the Left Orbital Cavity and a Lateral View of the Pterygopalatine Fossa

   NOTE: 1) that anteriorly on the thin medial wall of the orbital cavity is found the lacrimal fossa for the lacrimal sac. This fossa is limited in front by the anterior lacrimal crest of the maxilla and behind by the posterior lacrimal crest of the lacrimal bone.

   2) that the largest contribution to the medial wall of the orbit is made by the orbital lamina of the ethmoid bone. It is nearly rectangular in shape and articulates with the frontal bone above, the lacrimal bone anteriorly, the maxilla below, and the sphenoid and palatine bones posteriorly. Observe the anterior and posterior ethmoidal foramina through which course the anterior and posterior ethmoidal vessels and nerves.

   3) that below the apex of the orbital cavity (posteriorly) is located the pterygopalatine fossa and the sphenopalatine foramen.

Internal surface of frontal bone

Sphenofrontal suture

Parietal bone

Temporal bone

Lesser wing of
sphenoid bone

Tubercle for origin
of the small head
of the lat. rectus m.

←
Body of
sphenoid bone

gomatico-
orbital
foramina

Sphenoidal sinus

Pterygoid canal

Foramen rotundum

raorbital canal

Pterygopalatine fossa

Pterygoid process,
sphenoid bone

Pterygoid hamulus

Maxillary sinus

Greater palatine canal

Sockets for teeth (dental alveoli)

◀ Fig. 663: The Lateral Wall of the Right Orbital Cavity and a Medial View of the Pterygopalatine Fossa

   NOTE: 1) that the lateral wall of the orbit is formed posteriorly by the orbital surface of the greater wing of the sphenoid bone and anteriorly by the frontal process (i. e., the orbital surface) of the zygomatic bone. In this part of the zygomatic bone are found the small zygomatico-orbital foramina for the zygomaticofacial and zygomaticotemporal nerves. These two sensory nerves are derived from the zygomatic branch of the maxillary nerve. The zygomaticofacial nerve supplies the skin over the prominence of the cheek, while the terminal branch of the zygomaticotemporal nerve supplies the skin over the temple.

   2) the foramen rotundum, through which the maxillary division of the trigeminal nerve leaves the cranial cavity. Also observe the infraorbital canal (on the floor of the orbit), along which the infraorbital branch of the maxillary nerve courses to the infraorbital foramen on the anterior aspect of the face.

   3) the maxillary sinus, below most of the orbital floor, and the pterygopalatine fossa, inferior to the posterior part of the orbit. Observe the openings of the pterygoid canal and the greater palatine canal.

Frontal bone
Periorbita (periosteum)
Levator palpebrae superioris muscle
Superior rectus muscle
Eyeball
Lateral rectus muscle
Common tendinous ring

Cornea

Infraorbital margin

Inferior oblique muscle

Maxilla

Optic nerve

Sphenoid bone

Inferior rectus muscle

Infratemporal fossa

Maxillary sinus

Inferior orbital fissure

Fig. 664

Fig. 664: The Eye Muscles, Left Lateral View

NOTE: 1) with the lateral wall of the left orbit removed along with the bulbar fascia and eyelids, five of the seven extra-ocular muscles become exposed. Those evident from this view include the superior, lateral and inferior rectus muscles along with the levator palpebrae superioris and inferior oblique. The medial rectus and superior oblique cannot be seen.

2) of the seven muscles all except the levator palpebrae superioris and the inferior oblique take origin from the common tendinous ring which surrounds the optic nerve.

Superior rectus muscle

Tendon of superior oblique muscle

Pupil

Medial rectus muscle

Lateral rectus m.

Ocular conjunctiva

Inf. oblique m.

Cornea

Fig. 665

Inferior rectus muscle

Fig. 665: Right Eyeball and Muscle Insertions (Front)

Frontal bone
Trochlea
Tendon of superior oblique muscle
Superior oblique muscle
Superior rectus muscle
Levator palpebrae superioris muscle

Supraorbital margin

Eyeball

Lateral rectus muscle

Optic nerve

Sphenoid bone

Lateral rectus m.

Optic nerve

Maxilla

Inferior oblique muscle

Medial rectus muscle

Inferior orbital fissure

Fig. 667 Periorbita

Inferior rectus muscle

Maxillary sinus

Fig. 667: The Eye Muscles, Left Lateral View (Lateral Rectus Muscle and Optic Nerve Cut)

NOTE that the eyeball has been rotated 90° such that its posterior pole is directed laterally. This reveals to advantage the medial rectus muscle and the superior oblique muscle and tendon, as the latter bends around the trochlea to insert on the eyeball.

Fig. 666: Right Eyeball and Muscle Insertions (Behind)

Superior rectus muscle

Tendon of superior oblique muscle

Lateral rectus muscle

Medial rectus muscle

Inferior oblique

Fig. 666

Inferior rectus muscle

Optic nerve

Figs. 664–667

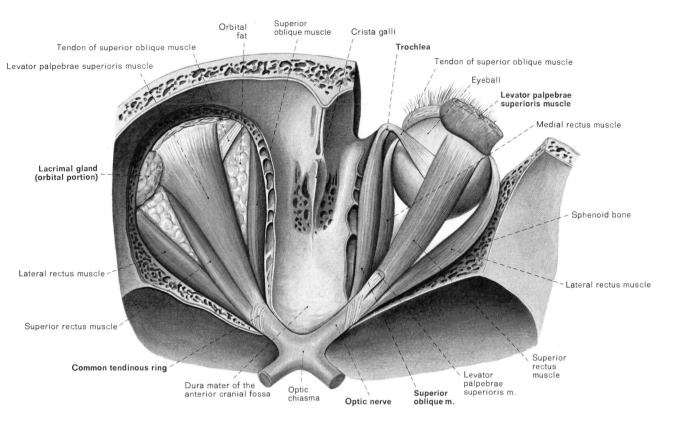

Fig. 668: The Muscles of the Orbital Cavity as seen from above

NOTE: 1) the orbital plates of the frontal bone have been removed from within the cranium. On the left side, only the bony roof of the orbit has been opened and the muscles, orbital fat and lacrimal gland have been left intact.

2) on the right side, the levator palpebrae superioris muscle has been resected and the orbital fat removed in order to expose the ocular muscles.

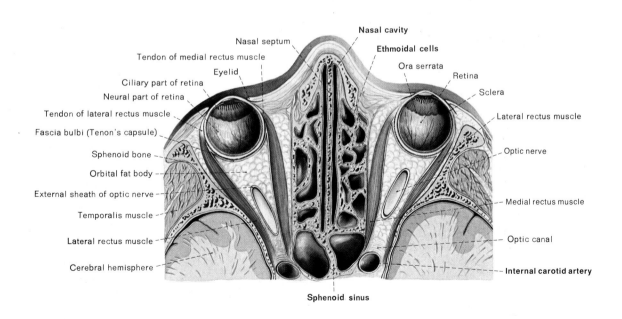

Fig. 669: A Horizontal Section Through Both Orbits at the Level of the Sphenoid Sinus

NOTE: 1) between the orbital cavities is situated the ethmoid bone containing the ethmoidal air sinuses (air cells). The vertically oriented perpendicular plate of the ethmoid serves as the nasal septum, which subdivides the nasal cavity into two symmetrical chambers.

2) the posterior portion of the orbits are separated by the sphenoidal sinuses, located within the body of the sphenoid bone. These sinuses usually are not symmetrical.

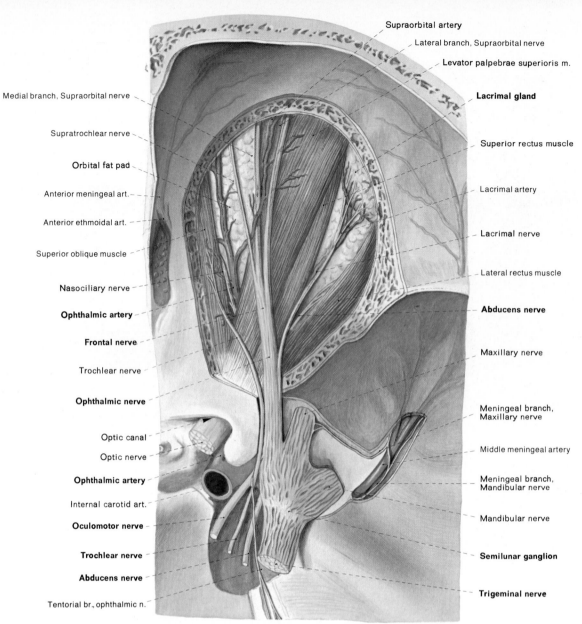

Supraorbital artery

Lateral branch, Supraorbital nerve

Levator palpebrae superioris m.

Lacrimal gland

Medial branch, Supraorbital nerve

Supratrochlear nerve

Orbital fat pad

Anterior meningeal art.

Anterior ethmoidal art.

Superior oblique muscle

Nasociliary nerve

Ophthalmic artery

Frontal nerve

Trochlear nerve

Ophthalmic nerve

Optic canal

Optic nerve

Ophthalmic artery

Internal carotid art.

Oculomotor nerve

Trochlear nerve

Abducens nerve

Tentorial br., ophthalmic n.

Superior rectus muscle

Lacrimal artery

Lacrimal nerve

Lateral rectus muscle

Abducens nerve

Maxillary nerve

Meningeal branch, Maxillary nerve

Middle meningeal artery

Meningeal branch, Mandibular nerve

Mandibular nerve

Semilunar ganglion

Trigeminal nerve

Fig. 670: Nerves and Arteries of the Orbit (Stage 1) Superior View: Ophthalmic Nerve and Artery

NOTE: 1) that the orbital plate of the frontal bone has been removed to expose the structures in the right orbit from above. Observe that the ophthalmic division of the trigeminal nerve divides into lacrimal, frontal and nasociliary branches. The lacrimal nerve courses anteriorly and laterally in the orbit and accompanies the lacrimal branch of the ophthalmic artery to supply the lacrimal gland.

2) that the frontal nerve overlies the levator palpebrae superioris and soon divides into a delicate supratrochlear branch and larger medial and lateral branches. These course toward the front of the orbit where they emerge on the forehead. Observe that the nasociliary nerve crosses the orbit anteromedially, deep to the superior rectus muscle, and accompanies the ophthalmic artery for a short distance.

3) the trochlear nerve entering the orbit medial to the ophthalmic nerve to supply the superior oblique muscle.

Fig. 671: The Extrinsic Muscle of the Left Eyeball, Anterolateral View

NOTE that the skin, eyelids and fascia have been removed. Observe that the tendon of the inferior oblique muscle inserts onto the lateral part of the eyeball, behind its equator and between the insertions of the superior and lateral recti muscles.

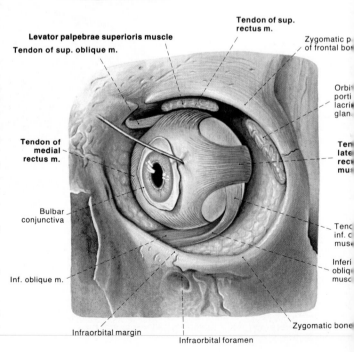

Tendon of sup. rectus m.

Levator palpebrae superioris muscle

Tendon of sup. oblique m.

Zygomatic p of frontal bo

Orbi porti lacri glan

Ten late rec mu

Tendon of medial rectus m.

Bulbar conjunctiva

Tend inf. c musc

Inferi obliq musc

Inf. oblique m.

Infraorbital margin

Infraorbital foramen

Zygomatic bone

Figs. 670, 671

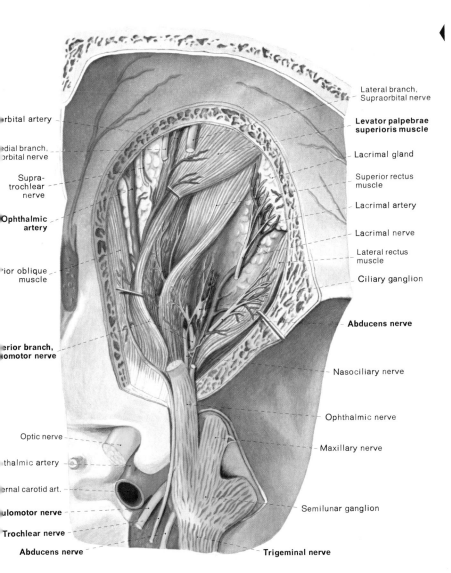

Lateral branch, Supraorbital nerve

Levator palpebrae superioris muscle

Lacrimal gland

Superior rectus muscle

Lacrimal artery

Lacrimal nerve

Lateral rectus muscle

Ciliary ganglion

Abducens nerve

Nasociliary nerve

Ophthalmic nerve

Maxillary nerve

Semilunar ganglion

Trigeminal nerve

rbital artery

dial branch, orbital nerve

Supra-trochlear nerve

Ophthalmic artery

ior oblique muscle

erior branch, omotor nerve

Optic nerve

thalmic artery

ernal carotid art.

ulomotor nerve

Trochlear nerve

Abducens nerve

Fig. 672: Nerves and Arteries of the Orbit (Stage 2) Superior View: The Trochlear and Abducens Nerves

NOTE: 1) that with the right orbit opened from above, the ophthalmic division of the trigeminal nerve and its lacrimal, supratrochlear and frontal branches have been cut. The levator palpebrae superioris and superior rectus muscles have been pulled medially to reveal their inferior surface where filaments from the *superior branch of the oculomotor nerve* innervate the two muscles.

2) that the *nasociliary branch* of the ophthalmic nerve is still intact, and it is seen turning medially deep to the superior rectus muscle. Observe that a fine communicating filament containing sensory fibers interconnects the ciliary ganglion with the nasociliary nerve.

3) the *trochlear nerve* as it supplies the superior oblique muscle along its upper surface. If this nerve is injured, the patient has difficulty turning the eyeball laterally and downward. When asked to look inferolaterally, the affected eye rotates medially, resulting in double vision or diplopia.

4) the *abducens nerve* as it supplies the lateral rectus muscle along its inner or medial surface. After emerging from the brainstem at the pontomedullary junction, the abducens nerve follows a long course in the floor of the cranial cavity to achieve the orbit by way of the superior orbital fissure. Injury to this nerve produces a diminished ability to move the eyeball laterally. From the resulting medial or convergent gaze of the affected eyeball, the patient complains of diplopia (double vision).

Fig. 673: Sagittal View of the Orbital Cavity and Eyeball

NOTE: 1) that bulbar fascia (also seen in Figure 677) is a thin membrane which encloses the posterior 3/4ths of the eyeball, separating the eyeball from the orbital fat and other contents of the orbital cavity. This fascia is pierced by the tendons of the ocular muscles, over which the fascia is prolonged like a tubular sheath.

2) the insertion of the levator palpebrae superioris is trilaminar. The superficial layer inserts into the upper eyelid, the middle into the superior tarsus and the deep layer inserts into the superior fornix of the conjunctiva.

3) the palpebral conjunctiva is a thin transparent mucous membrane on the innermost aspect of the eyelid. At the conjunctival angle (fornix), it reflects over the eyeball as far as the sclerocorneal junction.

4) that the optic nerve is located on the posterior aspect of the eyeball about 3 mm to the nasal side of the macula lutea and fovea centralis (see Fig. 680). The point at which the optic nerve pierces the eyeball is called the optic disc (optic papilla) and, because this site is devoid of neural retina, it is often referred to as the blind spot. The blood vessels that supply and drain the retina pass through the optic disc along with the axons of the ganglion cells of the retina that form the optic nerve.

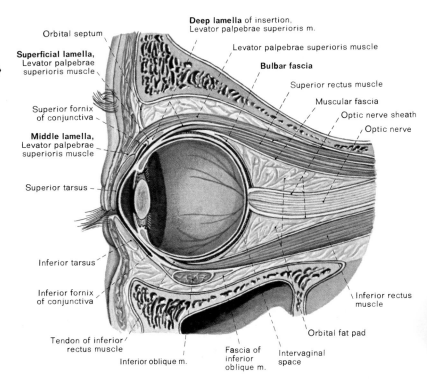

Orbital septum

Superficial lamella, Levator palpebrae superioris muscle

Superior fornix of conjunctiva

Middle lamella, Levator palpebrae superioris muscle

Superior tarsus

Inferior tarsus

Inferior fornix of conjunctiva

Tendon of inferior rectus muscle

Inferior oblique m.

Fascia of inferior oblique m.

Intervaginal space

Deep lamella of insertion, Levator palpebrae superioris m.

Levator palpebrae superioris muscle

Bulbar fascia

Superior rectus muscle

Muscular fascia

Optic nerve sheath

Optic nerve

Inferior rectus muscle

Orbital fat pad

Fig. 674: Nerves and Arteries of the Orbit (Stage 3) Superior View: The Optic Nerve and Ciliary Ganglion

NOTE: 1) that with the levator palpebrae superioris, superior rectus and superior oblique muscles cut and reflected, the nasociliary nerve and ophthalmic artery are seen crossing over the optic nerve from lateral to medial.

2) the optic nerve and the longitudinally oriented long ciliary arteries (from the ophthalmic) and long ciliary nerves (usually 2 or 3 branches of the nasociliary nerve).

3) the ciliary ganglion lateral to the optic nerve. Its *parasymphathetic root* comes from the oculomotor nerve and its *sensory root* from the nasociliary nerve. Postganglionic parasymphathetic fibers reach the eyeball by way of the short ciliary nerves.

4) that postganglionic parasympathetic nerve fibers supply the sphincter of the pupil and the muscle responsible for accommodation of the lens – the ciliary muscle.

5) that some sympathetic fibers (that arrive in the orbit along the ophthalmic artery from the cavernous plexus) also course through the ciliary ganglion. These are principally vasoconstrictor fibers to arteries that supply the eyeball. Sympathetic fibers that supply the dilator muscle of the pupil course to the posterior pole of the eyeball by way of the long ciliary nerves.

6) that although the supratrochlear nerve is derived from the frontal branch of the ophthalmic nerve, the infratrochlear nerve (as well as the anterior and posterior ethmoidal nerves) are derived from the nasociliary branch of the ophthalmic nerve.

Fig. 675: Origins of the Ocular Muscles, Apex of Left Orbit

NOTE: 1) this anterior view of the apex of the left orbit shows the stumps of the ocular muscles which have been cut close to their origins.

2) the four rectus muscles arise from a common tendinous ring surrounding the optic canal. The levator palpebrae superioris and superior oblique muscles arise from the sphenoid bone close to the tendinous ring, while the inferior oblique (not shown) arises from the orbital surface of the maxilla.

3) a. The **lateral rectus** *abducts* the eyeball;
   b. the **superior oblique** *abducts, depresses and medially rotates* the eyeball;
   c. the **inferior oblique** *abducts, elevates* and *laterally rotates* the eyeball;
   d. the **medial rectus** *adducts* the eyeball;
   e. the **inferior rectus** *adducts, depresses* and *laterally rotates* the eyeball;
   f. the **superior rectus** *adducts, elevates* and *medially rotates* the eyeball.

Figs. 674, 675

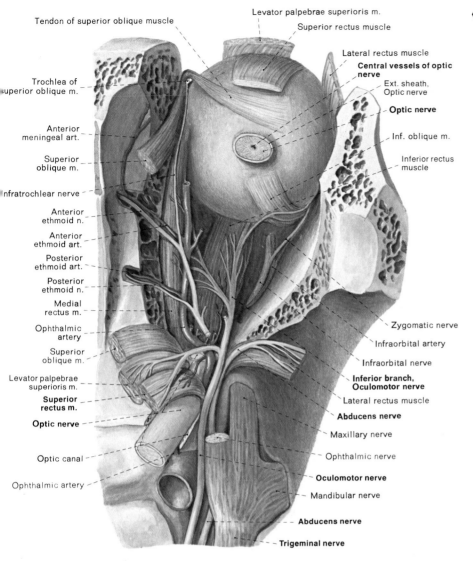

Tendon of superior oblique muscle

Trochlea of superior oblique m.

Anterior meningeal art.

Superior oblique m.

Infratrochlear nerve

Anterior ethmoid n.

Anterior ethmoid art.

Posterior ethmoid art.

Posterior ethmoid n.

Medial rectus m.

Ophthalmic artery

Superior oblique m.

Levator palpebrae superioris m.

Superior rectus m.

Optic nerve

Optic canal

Ophthalmic artery

Levator palpebrae superioris m.

Superior rectus muscle

Lateral rectus muscle

Central vessels of optic nerve

Ext. sheath, Optic nerve

Optic nerve

Inf. oblique m.

Inferior rectus muscle

Zygomatic nerve

Infraorbital artery

Infraorbital nerve

Inferior branch, Oculomotor nerve

Lateral rectus muscle

Abducens nerve

Maxillary nerve

Ophthalmic nerve

Oculomotor nerve

Mandibular nerve

Abducens nerve

Trigeminal nerve

Fig. 676: Nerves and Arteries of the Orbit (Stage 4) Superior View: The Oculomotor Nerve (Inferior Branch)

NOTE: 1) that the levator palpebrae superioris, superior rectus, superior oblique and lateral rectus muscles have been cut and reflected; the optic nerve has also been severed. The anterior half of the eyeball has been depressed and its posterior pole directed upward. Observe the central vessels of the optic nerve, as well as the insertions of the superior oblique and inferior oblique muscles.

2) that the *oculomotor nerve* enters the orbit through the superior orbital fissure and within the common tendinous ring. It quickly gives off its superior branch which courses upward in the orbit to the superior oblique and levator palpebrae superioris muscles. The inferior branch of the oculomotor nerve courses anteriorly in the deep part of the orbit to supply the inferior rectus, medial rectus and inferior oblique muscles.

3) the anterior and posterior ethmoidal arteries and nerves and the infratrochlear nerve medially in the orbit, and the infra-orbit to supply the inferior rectus, medial rectus and inferior oblique muscles.

4) that the ophthalmic artery is the first branch of the internal carotid artery within the cranial cavity and it immediately enters the orbit through the optic canal alongside the optic nerve. Although nearly all the blood vessels in the orbit are branches from the ophthalmic artery, perhaps the most important is the central artery of the optic nerve (or retina), seen with its accompanying vein in the center of the optic nerve. This artery is the only source of blood to the neural retina and increased pressure on the posterior part of the orbital cavity or edema of the optic nerve caused by an inflammatory process can seriously compromise vision either by blockage of the artery or by diminishing the flow in the central retinal vein.

Fig. 677: The Bulbar Fascia (Capsule of Tenon), Right Eye

NOTE: 1) longitudinal incisions have been made down the middle of each eyelid and the flaps have been reflected to expose the orbital cavity anteriorly.

2) the optic nerve has been severed at the optic disc and the eyeball, along with the insertions of the ocular muscles, has been removed from the orbital cavity.

3) the bulbar fascia which envelopes the posterior aspect of the eyeball (from the sclerocorneal junction to the optic nerve) has been left within the orbit. Observe how the bulbar fascia is perforated by the tendons of the ocular muscles. It is also pierced from behind by the ciliary vessels and nerves.

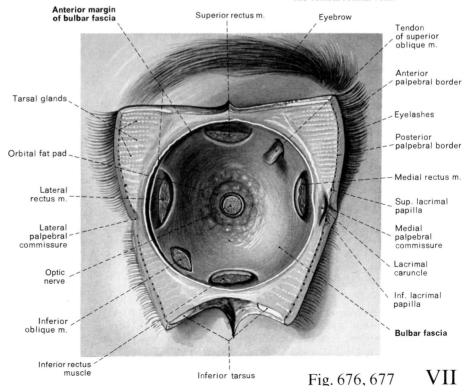

Anterior margin of bulbar fascia

Superior rectus m.

Eyebrow

Tendon of superior oblique m.

Anterior palpebral border

Eyelashes

Posterior palpebral border

Medial rectus m.

Sup. lacrimal papilla

Medial palpebral commissure

Lacrimal caruncle

Inf. lacrimal papilla

Bulbar fascia

Tarsal glands

Orbital fat pad

Lateral rectus m.

Lateral palpebral commissure

Optic nerve

Inferior oblique m.

Inferior rectus muscle

Inferior tarsus

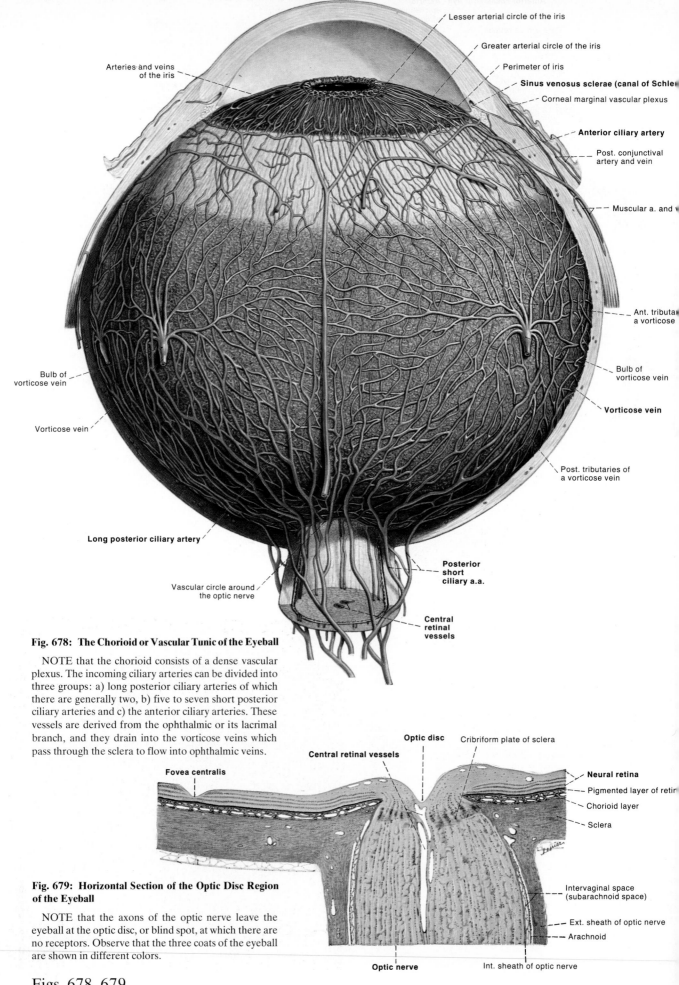

Lesser arterial circle of the iris

Greater arterial circle of the iris

Perimeter of iris

Sinus venosus sclerae (canal of Schle

Corneal marginal vascular plexus

Anterior ciliary artery

Post. conjunctival artery and vein

Muscular a. and v

Ant. tributa a vorticose

Bulb of vorticose vein

Vorticose vein

Post. tributaries of a vorticose vein

Arteries and veins of the iris

Bulb of vorticose vein

Vorticose vein

Long posterior ciliary artery

Vascular circle around the optic nerve

Posterior short ciliary a.a.

Central retinal vessels

Fig. 678: The Chorioid or Vascular Tunic of the Eyeball

NOTE that the chorioid consists of a dense vascular plexus. The incoming ciliary arteries can be divided into three groups: a) long posterior ciliary arteries of which there are generally two, b) five to seven short posterior ciliary arteries and c) the anterior ciliary arteries. These vessels are derived from the ophthalmic or its lacrimal branch, and they drain into the vorticose veins which pass through the sclera to flow into ophthalmic veins.

Optic disc Cribriform plate of sclera

Central retinal vessels

Neural retina

Pigmented layer of retir

Chorioid layer

Sclera

Fovea centralis

Intervaginal space (subarachnoid space)

Ext. sheath of optic nerve

Arachnoid

Fig. 679: Horizontal Section of the Optic Disc Region of the Eyeball

NOTE that the axons of the optic nerve leave the eyeball at the optic disc, or blind spot, at which there are no receptors. Observe that the three coats of the eyeball are shown in different colors.

Optic nerve Int. sheath of optic nerve

Figs. 678, 679

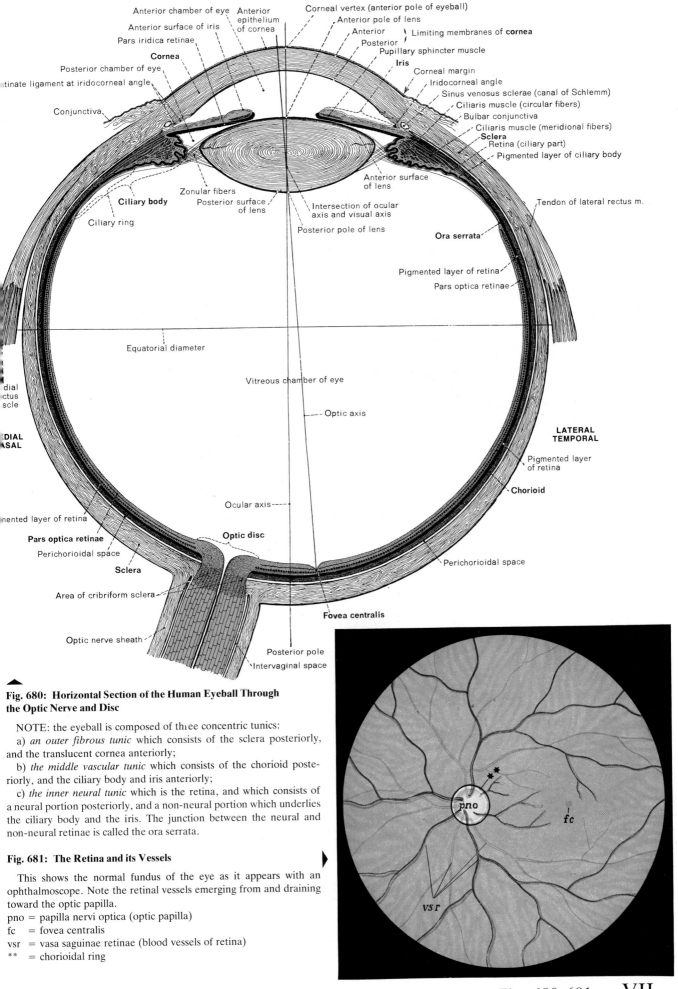

Anterior chamber of eye
Anterior surface of iris
Pars iridica retinae
Cornea
Posterior chamber of eye
tinate ligament at iridocorneal angle
Conjunctiva
Anterior epithelium of cornea
Anterior pole of lens
Corneal vertex (anterior pole of eyeball)
Anterior pole of lens
Anterior
Posterior
Pupillary sphincter muscle
Iris
Limiting membranes of **cornea**
Corneal margin
Iridocorneal angle
Sinus venosus sclerae (canal of Schlemm)
Ciliaris muscle (circular fibers)
Bulbar conjunctiva
Ciliaris muscle (meridional fibers)
Sclera
Retina (ciliary part)
Pigmented layer of ciliary body

Ciliary body
Ciliary ring
Zonular fibers
Posterior surface of lens
Anterior surface of lens
Intersection of ocular axis and visual axis
Posterior pole of lens

Tendon of lateral rectus m.

Ora serrata

Pigmented layer of retina
Pars optica retinae

Equatorial diameter

Vitreous chamber of eye

dial
ctus
scle

DIAL
ASAL

Optic axis

LATERAL
TEMPORAL

Pigmented layer of retina

Chorioid

Ocular axis

nented layer of retina
Pars optica retinae
Perichorioidal space
Sclera
Area of cribriform sclera
Optic nerve sheath

Optic disc

Perichorioidal space

Fovea centralis

Posterior pole
Intervaginal space

▲
Fig. 680: Horizontal Section of the Human Eyeball Through the Optic Nerve and Disc

NOTE: the eyeball is composed of three concentric tunics:
a) *an outer fibrous tunic* which consists of the sclera posteriorly, and the translucent cornea anteriorly;
b) *the middle vascular tunic* which consists of the chorioid posteriorly, and the ciliary body and iris anteriorly;
c) *the inner neural tunic* which is the retina, and which consists of a neural portion posteriorly, and a non-neural portion which underlies the ciliary body and the iris. The junction between the neural and non-neural retinae is called the ora serrata.

Fig. 681: The Retina and its Vessels
▶
This shows the normal fundus of the eye as it appears with an ophthalmoscope. Note the retinal vessels emerging from and draining toward the optic papilla.
pno = papilla nervi optica (optic papilla)
fc = fovea centralis
vsr = vasa saguinae retinae (blood vessels of retina)
** = chorioidal ring

pno
fc
vsr

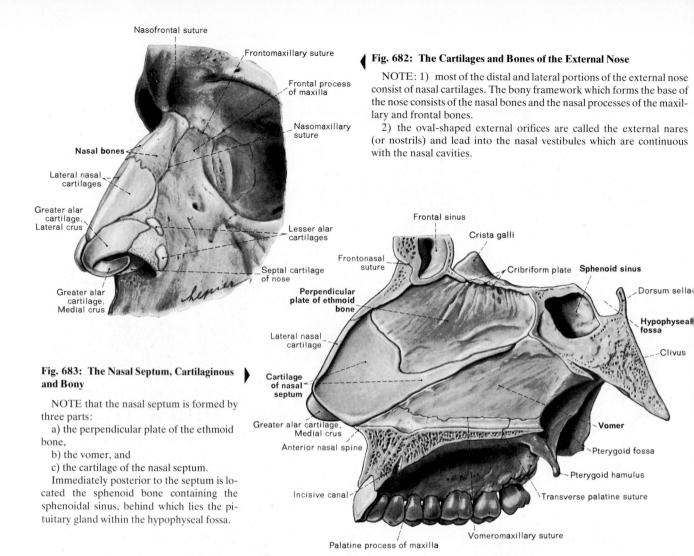

Nasofrontal suture
Frontomaxillary suture
Frontal process of maxilla
Nasomaxillary suture
Nasal bones
Lateral nasal cartilages
Greater alar cartilage, Lateral crus
Lesser alar cartilages
Greater alar cartilage, Medial crus
Septal cartilage of nose

Frontal sinus
Crista galli
Frontonasal suture
Cribriform plate
Sphenoid sinus
Perpendicular plate of ethmoid bone
Dorsum sellae
Lateral nasal cartilage
Hypophyseal fossa
Clivus
Cartilage of nasal septum
Greater alar cartilage, Medial crus
Anterior nasal spine
Vomer
Pterygoid fossa
Pterygoid hamulus
Transverse palatine suture
Incisive canal
Vomeromaxillary suture
Palatine process of maxilla

Fig. 682: The Cartilages and Bones of the External Nose

NOTE: 1) most of the distal and lateral portions of the external nose consist of nasal cartilages. The bony framework which forms the base of the nose consists of the nasal bones and the nasal processes of the maxillary and frontal bones.

2) the oval-shaped external orifices are called the external nares (or nostrils) and lead into the nasal vestibules which are continuous with the nasal cavities.

Fig. 683: The Nasal Septum, Cartilaginous and Bony

NOTE that the nasal septum is formed by three parts:
a) the perpendicular plate of the ethmoid bone,
b) the vomer, and
c) the cartilage of the nasal septum.

Immediately posterior to the septum is located the sphenoid bone containing the sphenoidal sinus, behind which lies the pituitary gland within the hypophyseal fossa.

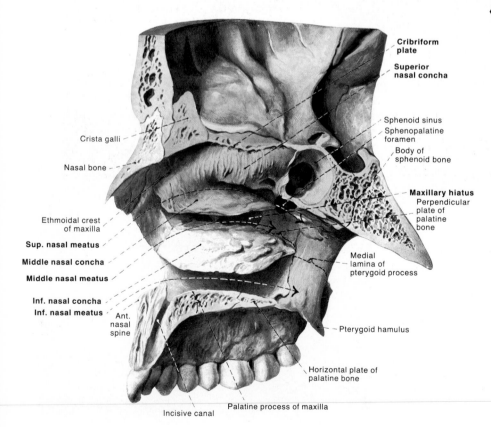

Cribriform plate
Superior nasal concha
Sphenoid sinus
Sphenopalatine foramen
Body of sphenoid bone
Maxillary hiatus
Perpendicular plate of palatine bone
Medial lamina of pterygoid process
Crista galli
Nasal bone
Ethmoidal crest of maxilla
Sup. nasal meatus
Middle nasal concha
Middle nasal meatus
Inf. nasal concha
Inf. nasal meatus
Ant. nasal spine
Pterygoid hamulus
Horizontal plate of palatine bone
Incisive canal
Palatine process of maxilla

Fig. 684: The Bony Lateral Wall of the Right Nasal Cavity

NOTE: 1) that the nasal septum has been removed and the mucosa stripped from the bones that form the irregular lateral wall of the nasal cavity and the hard palate. Observe that the crista galli, cribriform plate, superior nasal concha and middle nasal concha are all parts of the ethmoid bone (light orange). Below these is the thin, slightly curved inferior nasal concha (gray), which is a separate bone.

2) that in front of the nasal conchae are the nasal bone (gray), the small lacrimal bone (red, not labelled), and the maxilla (yellow), while behind is the perpendicular plate of the palatine bone (blue). The bony floor of the nasal cavity is the hard palate, which is formed by the palatine process of the maxilla and the horizontal plate of the palatine bone.

3) the three posteriorly directed curved arrows. These follow the courses of the superior, middle and inferior meatuses, each of which underlies its respective nasal concha, and is oriented posteroinferiorly to that part of the nasal cavity which becomes the nasopharynx.

4) the sphenoidal sinus in the body of the sphenoid bone, the sphenopalatine foramen and the opening of the maxillary sinus (maxillary hiatus).

Figs. 682, 683, 684

Labels (left side, top to bottom):
Frontal sinus
...henoethmoidal recess
Opening of ...henoidal sinus
Middle nasal concha
Superior nasal concha
Opening of frontal sinus
...us semilunaris; ...lla ethmoidalis
Limen nasi
...stibule of nose
Inferior nasal concha
...ening of naso-lacrimal duct; Lacrimal fold
...palate (bony); Soft ...ate (muscular)
...ramen cecum of tongue; Vallecula of epiglottis
Epiglottis; Entrance ...o larynx (→)

Labels (top):
Sphenoid sinus
Pharyngeal tonsil
Optic nerve; Internal carotid artery
Sella turcica; pituitary gland
Free margin of tentorium cerebelli

Labels (bottom):
Ventricle of larynx
Opening of auditory tube; Salpingopalatine fold; Ridge of levator veli palatini m.
Torus tubarius and pharyngeal recess
Vertebral artery

Fig. 685: Lateral Wall of the Right Nasal Cavity Showing Openings of the Paranasal Air Sinuses and the Nasopharynx

NOTE: 1) this median sagittal section of the adult head displays the right nasal cavity with the middle and inferior nasal conchae removed. The nasal cavity communicates anteriorly with the environment through the vestibule and nostril, and posteriorly with the pharynx (nasopharynx).

2) opening of the various paranasal sinuses and other structures. These include:

a) the *sphenoid sinus* which opens into the sphenoethmoidal recess above the superior concha.

b) the *frontal sinus* and *maxillary sinus* both of which open into a groove called the hiatus semilunaris in the middle meatus below the middle concha.

c) the *nasolacrimal duct* which opens into the inferior meatus below the inferior concha.

d) the *auditory tube* which opens into the nasopharynx just behind the inferior concha. This tube stretches between the cavity of the middle ear (tympanic cavity) and the nasopharynx, thereby allowing the cavity of the middle ear to alter its air pressure consistent with the environment. This mechanism equalizes the air pressure on both sides of the tympanic membrane.

3) the nasal cavity, oral cavity and laryngeal cavity all communicate with the pharynx, forming, in turn, the nasopharynx, oral pharynx and laryngeal pharynx.

Fig. 685   VII

Fig. 686: **The Paranasal Sinuses Viewed from Above**

NOTE: 1) that on the left side the frontal (reddish brown), anterior ethmoid (green), posterior ethmoid (lavender) and sphenoid (brown) sinuses are projected onto the bones of the base of the skull. On the right side portions of the frontal, ethmoid and sphenoid bones have been removed to bring the sinuses into view from above.

2) each of these sinuses drain into the nasal cavity, as indicated in Fig. 685. There is some variation in size and considerable variation in the geometry of the sinuses, but all are lined by a delicate mucosa formed by pseudostratified columnar epithelium with many goblet cells, and an underlying connective tissue layer containing many mucous glands.

Fig. 687: **Ethmoid Bone: Superior Surface, Viewed from Above**

NOTE the same orientation as Fig. 686.

Fig. 689: **The Frontal, Ethmoid and Nasal Bones Viewed from Below**

NOTE that the cribriform plate of the ethmoid bone (orange), which extends laterally from the midline on each side, is perforated by many foramina. Through the foramina course the nerve fibers of the primary olfactory receptor cells. These first order special sense afferent fibers enter the cranial cavity and synapse with second order neurons in the overlying olfactory bulbs of the brain (see Figs. 690 and 691).

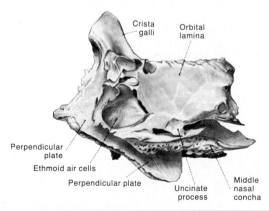

Fig. 688: **Ethmoid Bone, Left Lateral View**

Figs. 686–689

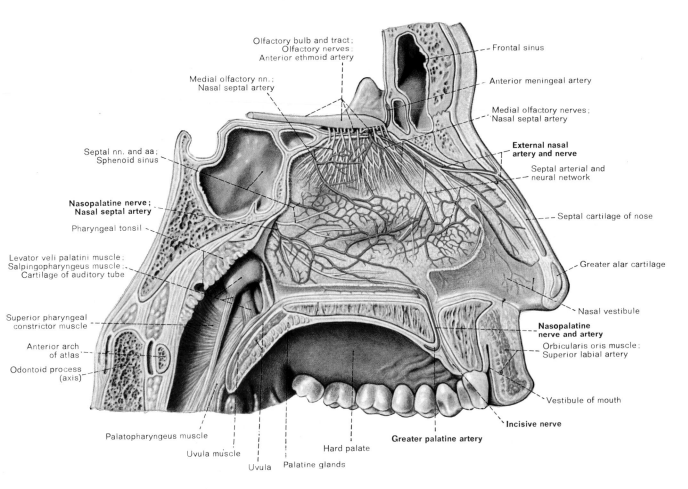

Fig. 690: Arteries and Nerves of the Nasal Septum

NOTE that the mucous membrane has been removed from the nasal septum and nasopharynx revealing the spetal vessels and nerves and the nasopharyngeal muscles.

Fig. 691: The Lateral Wall of the Left Nasal Cavity

NOTE: the mucous membrane overlying the lateral olfactory nerves has been removed. The lateral wall of the nasal cavity is marked by the superior, middle and inferior nasal conchae. Beneath each concha courses its corresponding nasal passage or meatus.

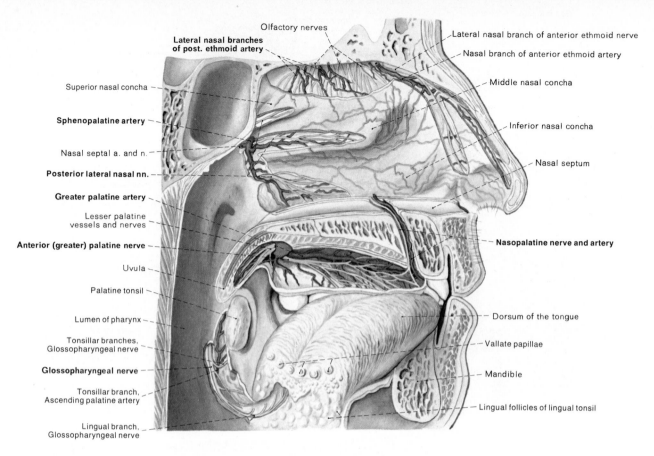

Fig. 692: **Nerves and Arteries of the Palate and Lateral Wall of the Nasal Cavity**

Olfactory nerves

Lateral nasal branches of post. ethmoid artery

Lateral nasal branch of anterior ethmoid nerve

Nasal branch of anterior ethmoid artery

Superior nasal concha

Middle nasal concha

Sphenopalatine artery

Inferior nasal concha

Nasal septal a. and n.

Nasal septum

Posterior lateral nasal nn.

Greater palatine artery

Nasopalatine nerve and artery

Lesser palatine vessels and nerves

Anterior (greater) palatine nerve

Uvula

Palatine tonsil

Dorsum of the tongue

Lumen of pharynx

Vallate papillae

Tonsillar branches, Glossopharyngeal nerve

Mandible

Glossopharyngeal nerve

Tonsillar branch, Ascending palatine artery

Lingual follicles of lingual tonsil

Lingual branch, Glossopharyngeal nerve

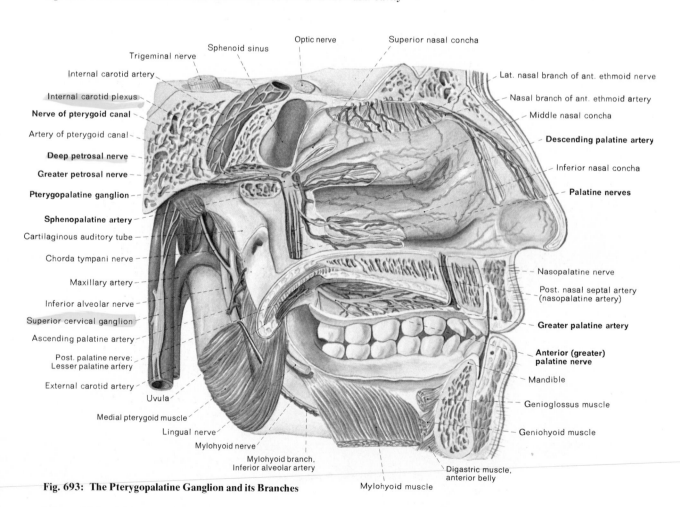

Fig. 693: **The Pterygopalatine Ganglion and its Branches**

Sphenoid sinus

Optic nerve

Superior nasal concha

Trigeminal nerve

Internal carotid artery

Lat. nasal branch of ant. ethmoid nerve

Internal carotid plexus

Nasal branch of ant. ethmoid artery

Nerve of pterygoid canal

Middle nasal concha

Artery of pterygoid canal

Descending palatine artery

Deep petrosal nerve

Inferior nasal concha

Greater petrosal nerve

Pterygopalatine ganglion

Palatine nerves

Sphenopalatine artery

Cartilaginous auditory tube

Chorda tympani nerve

Nasopalatine nerve

Maxillary artery

Post. nasal septal artery (nasopalatine artery)

Inferior alveolar nerve

Superior cervical ganglion

Greater palatine artery

Ascending palatine artery

Anterior (greater) palatine nerve

Post. palatine nerve: Lesser palatine artery

Mandible

External carotid artery

Genioglossus muscle

Uvula

Medial pterygoid muscle

Geniohyoid muscle

Lingual nerve

Mylohyoid nerve

Mylohyoid branch, Inferior alveolar artery

Digastric muscle, anterior belly

Mylohyoid muscle

Figs. 692, 693

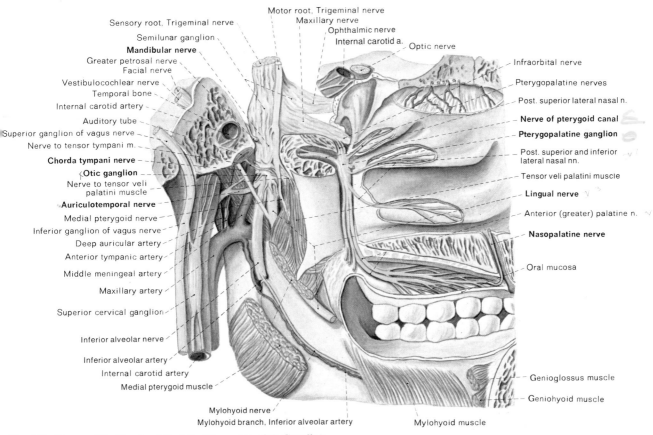

Fig. 694: Nerves of the Nasal and Oral Cavities and the Otic Ganglion

NOTE the junction of the chorda tympani nerve with the lingual nerve and the position of the otic ganglion in relation to the mandibular branch of the trigeminal. This ganglion receives preganglionic parasympathetic fibers by way of the tympanic branch of the glossopharyngeal nerve. Its postganglionic fibers supply the parotid gland.

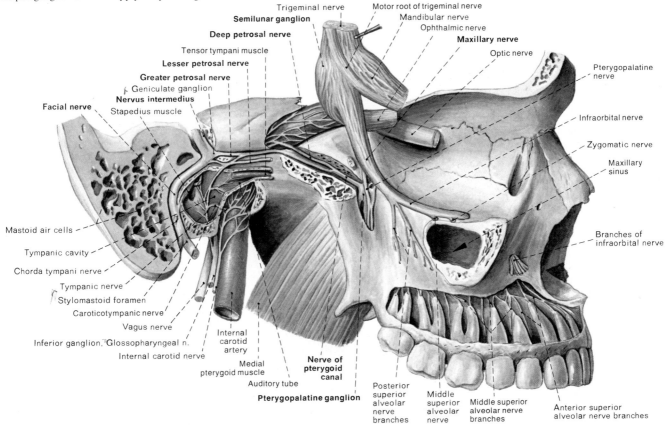

Fig. 695: The Maxillary Nerve, the Petrosal nerves and the Facial Nerve

NOTE that the nerve of the pterygoid canal is formed by the union of the deep petrosal and greater petrosal nerves. The deep petrosal nerve transmits postganglionic sympathetic fibers, while the greater petrosal nerve contains sensory fibers from the geniculate ganglion of the facial nerve and preganglionic parasympathetic fibers from the nervus intermedius portion of the facial nerve. The lesser petrosal nerve carries preganglionic fibers of the glossopharyngeal nerve to the otic ganglion.

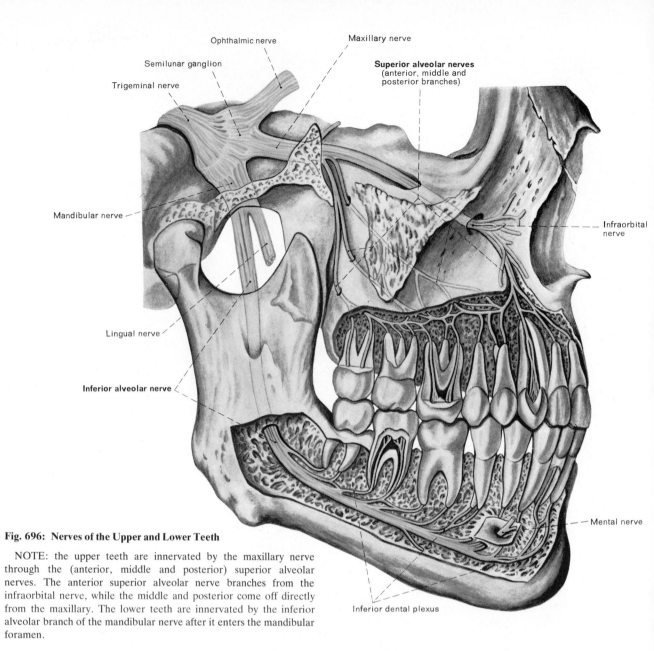

Ophthalmic nerve

Maxillary nerve

Semilunar ganglion

Superior alveolar nerves
(anterior, middle and
posterior branches)

Trigeminal nerve

Mandibular nerve

Infraorbital
nerve

Lingual nerve

Inferior alveolar nerve

Mental nerve

Inferior dental plexus

Fig. 696: Nerves of the Upper and Lower Teeth

NOTE: the upper teeth are innervated by the maxillary nerve through the (anterior, middle and posterior) superior alveolar nerves. The anterior superior alveolar nerve branches from the infraorbital nerve, while the middle and posterior come off directly from the maxillary. The lower teeth are innervated by the inferior alveolar branch of the mandibular nerve after it enters the mandibular foramen.

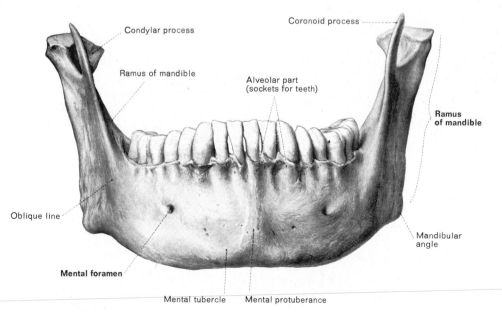

Condylar process

Coronoid process

Ramus of mandible

Alveolar part
(sockets for teeth)

**Ramus
of mandible**

Oblique line

Mandibular
angle

Mental foramen

Mental tubercle   Mental protuberance

Fig. 697: The Mandible as seen from the Front

NOTE: 1) the anterior aspect of the mandible forms the bony substructure of the mentum or chin. The two vertical rami of the mandible are continuous with the body of the mandible at the mandibular angle.

2) the mental foramen transmits the mental branch of the inferior alveolar nerve to the skin of the chin and lower lip on each side. The mental branch of the inferior alveolar artery accompanies the mental nerve and participates in the vascular supply of the lower lip.

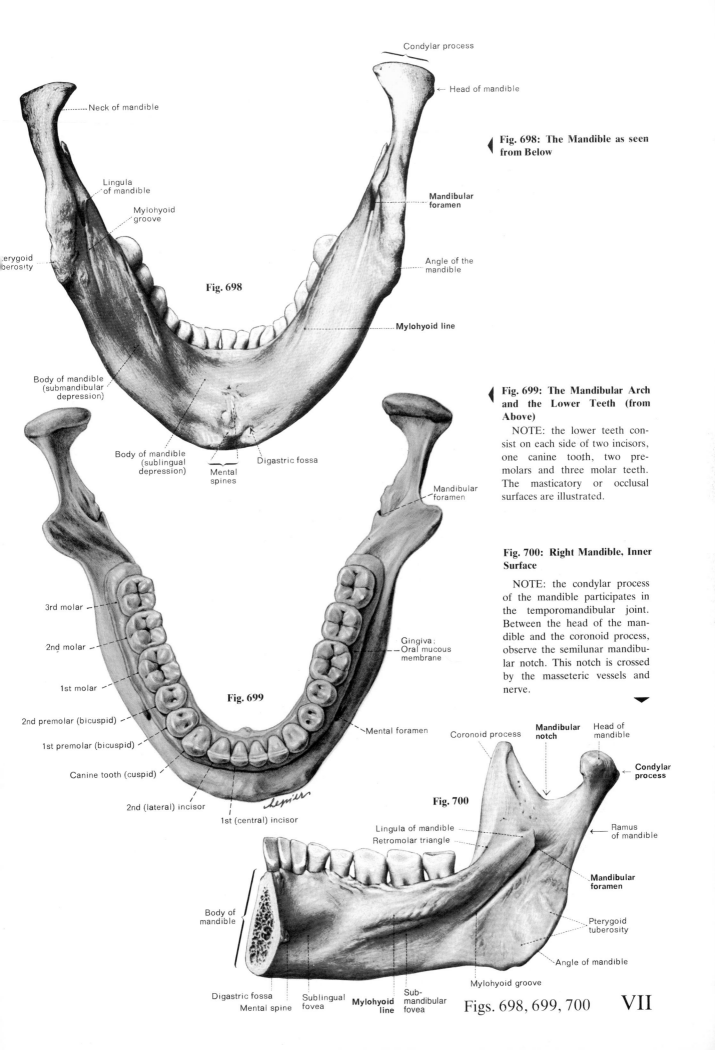

Neck of mandible

Condylar process

Head of mandible

Lingula of mandible

Mylohyoid groove

Mandibular foramen

Pterygoid tuberosity

Angle of the mandible

Fig. 698: The Mandible as seen from Below

Fig. 698

Mylohyoid line

Body of mandible (submandibular depression)

Body of mandible (sublingual depression)

Mental spines

Digastric fossa

Mandibular foramen

Fig. 699: The Mandibular Arch and the Lower Teeth (from Above)

NOTE: the lower teeth consist on each side of two incisors, one canine tooth, two premolars and three molar teeth. The masticatory or occlusal surfaces are illustrated.

Fig. 700: Right Mandible, Inner Surface

NOTE: the condylar process of the mandible participates in the temporomandibular joint. Between the head of the mandible and the coronoid process, observe the semilunar mandibular notch. This notch is crossed by the masseteric vessels and nerve.

3rd molar

2nd molar

1st molar

2nd premolar (bicuspid)

1st premolar (bicuspid)

Canine tooth (cuspid)

2nd (lateral) incisor

1st (central) incisor

Fig. 699

Gingiva; Oral mucous membrane

Mental foramen

Coronoid process

Mandibular notch

Head of mandible

Condylar process

Ramus of mandible

Lingula of mandible

Retromolar triangle

Mandibular foramen

Fig. 700

Body of mandible

Pterygoid tuberosity

Angle of mandible

Mylohyoid groove

Digastric fossa

Mental spine

Sublingual fovea

Mylohyoid line

Sub-mandibular fovea

Figs. 698, 699, 700   VII

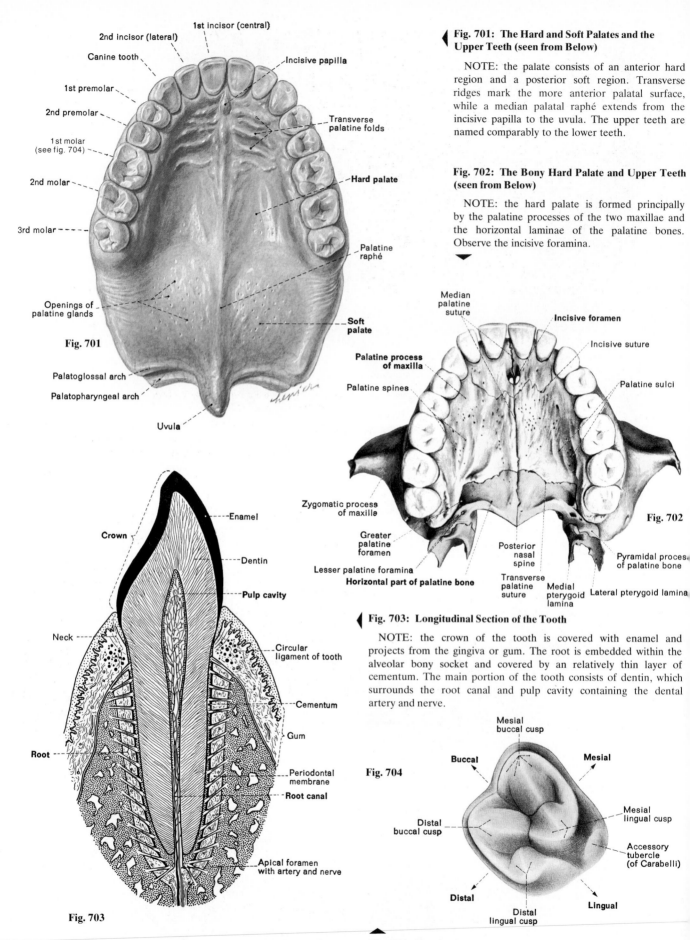

2nd incisor (lateral)

1st incisor (central)

Canine tooth

1st premolar

2nd premolar

1st molar (see fig. 704)

2nd molar

3rd molar

Openings of palatine glands

Fig. 701

Palatoglossal arch

Palatopharyngeal arch

Uvula

Incisive papilla

Transverse palatine folds

Hard palate

Palatine raphé

Soft palate

Fig. 701: The Hard and Soft Palates and the Upper Teeth (seen from Below)

NOTE: the palate consists of an anterior hard region and a posterior soft region. Transverse ridges mark the more anterior palatal surface, while a median palatal raphé extends from the incisive papilla to the uvula. The upper teeth are named comparably to the lower teeth.

Fig. 702: The Bony Hard Palate and Upper Teeth (seen from Below)

NOTE: the hard palate is formed principally by the palatine processes of the two maxillae and the horizontal laminae of the palatine bones. Observe the incisive foramina.

Median palatine suture

Incisive foramen

Incisive suture

Palatine process of maxilla

Palatine spines

Palatine sulci

Zygomatic process of maxilla

Greater palatine foramen

Lesser palatine foramina

Horizontal part of palatine bone

Posterior nasal spine

Transverse palatine suture

Medial pterygoid lamina

Lateral pterygoid lamina

Pyramidal process of palatine bone

Fig. 702

Crown

Enamel

Dentin

Pulp cavity

Neck

Circular ligament of tooth

Cementum

Gum

Root

Periodontal membrane

Root canal

Apical foramen with artery and nerve

Fig. 703

Fig. 703: Longitudinal Section of the Tooth

NOTE: the crown of the tooth is covered with enamel and projects from the gingiva or gum. The root is embedded within the alveolar bony socket and covered by an relatively thin layer of cementum. The main portion of the tooth consists of dentin, which surrounds the root canal and pulp cavity containing the dental artery and nerve.

Mesial buccal cusp

Buccal

Mesial

Fig. 704

Distal buccal cusp

Mesial lingual cusp

Accessory tubercle (of Carabelli)

Distal

Lingual

Distal lingual cusp

Fig. 704: The Occlusal Surface of the Right Upper First Molar

Figs. 701–704

in m	in l	c	pr 1	pr 2	mo 1	mo 2	mo 3

Superior

in m = Medial incisor
in l = Lateral incisor
c = Canine
pr 1 = 1st premolar
pr 2 = 2nd premolar
mo 1 = 1st molar
mo 2 = 2nd molar
mo 3 = 3rd molar

Inferior

Fig. 705

in m	in l	c	pr 1	pr 2	mo 1	mo 2	mo 3

▲ Fig. 705: The Maxillary and Mandibular Permanent Teeth (Buccal Surface)

Fig. 706: Diagram Showing Eruption Times of Permanent Upper Teeth

NOTE: on the left side of the illustration the times of eruption are shown in *years* for each tooth while the sequential order of appearance of the erupted *permanent* teeth is indicated on the right side by numbers.

6 to 8 Yr.
7 to 9 Yr.
9 to 13 Yr.
9 to 12 Yr.
10 to 13 Yr.
5 to 7 Yr.
11 to 14 Yr.
18 to 40 Yr.

Fig. 706

6 to 9 M.
8 to 12 M.
16 to 20 M.
12 to 16 M.
20 to 30 M.

Fig. 707

▲ Fig. 707: Diagram Showing Eruption Times of Deciduous Upper Teeth

NOTE: on the left side of the illustration the times of eruption are shown in *months* for each tooth, while the sequential order of appearance of the erupted *deciduous* teeth is indicated on the right side by numbers.

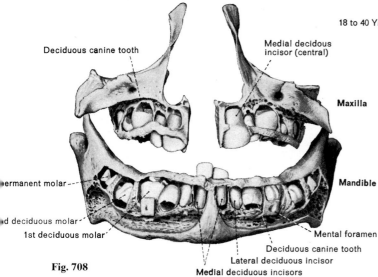

Deciduous canine tooth

Medial decidous incisor (central)

Maxilla

Mandible

Permanent molar
2nd deciduous molar
1st deciduous molar

Mental foramen
Deciduous canine tooth
Lateral deciduous incisor
Medial deciduous incisors

Fig. 708

◄ Fig. 708: Dentition of a Child of Nearly One Year of Age

NOTE: 1) the deciduous or "milk teeth" number 20 in all, including two incisors, one canine and two molars in each jaw quadrant. The earliest of these teeth to erupt are the incisors, which generally penetrate through the gum line before the end of the first year.

2) generally speaking:
a 1 year old child has 6 teeth,
a 1½ year old child has 12 teeth,
a 2 year old child has 16 teeth, and
a 2½ year old child has 20 teeth.

Figs. 705–708   **VII**

NOTE: 1) the deciduous teeth are shown as white, while the rudiments of the permanent teeth, shown in blue, have been exposed by removing the outer walls of the alveolar processes of both maxillae and the mandible.

2) all 20 deciduous teeth have erupted: eight incisors, four canines and eight molars. Normally, all the deciduous teeth are replaced by the 12th year.

Permanent lower
2nd molar tooth

Permanent lower
premolar teeth

Permanent lower
canine tooth

Deciduous
upper molars

Mandibular
canal

Permanent
lower 1st molar

Mental foramen

Permanent lower
incisors

Fig. 709

Fig. 710: The Maxillae and Mandible of a Nine Year Old Child

NOTE: 1) the deciduous teeth (white) have been partially replaced by the permanent teeth (blue). All eight permanent incisors (four upper and four lower) have grown into place, whereas the deciduous canine and molars are yet to be replaced by permanent teeth.

2) the deeply placed developing permanent canines. The permanent superior canines descend from positions in the maxilla lateral to the external nasal orifices (nares), and roots of the inferior canines develop from positions very deep in the mandible.

Upper permanent
canine tooth

Upper permanent
incisors

Lower permanent
incisors

Lower
deciduous
canine tooth

Lower permanent
1st premolar

Lower permanent
canine tooth

Fig. 710

Upper premolar
teeth

Upper canine
tooth

Lower canine
tooth

Upper 3rd molar

Mandibular
canal

Fig. 711

Mental foramen

Lower premolars

Lower 1st molar

Lower 2nd molar

Lower 3rd molar

Fig. 711: Dentition of a 20 Year Old Person, seen from the Left Side

NOTE: 1) the roots of the permanent teeth have been exposed by removal of the alveolar walls. Observe that all of the permanent teeth have erupted through the gums with the exception of the lower 3rd molar.

2) the canines and incisors have but one root, as generally do the premolars, although the latter teeth may have two roots. The 1st and 2nd molars usually have three roots, whereas the smaller 3rd molar may have less than three and may even be single rooted.

Figs. 709, 710, 711

Inl   Inm   Inm   Inl

Fig. 712: The Four Incisors

C   Inl   Inm

Fig. 713: The Two Right Incisors and Canine Teeth

Pr2   Pr1   C

Fig. 714: The Right Canine Tooth and Two Premolars

Mo3   Mo2   Mo1   Pr2

Fig. 715: The Right Second Premolar and Three Molars

Inl   Inm   Inm   Inl

Fig. 716: The Four Incisors

Inm   Inl   C   Pm1

Fig. 717: The Two Incisors, Canine and First Premolar

Pm1   Pm2   Mo1   Mo2

Fig. 718: The Two Premolars and First Two Molar Teeth

Mo1   Mo2   Mo3

Fig. 719: The Three Molar Teeth

Fig. 720: The Right Upper and Lower Teeth, Lateral View ▶

NOTE: 1) that the right upper eight and right lower eight teeth have been completely exposed by removal of the outer bony layers of the alveolar processes from both the maxilla and mandible. Each tooth has been cut along its longitudinal axis to reveal the pulp cavity and root canal.

2) the fine canaliculi leading to the root canals along which course the delicate vessels and nerves supplying the individual teeth.

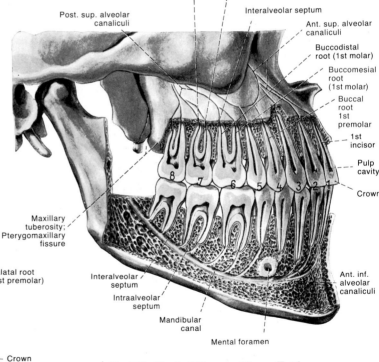

Alveolar foramen
Intraalveolar septum
Interalveolar septum
Post. sup. alveolar canaliculi
Ant. sup. alveolar canaliculi
Buccodistal root (1st molar)
Buccomesial root (1st molar)
Buccal root 1st premolar
1st incisor
Pulp cavity
Crown
Maxillary tuberosity; Pterygomaxillary fissure
Interalveolar septum
Intraalveolar septum
Mandibular canal
Mental foramen
Ant. inf. alveolar canaliculi

Hard palate
Palatal root (1st molar); Root canal
Palatal root (1st premolar)

...goid ...ulus
Maxillary ...erosity; ...ygomax. fissure
...ardibular canal
Interalveolar septum
Intraalveolar septum
Apex of root
Apex of root
Inf. alveolar canaliculus
Mental canal

Crown
Pulp cavity
Root
Apex of root
Ant. inf. alveolar canaliculi

L. SCHROTT

Fig. 721: The Left Upper and Lower Teeth, Medial View

NOTE that the inner aspect of the roots of the teeth on the left side have been exposed. Observe that the sockets for the canine teeth are the deepest, while those for the molar teeth are the widest. Interalveolar bony septa separate the sockets of individual teeth, and in the case of the multiple rooted molar teeth, intraalveolar septa separate each root.

Figs. 712–721   VII

Frontal sinus
Procerus muscle
Falx cerebri
Sphenoid sinus
Nasal bone
Medial pterygoid lamina;
Tendon and belly of tensor veli palatini muscle
Hypophyseal fossa
Palatine glands
Torus tubarius; **Levator veli palatini muscle**
Mucous membrane
of nasal septum
Pharyngeal tonsil; Lateral pterygoid muscle
Medial pterygoid muscle;
Sphenomandibular ligament
Hard palate
Ramus of mandible
Lateral cartilage of nose
Apical ligament of dens
Vibrissae
Tentorium
cerebelli
Cartilage of
apex of nose
Anterior atlanto
occipital memb
Median atlanto-
axial joint
Opening for
vertebral artery
and 1st cervical
Sebaceous glands
Transverse
ligament of atla
Orbicularis oris muscle
Labial glands
Posterior atlant
occipital memb
**Pterygoid hamulus;
Pterygomandibular
raphé;
Buccinator muscle**
**Styloid process
Styloglossus mu
Stylohyoid ligan**
Digastric muscle
Stylopharyngeus
Mylohyoid muscle
Opening for 2nd
cervical nerve
Mandible
**Stylomandibular
Stylohyoid musc**
Sublingual gland;
Sublingual caruncula
Longus capitis m
Genioglossus m.
Cervical fascia
Orbicularis oris m.
Greater horn
of hyoid bone
Hyoglossus m.
Thyrohyoid
membrane
Geniohyoid m.
Dura mater of the
vertebral canal
Mylohyoid muscle
Lesser horn of hyoid bone
Hyoid bone
Cervical fascia
Thyrohyoid muscle
Sternocleidomastoid muscle
Omohyoid muscle
Sternohyoid muscle
Cervical fascia

Fig. 722: Paramedian Sagittal View of the Face and Neck

NOTE: 1) this dissection has exposed the right half of the oral cavity and the nasal septum. The mucous membrane has been removed from the floor of the mouth exposing the mylohyoid muscle; the pharyngeal constrictors have been removed. Observe the pterygomandibular raphé and the buccinator muscle.

2) the tendon of the tensor veli palatini muscle as it turns medially around the pterygoid hamulus. The tendon has been severed at its insertion into the palatine aponeurosis. This muscle tightens the soft palate and, being derived from the first or mandibular branchial arch, it is innervated by the trigeminal nerve.

3) the stylohyoid ligament and the styloglossus and stylopharyngeus muscles which have been cut. These three structures all attach to the styloid process, as do the stylomandibular ligament and the stylohyoid muscles which have not been cut.

4) that the hyoid bone lies at the level of the third cervical vertebra and that the atlas (1st vertebra) and axis (2nd vertebra), which surround the uppermost part of the cervical spinal cord, lie directly behind the oral cavity and oropharynx. The spinomedullary junction and the lower medulla oblongata lie posterior to the palate and nasopharynx.

5) that the genioglossus and hyoglossus muscles have been cut. These attach the base and sides of the tongue to the mandible and hyoid bone.

Fig. 722

2) the *trigeminal field* (nerve of 1st branchial arch). The *dark blue* zones are supplied by the ophthalmic division of the trigeminal nerve through its anterior and posterior ethmoidal branches. This includes the mucosa of the anterior nasal cavity and the frontal sinus. At times the posterior ethmoidal branch reaches the sphenoid sinus.

The *blue-gray* zones, which include the posterior part of the nasal cavity, the upper nasopharynx, most of the palate and the upper gums of the oral cavity, are supplied by the maxillary division of the trigeminal nerve. This is achieved by branches from the greater and lesser palatine nerves and mucosal branches from the superior alveolar and superior labial nerves. Observe the *white dots* outlining the superior part of the nasal cavity. The mucosa at this site contains olfactory receptor cells for the special sense of smell.

The *blue-green* zones are supplied by the mandibular division of the trigeminal nerve. These include the anterior two-thirds of the tongue, the lower gums and lateral walls of the oral cavity by way of the lingual, buccal and inferior alveolar nerves. Note the *red dots* on the anterior tongue. These represent the field of the chorda tympani nerve which supplies the region with special sensory taste fibers.

3) the *glossopharyngeal field* (nerve of 3rd branchial arch). The *yellow* zones indicate the general sensory supply of the lingual and pharyngeal branches of the glossopharyngeal nerve. These include the posterior one-third of the tongue, part of the soft palate, the oropharynx and the lower part of the nasopharynx. The *white dots* indicate that this nerve also supplies the posterior one-third of the tongue with special sensory fibers of taste.

4) the *vagal field* (nerve of 4th and 6th branchial arches). The green zones represent fields supplied by fibers of general sensation from pharyngeal and laryngeal branches of the vagus nerve. These zones include the laryngopharynx, the larynx and trachea, as well as the esophagus.

723: The Sensory Fields of Cranial ~ves Supplying the Nasal and Oral Cavi- the Pharynx, Esophagus and Larynx

OTE: 1) various shades of *blue* = trige- ~l nerve; *yellow* = glossopharyngeal ~e; *green* = vagus nerve.

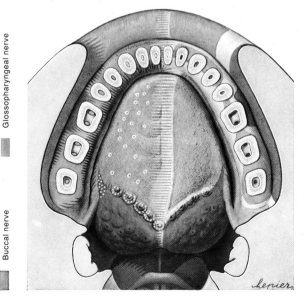

724: Sensory Innervation of the Tongue. Cheeks and Floor of the Cavity

OTE that on the right side are specific areas of distribution; on the left side, ~verlapping fields. *White circles:* taste zone of chorda tympani nerve; *white* ~ taste zone of glossopharyngeal nerve.

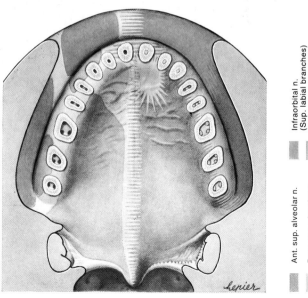

Fig. 725: Sensory Innervation of the Palate, Cheeks and Upper Gums of the Oral Cavity

NOTE that on the (reader's) left side are shown specific fields of distribution of the individual sensory nerves, while on the right side the overlapping fields of innervation are shown.

Nasal bone

Nasal septum (mucous membrane)

Opening of auditory tube; Torus tubarius

Spenoid sinus

Ala of vomer bone

Body of sphenoid bone

Nasal septum (cartilage)

Greater alar cartilage of nose

Pharyngeal tonsil and bursa;
Pharyngeal recess

Pharyngobasilar fascia
Anterior atlantooccipital membrane

Anterior arch of atlas;
Median atlantoaxial joint

Apical ligament of dens
Dura mater sheath for
hypoglossal nerve roots

Palatopharyngeal arch
Dura mater sheath for
vertebral artery and C-1 nerve

Transverse ligame
of atlas;
Occipital bone

Cutaneous portion of nasal septum

Nostril

Hard palate

Nasopharyngeal meatus;
Salpingopalatine fold;
Torus of lev. veli palatini m.

**Soft palate;
Salpingopharyngeal fold**
Sublingual caruncle
Genioglossus muscle

Mandible

Geniohyoid muscle

Mylohyoid muscle

Foramen cecum of tongue

Palatine tonsil

Hyoid bone

Median thyrohyoid lig.; Sternohyoid m. bursa

Hyoepiglottic ligament; **Cartilage of epiglottis**

Laryngeal fat pad

Thyroepiglottic ligament; **Thyroid cartilage**

**Vestibular fold; Ventrical of
larynx; Vocal fold**

Sup. thyroid a. and v. (cricothyroid branch);
Cricothyroid ligament

Arch of cricoid cartilage

Investing layer of cervical fascia

Pretracheal layer of cervical fascia

Isthmus of thyroid gland;
Paratracheal lymph node

Thyroid ima veins

Jugular venous arch

Interclavicular ligament;
Sternothyroid muscle

Manubrium of sternum

Left brachiocephalic vein

Thymus

Aortic arch;
Brachiocephalic
trunk

Cruciform ligament
of atlas

Pharyngoepiglottic fol

Dura mater sheaths
for spinal nerve roots

Cuneiform tubercle

Corniculate tubercle

Post. longitudinal ligament

Arytenoid muscle (transvers
Cricoid cartilage

Ant. longitudinal ligament

Epidural space

Dura mater

**Prevertebral layer
of cervical fascia**

Retroesophageal spa

Esophagus

Esophagotracheal space

Membranous wall of trachea

Trachea (anular ligaments and cartilages)

Fig. 726: The Viscera of the Head and Neck: Mid-sagittal Section

NOTE: 1) the closed oral cavity is occupied principally by the tongue. Observe that the posterior aspect of the oral cavity opens into the oropharanyx. Superiorly, the posterior nasal cavities are continuous with the nasopharynx, whereas inferiorly the laryngeal portion of the pharynx (between the levels of the epiglottis and cricoid cartilages) opens into the larynx.

2) the pharynx continues inferiorly as the esophagus, while the larynx becomes the trachea below the level of the cricoid cartilage.

3) during the act of swallowing (deglutition), as food is directed toward the posterior part of the oral cavity, the soft palate is both elevated and tensed (by the levator and tensor veli palatini muscles) and directed toward the posterior wall of the pharynx, thereby closing off the nasopharynx. Simultaneously the larynx is drawn superiorly toward the epiglottis to the level of the hyoid bone, and the pharynx also ascends. This action closes the laryngeal orifice, thereby preventing food from entering the larynx.

4) arrows I to V: surgical approaches to pharynx, larynx and trachea.

Fig. 726

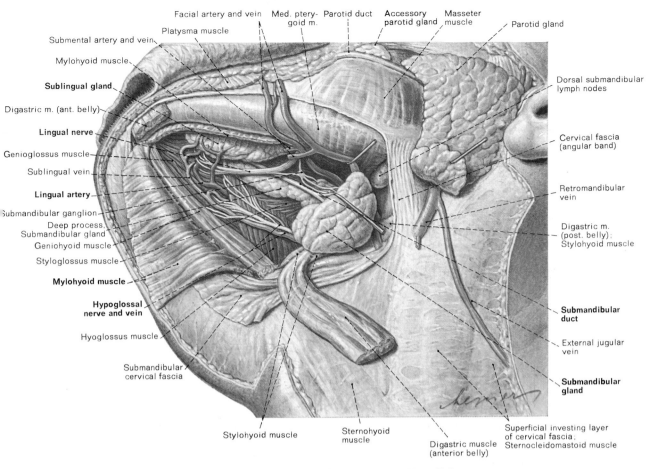

Facial artery and vein — Med. ptery- — Parotid duct — Accessory — Masseter — Parotid gland
gold m. — parotid gland — muscle

Platysma muscle

Submental artery and vein

Mylohyoid muscle

Sublingual gland

Digastric m. (ant. belly)

Lingual nerve

Genioglossus muscle

Sublingual vein

Lingual artery

Submandibular ganglion

Deep process;
Submandibular gland
Geniohyoid muscle

Styloglossus muscle

Mylohyoid muscle

**Hypoglossal
nerve and vein**

Hyoglossus muscle

Submandibular
cervical fascia

Dorsal submandibular
lymph nodes

Cervical fascia
(angular band)

Retromandibular
vein

Digastric m.
(post. belly);
Stylohyoid muscle

**Submandibular
duct**

External jugular
vein

**Submandibular
gland**

Stylohyoid muscle — Sternohyoid
muscle

Digastric muscle
(anterior belly)

Superficial investing layer
of cervical fascia;
Sternocleidomastoid muscle

Fig. 727: The Floor of the Oral Cavity Opened from the Submandibular Triangle, Viewed from Below

NOTE: 1) the anterior belly of the digastric muscle and the mylohyoid muscle have been reflected in order to reveal the following structures: the sublingual gland, the lingual nerve, the submandibular ganglion and duct, the hypoglossal nerve and vein and the lingual artery.

2) presynaptic parasympathetic fibers (VII) accompany the lingual nerve (V) to reach the submandibular ganglion, where they synapse with postganglionic neurons whose fibers innervate both the submandibular and sublingual glands.

3) the hypoglossal (XII) nerve is the motor nerve to all tongue muscles, except the palatoglossus, while the lingual nerve (V) supplies the anterior 2/3rds of the tongue with general sensation.

Fig. 728: The Mylohyoid and Geniohyoid Muscles (Viewed from Above)

NOTE that the mylohyoid muscles along with the geniohyoid muscles form the muscular floor of the oral cavity. The mylohyoids arise along the mylohyoid lines of the mandible and insert into the median fibrous raphé which extends from the hyoid bone to the symphysis menti. Observe that the genioglossal muscles have been severed near their origin.

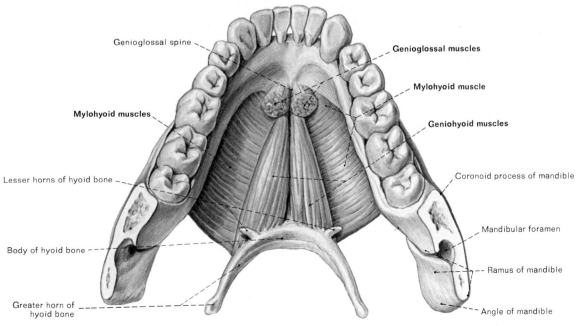

Genioglossal spine

Mylohyoid muscles

Lesser horns of hyoid bone

Body of hyoid bone

Greater horn of
hyoid bone

Genioglossal muscles

Mylohyoid muscle

Geniohyoid muscles

Coronoid process of mandible

Mandibular foramen

Ramus of mandible

Angle of mandible

Figs. 727, 728   VII

Fig. 729: The Oral Cavity

Frenulum of upper lip

Uvula and soft palate

Hard palate (palatine raphé)

Supratonsillar fossa

Palatopharyngeal arch

Buccinator m.

Posterior wall of oral pharynx

Palatoglossal arch

Buccal fat pad

Isthmus of the fauces

Cheek (cut)

Dorsum of tongue

Palatine tonsil

Gum (gingiva)

Fig. 729

Frenulum of lower lip

Vestibule of mouth

NOTE: 1) the position of the palatine tonsils located on each side of the oral cavity within fossae between the palatoglossal and palatopharyngeal arches. These soft folds are formed by correspondingly named muscles covered by oral mucous membrane (see Figure 731).

2) the passage between the oral cavity and the oral pharynx is called the fauces. This aperture or isthmus commences anteriorly at the palatoglossal arches on each side and is also bounded by the soft palate superiorly and the dorsum of the tongue inferiorly.

3) that portion of the oral cavity between the teeth and the lips anteriorly, and between the teeth and cheeks laterally, is called the vestibule. The vestibule communicates with the larger oral cavity proper behind the 3rd molar teeth.

Fig. 731: The Palate: Muscular Folds and Glands

NOTE: the oral mucosa has been removed from both the hard and soft palate revealing the palatal musculature, vessels and glands. Observe the palatoglossus and palatopharyngeus muscles along with the greater and lesser palatine nerves and vessels. A branch of the lesser palatine artery contributes to the tonsillar blood supply.

Levator labii superioris m.

Parotid duct

Orbicularis oris m.

Labial glands

Buccal glands

Levator anguli oris m.

Parotid duct

Zygomaticus major muscle

Buccinator muscle (inner surface)

Buccal glands

Risorius muscle

Fig. 730

Buccinator m. (outer surface)

Buccal and labial glands

Depressor labii inferioris m.

Mucous membrane of lip

Mentalis m.

Orbicularis oris m.

Fig. 730: The Lips Viewed from Within the Oral Cavity

NOTE: 1) this dissection demonstrates the muscles of the mouth from within the oral cavity after the oral mucous membrane has been removed. Observe the numerous small labial glands.

2) the contour of the lips as they surround the oral orifice depends on the arrangement of the muscular bundles which interlace at the labial margins. These include the elevators and depressors of the lips and their angles, along with the orbicularis oris and buccinator muscles.

3) the fibers of the buccinator muscle converging at the angle of the mouth. Many of these fibers decussate, becoming continuous with the fibers of the orbicularis oris muscle of both the upper and lower lips.

Figs. 729, 730

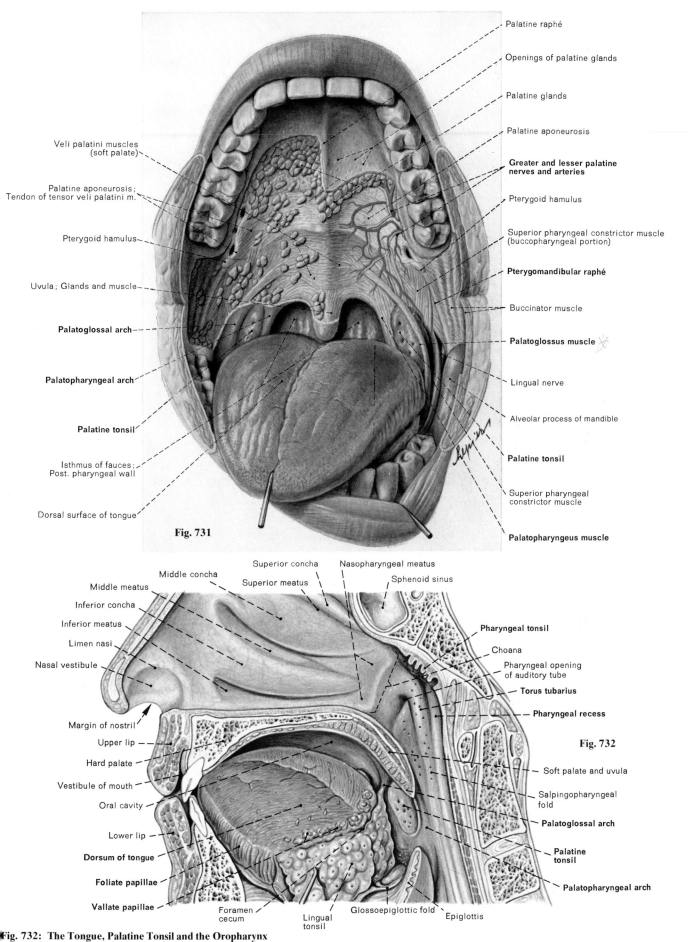

Fig. 731

Palatine raphé

Openings of palatine glands

Palatine glands

Palatine aponeurosis

Greater and lesser palatine nerves and arteries

Pterygoid hamulus

Superior pharyngeal constrictor muscle (buccopharyngeal portion)

Pterygomandibular raphé

Buccinator muscle

Palatoglossus muscle

Lingual nerve

Alveolar process of mandible

Palatine tonsil

Superior pharyngeal constrictor muscle

Palatopharyngeus muscle

Veli palatini muscles (soft palate)

Palatine aponeurosis; Tendon of tensor veli palatini m.

Pterygoid hamulus

Uvula; Glands and muscle

Palatoglossal arch

Palatopharyngeal arch

Palatine tonsil

Isthmus of fauces; Post. pharyngeal wall

Dorsal surface of tongue

Middle concha

Superior concha

Superior meatus

Nasopharyngeal meatus

Sphenoid sinus

Middle meatus

Inferior concha

Inferior meatus

Limen nasi

Nasal vestibule

Margin of nostril

Upper lip

Hard palate

Vestibule of mouth

Oral cavity

Lower lip

Dorsum of tongue

Foliate papillae

Vallate papillae

Foramen cecum

Lingual tonsil

Glossoepiglottic fold

Epiglottis

Pharyngeal tonsil

Choana

Pharyngeal opening of auditory tube

Torus tubarius

Pharyngeal recess

Fig. 732

Soft palate and uvula

Salpingopharyngeal fold

Palatoglossal arch

Palatine tonsil

Palatopharyngeal arch

Fig. 732: The Tongue, Palatine Tonsil and the Oropharynx

NOTE: 1) in this sagittal view, the tongue has been deviated to demonstrate the right palatoglossal arch and right palatine tonsil. Observe the large vallate papillae.

2) the opening of the auditory tube in the nasopharynx behind which is a cartilaginous elevation of the tube called the torus tubarius. Note also the pharyngeal tonsil (adenoids).

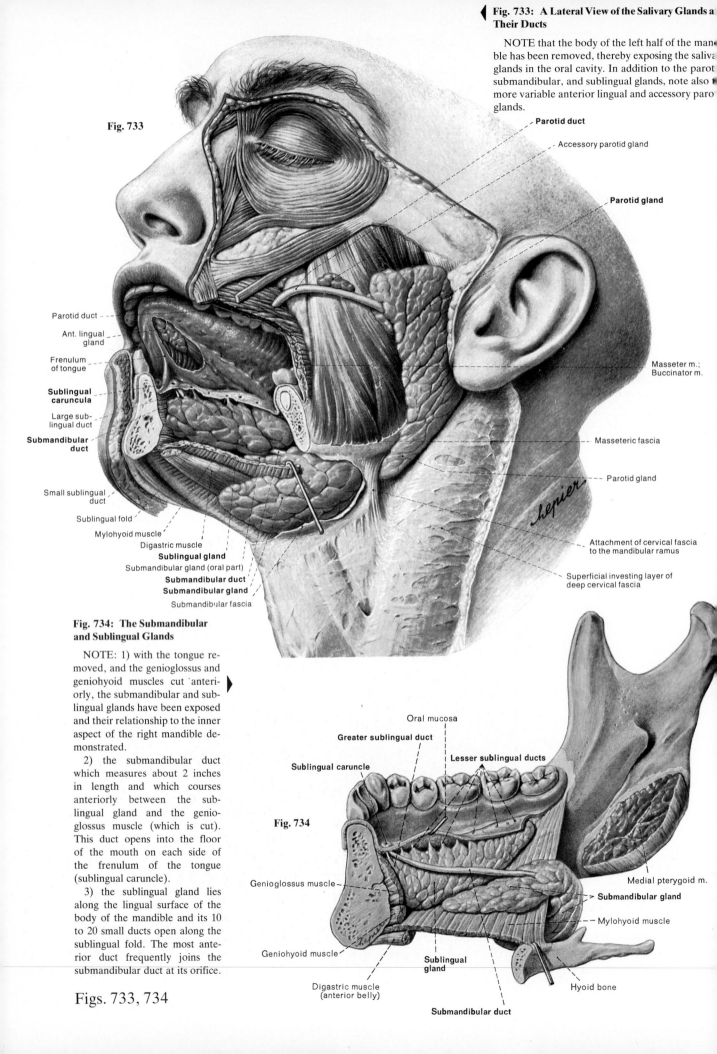

Fig. 733: A Lateral View of the Salivary Glands a[nd] Their Ducts

NOTE that the body of the left half of the man[di]ble has been removed, thereby exposing the saliva[ry] glands in the oral cavity. In addition to the parot[id,] submandibular, and sublingual glands, note also [the] more variable anterior lingual and accessory paro[tid] glands.

Parotid duct

Accessory parotid gland

Parotid gland

Fig. 733

Masseter m.;
Buccinator m.

Parotid duct

Ant. lingual gland

Frenulum of tongue

Sublingual caruncula

Large sublingual duct

Submandibular duct

Masseteric fascia

Parotid gland

hepier

Small sublingual duct

Sublingual fold

Mylohyoid muscle

Digastric muscle

Sublingual gland

Submandibular gland (oral part)

Submandibular duct

Submandibular gland

Submandibular fascia

Attachment of cervical fascia to the mandibular ramus

Superficial investing layer of deep cervical fascia

Fig. 734: The Submandibular and Sublingual Glands

NOTE: 1) with the tongue removed, and the genioglossus and geniohyoid muscles cut anteriorly, the submandibular and sublingual glands have been exposed and their relationship to the inner aspect of the right mandible demonstrated.

2) the submandibular duct which measures about 2 inches in length and which courses anteriorly between the sublingual gland and the genioglossus muscle (which is cut). This duct opens into the floor of the mouth on each side of the frenulum of the tongue (sublingual caruncle).

3) the sublingual gland lies along the lingual surface of the body of the mandible and its 10 to 20 small ducts open along the sublingual fold. The most anterior duct frequently joins the submandibular duct at its orifice.

Figs. 733, 734

Oral mucosa

Greater sublingual duct

Lesser sublingual ducts

Sublingual caruncle

Fig. 734

Genioglossus muscle

Medial pterygoid m.

Submandibular gland

Mylohyoid muscle

Geniohyoid muscle

Sublingual gland

Hyoid bone

Digastric muscle (anterior belly)

Submandibular duct

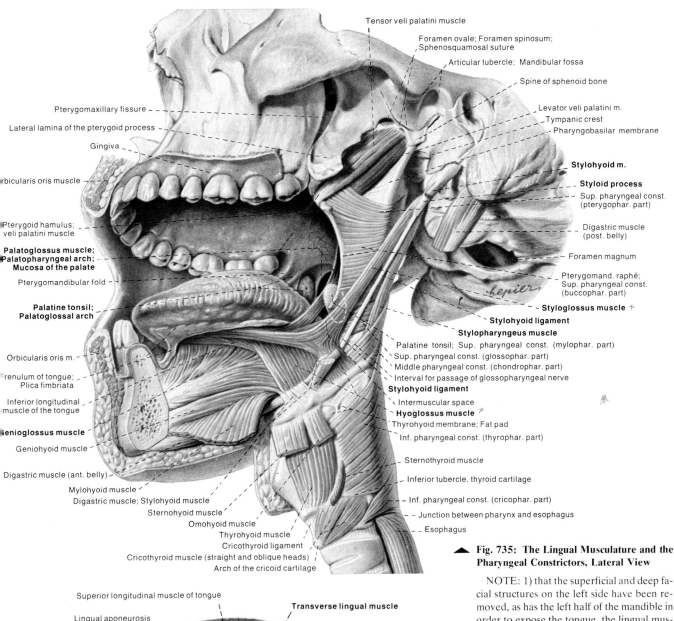

Tensor veli palatini muscle

Foramen ovale; Foramen spinosum;
Sphenosquamosal suture

Articular tubercle; Mandibular fossa

Spine of sphenoid bone

Pterygomaxillary fissure

Lateral lamina of the pterygoid process

Gingiva

rbicularis oris muscle

Pterygoid hamulus;
veli palatini muscle

**Palatoglossus muscle;
Palatopharyngeal arch;
Mucosa of the palate**

Pterygomandibular fold

**Palatine tonsil;
Palatoglossal arch**

Orbicularis oris m.

renulum of tongue;
Plica fimbriata

Inferior longitudinal
muscle of the tongue

enioglossus muscle

Geniohyoid muscle

Digastric muscle (ant. belly)

Mylohyoid muscle

Digastric muscle; Stylohyoid muscle

Sternohyoid muscle

Omohyoid muscle

Thyrohyoid muscle

Cricothyroid ligament

Cricothyroid muscle (straight and oblique heads)

Arch of the cricoid cartilage

Levator veli palatini m.

Tympanic crest

Pharyngobasilar membrane

Stylohyoid m.

Styloid process

Sup. pharyngeal const.
(pterygophar. part)

Digastric muscle
(post. belly)

Foramen magnum

Pterygomand. raphé;
Sup. pharyngeal const.
(buccophar. part)

Styloglossus muscle †

Stylohyoid ligament

Stylopharyngeus muscle

Palatine tonsil; Sup. pharyngeal const. (mylophar. part)

Sup. pharyngeal const. (glossophar. part)

Middle pharyngeal const. (chondrophar. part)

Interval for passage of glossopharyngeal nerve

Stylohyoid ligament

Intermuscular space

Hyoglossus muscle ⚹

Thyrohyoid membrane; Fat pad

Inf. pharyngeal const. (thyrophar. part)

Sternothyroid muscle

Inferior tubercle, thyroid cartilage

Inf. pharyngeal const. (cricophar. part)

Junction between pharynx and esophagus

Esophagus

Superior longitudinal muscle of tongue

Lingual aponeurosis

Lingual mucosa

Transverse lingual muscle

Septum of the tongue

Foramen cecum

wer lip

stibule
mouth

Lingual tonsil

Vallecula of
epiglottis

Cartilage
of epi-
glottis

dible

oglossus
muscle

Superior
aperture
of larynx

Mylohyoid muscle

**Geniohyoid
muscle**

Hyoid
bone

Thyroid
cartilage

Ventricle of larynx

▲ **Fig. 735: The Lingual Musculature and the
Pharyngeal Constrictors, Lateral View**

NOTE: 1) that the superficial and deep facial structures on the left side have been removed, as has the left half of the mandible in
order to expose the tongue, the lingual muscles, and the pharyngeal constrictors. Observe
that the buccinator has been removed but
that the superior pharyngeal constrictor is
still attached to the pterygomandibular raphé.

2) that the stylohyoid muscle has been cut,
but the stylohyoid ligament and the stylopharyngeus and styloglossus muscles are still intact. Observe the hyoglossus, geniohyoid,
and genioglossus muscles and that the palatoglossus descends into the tongue from the
soft palate.

◀ **Fig. 736: The Genioglossus and the Intrinsic Muscles of the Tongue**

NOTE: 1) that in this mid-sagittal section
can be seen the median fibrous septum of the
tongue and that the intrinsic tongue musculature includes the longitudinal, transverse,
and vertical muscles of the tongue.

2) that the genioglossus constitutes most of
the tongue musculature and that its fibers radiate backward and upward in a fan-like
manner from the uppermost of the mental
spines (genial tubercles) on the inner surface
of the mandible, just above the origin of the
geniohyoid muscles.

Figs. 735, 736   **VII**

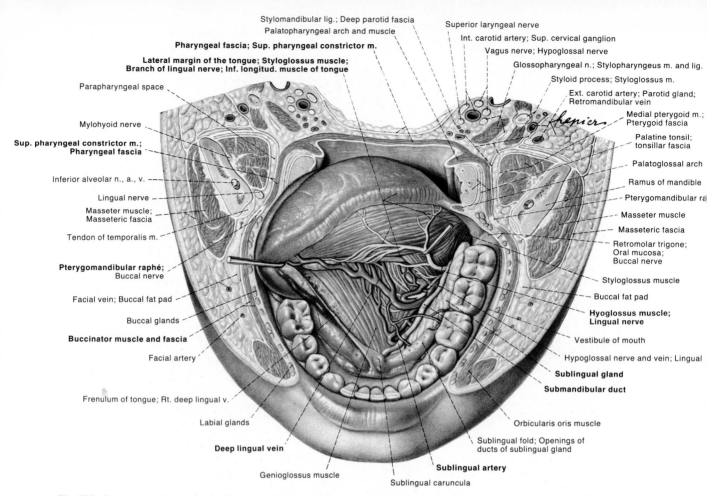

Fig. 737: Vessels and Nerves in the Floor of the Oral Cavity, Viewed from Above and Anteriorly, Stage 1: With Salivary Glands in Place

NOTE that the tongue has been deflected to the (specimen's) right, and the left lingual nerve and vessels and the hypoglossal nerve, sublingual gland and submandibular duct exposed in the floor of the oral cavity. Observe also that the lateral walls of the oral cavity and the oropharynx have been cut in cross section, showing the muscles of mastication laterally, the buccinator muscles medially and the superior pharyngeal constrictor posteriorly.

Fig. 738: Anterior Sublingual Region, Superficial View

NOTE that the mucous membrane covering the floor of the oral cavity continues over the inferior surface of the tongue, meeting at the midline as an elevated fold called the frenulum of the tongue. Observe the sublingual folds. Along these open the ducts of the sublingual glands, and at their anterior end on each side is an orifice for the submandibular duct called the sublingual caruncula.

Fig. 739: Frontal Section Through the Tongue, Sublingual and Submandibular Regions

NOTE the locations of the lingual nerve, submandibular duct and hypoglossal nerve and its accompanying vein. Observe that the mylohyoid muscle separates the sublingual and submandibular regions.

Figs. 737, 738, 739

Labels on the figure:

Sympathetic trunk
Vagus nerve; Internal jugular vein
Ascending pharyngeal artery; Cervical fat pad;
Superior laryngeal nerve; Internal carotid artery
Hypoglossal nerve
Glossopharyngeal nerve
Pharyngeal fascia; Retropharyngeal space;
Deep cervical fascia (prevertebral layer)
External carotid artery;
Retromandibular vein

Ascending
palatine art.
(from facial art.)

Lingual n.;
Mylohyoid n. and art.;
Mandibular n.;
Inf. alveolar
art. and vein

Pterygomandibular
raphé; Retromolar
trigone of mandible;
Branch of lingual n.;
Tendon, Temporalis m.;
Masseteric n. a. v.

Submandibular
ganglion;
Lingual nerve

Hypoglossal nerve
and accompanying v.;
Sublingual nerve

Buccal nerve branches
(from trigeminal n.)

Facial vein

Facial artery

Buccal nerve branches
(from trigeminal n.)

Inferior labial branches of
mental artery and nerve

ngual nerve (branches
to the tongue)

Artery and vein of the
apex of the tongue

renulum of the tongue

Deep lingual artery;
lingual nerve (commun. br. with XII);
Lingual artery;
Submandibular nerve

Sublingual artery; Submandibular duct;
Major sublingual duct; Sublingual caruncula

Sublingual vessels and nerve;
Minor sublingual duct

Gingiva; Interdental papilla

Fig. 740: Vessels and Nerves in the Floor of the Oral Cavity, Viewed from Above and Anteriorly, Stage 2: With the Sublingual Gland Mobilized and the Vestibule of the Mouth Exposed

A = Dorsum of the tongue	J = Sup. pharyng. constrictor m.	S = Ramus of mandible
B = Posterior wall of the pharynx	K = Genioglossus muscle	T = Med. pterygoid muscle
C₁ = Sup. long. muscle of tongue	L = Hyoglossus muscle	U = Parotid gland
C₂ = Inf. long. muscle of tongue	M = Sublingual gland	U₁ = Stylomandibular lig.
D = Styloglossus muscle	M₁ = Submandibular gland	V = Buccal fat pad
E = Palatoglossus muscle	N = Mylohyoid muscle	W = Digastric m. (ant. belly)
F = Palatopharyngeus muscle	O = Buccinator muscle	X₁ = Stylopharyngeus muscle
G = Glossopharyngeal part ⎱ Sup. pharyng.	P = Depressor labii inf. m.	X₂ = Styloglossus muscle
H₁ = Mylopharyngeal part ⎰ constrictor	Q = Orbicularis oris muscle	X₃ = Stylohyoid muscle
H₂ = Buccopharyngeal part ⎰ muscle	R = Masseter muscle	Y = Styloid process

NOTE: 1) that the tongue has been directed to the right, and the sublingual gland (M) has been elevated from its bed; this exposes the intraoral portion of the submandibular gland (M₁) and the mylohyoid muscle (N). Observe the submandibular ganglion attached to the lingual nerve. Preganglionic parasympathetic fibers course to this ganglion successively by way of the nervus intermedius (facial nerve), chorda tympani, and lingual nerves. These fibers synapse in the ganglion and then the postganglionic fibers course forward again through the lingual nerve to the sublingual and submandibular glands.

2) the branches of the buccal nerve that supply the mucous membrane lining the vestibule of the mouth. These are sensory nerves and are derived from the mandibular division of the trigeminal nerve. Observe that the vestibule is limited by the cheeks and lips externally and by the teeth and gums internally.

Fig. 740   VII

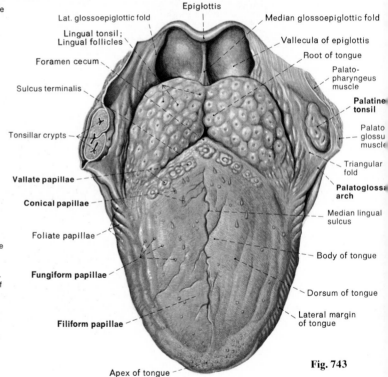

Apex of tongue
Plica fimbriata
Septum of tongue
Mucous membrane
Inferior longitudinal muscle of tongue
Hyoglossus muscle
Genioglossus muscle
Palatoglossus muscle
Styloglossus muscle
Chondroglossus muscle (part of hyoglossus arising from lesser horn of hyoid)
Middle pharyngeal constrictor muscle
Hyoglossus muscle
Hyoglossus muscle
Geniohyoid muscles
Hyoid bone (greater horn)
Superior laryngeal n.a.v.
Inferior pharyngeal constrictor muscle
Thyrohyoid muscle
Subhyoid bursa; Med. thyrohyoid ligament
Laryngeal prominence
Omohyoid muscle
Sternohyoid muscle

Fig. 741: Extrinsic Muscles of the Tongue (seen from Below)

NOTE: 1) the tongue is attached to three bony structures by way of extrinsic muscles. The genioglossus, hyoglossus and styloglossus muscles each blend into the tongue musculature from their respective bony origins: the mental spine of the mandible, the hyoid bone and the styloid process.

2) in this dissection the symphysis of the mandible has been removed from its position anterior to the base of the tongue. Thus, the severed geniohyoid and genioglossaι muscles can be observed.

3) the base of the tongue is attached to the hyoid bone by way of the hyoglossus. Arising from the body and greater horn of the hyoid bone, the hyoglossus courses vertically to insert into the tongue medial to the fibers of the styloglossus.

4) the styloglossus is a thin muscle which descends from the styloid process to insert on the lateral aspect of the tongue in relationship to the hyoglossus and the inferior longitudinal muscle of the tongue (which is an intrinsic muscle). Observe also the palatoglossal muscle inserting into the side of the tongue, somewhat anterior and superior to the styloglossus.

Geniculate ganglion
Chorda tympani n.
Nucleus of tractus solitarius
Lingual n.
Glossopharyngeal n.

Fig. 742

Epiglottis
Lat. glossoepiglottic fold
Median glossoepiglottic fold
Lingual tonsil; Lingual follicles
Vallecula of epiglottis
Foramen cecum
Root of tongue
Palato-pharyngeus muscle
Sulcus terminalis
Palatine tonsil
Tonsillar crypts
Palato glossu muscle
Triangular fold
Vallate papillae
Palatoglossa arch
Conical papillae
Median lingual sulcus
Foliate papillae
Body of tongue
Fungiform papillae
Dorsum of tongue
Lateral margin of tongue
Filiform papillae
Apex of tongue

Fig. 743

Fig. 742: The Principal Pathways for Taste

NOTE: 1) that the two principal pathways for taste are by means of the chorda tympani nerve for the anterior two-thirds of the tongue and the glossopharyngeal nerve for the posterior one-third of the tongue;

2) that two lesser pathways also exist (not shown in this figure). From the epiglottis, taste fibers enter the brain by way of the internal laryngeal branch of the vagus, and taste fibers from the palate course through the palatine nerves and nerve of the pterygoid canal to the greater petrosal nerve and nervus intermedius of the facial nerve.

Fig. 743: Dorsal Surface of the Tongue

NOTE:1) the dorsum of the tongue is marked by numerous elevations called papillae. These serve as receptor sites for the special sense of taste. Observe the inverted V-shaped group of large vallate papillae.

2) the fungiform papillae which are found principally at the sides and apex of the tongue. These are relatively large and round and have a deep red color.

3) the filiform (conical) papillae. These are very small and generally arranged in rows which course parallel to the vallate papillae.

Figs. 741, 742, 743

Fig. 744: The Extrinsic Tongue Muscles: the External Larynx and Pharynx (Lateral View 1)

NOTE: 1) the posterior fibers of the genioglossus draw the tongue forward, while its anterior fibers retract the tongue back into the mouth. The hyoglossus depresses the tongue, while the styloglossus elevates the tongue and pulls it backward. All three of these muscles and the intrinsic tongue muscles as well are innervated by the hypoglossal nerve.

2) the inferior pharyngeal constrictor arises from the cricoid and thyroid cartilages, while the middle pharyngeal constrictor arises from the entire length of the greater horn of the hyoid bone, from the stylohyoid ligament and from the lessern horn (seen in Fig. 745).

3) the thyrohyoid muscle covering the lateral surface of the thyroid cartilage and the two parts of the cricothyroid muscle.

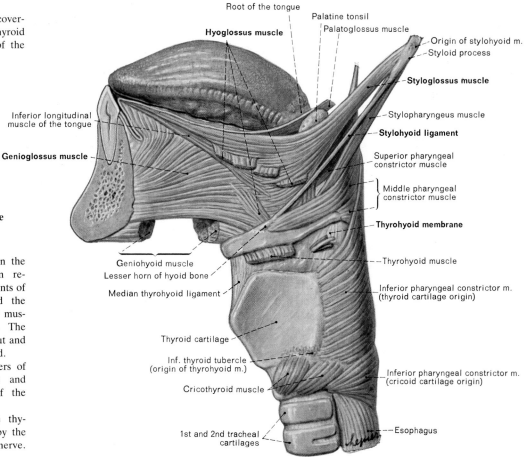

Fig. 745: The Extrinsic Tongue Muscles: the External Larynx and Pharynx (Lateral View 2)

NOTE: 1) in this dissection the hyoglossus muscle has been removed, revealing the attachments of the stylohyoid ligament and the middle pharyngeal constrictor muscle along the hyoid bone. The geniohyoid muscle has been cut and the thyrohyoid muscle removed.

2) the blending of the fibers of the styloglossus, hyoglossus and genioglossus at the base of the tongue.

3) the penetration of the thyrohyoid membrane laterally by the internal laryngeal vessels and nerve.

Figs. 744, 745   VII

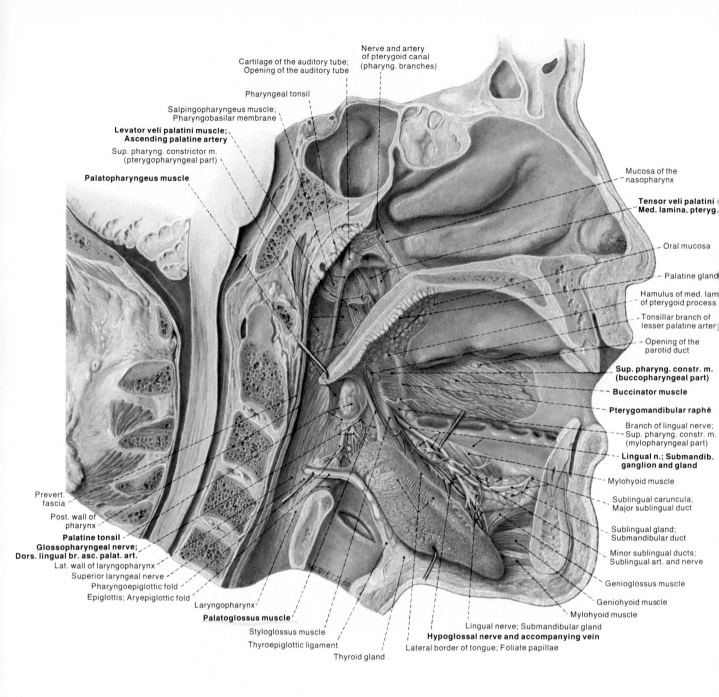

Nerve and artery
of pterygoid canal
(pharyng. branches)

Cartilage of the auditory tube;
Opening of the auditory tube

Pharyngeal tonsil

Salpingopharyngeus muscle;
Pharyngobasilar membrane

**Levator veli palatini muscle;
Ascending palatine artery**

Sup. pharyng. constrictor m.
(pterygopharyngeal part)

Palatopharyngeus muscle

Mucosa of the
nasopharynx

**Tensor veli palatini
Med. lamina, pteryg.**

Oral mucosa

Palatine gland

Hamulus of med. lam
of pterygoid process

Tonsillar branch of
lesser palatine arter

Opening of the
parotid duct

**Sup. pharyng. constr. m.
(buccopharyngeal part)**

Buccinator muscle

Pterygomandibular raphé

Branch of lingual nerve;
Sup. pharyng. constr. m.
(mylopharyngeal part)

**Lingual n.; Submandib.
ganglion and gland**

Mylohyoid muscle

Sublingual caruncula;
Major sublingual duct

Sublingual gland;
Submandibular duct

Minor sublingual ducts;
Sublingual art. and nerve

Genioglossus muscle

Geniohyoid muscle

Mylohyoid muscle

Lingual nerve; Submandibular gland

Hypoglossal nerve and accompanying vein

Lateral border of tongue; Foliate papillae

Lateral border of tongue; Foliate papillae

Prevert.
fascia

Post. wall of
pharynx

Palatine tonsil
**Glossopharyngeal nerve;
Dors. lingual br. asc. palat. art.**

Lat. wall of laryngopharynx

Superior laryngeal nerve

Pharyngoepiglottic fold

Epiglottis; Aryepiglottic fold

Laryngopharynx

Palatoglossus muscle

Styloglossus muscle

Thyroepiglottic ligament

Thyroid gland

**Fig. 746: The Left Side of the Oral Cavity and Pharynx, Viewed From the Right, Stage 1: Muscles in the Nasopharynx and Oropharynx and the
Nerves and Vessels at the Base of the Tongue and Within the Oral Cavity**

NOTE: 1) that the mucosa has been stripped from the surface of the palatoglossus and styloglossus muscles anterior to the palatine tonsil. Observe the glossopharyngeal nerve which has been dissected in the oropharynx below the palatine tonsil, near the base of the tongue. At this point, the glossopharyngeal nerve is entirely sensory, supplying both general sensation and the special sense of taste to the posterior one-third of the tongue.

2) the levator and tensor veli palatini muscles coursing toward the soft palate on the lateral side of the posterior opening of the nasal cavity. Observe the cartilaginous auditory tube and the delicate salpingopharyngeus muscle. This muscle arises from the inferior part of the cartilage of the auditory tube and its fibers descend to blend with the palatopharyngeus muscle prior to inserting into the pharyngeal wall. The salpingopharyngeus muscle elevates the lateral wall of the pharynx and with other muscles helps to displace the pharynx upward during swallowing.

3) the buccinator and the superior pharyngeal constrictor muscle (buccopharyngeal part), which becomes visible after removal of the mucosa on the inner surface of the cheek. See the pterygomandibular raphé at which these two muscles are juxtaposed. Turn to Figure 722 and observe that this raphé is formed by decussating tendon-like fibers and that it extends from the hook-like hamulus of the medial pterygoid plate of the sphenoid bone to the posterior end of the mylohyoid line on the inner surface of the mandible.

4) the hypoglossal nerve coursing toward the tongue with the accompanying vein to the hypoglossal nerve. This nerve supplies all of the intrinsic muscles of the tongue (i. e., the longitudinal, vertical, and transverse) and all of the extrinsic muscles of the tongue except the palatoglossus muscle. Thus, the styloglossus, hyoglossus (including the chondroglossus), and the genioglossus muscles are all supplied by the hypoglossal nerve, while the palatoglossus is supplied by the pharyngeal branch of the vagus nerve.

Fig. 746

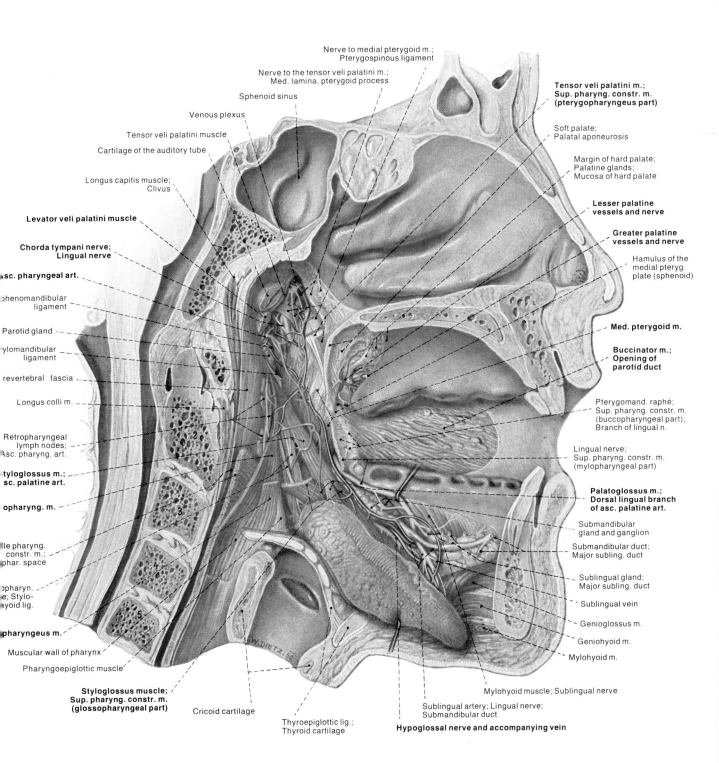

Nerve to medial pterygoid m.;
Pterygospinous ligament

Nerve to the tensor veli palatini m.;
Med. lamina, pterygoid process

Sphenoid sinus

Venous plexus

Tensor veli palatini muscle

Cartilage of the auditory tube

Longus capitis muscle;
Clivus

Levator veli palatini muscle

**Chorda tympani nerve;
Lingual nerve**

sc. pharyngeal art.

phenomandibular
ligament

Parotid gland

ylomandibular
ligament

revertebral fascia

Longus colli m.

Retropharyngeal
lymph nodes;
Asc. pharyng. art.

tyloglossus m.;
sc. palatine art.

opharyng. m.

le pharyng.
constr. m.;
phar. space

opharyn.
e; Stylo-
yoid lig.

pharyngeus m.

Muscular wall of pharynx

Pharyngoepiglottic muscle

**Styloglossus muscle;
Sup. pharyng. constr. m.
(glossopharyngeal part)**

Cricoid cartilage

Thyroepiglottic lig.;
Thyroid cartilage

Hypoglossal nerve and accompanying vein

**Tensor veli palatini m.;
Sup. pharyng. constr. m.
(pterygopharyngeus part)**

Soft palate;
Palatal aponeurosis

Margin of hard palate;
Palatine glands;
Mucosa of hard palate

**Lesser palatine
vessels and nerve**

**Greater palatine
vessels and nerve**

Hamulus of the
medial pteryg.
plate (sphenoid)

Med. pterygoid m.

**Buccinator m.;
Opening of
parotid duct**

Pterygomand. raphé;
Sup. pharyng. constr. m.
(buccopharyngeal part);
Branch of lingual n.

Lingual nerve;
Sup. pharyng. constr. m.
(mylopharyngeal part)

**Palatoglossus m.;
Dorsal lingual branch
of asc. palatine art.**

Submandibular
gland and ganglion

Submandibular duct;
Major subling. duct

Sublingual gland;
Major subling. duct

Sublingual vein

Genioglossus m.

Geniohyoid m.

Mylohyoid m.

Mylohyoid muscle; Sublingual nerve

Sublingual artery; Lingual nerve;
Submandibular duct

**Fig. 747: The Left Side of the Oral Cavity and Pharynx, Viewed From the Right, Stage 2: Exposure of the Pharyngeal, Palatine, and Oral Vessels
and Nerves After Dissection of the Pharyngeal Muscles and Mucosa**

NOTE: 1) that in the lateral wall of the nasopharynx, the cartilaginous auditory tube and the salpingopharyngeus muscle have been cut and removed, as have the levator and tensor veli palatini muscles. Additionally, the superior constrictor muscle (all of its parts: pterygo, bucco, mylo, and glosso; see Figs. 749 and 750) has been cut in such a way that the medial pterygoid muscle becomes visible from this medial view (see also Fig. 722).

2) that above and behind the medial pterygoid muscle, the lingual nerve has been exposed at the site at which it is joined at an acute angle by the chorda tympani nerve. The lingual nerve descends to the oral cavity, coursing lateral to the medial pterygoid muscle. It then enters the oral cavity just below the pterygomandibular raphé, a short distance behind the last molar tooth, where it is covered only by mucous membrane. The lingual nerve can again be seen lateral to the styloglossus, where it passes forward toward the tip of the tongue. The lingual nerve is the general sensory nerve to the anterior two-thirds of the tongue, but also it supplies the floor of the oral cavity and the inner surface of the mandibular gums.

3) that in the oropharynx, both the palatoglossus and palatopharyngeus muscles have been cut and the palatine tonsil has been removed. This allows a more complete exposure of the glossopharyneal nerve deep in the tonsillar bed. Observe also the ascending pharyngeal artery (a branch of the external carotid artery) and the ascending palatine artery (a branch of the facial artery) in the oropharynx.

Fig. 747   VII

Procerus muscle

Nasalis muscle

Lev. labii sup. alaeque nasi m.

Levator labii superioris m.

Zygomaticus major m.

Zygomaticus minor m.

Levator anguli oris m.

Parotid duct; Buccinator muscle

** Zygomaticus major muscle

Orbicularis oris muscle

Depressor anguli oris muscle

Mentalis muscle

Platysma muscle

Anterior belly of digastric m.

Mylohyoid muscle

Sternohyoid muscle

Omohyoid muscle

Thyrohyoid muscle

Thyroid cartilage

Cricothyroid muscle

Tracheal cartilages

Lateral pterygoid plate

Zygomatic arch

Tensor veli palatini muscle

Levator veli palatini muscle

Articular capsule of temporomandibular joint

An accessory muscular fascicle

External acoustic meatus

Pharyngobasilar fascia

Pterygoid hamulus; Pterygomandibular rap

Stylohyoid muscle

Occipital condy

Mastoid process

Post. belly of digastric m.

Styloid process; Stylohyoid lig.

Styloglossus muscle

Stylopharyngeus muscle

Post. belly of digastric m.

Stylohyoid muscle

Middle pharyngeal constrictor muscle

Greater horn of hyoid bone

Superior laryngeal artery, nerve and vein

Thyrohyoid membrane

Inferior pharyngeal constrictor muscle

Esophagus

Fig. 748: The Oropharyngeal Muscles (Lateral View)

NOTE: 1) the tendinous pterygomandibular raphé. This structure extends between the pterygoid hamulus superiorly and the mylohyoid line of the mandible inferiorly, and serves as a common site of origin for the buccinator and superior pharyngeal constrictor muscles.

2) the origin of the superior constrictor is divisible into four parts: from the hamulus of the medial pterygoid plate (1); from the pterygomandibular raphé (2); from the mylohyoid line of the mandible (3); and by certain fibers which blend with tongue muscle fibers and whose origin emerges from the side of the tongue (4).

3) the middle constrictor arises from the greater and lesser horns of the hyoid bone, while the larger and thicker inferior constrictor arises from the thyroid and cricoid cartilages.

Sup. pharyngeal constrictor m.

Stylopharyngeus muscle

Middle pharyngeal constrictor m.

Inf. pharyngeal constrictor m.

Cricothyroid muscle

Fig. 749: Diagram of the Origins of the Pharyngeal Constrictor Muscles

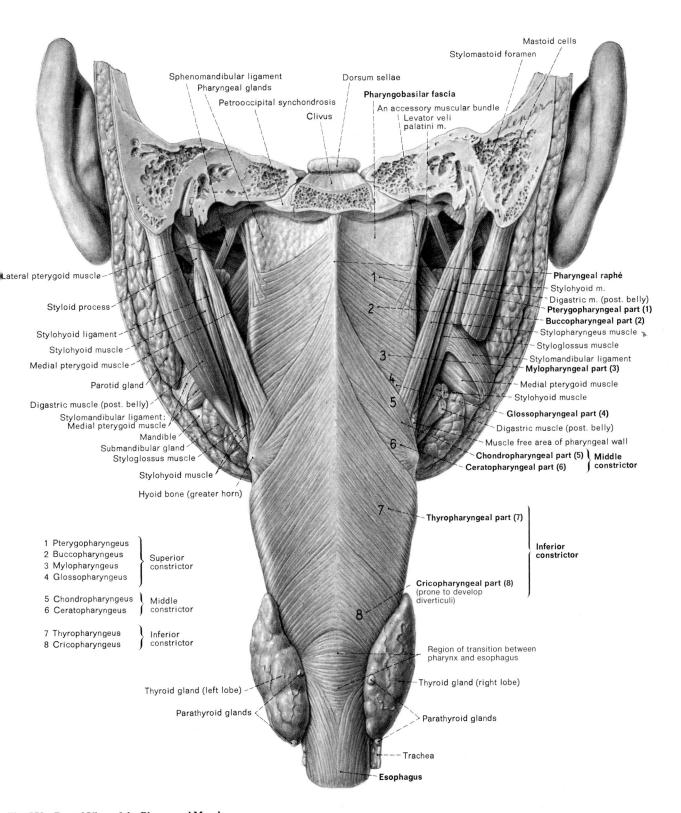

Mastoid cells
Stylomastoid foramen
Sphenomandibular ligament
Pharyngeal glands
Dorsum sellae
Pharyngobasilar fascia
Petrooccipital synchondrosis
Clivus
An accessory muscular bundle
Levator veli palatini m.

Lateral pterygoid muscle
Styloid process
Stylohyoid ligament
Stylohyoid muscle
Medial pterygoid muscle
Parotid gland
Digastric muscle (post. belly)
Stylomandibular ligament;
Medial pterygoid muscle
Mandible
Submandibular gland
Styloglossus muscle
Stylohyoid muscle
Hyoid bone (greater horn)

Pharyngeal raphé
Stylohyoid m.
Digastric m. (post. belly)
Pterygopharyngeal part (1)
Buccopharyngeal part (2)
Stylopharyngeus muscle
Styloglossus muscle
Stylomandibular ligament
Mylopharyngeal part (3)
Medial pterygoid muscle
Stylohyoid muscle
Glossopharyngeal part (4)
Digastric muscle (post. belly)
Muscle free area of pharyngeal wall
Chondropharyngeal part (5) } **Middle**
Ceratopharyngeal part (6) } **constrictor**

Thyropharyngeal part (7)
Inferior constrictor
Cricopharyngeal part (8)
(prone to develop diverticuli)
Region of transition between pharynx and esophagus
Thyroid gland (right lobe)
Parathyroid glands

1 Pterygopharyngeus
2 Buccopharyngeus } Superior constrictor
3 Mylopharyngeus
4 Glossopharyngeus

5 Chondropharyngeus } Middle
6 Ceratopharyngeus } constrictor

7 Thyropharyngeus } Inferior
8 Cricopharyngeus } constrictor

Thyroid gland (left lobe)
Parathyroid glands
Trachea
Esophagus

Fig. 750: Dorsal View of the Pharyngeal Muscles

NOTE: 1) this posterior view of the pharynx was achieved by making a frontal transection through the petrous and mastoid portions of the temporal bones and through the body of the occipital bone. The styloid processes and their muscular attachments have been left intact.

2) the arrangement of the divisions of the pharyngeal constrictors. Their muscle fibers arise laterally to insert in a posterior median pharyngeal raphé. The superior constrictor is divisible into four parts while the middle and inferior constrictor are each divisible into two. Above the superior constrictor, observe the fibrous pharyngobasilar fascia which attaches to the basal portion of the occipital bone and to the temporal bones. Below the inferior constrictor, the pharynx is continuous with the muscular esophagus.

3) the *superior* and *middle constrictor* muscles and the *thyropharyngeal part of the inferior constrictor* are innervated by the pharyngeal branch of the vagus nerve. These fibers have their cell bodies in the nucleus ambiguus in the brain stem, emerge from the brain with the rootlets of the bulbar part of the accessory nerve and then, by a communicating branch, join the vagus. The cricopharyngeal part of the inferior constrictor is supplied by the recurrent laryngeal branch of the vagus nerve.

Fig. 750   VII

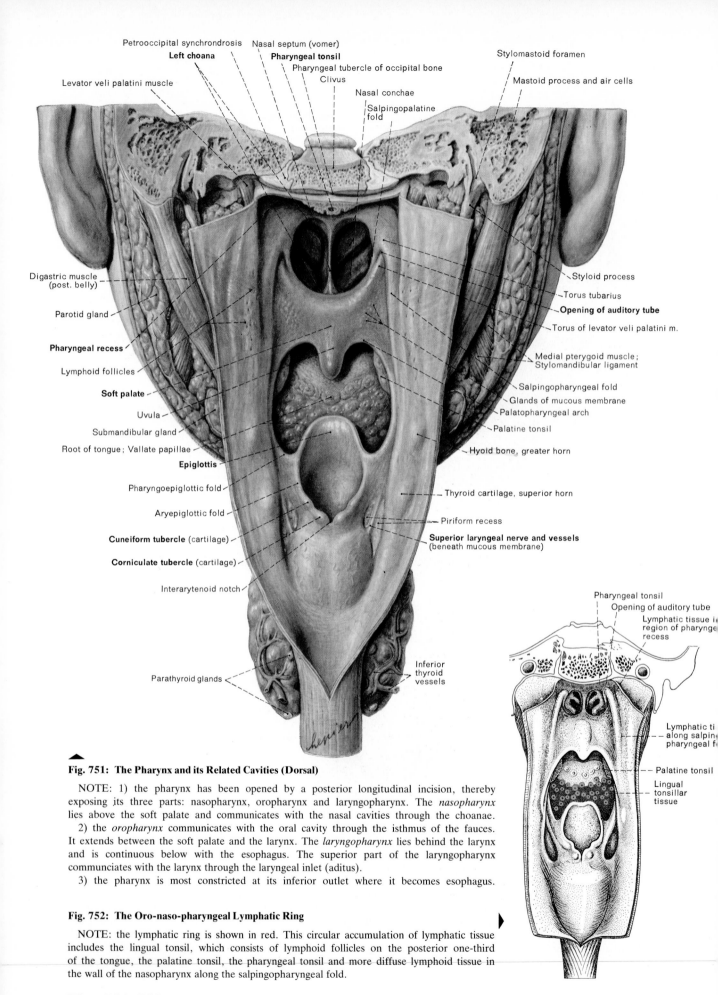

Petrooccipital synchrondrosis
Left choana
Levator veli palatini muscle
Nasal septum (vomer)
Pharyngeal tonsil
Pharyngeal tubercle of occipital bone
Clivus
Nasal conchae
Salpingopalatine fold
Stylomastoid foramen
Mastoid process and air cells

Digastric muscle (post. belly)
Parotid gland
Pharyngeal recess
Lymphoid follicles
Soft palate
Uvula
Submandibular gland
Root of tongue; Vallate papillae
Epiglottis
Pharyngoepiglottic fold
Aryepiglottic fold
Cuneiform tubercle (cartilage)
Corniculate tubercle (cartilage)
Interarytenoid notch
Parathyroid glands

Styloid process
Torus tubarius
Opening of auditory tube
Torus of levator veli palatini m.
Medial pterygoid muscle; Stylomandibular ligament
Salpingopharyngeal fold
Glands of mucous membrane
Palatopharyngeal arch
Palatine tonsil
Hyoid bone, greater horn
Thyroid cartilage, superior horn
Piriform recess
Superior laryngeal nerve and vessels (beneath mucous membrane)
Inferior thyroid vessels

Pharyngeal tonsil
Opening of auditory tube
Lymphatic tissue i region of pharynge recess
Lymphatic ti along salpin pharyngeal f
Palatine tonsil
Lingual tonsillar tissue

Fig. 751: The Pharynx and its Related Cavities (Dorsal)

NOTE: 1) the pharynx has been opened by a posterior longitudinal incision, thereby exposing its three parts: nasopharynx, oropharynx and laryngopharynx. The *nasopharynx* lies above the soft palate and communicates with the nasal cavities through the choanae.

2) the *oropharynx* communicates with the oral cavity through the isthmus of the fauces. It extends between the soft palate and the larynx. The *laryngopharynx* lies behind the larynx and is continuous below with the esophagus. The superior part of the laryngopharynx communciates with the larynx through the laryngeal inlet (aditus).

3) the pharynx is most constricted at its inferior outlet where it becomes esophagus.

Fig. 752: The Oro-naso-pharyngeal Lymphatic Ring

NOTE: the lymphatic ring is shown in red. This circular accumulation of lymphatic tissue includes the lingual tonsil, which consists of lymphoid follicles on the posterior one-third of the tongue, the palatine tonsil, the pharyngeal tonsil and more diffuse lymphoid tissue in the wall of the nasopharynx along the salpingopharyngeal fold.

Figs. 751, 752

Cartilaginous auditory tube
Pharyngobasilar fascia
Nasal septum
Nasal conchae
Pharyngeal tonsil
Cartilages of **auditory tube**
Petrooccipital synchrondrosis
Levator veli palatini m.

Opening of auditory tube

Pharyngobasilar fascia

Levator veli palatini m.
Digastric muscle (post. belly)
alpingopharyngeus muscle (insertion)

Palatopharyngeus muscle

Pharyngeal constrictor muscles

Epiglottis

Greater horn of hyoid bone

Stylopharyngeus muscle

Aryepiglottic fold and muscle

Arytenoid muscles (oblique and transverse)

Posterior cricoarytenoid muscle

Cricoesophageal tendon

Sphenomandibular ligament
Lateral pterygoid muscle
Styloid process;
Stylopharyngeus m.;
Stylohyoid m.
Medial pterygoid muscle
Tensor veli palatini muscle and tendon
Superior pharyngeal constrictor m.
Pterygoid hamulus
Levator veli palatini muscle
Uvula and muscle
Dorsum of tongue
Palatine tonsil
Vallate papillae
Foramen cecum; Sulcus terminalis
Root of tongue; Lingual tonsil
Mucous membrane of isthmus of fauces
Pharyngoepiglottic fold
Inlet of the larynx (aditus)
Sup. horn of thyroid cartilage
Cuneiform cartilage (tubercle)
Corniculate cartilage (tubercle)
Interarytenoid notch
Superior laryngeal nerve and vessels (fold)
Piriform recess

Thyroid gland, Right lobe
Parathyroid glands

Tracheal cartilages
Esophagus

III = Laryngopharynx
II = Oropharynx
I = Nasopharynx

Fig. 753: Muscles of the Soft Palate, Pharynx, and Posterior Larynx

NOTE: 1) the dissection in this figure is similar to that in Figure 751. The pharynx has been opened dorsally by a midline incision and the mucous membrane has been removed from the soft palate, pharynx and the left posterior larynx. On the right side, a portion of the levator veli palatini muscle has been removed in order to expose the adjacent belly and tendon of the tensor veli palatini muscle.

2) the muscles of the soft palate. Both the muscle of the uvula and the levator veli palatini muscle are innervated by the vagus and accessory nerve contributions to the pharyngeal plexus, whereas the tensor veli palatini muscle is innervated by the mandibular division of the trigeminal nerve.

3) the palatopharyngeus muscle arising by two fascicles from the soft palate. The muscle fibers of these two fascicles arise posterior and anterior to the insertion of the levator veli palatini muscle. The fascicles descend and merge and then insert into the posterior border of the thyroid cartilage and onto the adjacent pharyngeal wall.

Fig. 753   VII

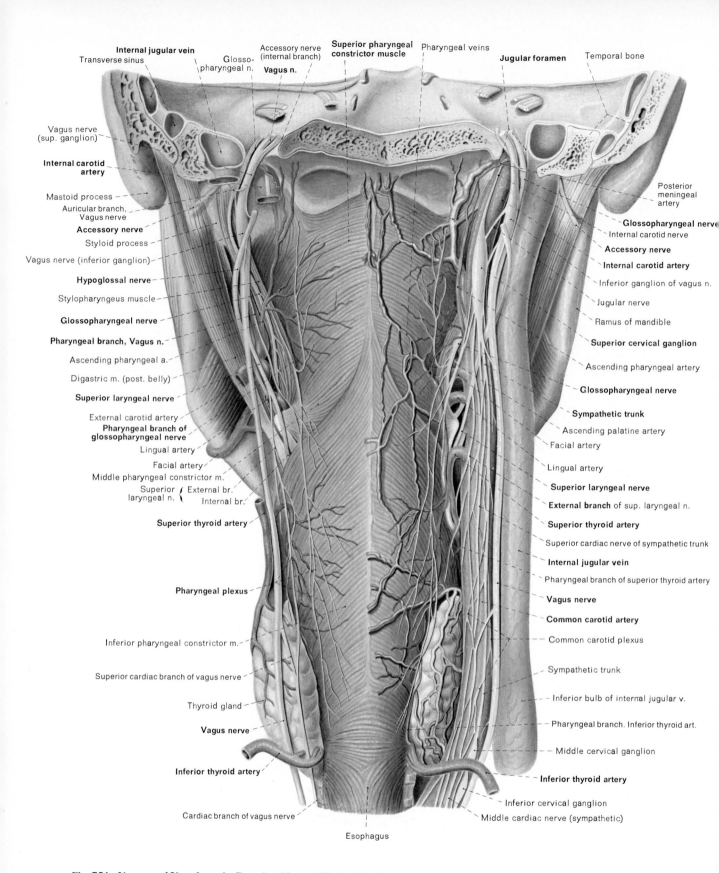

Fig. 754: Nerves and Vessels on the Dorsal and Lateral Walls of the Pharynx

NOTE: 1) the head has been split longitudinally. The pharynx, larynx and facial structures were separated from the vertebral column and its associated muscles. This posterior view of the pharynx also shows the large nerves and blood vessels which course through the neck. On the right side, observe the carotid artery, internal jugular vein, vagus nerve and sympathetic trunk.

2) on the left side, the glossopharyngeal and hypoglossal nerves were exposed by the removal of the carotid arteries and internal jugular vein. Along with the jugular vein, the jugular foramen transmits the 9th, 10th and 11th cranial nerves.

3) the thyroid gland and its superior and inferior thyroid arteries. The superior and middle thyroid veins drain into the internal jugular vein, while the inferior thyroid veins (not shown) usually drain into the left brachiocephalic vein.

Fig. 754

Vagus n.
Accessory nerve (internal branch)
Pharyngeal tonsil
Cartilage and opening of auditory tube
Hypoglossal n.
Glossopharyngeal nerve
Pharyngo-basilar fascia
Vagus n.
Accessory n.

VII VIII V III   III V
VI   VI   VII VIII

Sigmoid portion of transverse sinus
Int. jugular vein
Vagus nerve (inferior ganglion)
Accessory n. (ext. branch)
Ext. branch of accessory n.
Occipital artery
Mastoid process
Internal carotid artery
Hypoglossal nerve
Superior cervical ganglion
Digastric muscle (post. belly)
Tensor veli palatini m.
Superior pharyngeal constrictor m.
Torus tubarius
Salpingopharyngeus muscle
Palatopharyngeus muscle
Uvula
Salpingopharyngeal fold
Root of tongue; Vallate papillae
Palatine tonsil
Palatopharyngeal arch
Epiglottis
Pharyngoepiglottic fold
Pharyngoepiglottic muscle
Greater horn of hyoid bone
Aryepiglottic fold
Superior laryngeal nerve, artery and vein
Cuneiform tubercle (cartilage)
Corniculate tubercle (cartilage)
Aryepiglottic muscle
Fold of superior laryngeal nerve;
Arytenoid muscle (oblique and transverse)
Piriform recess
Interarytenoid notch
Right vagus nerve
Posterior cricoarytenoid muscle
Left vagus nerve
Sympathetic trunk; Carotid plexus
Esophageal muscles (circular and longitudinal)
Thyroid gland
Superior parathyroid gland
Middle cervical ganglion
Inferior parathyroid gland
Inferior thyroid artery
Inferior cervical ganglion
Thyrocervical trunk
Thyrocervical trunk
Superior cardiac branch (vagus nerve)
Internal jugular vein
Internal jugular v. (inferior bulb)
1st thoracic ganglion
Right subclavian artery
Left subclavian artery and vein
Right subclavian vein
Right vagus nerve
Left brachiocephalic vein
Right recurrent laryngeal nerve
Left common carotid artery
Right brachiocephalic vein
Left recurrent laryngeal nerve
Trachea and tracheal glands
Left vagus nerve
Brachiocephalic trunk
Superior vena cava
Arch of aorta

Fig. 755: Posterior View of Cervical Viscera: Muscles, Vessels and Nerves

NOTE: 1) in this posterior view of the vessels and nerves of the neck, the dorsal wall of the pharynx has been opened longitudinally, revealing the nasal, oral and laryngeal orifices which communicate with the pharynx. Observe the superior laryngeal artery, vein and nerve entering the larynx from above.

2) the recurrent laryngeal nerves ascending from the thorax to the larynx in the tracheoesophageal groove. On the left side, the recurrent laryngeal nerve courses around the arch of the aorta to reach this groove, while on the right side the recurrent laryngeal nerve curves around the subclavian artery.

3) the inferior cervical ganglion (at the level of 7th cervical vertebra). This ganglion is fused with the 1st thoracic sympathetic ganglion in about 80% of cases. The fused 1st thoracic and inferior cervical ganglion is called the stellate ganglion.

Fig. 755   VII

Plica fimbriata

Anastomosing branch,
Lingual artery

Genioglossus muscles

Sublingual gland

**Sublingual artery
and vein**

Sublingual artery

Sublingual nerve

Lingual nerve

Hyoglossus muscle

Deep lingual artery

Sublingual artery

Lingual artery

Hyoglossus muscle

Superior thyroid art.

Ext. carotid artery

Geniohyoid muscle

Hyoid bone

Cricothyroid muscle

Branches of superior
thyroid artery

Isthmus of thyroid gland

Lingual nerve

Deep lingual artery

Styloglossus muscle

Deep lingual veins

Hypoglossal nerve

Lingual vein

Hyoglossus muscle

Ext. carotid artery

Internal laryngeal n.

Superior thyroid art.

Superior laryngeal a.

Thyrohyoid membrane

Common carotid art.

Thyroid cartilage

Cricothyroid ligament

Trachea

Fig. 756: Ventral View of Larynx, Tongue and Thyroid Gland: Vessels and Nerves

NOTE: 1) the superior thyroid arteries descending to the thyroid gland. In their course they give off the superior laryngeal arteries, which penetrate the thyrohyoid membrane to gain entrance to the interior of the larynx, accompanied by the internal laryngeal branch of the superior laryngeal nerve. Observe also the cranial and medial course of the lingual artery deep to the hyoglossus muscle and its suprahyoid, sublingual and deep lingual branches.

2) the lingual nerves as they enter the tongue to supply its anterior two-thirds with general sensation. The motor nerve to the tongue is the hypoglossal, and it is seen coursing along with accompanying veins (venae comitantes). The hypoglossal nerve enters the base of the tongue just above the hyoid bone, passing anteriorly across the external carotid and lingual arteries.

3) that the common carotid artery bifurcates at about the level of the upper border of the thyroid cartilage. Observe also that the lingual artery branches from the external carotid above the hyoid bone, while the superior laryngeal artery arises at the level of the thyrohyoid membrane.

Fig. 757: The Cartilages and Ligaments of the Larynx (Ventral View)

NOTE: 1) the laryngeal cartilages comprise the skeletal framework of the larynx and they are interconnected by ligaments and membranes. There are *three larger unpaired* cartilages, the cricoid, thyroid and epiglottis and *three sets of paired* cartilages, the arytenoid, cuneiform and corniculate. In this anterior view the unpaired cricoid, thyroid and epiglottis cartilages are all visible.

2) the thyrohyoid membrane and the centrally located thyrohyoid ligament. Attached at the cranial border of the thyroid cartilage, this membrane stretches across the posterior surfaces of the greater horns of the hyoid bone. The medial thyrohyoid ligament extends from the thyroid notch to the body of the hyoid bone. The membrane is pierced by the superior laryngeal vessels and the internal laryngeal nerve.

3) the cricothyroid ligament attaching the contiguous margins of the cricoid and thyroid cartilages. This is a strong ligament and its lateral portions underlie the cricothyroid muscles. Below, the cricotracheal ligament connects the inferior margin of the cricoid cartilage with the first tracheal ring.

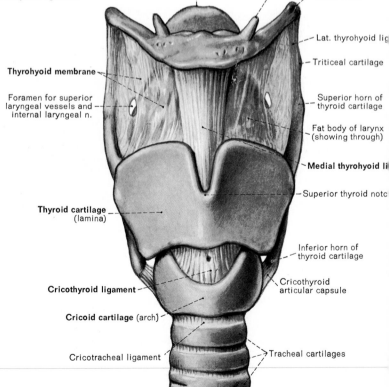

Epiglottis

Lesser horn of
hyoid bone

Greater horn of
hyoid bone

Lat. thyrohyoid lig.

Triticeal cartilage

Superior horn of
thyroid cartilage

Fat body of larynx
(showing through)

Medial thyrohyoid li

Superior thyroid notc

Inferior horn of
thyroid cartilage

Cricothyroid
articular capsule

Tracheal cartilages

Thyrohyoid membrane

Foramen for superior
laryngeal vessels and
internal laryngeal n.

Thyroid cartilage
(lamina)

Cricothyroid ligament

Cricoid cartilage (arch)

Cricotracheal ligament

Figs. 756, 757

Fig. 758: Dorsal View of Larynx, Tongue and Thyroid Gland: Vessels and Nerves

NOTE: 1) the glossopharyngeal nerves (IX) as they enter the root or pharyngeal part of the tongue in order to supply the posterior one-third of the surface of the tongue with both general sensation and the special sense of taste. Observe the relationship of the tonsillar branch of the ascending palatine artery with the glossopharyngeal nerve.

2) the courses of the internal branch of the superior laryngeal nerve and the recurrent laryngeal nerve. The internal branch of the superior laryngeal nerve is sensory to the laryngeal mucous membrane as far down as the level of the vocal folds. The recurrent laryngeal nerve is the principal motor nerve of the larynx and supplies all laryngeal muscles except the cricothyroid (which is supplied by the external branch of the superior laryngeal nerve). Additionally, the recurrent nerve supplies sensory innervation to the mucous membrane of the larynx below the level of the vocal folds.

3) the relationships of recurrent laryngeal nerves to the inferior thyroid artery and its inferior laryngeal branches. Observe also the proximity of the recurrent laryngeal nerves to the posterior aspect of the thyroid glands.

Vallate papillae

Lingual branches, Glossopharyngeal nerve

Glossopharyngeal nerve (IX)

Tonsillar artery

Epiglottis

Greater horn of hyoid bone

Superior laryngeal nerve

Superior laryngeal artery

Superior horn of thyroid cartilage

Internal branch of superior laryngeal n.

Interarytenoid notch

Piriform recess

Thyroid cartilage

Inferior horn of thyroid cartilage

Inferior laryngeal artery

Tracheal branches, Inf. thyroid artery

Tracheal and esophageal branches, Recurrent laryngeal nerve

Trachea

Mucous membrane of tongue

Glossopharyngeal nerve (IX)

Tonsillar branch of Glossopharyngeal n.

Palatine tonsil

Epiglottic vallecula

Inlet of the larynx (aditus)

Oblique arytenoid m.

Inf. laryngeal nerve

Post. cricoarytenoid muscle

Thyroid gland

Inferior thyroid artery

Recurrent laryngeal nerve

Epiglottis

Hyoid bone

Lesser horn   Greater horn

Triticeal cartilage

Foramen for sup. laryngeal vessels and nerve

Fat pad

Thyroid cartilage

Arytenoid cartilage

Cricothyroid articular capsule

Cricotracheal ligament

Tracheal cartilages

Tracheal membranous wall; Tracheal glands

Lat. thyro-hyoid lig.

Thyrohyoid membrane

Superior horn thyroid cartilage

Stem of epiglottis

Corniculate cartilage

Corniculopharyngeal lig.

Cricoarytenoid joint (capsule and post. cricoarytenoid ligament)

Inferior horn (thyroid cartilage)

Cricothyroid articular capsule

Cricopharyngeal ligament

Anular tracheal ligaments

Fig. 759: The Cartilages and Ligaments of the Larynx

NOTE: 1) the articulation of the paired arytenoid cartilages with the cricoid cartilage below. These synovial cricoarytenoid joints are surrounded by articular capsules and strengthened by the posterior cricoarytenoid ligaments.

2) the cricoarytenoid joints allow for a) *rotation of the arytenoid cartilage* on an axis which is nearly vertical and b) *the horizontal gliding movement* of the arytenoid cartilages.

3) rotation of the arytenoid cartilages results in medial or lateral displacement of the vocal folds, thereby increasing or decreasing the size of the opening between the folds, the rima glottidis. The horizontal gliding action of the arytenoid cartilages permits the bases of these cartilages to be approximated or moved apart. Medial rotation and medial gliding of the arytenoid cartilages occur simultaneously as do the two lateral movements.

Epiglottis

Thyrohyoid membrane

Body of hyoid bone

Subhyoid bursa

Superior horn of thyroid cartilage

Probe inserted lateral → to epiglottis

Hyoepiglottic ligament

Thyrohyoid ligament

Thyroid cartilage

Fat body

Corniculopharyngeal ligament

Stem of epiglottis; Thyroepiglottic ligament

Arytenoid cartilage

Vestibular ligament

Vocal ligament

Cricopharyngeal lig.

Cricothyroid ligament

Cricoid cartilage

Pharynx

Anular tracheal ligaments; Tracheal glands

Tracheal wall

Fig. 760: The Right Half of the Larynx Showing the Cartilages and the Vestibular and Vocal Ligaments

NOTE: 1) the vestibular ligament is a compact band of fibrous tissue attached anteriorly to the thyroid cartilage and posteriorly to the anterior and lateral surface of the arytenoid cartilage. It is enclosed by mucous membrane to form the vestibular fold (or false vocal fold).

2) the vocal ligament consists of elastic tissue which is attached anteriorly to the thyroid cartilage and posteriorly to the vocal process of the arytenoid cartilage. It, too, is surrounded by mucous membrane which, along with the vocalis muscle, forms the vocal fold. Laryngeal sound waves are produced by oscillations of the vocal folds initiated by puffs of air.

Fig. 761: The Vocal Ligaments and Conus Elasticus from Above

NOTE that the conus elasticus is a membrane consisting principally of yellow elastic fibers which interconnects the thyroid, cricoid and arytenoid cartilages. It underlies the mucous membrane below the vocal folds and is overlain to some extent by the circothyroid muscle on the exterior of the larynx. Observe the symmetry of the arytenoid cartilages and their related vocal ligaments.

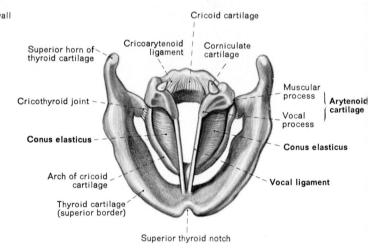

Cricoid cartilage

Superior horn of thyroid cartilage

Cricoarytenoid ligament

Corniculate cartilage

Cricothyroid joint

Muscular process

Arytenoid cartilage

Vocal process

Conus elasticus

Conus elasticus

Arch of cricoid cartilage

Vocal ligament

Thyroid cartilage (superior border)

Superior thyroid notch

Thyrohyoid membrane

Body of hyoid bone

Foramen for superior laryngeal vessels and internal laryngeal nerve

Epiglottis

Median thyro-hyoid ligament

Stem of epiglottis; Thyroepiglottic lig.

Vocal ligaments

Corniculopharyngeal lig.

Thyroid cartilage

Arytenoid cartilage

Conus elasticus

Cricothyroid ligament

Cricoid cartilage; Articular facet for thyroid cartilage

Cricoid cartilage

Tracheal cartilages

Fig. 762: The Upper Left Part of the Larynx

NOTE: 1) the right halves of the hyoid bone, epiglottis and thyroid cartilage have been removed to reveal the interior of the upper left portion of the larynx. The two vocal ligaments, the arytenoid cartilages and the conus elasticus are also displayed.

2) the broad thyrohyoid membrane and its foramen. Observe the attachment of the stem of the epiglottis to the thyroid cartilage by means of the thyroepiglottic ligament.

3) the conus elasticus as it attaches to the vocal fold and the arytenoid, thyroid and cricoid cartilages.

4) although laryngeal sounds are initiated at the vocal folds, the pitch, quality, volume, range, tone and overtone characteristics of the human voice incorporate not only the vocal folds but also the structures in the mouth (tongue, teeth, and palate), the nasal cavities (sinuses), the pharynx, the rest of the larynx, the lungs, diaphragm and abdominal musculature.

Figs. 760, 761, 762

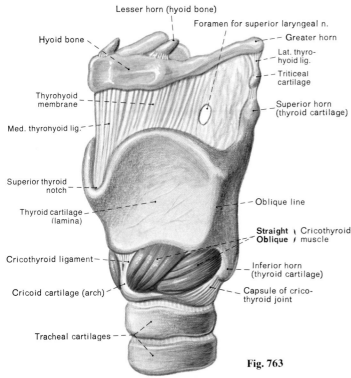

Fig. 763

Fig. 763: Ventrolateral View of the Exterior Larynx and the Cricothyroid Muscle

NOTE: 1) the cricothyroid muscle consists of straight and oblique heads. The *straight head* is more vertical and inserts into the lower border of the lamina of the thyroid cartilage, while the *oblique head is* more horizontal and inserts onto the inferior horn of the thyroid cartilage.

2) the cricothyroid muscle tilts the anterior part of the cricoid cartilage superiorly. In so doing, the arytenoid cartilages which are attached to the cricoid are pulled dorsally. In addition, the thyroid cartilage is pulled forward and downward. These actions increase the distance between the arytenoid and thyroid cartilages, thereby increasing the tension of and elongating the vocal folds.

Fig. 764: Laryngeal Muscle (Dorsal)

NOTE: 1) the *arytenoid muscle* consisting of a *transverse portion* which spans the zone between the two arytenoid cartilages horizontally, and an *oblique portion* which consists of two muscular fascicles that cross one another. Thus, each of the two fascicles of the oblique portion extends from the base of one arytenoid cartilage to the apex of the other cartilage. Some oblique arytenoid fibers continue to the epiglottis along the aryepiglottic fold. These constitute the *aryepiglottis muscle.*

2) the *transverse arytenoid* approximates the arytenoid cartilages, and, therefore, closes the posterior part of the rima glottis. The *oblique arytenoid and aryepiglottic muscles* tend to close the inlet into the larynx by pulling the aryepiglottic folds together and approximating the arytenoid cartilages and the epiglottis.

3) the *posterior cricoarytenoid* muscle extends from the lamina of the cricoid cartilage to the muscular process of the arytenoid cartilage while the *lateral cricoarytenoid* muscle arises laterally from the arch of the cricoid cartilage to insert with the posterior cricoarytenoid muscle onto the arytenoid cartilage.

4) the *posterior cricoarytenoids* are the only abductors of the vocal folds, while the *lateral cricoarytenoids* act as antagonists, and adduct the vocal folds. The posterior muscle abducts by pulling the base of the arytenoid cartilages medially and posteriorly, while the lateral muscle adducts by pulling these same cartilages anteriorly and laterally.

5) the *thyroarytenoid muscle* (Fig. 765) is a thin sheet of muscle radiating from the thyroid cartilage principally backward toward the arytenoid cartilage. Its upper fibers continue to the epiglottis and, joining the aryepiglottic fibers, become the *thyroepiglottic muscle.* Its deepest (and most medial) fibers form the *vocalis muscle* which is attached to the lateral aspect of the vocal fold.

6) the thyroarytenoid muscles draw the arytenoid cartilages toward the thyroid cartilage and, thus, shorten (relax) the vocal folds.

Fig. 764

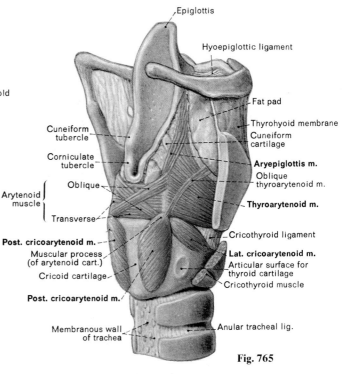

Fig. 765

Fig. 765: Laryngeal Muscles (Lateral)

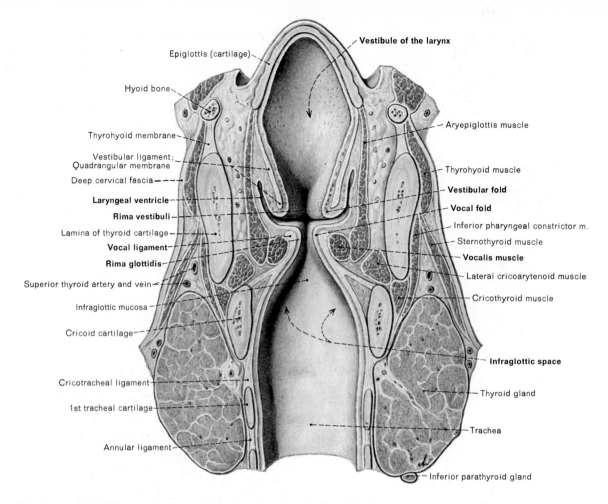

Fig. 766: Frontal Section Through the Larynx Showing the Laryngeal Folds and Cavities in its Anterior One-Half

NOTE: 1) the paired vocal folds consisting of mucous membrane overlying the vocal ligaments and vocalis muscles. Just superior to the vocal folds observe the vestibular folds. On each side, the vestibular fold is separated from the vocal folds by a recess called the laryngeal ventricle (or sinus).

2) that above the vestibular folds is the vestibule of the larynx which lies just below the laryngeal inlet. Below the vocal folds observe the infraglottic space. This space communicates with the trachea below and is limited by the rima glottidis between the vocal folds above.

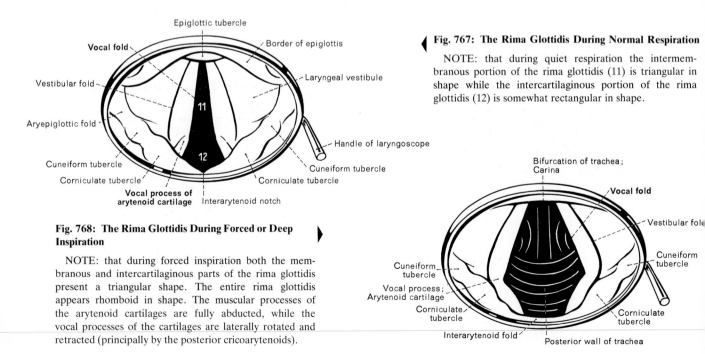

Fig. 767: The Rima Glottidis During Normal Respiration

NOTE: that during quiet respiration the intermembranous portion of the rima glottidis (11) is triangular in shape while the intercartilaginous portion of the rima glottidis (12) is somewhat rectangular in shape.

Fig. 768: The Rima Glottidis During Forced or Deep Inspiration

NOTE: that during forced inspiration both the membranous and intercartilaginous parts of the rima glottidis present a triangular shape. The entire rima glottidis appears rhomboid in shape. The muscular processes of the arytenoid cartilages are fully abducted, while the vocal processes of the cartilages are laterally rotated and retracted (principally by the posterior cricoarytenoids).

Figs. 766, 767, 768

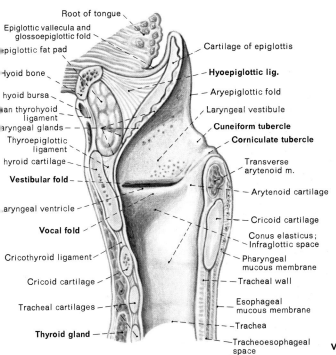

Root of tongue

Epiglottic vallecula and glossoepiglottic fold

piglottic fat pad

Cartilage of epiglottis

Hyoid bone

Hyoepiglottic lig.

hyoid bursa

Aryepiglottic fold

an thyrohyoid ligament

Laryngeal vestibule

aryngeal glands

Cuneiform tubercle

Thyroepiglottic ligament

Corniculate tubercle

hyroid cartilage

Transverse arytenoid m.

Vestibular fold

Arytenoid cartilage

aryngeal ventricle

Cricoid cartilage

Vocal fold

Conus elasticus; Infraglottic space

Cricothyroid ligament

Pharyngeal mucous membrane

Cricoid cartilage

Tracheal wall

Tracheal cartilages

Esophageal mucous membrane

Thyroid gland

Trachea

Tracheoesophageal space

Fig. 770: Cross Section of Larynx at the Vocal Folds ▶

I = intermembranous portion of rima glottidis

II = intercartilaginous portion of rima glottidis

NOTE: the orientation of the arytenoid cartilages and their articulations with the cricoid cartilage. The vocal folds consist of mucous membrane overlying the vocal ligaments, lateral to which extend the deeper vocalis portions of the thyroarytenoid muscle. By drawing the arytenoid cartilages forward, the thyroarytenoids shorten and relax the vocal folds. Simultaneously, they medially rotate the arytenoid cartilages and, thus, approximate the vocal folds.

Fig. 769: Midsagittal Section of Larynx

NOTE: 1) the laryngeal inlet through which the larynx communicates with the pharynx. This aperture leads to the laryngeal vestibule, the anterior border of which is the epiglottis. On each side the aryepiglottic folds define the borders of the inlet, which are marked by oval elevations, the cuneiform and corniculate cartilages.

2) the space between the vestibular folds and the vocal folds is known as the ventricle or laryngeal sinus. Below the vocal fold observe how the conus elasticus bounds the infraglottic space laterally, and the communication of this space with the trachea.

3) the attachments of the epiglottis. Superiorly, its hyoepiglottic ligament stretches to the hyoid bone; inferiorly, the thyroepiglottic ligament connects the stem of the epiglottis to the thyroid cartilage; laterally, the aryepiglottic folds extend between the epiglottis and the arytenoid cartilages.

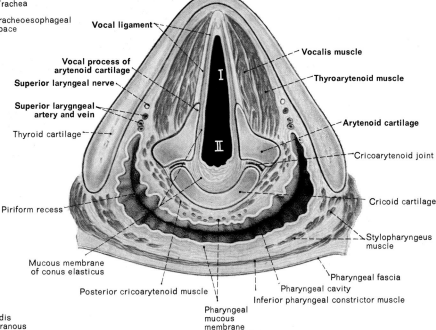

Vocal ligament

Vocalis muscle

Vocal process of arytenoid cartilage

Thyroarytenoid muscle

Superior laryngeal nerve

Superior laryngeal artery and vein

Arytenoid cartilage

Thyroid cartilage

Cricoarytenoid joint

Cricoid cartilage

Piriform recess

Stylopharyngeus muscle

Mucous membrane of conus elasticus

Pharyngeal fascia

Pharyngeal cavity

Posterior cricoarytenoid muscle

Inferior pharyngeal constrictor muscle

Pharyngeal mucous membrane

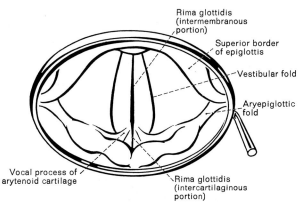

Rima glottidis (intermembranous portion)

Superior border of epiglottis

Vestibular fold

Aryepiglottic fold

Vocal process of arytenoid cartilage

Rima glottidis (intercartilaginous portion)

Fig. 772: The Rima Glottidis During Whispering ▶

NOTE: that during the production of whispering sounds the intermembranous portion of the vocal folds are approximated, while the intercartilaginous portion of the folds are kept separated. The anterior part of the rima glottidis is narrow and slit-like and the posterior, intercartilaginous portion remains open.

◀ Fig. 771: The Rima Glottidis During Phonation (Shrill Tones)

NOTE: that during the emission of shrill tones, the vocal folds are approximated and the vocal ligaments tensed resulting in a narrowing of the rima glottidis to a thin slit.

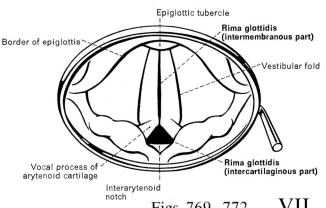

Epiglottic tubercle

Rima glottidis (intermembranous part)

Border of epiglottis

Vestibular fold

Vocal process of arytenoid cartilage

Interarytenoid notch

Rima glottidis (intercartilaginous part)

Figs. 769–772   VII

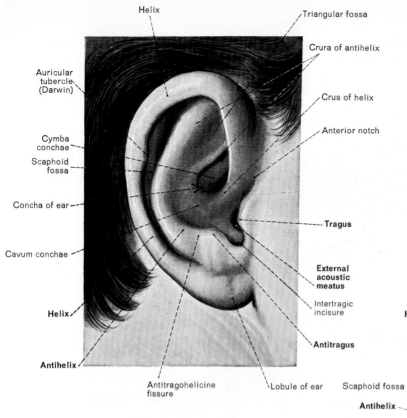

Helix

Triangular fossa

Crura of antihelix

Auricular tubercle (Darwin)

Crus of helix

Anterior notch

Cymba conchae

Scaphoid fossa

Concha of ear

Cavum conchae

Tragus

External acoustic meatus

Intertragic incisure

Helix

Antitragus

Antihelix

Antitragohelicine fissure

Lobule of ear

Fig. 773: The Right External Ear (Lateral View)

NOTE: 1) the external ear (or auricle) consists of skin overlying elastic fibrocartilage. It is irregularly shaped and the external acoustic meatus courses through the external ear to the tympanic membrane.

2) the external rim of the auricle is called the helix. Another curved prominence anterior to the helix is the antihelix. Inferiorly, a notch in the cartilage (the intertragic incisure) separates the tragus anteriorly from the antitragus posteriorly.

3) the ear lobe or lobule does not contain cartilage. Instead, it is soft and contains connective tissue and fat.

4) the external acoustic meatus is an oval canal which extends for about 2.5 cm in a S-shaped curve from the concha to the tympanic membrane. It consists of an outer cartilaginous part (1 cm) and a narrower more medial osseous part (1.5 cm).

Helix

Spine of helix

Squamous portion of temporal bone

Incisures in the cartilage of the acoustic meatus

Scaphoid fossa

Antihelix

Lamina of tragus

Tympanic part of temporal b...

Antitragohelicine fissure

Tail of helix

Cartilage of acoustic meatus

Styloid process

Mastoid process

Fig. 774: The Cartilage of the Right External Ear (seen from Front)

NOTE: 1) with the skin of the external ear removed, the contours of the single cartilage conform generally with those of the intact auricle. The cartilage is seen to be absent inferiorly at the site of the ear lobe.

2) the attachment of the auricular cartilage to the temporal bone. This attachment is strengthened by the anterior and posterior ligaments (not shown in this figure) which articulate the tragus and spine of the helix to the temporal bone anteriorly, and the concha to the mastoid process posteriorly. The continuous overlying skin completes the attachment.

Helicis major muscle

Helicis minor muscle

Tragicus muscle

Tail of helix

Antitragicus muscle

Fig. 775: Intrinsic Muscles of External Ear (Lateral Surface)

Superior auricular muscle

Oblique auricular muscle

Transverse auricular mus...

External acoustic meatus

Posterior auricular muscle

Fig. 776: Muscles Attaching to the Medial Surface of External Ear

Figs. 773–776

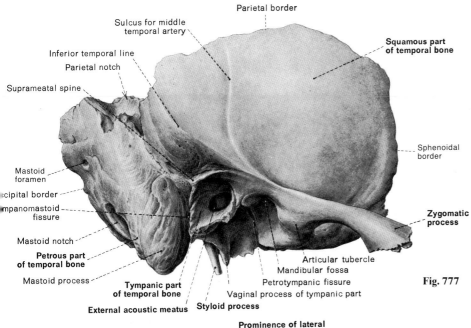

Parietal border

Sulcus for middle
temporal artery

Inferior temporal line

Parietal notch

Suprameatal spine

**Squamous part
of temporal bone**

Sphenoidal
border

Mastoid
foramen

cipital border

mpanomastoid
fissure

Mastoid notch

**Petrous part
of temporal bone**

Mastoid process

**Zygomatic
process**

Articular tubercle
Mandibular fossa
Petrotympanic fissure

**Tympanic part
of temporal bone**

Vaginal process of tympanic part

External acoustic meatus **Styloid process**

Fig. 777

Fig. 777: The Right Temporal Bone (Lateral View)

NOTE: 1) the temporal bone which forms the osseous encasement for the middle and internal ear, consists of three parts: *squamous, tympanic* and *petrous.*

2) the *squamous part* is broad in shape, thin and flat. From it extends the zygomatic process. The *tympanic part* is interposed below the squamous, and anterior to the petrous parts. The external acoustic meatus, which leads to the tympanic membrane, is surrounded by the tympanic part of the temporal bone.

3) the hard *petrous part* contains the organ of hearing and the vestibular canals. Its mastoid process is not solid but contains many air cells, and its external surface affords attachment to several muscles.

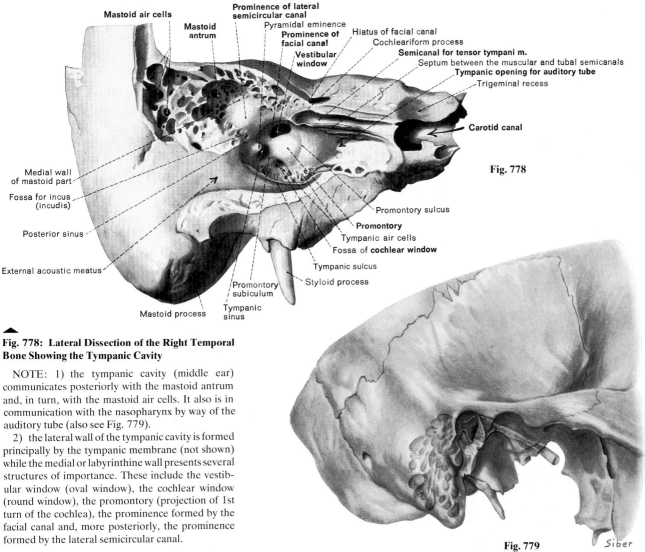

Mastoid air cells

**Mastoid
antrum**

**Prominence of lateral
semicircular canal**

Pyramidal eminence

**Prominence of
facial canal**

**Vestibular
window**

Hiatus of facial canal

Cochleariform process

Semicanal for tensor tympani m.

Septum between the muscular and tubal semicanals

Tympanic opening for auditory tube

Trigeminal recess

Carotid canal

Fig. 778

Medial wall
of mastoid part

Fossa for incus
(incudis)

Posterior sinus

External acoustic meatus

Promontory sulcus

Promontory
Tympanic air cells

Fossa of **cochlear window**

Tympanic sulcus

Promontory
subiculum

Tympanic
sinus

Styloid process

Mastoid process

Fig. 778: Lateral Dissection of the Right Temporal Bone Showing the Tympanic Cavity

NOTE: 1) the tympanic cavity (middle ear) communicates posteriorly with the mastoid antrum and, in turn, with the mastoid air cells. It also is in communication with the nasopharynx by way of the auditory tube (also see Fig. 779).

2) the lateral wall of the tympanic cavity is formed principally by the tympanic membrane (not shown) while the medial or labyrinthine wall presents several structures of importance. These include the vestibular window (oval window), the cochlear window (round window), the promontory (projection of 1st turn of the cochlea), the prominence formed by the facial canal and, more posteriorly, the prominence formed by the lateral semicircular canal.

Fig. 779

Siber

Fig. 779: A Projection of the Middle Ear Air Spaces on the Lateral Surface of the Skull

NOTE that the mastoid air cells within the mastoid process of the temporal bone (shown in red) communicate with the tympanic cavity (blue). Coursing between the middle ear and the nasopharynx is the auditory tube (yellow). This communication allows the air pressure in the tympanic cavity to be the same as external atmospheric pressure and, thus, equivalent on both sides of the tympanic membrane.

Fig. 780: Frontal Section Through Left External, Middle and Internal Ear

NOTE: 1) the external acoustic meatus commences at the auricle and leads to the external surface of the tympanic membrane. Through the meatus course the sound waves which cause vibration of the tympanum.

2) the middle ear (or tympanic cavity) contains three ossicles (malleus, incus and stapes) and two muscles (tensor tympani and stapedius [not shown]). The cavity of the middle ear communicates with the mastoid antrum and mastoid air cells posteriorly, and the nasopharynx by way of the auditory tube. From the middle ear this tube courses downward, forward and medially. The ossicles interconnect the tympanic membrane with the inner ear.

3) the inner ear contains the coiled cochlea (or organ of hearing) and the three semicircular canals (the vestibular organ) and their associated structures and nerves.

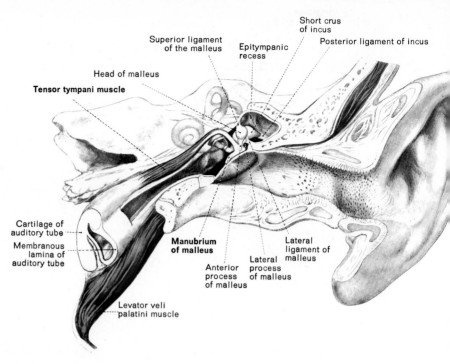

Fig. 781: Frontal Section Through Right External and Middle Ear

NOTE: 1) the slender tendon of the tensor tympani muscle, as it turns sharply upon reaching the tympanic cavity to terminate on the manubrium of the malleus.

2) the tympanic cavity is extended superiorly by the epitympanic recess and, inferiorly, by the hypotympanic recess. On the medial wall of the middle ear observe the promontory which protrudes into the tympanic cavity and which contains the spiral cochlea.

3) the lateral and superior ligaments attaching to the head of the malleus.

Fig. 782: Frontal Section of Left Ear Through the Middle Ear Bones

NOTE: 1) when sound waves are received at the tympanic membrane, they cause medial displacements of the manubrium of the malleus. The head of the malleus is tilted laterally, pulling with it the body of the incus. At the same time the long process of the incus is displaced medially, as is the articulation between the incus and the stapes.

2) the base of the stapes rocks as though it were on a fulcrum at the vestibular window, thereby establishing waves in the perilymph. These waves stimulate the auditory receptors and become dissipated at the secondary tympanic membrane covering the cochlear window.

Figs. 780, 781, 782

10–11 mm
9 mm

Fig. 784: Labeled Diagram of Fig. 783

NOTE: 1) the tympanic membrane has been divided into quadrants. The most depressed point is the umbo and is found at the rounded extremity of the handle of the malleus.

2) the anterior and posterior malleolar folds. The more lax part (pars flaccida) of the tympanic membrane lies above and between these folds, while the rest is more tightly stretched (pars tensa).

Fig. 783: Right Tympanic Membrane as seen with an Otoscope in a Living Person

NOTE: that the tympanic membrane is oval in shape and measures about 9 mm across and from 10 to 11 mm vertically (upper inset, actual size). Its blood supply is derived from the deep auricular and anterior tympanic branches of the maxillary artery, and the stylomastoid branch of the posterior auricular artery.

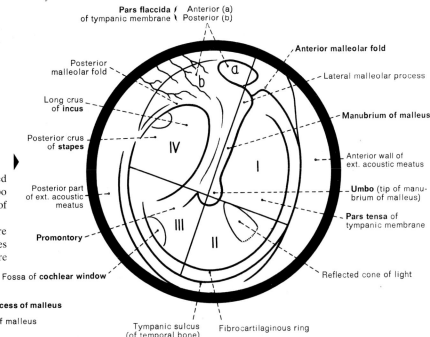

Pars flaccida / Anterior (a)
of tympanic membrane \ Posterior (b)

Posterior malleolar fold

Long crus of incus

Posterior crus of stapes

Posterior part of ext. acoustic meatus

Promontory

Fossa of cochlear window

Anterior malleolar fold

Lateral malleolar process

Manubrium of malleus

Anterior wall of ext. acoustic meatus

Umbo (tip of manubrium of malleus)

Pars tensa of tympanic membrane

Reflected cone of light

Tympanic sulcus (of temporal bone)

Fibrocartilaginous ring

Fig. 785: Right Tympanic Cavity seen After Removal of Tympanic Membrane

NOTE: that from this lateral view, the lateral process and manubrium of the malleus, the lenticular process and long crus of the incus, as well as the stapes can be observed upon the removal of the tympanic membrane. Note also the chorda tympani nerve and the tendons of the stapedius and tensor tympani muscles.

Lesser tympanic spine

Tympanic notch

Lateral process of malleus

Neck of malleus

. acoustic meatus

Greater tympanic spine

Ant. malleolar fold; Chorda tympani nerve

Tendon of tensor tympani muscle

Manubrium of malleus

Septum covering tensor tympani m (septum canalis musculotubarii)

rda ani rve old

Long f incus

ramidal ninence

artilaginous ring

Tendon of tapedius muscle

ssa of cochlear window

Lenticular process of incus

Stapes

Promontory

Fig. 786: Lateral Wall of the Right Middle Ear (Tympanic Membrane Viewed from within the Tympanic Cavity)

NOTE: 1) the manubrium of the malleus has been severed from the remainder of the ossicle and left attached to the tympanic membrane. The fibrocartilaginous tympanic ring is deficient superiorly, forming the tympanic notch (of Rivinus). The looser portion of the tympanic membrane (pars flaccida) covers this zone.

2) the tympanic membrane below the malleolar folds is the pars tensa. This portion is made taut by the tensor tympani muscle which attaches to the manubrium of the malleus.

3) the innervation of external surface of the tympanic membrane comes from the auriculotemporal branch of the mandibular nerve (V) and the auricular branch of the vagus (X). The inner surface of the membrane receives innervation from the tympanic branch of the glossopharyngeal nerve (IX).

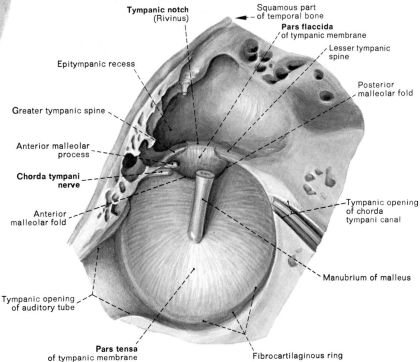

Tympanic notch (Rivinus)

Squamous part of temporal bone

Pars flaccida of tympanic membrane

Lesser tympanic spine

Epitympanic recess

Greater tympanic spine

Anterior malleolar process

Chorda tympani nerve

Anterior malleolar fold

Posterior malleolar fold

Tympanic opening of chorda tympani canal

Manubrium of malleus

Tympanic opening of auditory tube

Pars tensa of tympanic membrane

Fibrocartilaginous ring

Figs. 783–786   VII

Fig. 787: Lateral Dissection of the Right Temporal Bone: The Tympanic Membrane, Middle Ear, and Facial Canal

NOTE: 1) that this dissection has proceeded through the mastoid region of the temporal bone, much of which has been removed, as has the posterior wall of the external acoustic meatus. The descending part of the facial canal and the lateral semicircular canal have been opened.

2) the lateral or outer surface of the tympanic membrane. Observe the manubrium of the malleus on the inner surface of the membrane, and the head of the malleus, the incus and the incudomalleolar joint within the tympanic cavity.

3) the junction of the chorda tympani nerve with the facial nerve.

Fig. 788: The Intracranial Course of the Facial Nerve, View from Behind

NOTE: 1) that a frontal section has been made through the temporal bone at an angle which opens the facial canal and tympanic cavity from behind. Observe the chorda tympani nerve coursing anteroposteriorly across the middle ear cavity to its junction with the facial nerve.

2) that the internal acoustic meatus in the floor of the cranial cavity can be seen transmitting the facial nerve with its nervous intermedius, as well as the vestibulocochlear nerve. Peripheral to the geniculate ganglion (which serves as the sensory ganglion of VII), the facial nerve enters the facial canal. Within the canal, the facial nerve initially courses laterally and then turns sharply backward and inferiorly (see Figs. 787, 793 and 794).

3) that beyond its junction with the chorda tympani nerve, the main trunk of the facial nerve continues its descent in the temporal bone to emerge on the lateral aspect of the face through the stylomastoid foramen.

Figs. 787, 788

Anterior semicircular canal

Lateral semicircular canal; Facial nerve;
Prominence of the facial canal

Supramastoid crest

Post. semicircular canal;
Petrous part of temporal bone

Head of malleus; Cochleariform process

Zygomatic process of
temporal bone

Tegmen tympani

Bony wall of posterior
cranial fossa

Parotid gland
(retromandibular part)

Sigmoid sinus

Posterior
semicircular canal

Stapedius muscle, nerve and artery;
Chorda tympani nerve; Post. tympanic artery

Auricular branch of vagus nerve;
Communicating branch with facial nerve

Head of stapes; Umbo;
Manubrium of malleus

Promontory;
Fossa of cochlear window

**Fig. 789: Lateral Dissection of the Right Temporal Bone:
The Semicircular Canals and Facial Nerve**

NOTE: 1) that the facial canal has been opened more extensively than in Figure 787, exposing further the chorda tympani nerve and the posterior tympanic artery. This vessel branches from the stylomastoid artery and helps to supply the internal surface of the tympanic membrane. Observe the nerve to the stapedius muscle which arises from the facial nerve near the pyramidal eminence on the posterior wall of the tympanic cavity. Coursing with the nerve is the stapedial artery, and more inferiorly is found the auricular branch of the vagus nerve.

2) that the incus has been removed, thereby revealing the head of the stapes, which is directed laterally. The stapedius muscle inserts onto the posterior surface of the head of the stapes.

3) the anterior, posterior and lateral semicircular canals. These become exposed after removal of the bony prominence over the lateral canal, and additional bone above and behind that prominence.

**Fig. 790: The Right Temporal Bone Opened Laterally ▶
to Demonstrate the Medial Wall of the Tympanic Cavity**

NOTE: 1) that the irregularly shaped mastoid portion of the temporal bone has been dissected laterally and that its interior is marked by a number of cavities called the mastoid cells. These are organized into three groups: anterosuperior, middle, and apical. The anterosuperior and middle mastoid cells are lined with mucous membrane, filled with air, and communicate with the tympanic cavity of the middle ear. Because of this, middle ear infections can spread directly to the mastoid air cells. The apical mastoid cells are quite different for they are small and contain bone marrow instead of air.

2) that the medial wall of the tympanic cavity contains a convex elevation of bone called the promontory, which is formed by the projection laterally of the first turn of the cochlea. Behind the middle ear cavity the curved facial canal has been opened, as have the lateral semicircular canal and the sigmoid sinus.

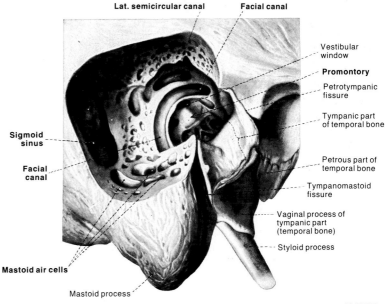

Lat. semicircular canal

Facial canal

Vestibular
window

Promontory

Petrotympanic
fissure

Tympanic part
of temporal bone

Petrous part of
temporal bone

Tympanomastoid
fissure

Vaginal process of
tympanic part
(temporal bone)

Styloid process

Sigmoid
sinus

Facial
canal

Mastoid air cells

Mastoid process

Fig. 791: **Lateral Wall of the Right Tympanic Cavity (Viewed From the Medial Aspect)**

NOTE: 1) that the tympanic cavity is lined completely with a mucous membrane that attaches onto the surface of all of the structures of the middle ear. This tympanic mucosa is continuous with that lining the mastoid air cells posteriorly and the auditory tube anteriorly.

2) that reflections of the tympanic mucous membrane form the anterior and posterior malleolar folds. These are also reflected around the chorda tympani nerve as it curves along the medial side of the manubrium of the malleus.

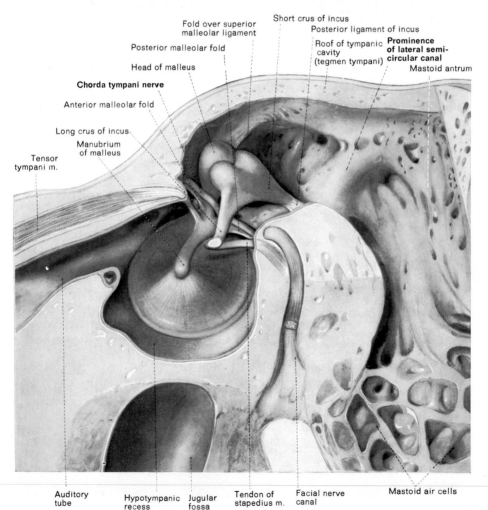

Fig. 792: The Muscles, Chorda Tympani Nerve, and Ossicles of the Right Middle Ear

NOTE: 1) the tendon of the tensor tympani muscle inserting on the manubrium of the malleus and the short tendon of the stapedius as it inserts onto the neck of the stapes close to its articulation with the incus. The tensor tympani draws the manubrium medially, thereby making the tympanic membrane taut. It is innervated by the mandibular division of the trigeminal nerve.

2) the stapedius is the smallest of the skeletal muscles in the body and it is supplied by the facial nerve. It pulls the head of the stapes posteriorly, thereby tilting the base of the stapes in the vestibular window.

3) the direct communication between the nasopharynx, tympanic cavity and mastoid air cells has important clinical meaning, since oro-respiratory tract infections reach the middle ear readily by way of the auditory tube.

Figs. 791, 792

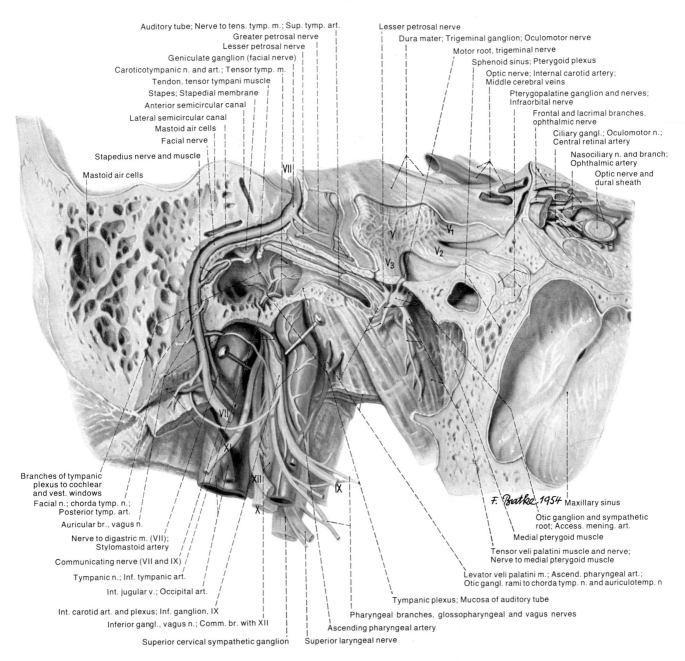

Auditory tube; Nerve to tens. tymp. m.; Sup. tymp. art.
Greater petrosal nerve
Lesser petrosal nerve
Geniculate ganglion (facial nerve)
Caroticotympanic n. and art.; Tensor tymp. m.
Tendon, tensor tympani muscle
Stapes; Stapedial membrane
Anterior semicircular canal
Lateral semicircular canal
Mastoid air cells
Facial nerve
Stapedius nerve and muscle
Mastoid air cells

Lesser petrosal nerve
Dura mater; Trigeminal ganglion; Oculomotor nerve
Motor root, trigeminal nerve
Sphenoid sinus; Pterygoid plexus
Optic nerve; Internal carotid artery;
Middle cerebral veins
Pterygopalatine ganglion and nerves;
Infraorbital nerve
Frontal and lacrimal branches,
ophthalmic nerve
Ciliary gangl.; Oculomotor n.;
Central retinal artery
Nasociliary n. and branch;
Ophthalmic artery
Optic nerve and
dural sheath

VII

V V₁
V₂
V₃

VII
XI
XII
X
IX

F. Batke 1954 Maxillary sinus

Branches of tympanic
plexus to cochlear
and vest. windows
Facial n.; chorda tymp. n.;
Posterior tymp. art.
Auricular br., vagus n.
Nerve to digastric m. (VII);
Stylomastoid artery
Communicating nerve (VII and IX)
Tympanic n.; Inf. tympanic art.
Int. jugular v.; Occipital art.
Int. carotid art. and plexus; Inf. ganglion, IX
Inferior gangl., vagus n.; Comm. br. with XII
Superior cervical sympathetic ganglion

Superior laryngeal nerve
Ascending pharyngeal artery
Pharyngeal branches, glossopharyngeal and vagus nerves
Tympanic plexus; Mucosa of auditory tube

Otic ganglion and sympathetic
root; Access. mening. art.
Medial pterygoid muscle
Tensor veli palatini muscle and nerve;
Nerve to medial pterygoid muscle
Levator veli palatini m.; Ascend. pharyngeal art.;
Otic gangl. rami to chorda tymp. n. and auriculotemp. n

Fig. 793: Lateral View of the Right Facial Canal, Medial Wall of the Tympanic Cavity, the Semicircular Canals and the Auditory Tube

**Fig. 794: The Facial, Glossopharyngeal and
Vagus Nerves Projected Onto the Temporal Bone,
Lateral View**

NOTE: 1) the tympanic branch of the glossopharyngeal nerve which, along with sympathetic fibers from
the caroticotympanic nerve, contributes to the formation of the tympanic plexus (see Figure 799). From this
plexus emerges the lesser petrosal nerve which courses
to the otic ganglion.

2) the greater petrosal nerve joining with sympathetic branches of the internal carotid plexus (actually the
deep petrosal nerve) to form the nerve of the pterygoid
canal.

3) the auricular branch of the vagus nerve which is
distributed to the upper surface of the external auricle.
to the posterior wall and floor of the external acoustic
meatus and part of the lateral (outer) surface of the
tympanic membrane.

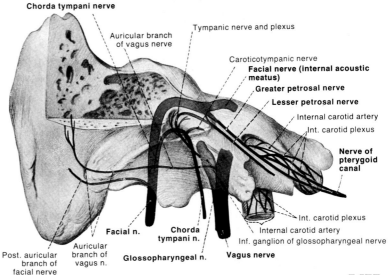

Chorda tympani nerve
Auricular branch
of vagus nerve
Tympanic nerve and plexus
Caroticotympanic nerve
**Facial nerve (internal acoustic
meatus)**
Greater petrosal nerve
Lesser petrosal nerve
Internal carotid artery
Int. carotid plexus
**Nerve of
pterygoid
canal**
Int. carotid plexus
Internal carotid artery
Inf. ganglion of glossopharyngeal nerve
Facial n.
**Chorda
tympani n.**
Glossopharyngeal n.
Vagus nerve
Post. auricular
branch of
facial nerve
Auricular
branch of
vagus n.

Figs. 793, 794   VII

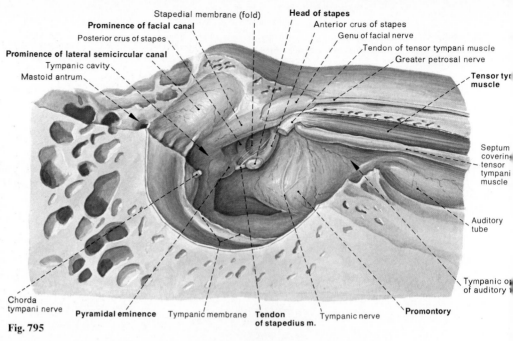

NOTE: 1) the tympanic membrane has been removed along with the bony roof of the tympanic cavity. The malleus and incus have also been removed and the tendon of the tensor tympani severed. Observe the stapes with its base directed toward the vestibular window and the stapedius muscle still attached to its neck.

2) several bony markings: a) the prominence containing the lateral semicircular canal, b) the curved prominence of the facial canal with its facial nerve, c) the rounded promontory, which is the thin bony covering over the cochlea and d) the hollow pyramidal eminence from which arises the stapedius muscle.

Stapedial membrane (fold)
Prominence of facial canal
Posterior crus of stapes
Prominence of lateral semicircular canal
Tympanic cavity
Mastoid antrum
Head of stapes
Anterior crus of stapes
Genu of facial nerve
Tendon of tensor tympani muscle
Greater petrosal nerve
Tensor tympani muscle
Septum covering tensor tympani muscle
Auditory tube
Tympanic opening of auditory tube
Chorda tympani nerve
Pyramidal eminence
Tympanic membrane
Tendon of stapedius m.
Tympanic nerve
Promontory

Fig. 795

The crura of the stapes
Tendon of tensor tympani muscle
Cochleariform process
Lateral semicircular canal
Genu of facial nerve
Lateral semicircular duct
Greater petrosal nerve
Tensor tympani muscle
Semicanal for tensor tympani muscle
Stapedial membrane
Septum covering tensor tympani (septum canalis musculotubarii)
Pyramidal eminence
Semicanal of auditory tube
Promontory
Tympanic nerve
Tendon of stapedius muscle
Tympanic cavity
Head of stapes
Fig. 796
Facial nerve
Facial canal at stylomastoid foramen
Tympanic sinus

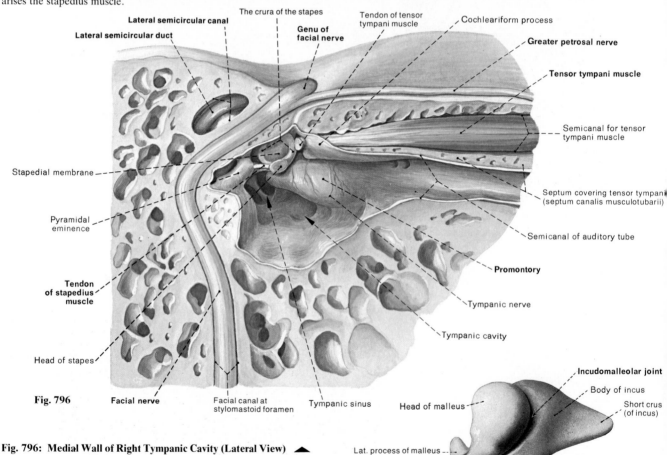

Fig. 796: Medial Wall of Right Tympanic Cavity (Lateral View) ▲

NOTE: 1) that the bone forming the prominence of the lateral semicircular canal and the curved prominence of the facial canal has been removed to reveal their internal structures.

2) the greater petrosal nerve which carries preganglionic parasympathetic fibers from the facial nerve to the pterygopalatine ganglion and many taste fibers from the soft palate.

Fig. 797: Right Auditory Ossicles ▶

NOTE: that the malleus, incus and stapes articulate to form an osseous bridge for transmission of sound waves from the tympanic membrane to the vestibular window of the inner ear.

Head of malleus
Incudomalleolar joint
Body of incus
Short crus (of incus)
Lat. process of malleus
Long crus (of incus)
Anterior process (of malleus)
Incudostapedial joint
Posterior crus (of stapes)
Manubrium of malleus
Anterior crus (of stapes)
Fig. 797
Base of stapes

Figs. 795, 796, 797

Fig. 798: Medial Wall of the Right Tympanic Cavity Showing the Stapedius Muscle (Lateral View)

NOTE: 1) the lateral aspect of the pyramidal eminence was removed in order to demonstrate the stapedius muscle. Its tendon emerges through the apex of the eminence and inserts on the neck of the stapes. This muscle measures about 4 mm in length and its action on the base of the stapes (pulling it laterally) protects the inner ear from damage caused by loud sounds.

2) the tympanic branch of the glossopharyngeal nerve (IX) coursing along the promontory. This nerve is sensory to the mucous membrane of the middle ear and is also known as the nerve of Jacobson. Its fibers are joined by sympathetic fibers and by branches from the facial nerve to form the tympanic plexus.

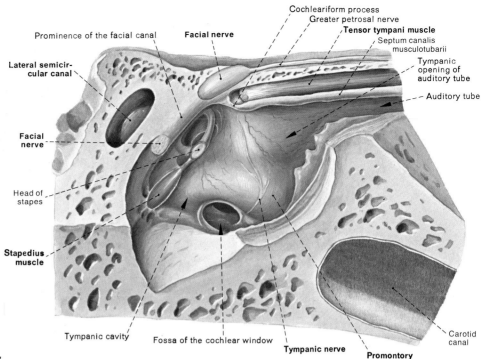

Prominence of the facial canal — Facial nerve — Cochleariform process — Greater petrosal nerve — **Tensor tympani muscle** — Septum canalis musculotubarii — Tympanic opening of auditory tube — Auditory tube

Lateral semicircular canal — Facial nerve — Head of stapes — **Stapedius muscle** — Tympanic cavity — Fossa of the cochlear window — **Tympanic nerve** — **Promontory** — Carotid canal

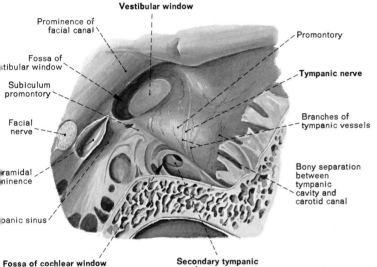

Vestibular window — Prominence of facial canal — Promontory — **Tympanic nerve** — Fossa of vestibular window — Subiculum promontory — Facial nerve — Branches of tympanic vessels — Pyramidal eminence — Bony separation between tympanic cavity and carotid canal — Tympanic sinus — **Fossa of cochlear window** — **Secondary tympanic membrane**

Fig. 799: The Vestibular and Cochlear Windows of the Right Tympanic Cavity

NOTE: the three ossicles and the stapedius and tensor tympani muscles have been removed. The pyramidal eminence has been opened. On the medial wall of the tympanic cavity observe the oval vestibular window and the round cochlear window which communicate with the internal ear. Coursing along the surface of the promontory can be seen the tympanic vessels and nerve.

Fig. 800: The Right Membranous Labyrinth Partially Exposed within the Temporal Bone

NOTE: 1) the membranous labyrinth is in blue, while the roots of the vestibulocochlear nerve are in yellow. The membranous labyrinth lies within the bony labyrinth and generally conforms to it in shape. Between them is found the perilymphatic fluid.

2) within the bony cochlea lie the coils of the cochlear duct. The bony labyrinth consists of the cochlea and the semicircular canals interconnected by the vestibule. In the lateral wall of the vestibule is situated the vestibular window where the stapes has access to the perilymph.

3) the basal end of the cochlear duct communicates with the saccule through the ductus reuniens. The saccule communicates with the utricle and the semicircular canals through the utriculosaccular duct.

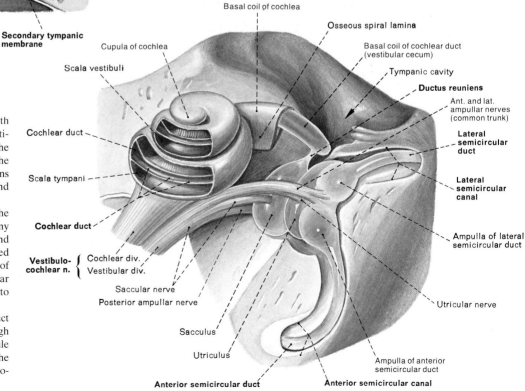

Basal coil of cochlea — Osseous spiral lamina — Basal coil of cochlear duct (vestibular cecum) — Tympanic cavity — **Ductus reuniens** — Ant. and lat. ampullar nerves (common trunk) — **Lateral semicircular duct** — **Lateral semicircular canal** — Ampulla of lateral semicircular duct — Utricular nerve — Cupula of cochlea — Scala vestibuli — Cochlear duct — Scala tympani — **Cochlear duct** — **Vestibulocochlear n.** { Cochlear div. / Vestibular div. } — Saccular nerve — Posterior ampullar nerve — Sacculus — Utriculus — **Anterior semicircular duct** — **Anterior semicircular canal** — Ampulla of anterior semicircular duct

Internal carotid artery;
Ant. petroclinoid fold

Oculomotor n.

Cavern. sinus;
Trochlear n.;
Sup. petr.
sinus;
Petroclinoid
fold (post.)

Trigeminal n.
(sensory root)

Trigeminal n.
(motor root);
Abducens n.

**Cochlear n.;
Labyrinthine
artery**

Glossopharyng.
nerve

Hypoglossal n.

Vagus n.

Ophthalmic nerve
Maxillary nerve
Trigeminal (semilunar) ganglion
Mandibular nerve

Petrous part of temporal bone; Greater petrosal nerve
Middle meningeal art.; Auditory tube; Sup. tymp. art.; Lesser petrosal n.
Tensor tympani m.; Geniculate ganglion; Facial nerve
Auditory tube (osseous part)
Tendon of tens. tymp. m.; Ligament overlying t

Chorda tym
Ant. tymp. a

Head of
malleus;
Sup. mall.
ligament

Epitympan
recess

Joint betw
incus and
malleus

Short crus
post. lig.
of incus;
Tympanic
antrum

Mastoid
air cells

**Lateral
semicircu
canal**

F. Batke 54.

Accessory nerve (spinal and bulbar roots)
Dural septum between IX and X
Vestibular nerve
Fundus of int. acoustic meatus; Facial nerve; Nervus intermedius
Post. ampullar nerve; Endolymphatic duct
Common crus to ant. and post. semicir. canals

Mastoid air cells;
Sigmoid sinus
Anterior semicircular canal
Posterior semicircular canal

Fig. 801: The Right Tympanic Cavity, Auditory Tube, and Semicircular Canals Opened from the Floor of the Cranial Cavity and View from Above

NOTE: 1) that the orientation of this dissection is the same as that seen in Figure 802. The petrous portion of the right temporal bone (including the arcuate eminence), the tegmen tympani (which is the thin roof of the tympanic cavity), and the mastoid part of the temporal bone have all been dissected from the surface of the floor of the cranial cavity. This dissection has also opened the internal acoustic meatus, exposing within it the facial nerve and its accompanying nervus intermedius, the cochlear and vestibular divisions of the vestibulocochlear nerve, and the labyrinthine artery.

2) the geniculate ganglion at the fundus of the internal acoustic meatus. This sensory ganglion of the facial nerve contains the cell bodies of the primary afferent neurons (both general sensory and the special sense of taste) that course in the facial nerve. Attached to the ganglion are: a) the main trunk of the facial nerve, which descends into the facial canal behind the tympanic cavity (it cannot be seen in this figure, but is shown well in Figures 640, 793, and 796), and b) the greater petrosal nerve, which courses along a shallow groove (called the hiatus of the facial canal) that extends between the geniculate ganglion and the foramen lacerum (through which the greater petrosal nerve reaches the pterygoid canal, see Figure 640).

3) the auditory tube and its tympanic opening. Observe also that the tensor tympani muscle lies in a thin, bony canal just above the auditory tube. Its tendon bends around the cochleariform process to attach to the handle of the malleus. This muscle is supplied by a small nerve, the fibers of which are derived from the mandibular division of the trigeminal nerve but course through the otic ganglion (no synapse) before reaching the muscle (see Figure 793).

4) that the anterior and posterior semicircular canals have been opened, but the bone that forms the lateral semicircular canal is still intact. Observe that behind these canals is found an opening for the small endolymphatic sac called the aqueduct of the vestibule. Also note the direct communication that exists between the tympanic cavity, its antrum, and the mastoid air cells.

Fig. 801

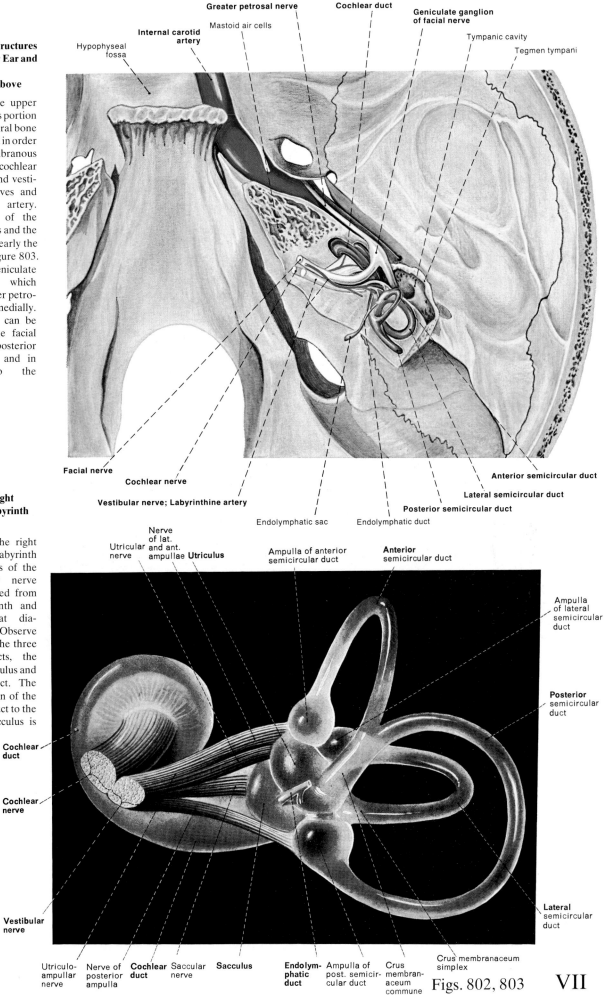

Hypophyseal fossa

Internal carotid artery

Greater petrosal nerve

Mastoid air cells

Cochlear duct

Geniculate ganglion of facial nerve

Tympanic cavity

Tegmen tympani

Facial nerve

Cochlear nerve

Vestibular nerve; Labyrinthine artery

Endolymphatic sac

Endolymphatic duct

Posterior semicircular duct

Lateral semicircular duct

Anterior semicircular duct

Nerve of lat. and ant. ampullae

Utricular nerve

Utriculus

Ampulla of anterior semicircular duct

Anterior semicircular duct

Ampulla of lateral semicircular duct

Posterior semicircular duct

Cochlear duct

Cochlear nerve

Vestibular nerve

Lateral semicircular duct

Utriculo-ampullar nerve

Nerve of posterior ampulla

Cochlear duct

Saccular nerve

Sacculus

Endolym-phatic duct

Ampulla of post. semicir-cular duct

Crus membran-aceum commune

Crus membranaceum simplex

Figs. 802, 803   VII

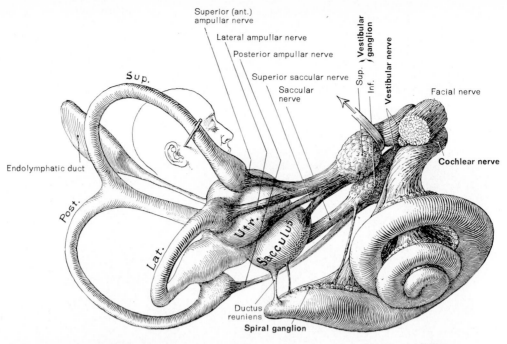

Fig. 804: The Right Membranous Labyrinth Viewed from the Lateral Aspect (Drawing by Max Brödel, 1934)

NOTE: 1) nerve branches from each of the ampullae of the semicircular ducts and from the utriculus and sacculus join to form the vestibular division of the vestibulocochlear nerve. The ganglion containing the sensory nerve cell bodies for this division is the vestibular (Scarpa's) ganglion and it has two parts, superior and inferior.

2) the cochlear division of the vestibulocochlear nerve serves the cochlear duct. Its ganglion, the spiral ganglion, is long and coiled. Observe the close relationship between the facial nerve and the vestibulocochlear nerve within the internal acoustic meatus. (Note that the superior semicircular duct is synonymous with the anterior semicircular duct.)

Fig. 805: Diagram of the Membranous Labyrinth Showing the Stapes

NOTE: 1) the bony structures are shown as cross hatched, while the perilymphatic spaces are diagrammed as white. The membranous labyrinthine duct system (endolymphatic spaces) which contains the receptors is shown as black.

2) the stapes at the vestibular window. The cochlear window, shown close by, in life is covered by the second tympanic membrane.

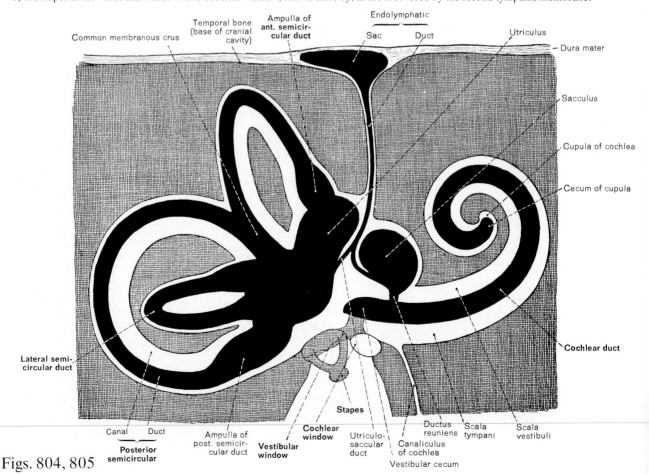

Figs. 804, 805

Index

(Numbers refer to Figures in this *Atlas*.)

Abdomen, 215, 231–342
  inferior, nerves of, 340
    vessels of, 340
  muscles of, deep layer, 238
    superficial layer, 12
  section of, frontal, 215
    transverse, at L-2, 331
      at L-3, 332
      at T-10, 299
      between T-12 and L-1, 300
  upper, sympathetic trunk of, 224
  vagus nerve in, 224
Abdominal cavity, 260, 265, 266, 297, 301–303,
    305, 316–318, 320, 321, 399
  during pregnancy, 399
  organs of, male retroperitoneal, 317
  structures of, posterior abdominal
    retroperitoneal, in lumbar region, 320
  viscera of, intact, 257–259
  wall of, posterior abdominal, 321
Abdominal region, lateral view, 1
Abdominal wall, above umbilicus, 241
  anterior, inner aspect, 242, 243
    anastomosis of, epigastric, 240
    region of, inguinal, 244–246
    section of, transverse, 241
    vessels and nerves of, cutaneous, 239
  below arcuate line, 241
  musculature of, superficial, 231
  nerves and vessels of, 232, 239
    superficial, 232
  posterior, 321, 337
  ventral, posterior aspect, 243, 359
Acetabulum, 235, 253, 339, 386, 387, 389, 401
Acromion, 15, 21, 23, 26–31, 33–37, 51, 61, 137,
    138, 151, 233, 257, 258, 524, 574, 576
  articular surface of, 27, 138
Adminiculum, of linea alba, 240, 242, 243
Air cells, ethmoid, 595, 669, 675, 686–688, 750
  mastoid, 595, 640, 695, 750, 751, 778, 779, 790,
    792, 793, 801, 802
  tympanic, 778
Amnion, 181
  cavity of, 181
Ampulla, of canaliculus, 658, 660
  of duodenum, 331
  of rectum, 312, 314, 343, 377
  of semicircular duct, anterior, 800, 803, 805
    lateral, 800, 803
    posterior, 803, 805
  of uterine tube, 310, 316, 318, 374, 375, 377–380
  of vas deferens, 340, 352, 357–359, 362
Anastomosis, at elbow joint, 62
  at wrist, 76
  cubital, 58, 60, 76
  epigastric, 240
Angle, costal, 143
  costodiaphragmatic, 136, 227, 257
  iridocorneal, 680
  of eye, lateral, 648, 653
    medial, 648, 649, 653
  of mandible, 574, 612, 613, 647, 697, 698, 700,
    728
  of scapula, inferior, 26, 27, 34, 36, 258
    lateral, 26, 27
    superior, 21, 26, 27, 34, 36, 51, 258, 523
  scalenovertebral, 593
  sternal, 141, 142, 144
  submental, 574
Ankle, 512
Ansa, thyroid, 226
Ansa cervicalis, 579–582, 585, 591, 592, 625
  branch of, inferior, 20
  root of, inferior, 580, 592
    superior, 580, 592, 600
Ansa subclavia, 219, 220, 224, 226, 592, 593, 755
  strand of, deep, 228
    superficial, 228

Antebrachium, 1, 98, 99
Antihelix, 773, 774
Antitragus, 773
Antrum, cardiac, 216
  mastoid, 778, 792, 795
  pyloric, 268–270, 331
  tympanic, 801
Anus, 258, 313, 314, 344, 367, 368, 370, 387, 388
Aorta, 158, 178, 202, 204, 206, 229, 264, 285, 300,
    319, 320, 331, 332, 355
  abdominal, 182, 215, 216, 218, 224, 262, 265, 272,
    303, 314, 317, 333, 335, 338, 340–342, 383
  arch of, 136, 150, 157, 172, 176, 178, 182, 186,
    188–190, 192, 194, 195, 208, 209, 212,
    214–219, 257, 258, 588, 594, 595, 726, 755
  ascending, 136, 172, 176, 181, 188, 190, 195,
    207–209, 212, 214, 218, 224, 586, 588
  bifurcation of, 303, 364
  descending, 159, 214, 219, 230, 299
  groove for, 158
  hiatus of, 170, 214, 216, 285, 317, 320, 333–335
  isthmus of, 176
  thoracic, 182, 185, 216–218, 224, 573
    descending, 195
Aperture, vena caval, in diaphragm, 299
Aponeurosis, bicipital, 47, 49, 53, 54, 65, 67, 71, 98
  extensor, dorsal digital, 123, 124, 469
  lingual, 736
  lumbodorsal, 320
  of gastrocnemius muscle, 473
  of latissimus dorsi muscle, 524
  of levator labii superioris muscle, 657
  of levator palpebrae superioris muscle, 656, 657
  of oblique muscle, external, 12, 151, 232, 235,
    236, 239–241, 244–246, 248, 251, 253, 255
    internal, 233, 238, 239, 241
  of rectus abdominis muscle, 241
  palatal, 615, 647, 731, 747
  palatine, 615, 647, 731, 747
  palmar, 106, 120, 121
  plantar, 492–494, 515, 516
Appendices epiploicae, 260, 307, 317, 318, 354, 399
Appendix, vermiform, 257, 258, 297, 301, 302,
    304–306, 309–311, 374, 378
  blood supply to, 309
  location of, variations in, 310
  orifice of, 306
  vesicular, 372, 379–381
Appendix epididymis, 247, 249, 253
Appendix fibrosa hepatis, 273, 282
Appendix testis, 247–249, 253, 363
Arachnoid, 343, 570, 571, 573, 633, 679
Arachnoid granulations, 633–635
Arc, tendinous, 365, 376, 386
Arch(es), aortic. See *Aorta, arch of.*
  costal, 233, 242
  iliopectineal, 318
  jugular venous, 585, 726
  lumbocostal, lateral, 335
    medial, 219, 335
  mandibular, 699
  of atlas, anterior, 531, 540, 690, 726
    posterior, 528, 531, 536, 540
  of axis, 532–534
    posterior, 536
  of cricoid cartilage, 726, 735, 761
  palatoglossal, 729, 731, 732, 735, 737, 743
  palatopharyngeal, 726, 729, 731, 732, 735, 737,
    751, 755
  palmar, deep, 61, 111, 113, 182
    superficial, 62, 110, 111, 113, 182, 183
  palpebral arterial, inferior, 654, 655
    superior, 655
  plantar, 403, 497
  tendinous, of psoas major muscle, 333
    of soleus muscle, 434, 475
  venous, dorsal, of foot, 468
  vertebral, 543, 552, 553

Arch(es), vertebral, *continued*
    inferior, 548
    lamina of, 547, 549, 554
    lumbar, 565
    of 7th cervical vertebra, 542
    pedicles of, 557, 573
    zygomatic, 606, 608, 614, 615, 624, 625, 635, 646,
      748
Area, cardiac, 153
  of superficial cardiac dullness, 170
  interpleural, inferior, 153
    superior, 153
  thymic, 153
Area cribrosa, 325
Areola, 4, 257
Arm, 1, 37–40, 42, 47, 48, 53–64, 67, 68
  anatomy of, surface, 37
  arteries of, 54, 56, 58, 60, 62, 67, 68, 73
  arteriogram of, 73
  muscles of, 37, 47–49, 51, 53, 55, 57, 59
  nerves of, 38–40, 42, 47, 48, 54, 56, 58, 60, 67, 68
    cutaneous, distribution of, 39
  upper, deep fascia, 47, 48
  veins of, 40, 42, 47, 54
Arterial supply, of genitalia, female, 367, 368, 378,
    381, 388
  of menisci, 454
Arterial system, coronary, 196, 197
Arteriogram, brachial, 73
  of the hand, 113
Artery (arteries), alveolar, inferior, 618, 623–625,
    694, 737, 739, 740
    posterior superior, 618, 624
  angular, 618, 622–625, 654–657
    nasal branch of, 654
  anococcygeal, 346, 371
  appendicular, 296, 298, 309
  arcuate, of foot, 182, 402, 471
    of kidney, 325
  auricular, deep, 624, 625, 694
    posterior, 618, 622–625, 787
      occipital branch of, 527, 577, 580, 618
  axillary, 17, 20, 22, 54, 56, 62, 63, 182, 185, 187,
    188, 227, 581, 582, 596
  basilar, 569, 595, 643, 644
  brachial, 17, 18, 21, 22, 51, 54, 56, 58, 60, 62, 64,
    67, 68, 70–73, 82, 98, 182
    profunda, 54, 62, 64, 73, 182
  brachiocephalic, 172, 177, 182, 186, 189, 194,
    195, 216–218, 228, 586, 588
  bronchial, 184, 188, 218, 220, 229
  buccal, 618, 623–625
  bulbovestibular, 369
  cardiac, anterior, 190, 191
  caroticotympanic, 793
  carotid, 674
    common, 17, 20, 182, 188, 216, 224, 228, 576,
      579–585, 588, 591, 593, 595, 596, 608,
      618, 621, 625, 754, 756
    left, 151, 152, 172, 177, 178, 185, 186, 189,
      194, 195, 212, 214, 216, 217, 219, 586
    right, 172, 217, 594
    external, 182, 579–582, 588, 595, 600, 608,
      618, 623, 624, 693, 737, 740, 754, 756
      branches in skull, 618
    internal, 182, 581, 582, 588, 595, 618, 621, 623,
      637, 638, 640–644, 669, 670, 672, 685,
      693–695, 737, 740, 754, 755, 788, 793,
      794, 801, 802
  cerebellar, inferior, anterior, 595, 643, 644
    middle, 643
    posterior, 643, 644
    superior, 595, 643, 644
  cerebral, anterior, 595, 643, 644
    middle, left, 595, 643, 644
    posterior, 595, 643, 644
  cervical, ascending, 580–582, 596
    deep branch, 596

Artery (arteries), cervical, *continued*
  deep, 218, 528, 593, 596
  superficial, 11, 579–582, 592, 593, 596
  transverse, 579, 588, 592, 593, 596
    deep branch, 528, 579, 580
    superficial branch, 528, 579, 580, 582, 586
  choroidal, 643, 644
  ciliary, 674
    anterior, 678
    posterior, 678
      long, 678
  circumflex, femoral, lateral, 182, 402, 421
    ascending branch, 402
    descending branch, 402, 421
    medial, 182, 402, 421, 422
      acetabular branch, 428
      transverse branch, 421, 428
    humeral, anterior, 17, 22, 54, 62, 182
      posterior, 17, 19, 22, 24, 60, 62, 63, 182
        superficial branches, 42
    iliac, deep, 239, 245, 317, 338, 342, 376, 418
      lateral, 422
        ascending branch, 422
        descending branch, 422
      superficial, 11, 232, 239, 240, 245, 246
    scapular, 19, 22, 24
  colic, 320
    left, 296, 297, 303, 304, 317, 320, 321, 332
    middle, 277, 285, 296, 298, 302
    right, 285, 296–298
  communicating, anterior, 595, 643, 644
    posterior, 595, 643, 644
  conjunctival, 678
  coronary, complete arterial system, 196
    distribution of, balanced, 197
      left dominant, to heart wall, 198
      right dominant, to heart wall, 198
    left, 190, 191, 196–201, 215
      atrial branch, 196–199
      atrioventricular branch, 197, 198
      branch to atrioventricular node, 198
      branch to pulmonary trunk, 196
      circumflex branch, 190–192, 194–200
      diagonal branch, 196–199
      distribution of, dominant, to heart wall, 198
      interventricular branch, anterior, 190, 191, 194–199
        posterior, 198
      lateral branch, 198, 199
      marginal branch, 192, 196–199
      opening of, 212
      posterolateral branch, 197, 198
      septal branch, anterior, 196–199
        posterior, 198
    right, 190–192, 194–199, 201, 207, 214
      atrial branch, 196–199
      atrioventricular branch, 197, 199
      branch to atrioventricular node, 196, 197, 199
      branch to pulmonary trunk, 196–199
      branch to sinoatrial node, 196–199
      cardiac branch, anterior, 191
      distribution of, dominant, to heart wall, 198
      interventricular branch, posterior, 191, 192, 195–197, 199
      marginal branch, 196–199
      opening of, 212
      posterolateral branch, 196, 197, 199
      septal branch, posterior, 197, 199
      ventricular branch, 196–199
        posterior, 200
  cremasteric, 239, 246, 254, 347, 365
  cystic, 265
  deep, of penis, 248, 348, 361
  digital, dorsal, of hand, 112, 122
    of foot, 182, 402, 465, 471, 515
    palmar, common, 106, 110, 113
      proper, 106, 110, 111, 113, 122–124
    proper, of foot, 493, 496
  dorsal, of clitoris, 245, 369
    of penis, 347, 355, 366
  dorsalis pedis, 182, 402, 465, 471, 515
  epigastric, inferior, 11, 149, 182, 239, 243, 245, 253, 256, 297, 317, 318, 321, 338, 340, 342, 352, 364, 376, 383
    pubic branch, 243, 364
    superficial, 11, 232, 239, 240, 245, 246, 414
    superior, 11, 149, 230, 243, 255
  esophageal, 218, 220, 573
  ethmoid, anterior, 638, 670, 674, 676, 690, 693
    posterior, 674, 676

Artery (arteries), *continued*
  facial, 182, 581, 582, 585, 586, 597, 599, 600, 618, 622–625, 727, 737, 754
    transverse, 618, 622, 624, 654
  femoral, 182, 335, 341, 342, 402, 414, 418, 421, 422, 442, 486
    deep, 182, 342, 402, 418, 421, 422
  gastric, left, 182, 265, 266, 270–273, 277, 285, 300, 317, 318, 341
    right, 265, 270, 271, 300
    short, 266, 270
  gastroduodenal, 265, 266, 271, 331
  gastroepiploic, 273
    left, 265, 271
    right, 266, 270–272, 316
  genicular, descending, 182, 402, 414, 421, 422, 443, 486
    articular branch, 418, 422
    lateral, inferior, 402, 403, 443, 454, 465
      superior, 402, 441–443, 465
    medial, inferior, 402, 403, 422, 443, 454, 479
      superior, 402, 403, 422, 443, 465, 476, 487
    middle, 403, 442, 443
      anterior branch, 455
      posterior branch, 454
  gluteal, inferior, 182, 364, 403, 428, 430
    superior, 182, 314, 342, 364, 428, 430
  helicine, 361
  hemorrhoidal, 346
  hepatic, common, 182, 265, 266, 270, 271, 285, 300, 317
    left, 271
    middle, 271
    peritoneal fold over, 300
    proper, 270, 272, 277, 285
    right, 271, 300
  hypogastric, 364. See also *Artery, iliac, internal*
  ileal, 296–298
  ileocolic, 296–298, 309
  iliac, common, 178, 182, 304, 314, 316, 317, 320, 321, 338, 340–342, 354, 355, 364, 376, 382, 569
    external, 149, 178, 182, 243, 314, 317, 338, 340, 342, 352, 355, 359, 364, 376, 377, 383, 418
    internal, 178, 182, 314, 321, 342, 355, 364, 382, 418
  iliolumbar, 321, 338, 342, 364
  infraorbital, 618, 622–625, 655, 656, 676
    branch of, 654
  intercostal, 182, 184, 185, 195, 214, 217, 218, 227, 229, 230, 239, 240, 243, 255, 299, 526, 573
    anterior, 149, 596
    spinal branch of, 226, 569, 572
    supreme, 218, 219, 226, 593, 596
  interlobar, of kidney, 330, 332
  interosseous, anterior, 62, 70, 73, 76, 77, 100, 105, 113
    common, 62, 68, 70, 73, 99
    posterior, 62, 70, 73, 76, 78, 100
    recurrent, 62, 72, 73, 78
  interventricular, anterior, 204
  jejunal, 296–298, 332
  labial, anterior, 244, 245
    inferior, 618, 622
    posterior, 244, 245, 371
    superior, 618, 690
  labyrinthine, 595, 638, 642–644, 801, 802
  lacrimal, 653, 659, 670, 672, 674
    palpebral branch, lateral inferior, 656
      lateral superior, 656
  laryngeal, inferior, 588, 758
    internal, 588
    superior, 581, 593, 600, 741, 744, 748, 755, 756, 758, 770
  lingual, 182, 580, 600, 618, 623, 625, 727, 737, 739, 740, 754, 756
    deep, 740
    suprahyoid branch, 579
  lumbar, 182, 317, 321, 332, 338, 340, 342, 354
  malleolar, lateral, 402, 403, 465, 479
    medial, 402, 403, 471
  mammary, external, 11
  marginal, 296, 298
  masseteric, 623, 624, 740
  maxillary, 182, 618, 624, 640, 693, 694
  median, 62, 70, 100
  meningeal, accessory, 793
    anterior, 638, 670, 674, 676, 690
    middle, 182, 618, 624, 625, 634, 635, 638, 642, 670, 694, 801
      anterior branch, 634
      frontal branch, 635, 638

Artery (arteries), meningeal, *continued*
    orbital branch, 635
    parietal branch, 635
    petrosal branch, 638
    posterior branch, 634
    posterior, 754
  mental, 618, 622–624
    labial branches, 740
  mesenteric, inferior, 182, 285, 303, 304, 314, 316, 317, 320, 321, 338, 339, 355, 364
    superior, 182, 218, 226, 266, 272, 285, 286, 296–298, 303, 316, 317, 321, 331, 332, 338, 339, 341
  metacarpal, dorsal, 112
    palmar, 111
  metatarsal, dorsal, 182, 402, 465, 471, 516
    plantar, 493, 496, 497, 516
    perforating branch, 516
  musculophrenic, 149, 230
  mylohyoid, 624, 693, 694, 739, 740
  nasal, dorsal, 622, 623, 654, 674
    external, 654–657, 690
  nasopalatine, 690, 692, 693
  obturator, 182, 243, 314, 340, 342, 359, 364, 376, 383, 421, 422
    acetabular branch, 421
    anterior branch, 421
    pubic branch, 243, 364
  occipital, 527, 528, 577, 579, 581, 582, 618, 622–625, 638, 640, 755, 793
    descending branch, 527, 528
    mastoid branch, 527, 528, 582, 618
    sternocleidomastoid branch, 581, 618
  of ductus deferens, 254, 340, 355
  of foot, 471, 493, 496, 497
  of forearm, 67, 68, 70–72
  of hand, 112, 113
  of nasal septum, 690
  of palm, 62, 106, 110, 111
  of penile bulb, 346, 366
  of penis, 248, 348, 354, 361
  of pterygoid canal, 640, 693, 746
  of tongue, apex of, 740
  of upper extremity, 62
  ophthalmic, 638, 642, 643, 670, 672, 674, 676, 793
    palpebral branch, inferior medial, 656
  ovarian, left, 285, 318, 381, 383
    right, 318
  palatine, ascending, 618, 625, 693, 740, 746, 747, 754
    dorsal lingual branch, 746, 747
    descending, 618, 640, 693
    greater, 690, 692, 693, 731
    lesser, 693, 731
    tonsillar branch, 746
  palmar digital, common, 106, 110, 113
    proper, 106, 110, 111, 113, 122–124
    to thumb, 106, 111
  palpebral, medial, 622
  pancreaticoduodenal, inferior, 266, 296, 303
    superior, 266, 272
  perforating, 182, 402, 403, 422, 428, 430, 442, 443, 486
    anterior, 232
  pericardiacophrenic, 149, 175, 184, 186–188, 230, 573, 593
  perineal, 346
  peroneal, 182, 403, 442, 443, 476, 479, 490, 491
    perforating branch, 402, 465, 471
  pharyngeal, ascending, 618, 640, 740, 747, 754, 793
  phrenic, inferior, 216, 243, 265, 266, 300, 321, 338, 341
    superior, 230
  plantar, 471, 496
    lateral, 403, 496, 497, 515
    medial, 182, 403, 496, 497, 515
  popliteal, 182, 403, 426–428, 441–443, 454, 476, 479, 487, 489
  princeps pollicis, 105, 111, 113, 121
  profunda brachii, 56, 58, 60, 73
    deltoid branch, 58, 60
  pudendal, external, 11, 245, 246, 414
    superficial, 244
    internal, 314, 342, 346, 364, 371, 383, 428, 430
  pulmonary, 136, 164, 165, 176, 184, 185, 187–190, 192, 194, 195, 204, 208, 209, 212, 214, 215, 227
  radial, 41, 62, 67, 68, 70–73, 99–101, 105, 108, 110–113, 120, 182
    carpal branch, 62, 105, 111
    dorsal, 112

Artery (arteries), radial, *continued*
  carpal network of, dorsal, 112
    palmar branch, superficial, 67, 68, 70,
      110–112, 120
    perforating branch, 105, 112
  radial collateral, 58, 60, 62, 67, 70, 72, 73, 76, 78, 98
  radial recurrent, 62, 67, 68, 70, 72, 73
  radialis indicis, 112, 113
  rectal, inferior, 314, 315, 346
    middle, 314, 315, 364, 383
    superior, 303, 304, 314, 316, 317, 321, 382, 383
  renal, 178, 182, 226, 272, 285, 321–323, 325, 326,
    330–332, 339, 341, 569
    accessory, 321
  retinal, central, 678, 793
  sacral, lateral, 342, 354, 364
    middle, 182, 303, 314, 317, 320, 321, 338, 342,
      355, 364, 377, 382, 383
  scaphenous, 402
  scapular, descending, 20
    dorsal, 20, 527
  scrotal, anterior, 246
    posterior, 246, 346
  sigmoid, 303, 304, 316, 317, 321
  spermatic, 182, 248, 285
  sphenopalatine, 618, 625, 692, 693
  spinal, anterior, 226, 569, 572, 573, 643, 644
    posterior, 572, 643
  splenic, 182, 265, 266, 271, 272, 275, 278, 285,
    300, 317
  stapedius, 640, 789
  sternocleidomastoid, 618
  stylomastoid, 618, 624, 640, 793
  subclavian, 17, 20, 177, 182, 220, 569, 579–582,
    592, 593, 595, 596
    left, 151, 172, 176, 177, 185, 188, 189, 194, 195,
      215, 216, 218–220, 224, 586, 588, 593, 594,
      755
    right, 18, 172, 216–219, 224, 586, 594, 596, 755
  subcostal, 182, 218, 220, 300
  sublingual, 625, 737, 740, 746, 747, 756
  submental, 580–582, 597, 599, 600, 618, 624,
    625, 727
  subscapular, 17, 22, 182
    acromial branch, 24
  supraorbital, 622, 623, 654–657, 670, 672, 674
  suprarenal, 320, 321
    inferior, 318, 320, 322, 323
    middle, 320, 322, 323
    superior, 322, 323
  suprascapular, 22, 24, 579–582, 592, 593, 596
  supratrochlear, 622–625, 654, 655, 657, 674
  sural, 403, 441–443
  tarsal, 402, 471
  temporal, deep, 618, 624, 625
    middle, 618, 623–625
    superficial, 604, 618, 622–625
  testicular, 243, 254, 255, 317, 320, 321, 332, 338,
    340, 347
  thoracic, internal, 11, 17, 20, 149, 182, 184,
    186–188, 218, 220, 243, 581, 582, 585,
    592–594, 596
    perforating branches, 13
    lateral, 11, 13, 14, 17, 19, 20, 182
    supreme, 17, 182
  thoracoacromial, 13, 15, 17, 20, 24, 42, 182, 579,
    581, 582
    acromial branch, 582
  thoracodorsal, 7, 13, 14, 17, 19, 20, 22
  thymic, 175
    superior, 592
  thyroid, inferior, 226, 581, 582, 588, 591–593,
    596, 754–756, 758
    cervical branches, ascending, 592
    esophageal branch, 219
    superior, 152, 579–582, 588, 592, 593, 597,
      600, 618, 625, 726, 754, 756, 766
    cricothyroid branch, 592, 593
  tibial, anterior, 182, 402, 403, 442, 443, 465, 466,
    471, 479, 489–491
    posterior, 182, 403, 434, 442, 443, 476, 479,
      490, 491, 493, 496, 497
  tibial recurrent, anterior, 402, 442, 465
    posterior, 403, 443
  to sternoclavicular joint, 592
  tonsillar, 758
  tympanic, anterior, 624, 625, 694, 801
    inferior, 640, 754, 793
    posterior, 640, 787, 789, 793
    superior, 638, 642, 793, 801
  ulnar, 62, 67, 68, 70, 71, 73, 99–101, 105, 106,
    108, 110, 111, 113, 120, 182

Artery (arteries), *continued*
  carpal branch, dorsal, 62, 67
    palmar, 62
    palmar branch, deep, 113
  ulnar collateral, inferior, 54, 56, 58, 60, 62, 67,
    70, 71, 73, 78, 98
    superior, 54, 56, 62, 64, 67, 70, 71, 73, 98
  ulnar recurrent, 60, 62, 68, 70, 71, 73, 76, 99
  umbilical, 178, 181, 253, 255, 256, 259, 261, 319,
    352, 355, 364, 377, 382
    obliterated, 243, 340, 359
  uterine, 342, 381–383
    ovarian branch, 381
    tubal branch, 381, 382
  uteroplacental, 181
  vaginal, 381–383
  vertebral, 17, 20, 151, 182, 528, 529, 569, 581,
    582, 591–593, 595, 596, 638, 642–644, 685
    groove for, 530, 534, 543
    meningeal branch, 638
    spinal branch, 569
  vesicle, inferior, 243, 355, 364, 381, 382
    vaginal branch, 381, 382
    superior, 240, 243, 255, 340, 355, 383
  zygomaticofacial, 656, 657
  zygomatico-orbital, 618, 623, 624, 645–657
  zygomaticotemporal, 622
Articular capsule, cricothyroid, 757, 759
  of atlas, 539
  of axis, 539
  of elbow joint, 82, 91, 98
  of hip joint, 394–396, 437, 438
  of intervertebral joint, 526, 529
  of knee joint, 446, 448, 459
  of metacarpophalangeal joint, 114, 129
  of shoulder joint, 24, 30, 32–35, 49–51
  of talocalcaneonavicular joint, 515
  of tibiofibular joint, 459
  temporomandibular, 606, 608, 612, 614, 647, 748
Articulations, costosternal, 147
  costovertebral, 551
  of rib, head of, 554
Aryepiglottic fold, 746, 751, 753, 755, 764, 767, 769,
  771
Atlas, 151, 530, 531, 533–540, 543, 565
  arch of, anterior, 531, 540, 690, 726
    posterior, 528, 531, 533, 536, 540
  body of, 530, 531, 533–536, 540
  facet of, articular, inferior, 531, 533
    superior, 530, 531, 533, 537
  foramen of, transverse, 530, 531
    vertebral, 530, 531
  fovea for dens, 530, 533, 537
  ligament of, transverse, 537, 540, 722, 726
  mass of, lateral, 530, 531
  process of, transverse, 258, 526, 529–531, 534,
    539, 594
  tubercle of, anterior, 530, 531, 594
    posterior, 523, 526, 530, 531, 540
Atrioventricular bundle, 191, 210, 213
  left branch, 210–213
  right branch, 213
Atrioventricular opening, 213, 215
  left, 206, 212
  right, 202–204, 214
Atrium, of heart, left, 136, 158, 159, 181, 190, 192,
  195, 201, 206, 207, 211, 214, 215, 257
  right, 136, 150, 158, 159, 181, 190, 192, 194, 195,
    201–203, 257
Auditory tube. See *Tube, auditory*
Auricle, of heart, left, 150, 176, 188, 190, 192, 194,
  195, 204, 206, 208, 210, 212, 215
  right, 136, 176, 188, 190, 194, 202, 208, 209
Axilla, 14, 19, 20, 63
  nerves and vessels of, 37
Axis, 532–540, 543
  arch of, anterior, 531–534, 540, 690, 726
    posterior, 528, 531, 536, 540
  body of, 532, 533, 535–540
    capsule of, articular, 539
  dens of, 532, 533, 538, 540, 543, 690
  foramen of, transverse, 532, 533
  process of, articular, 532, 533
    inferior, 532, 533
    superior, 532
    odontoid, 532, 533, 538, 690
    spinous, 528, 533, 537
    bifid, 532
    transverse, 529, 532, 533
  surface of, articular, posterior, 532
    superior, 533
Azygos system of veins, 221

Back, cross section of, 522
  muscles of, 523–526
    deep, 524–526
    intermediate layer, 524
  region of, lumbosacral, 521
  vessels and nerves of, 527, 528
Bicuspid tooth, 699
Bifurcation, aortic, 303, 364
  tracheal, 157, 168, 214–216, 768
Bile duct, common, 265, 268, 272, 283, 284,
  286–293, 300, 317, 331
Bladder, urinary, 240, 243, 253, 255–257, 305, 310,
  316, 317, 319, 321, 335, 340, 353–355,
  359–361, 363, 372–374, 378, 382, 383, 385,
  399
  apex of, 318, 343, 352, 356, 358
  base of, 357
  body of, 352
  fundus of, 352
  surface of, posterior, 358
  uvula of, 356
Blood vessels. See *Artery (Arteries); Vein(s);
  Vessel(s)*
Bone(s), calcaneus, 501, 502, 504, 508, 511
  tuberosity of, 413, 467, 473, 474, 477, 492, 494,
    495, 503, 509, 511, 513, 514
  capitate, 118, 120, 129, 131–135
  carpal, 118
  clavicle, 6, 16, 20–22, 24, 25, 29, 31, 34, 36, 49,
    51–53, 55, 57, 61, 136–138, 140, 144, 148,
    150–152, 176, 184–186, 188, 227, 231, 233,
    256–258, 524, 574–576, 579, 582, 583, 586
    border of, anterior, 138
    extremity of, acromial, 33, 34, 139
      sternal, 138, 139
    foramen of, nutrient, 138
  coccyx, 25, 344, 370, 387, 393, 544, 546, 561, 562
    body of, 377
    horn of, 561, 562
    vertebral column, part of, 544–546
  cuboid, 501–504, 510, 511, 515
  cuneiform of foot, 462, 501–504, 510, 513
  ethmoid, 601, 687–689
    lamina of, orbital, 610, 661, 662, 687, 688
    plate of, cribriform, 645, 683, 684, 686, 687,
      689
    perpendicular, 613, 683, 687–689
    process of, uncinate, 688
  femur, 25, 423, 431–434, 445, 447–450, 457, 458,
    486, 487
    body of, 432, 446, 457
    condyle of, lateral, 433, 442, 446, 449–451,
      457–459
      medial, 417, 419, 420, 433, 442, 446, 448,
        450, 451, 457, 459, 464
    end of, distal, 449, 450
    epicondyle of, 432, 433
      lateral, 412, 446, 449, 450, 457
      medial, 446, 450, 457
    foramen of, nutrient, 434
    fossa, intercondylar, 433, 442, 448, 450, 457,
      459
    head of, 401, 433, 438, 439
      fovea of, 401, 432, 433
    line of, epiphysial, distal, 459
    linea aspera, 430, 433, 440, 448, 486
    neck of, 401, 432, 433, 436
    of fetus, 400
    popliteus muscle, notch for attachment of, 449
    surface of, articular, 450
      meniscofemoral, 448, 459
      patellar, 432, 442, 446, 450, 451
      popliteal, 433, 440, 443, 448, 477
  fibula, 447, 448, 451, 452, 457, 482, 483, 485, 489,
    491, 505, 508, 512
    body of, 457
    crest of, medial, 477, 478, 490
    end of, proximal, 452
    head of, 442, 444–446, 452, 457, 459, 463, 466,
      467, 480, 485
      apex of, 452, 457
      ligament of, anterior, 446
        posterior, 448
      margin of, anterior, 490
        interosseous, 490
        posterior, 485, 490
    of fetus, 400
    process of, styloid, 485
    surface of, lateral, 485, 490
      posterior, 490
  frontal, 601, 635, 645, 659, 662, 664, 667, 675, 689
    process of, zygomatic, 671, 689

Bone(s), frontal, *continued*
  squama of, 610
  surface of, internal, 663
    orbital, 728
hamate, 118, 120, 129, 132–135
  hamulus of, 108, 118, 131, 133, 135
humerus, 17, 30, 31, 34, 49, 52, 63, 64, 83–86
  body of, 34, 51, 55, 82, 83, 91, 92, 96, 97
  capitulum of, 84, 86, 94–97
  diaphysis of, 94, 95
  epicondyle of, lateral, 42, 48, 51, 57, 58, 60, 61,
      74–77, 81, 83, 84, 86, 91, 92, 97, 98, 303
    medial, 37, 49, 50, 53, 55, 56, 65–68, 70, 71,
      76, 81, 83, 84, 86, 91, 92, 96–98, 303
  epiphysis of, 94
  extremity of, distal, 86
  foramen of, nutrient, 52, 84
  fossa of, coronoid, 82, 84, 98
    olecranon, 82, 83, 96, 97
    radial, 84, 96
  groove, for ulnar nerve, 86
    radial, 83
  head of, 6, 25, 26, 34, 50, 63, 83, 85
  muscle attachment, sites of, 85
  neck of, anatomical, 34, 36, 83–85
    surgical, 23, 34, 36, 59, 83
  of fetus, 400
  process of, coronoid, 84
  sulcus of, intertubercular, 84, 85
  trochlea of, 82–84, 86, 96–98
  tubercle of, greater, 30, 32, 36, 83–85
    lesser, 84, 85
    crest of, 36, 84
  tuberosity of, deltoid, 84
hyoid, 151, 217, 233, 257, 576, 583, 586, 588, 592,
    593, 598, 599, 608, 625, 722, 726, 734, 736,
    756, 763, 764, 766, 769
  body of, 574, 589, 598, 615, 728, 760
  horn of, greater, 589, 590, 598, 722, 728, 741,
    744, 748, 750, 751, 753, 755, 757–759, 763
    lesser, 589, 615, 722, 728, 745, 757, 759, 763
ilium, 25, 386, 387
  ala of, 389–391, 401
  body of, 389–392
  crest of, 232, 257, 258, 298, 333, 335, 339, 359,
    387, 389–393, 401, 424, 430, 521, 523
  of newborn, 563
  tuberosity of, 390
incus, body of, 781, 782, 791, 797
  crus of, long, 784, 785, 791, 792, 797
    short, 780, 787, 791, 792, 797, 801
  fossa for, 778, 791
  ligaments of, 801
    superior 791
  process of, lenticular, 785, 791
ischium, 359, 388–393
lacrimal, 601, 728
lunate, 118, 120, 131–135
malleus, head of, 780–782, 787–789, 791, 792,
    797, 801
  ligament of, 791, 801
  manubrium of, 789, 791
  neck of, 785
  process of, lateral, 780, 787, 797
mandible, 599, 601, 625, 629, 631, 692, 693, 697,
    698, 708, 722, 726, 736, 744, 750
  angle of, 574, 612, 613, 647, 697, 698, 700, 728
  arch of, 699
  base of, 610, 647
  body of, 574, 583, 598, 601, 700, 728
    depression of, sublingual, 698
      submandibular, 698
  canal of, 709, 711, 720, 721
  head of, 615, 698, 700
  line of, oblique, 697
  lingula of, 613, 698, 700
  neck of, 647, 698
  notch of, 700
  of 9-year-old child, 710
  part of, alveolar, 697
  process of, condyloid, 574, 598, 610, 612, 614,
      697, 698, 700
    coronoid, 598, 610, 612, 697, 700, 728
  ramus of, 601, 608, 613, 697, 700, 722, 728,
    737, 740, 754
  trigone of, retromolar, 740
  tuberosity of pterygoid, 614, 730
maxilla, 601, 629, 640, 664, 667, 708, 710
  crest of, ethmoidal, 684
  hiatus of, 684
  process of, alveolar, 601, 662, 731
    frontal, 601, 651, 658, 660, 682

Bone(s), maxilla, *continued*
  palatine, 631, 683, 684, 702
    zygomatic, 646, 662, 702
  metacarpal, 79, 109, 112, 118, 121, 132–135
    base of, 132, 133, 135
    body of, 132
    head of, 132, 135
  metatarsal, 462, 501, 503, 508–511
    base of, 510, 511, 513
    tuberosity of, 501, 503, 510, 511, 513
  nasal, 601, 603, 606, 610, 626, 651, 661, 662, 682,
    684, 689, 722, 726
  navicular, 501–504, 510, 511, 515
    tuberosity of, 513
  occipital, 534, 535, 538, 539, 563, 626, 629, 637,
    645, 726
    condyle of, 615, 647
    part of, basilar, 535, 536, 540, 594, 645
      lateral, 535, 629, 631
    process of, jugular, 645
    squama of, 540, 630, 631
    tubercle of, pharyngeal, 646, 751
  of fetus, 400
  of skull. See names of specific bones
palatine, 631, 646, 702
  lamina of, horizontal, 631, 646, 684, 702
  plate of, perpendicular, 684
  process of, orbital, 662
    pyramidal, 646, 702
parietal, 601, 626, 631, 633, 635, 645, 663
  diploë of, 635
  line of, superior temporal, 610
  table of, external, 635
    internal, 635
patella, 412, 416, 417, 419, 420, 424, 442,
    444–446, 457, 458, 461, 468
  apex of, 446
  base of, 446
  surface of, articular, 458
    posterior, ridge of, 446
pelvic, 389–392. See also *Pelvis*
phalanx (phalanges), of foot, 501, 503
  of hand, 109, 118, 119, 123, 124, 132, 135
    distal phalanx, base of, 4th finger, 132
      tuberosity of, 118, 132
    middle phalanx, 4th finger, 132
      middle finger, 124
      head of, 4th finger, 132
      tuberosity of, little finger, 132
    proximal, 4th finger, 132
      middle finger, 123
      base of, little finger, 132
pisiform, 108, 110, 114, 120, 131, 133, 135
pubic, surface for symphysis pubis, 439
radius, 48, 61, 75, 77, 79, 89–93, 96, 97, 99–101,
    114, 118, 129, 131–135
  body of, 79, 90, 96, 97
  crest of, interosseous, 89, 90
  diaphysis of, 95
  epiphysis of, 94
  extremity of, distal, 69
  foramen of, nutrient, 89
  head of, 69, 79, 88, 90, 91, 93, 95–97
  margin of, interosseous, 132
  neck of, 88, 90, 96, 97
  notch of, ulnar, 133
  of fetus, 400
  process of, styloid, 37, 89, 90, 118, 129, 131, 133
  surface of, posterior, 132
  tuberosity of, 89, 96, 97
rib(s), 146, 157, 158, 518, 550, 553
  1st, 137, 140, 143, 145, 146, 150, 152, 184, 185,
    219, 227, 524, 574, 582, 586–588, 593, 594
  2nd, 25, 36, 137, 140, 143, 146, 148, 149, 175,
    574, 587, 593, 594
  3rd, 143, 146, 148, 149
  4th, 137, 146, 148, 149, 186
  5th, 146, 186
  6th, 137, 227, 231, 523
  7th, 137, 148
  8th, 143, 146
  9th, 146, 238
  10th, 146, 238, 299, 359
  11th, 25, 137, 140, 320, 339, 359, 521
  12th, 16, 25, 137, 140, 218, 320, 333, 526
  angle of, 146
    costodiaphragmatic, 170
  body of, 143, 573
  cartilage of, costal, 144, 146–148, 158, 237,
    238, 255
  crest of, 143
  extremity of, sternal, 143

Bone(s), rib(s), *continued*
  head of, 143, 551, 573
    ligaments of, 299
  neck of, 143, 554, 573
    ligaments of, 299
  of fetus, 298
  osseous part of, 146
  spaces of, intercostal, 146
  tubercle of, 143, 551, 554
sacrum, 25, 258, 320, 354, 386, 387, 544, 546, 557,
    561, 565
  ala of, anterior aspect, 559
  apex of, 559, 560
  coccyx and, lateral view, 561
  crest of, intermediate, 560
    lateral, 560
    median, 386, 394, 560, 561
  foramina of, dorsal, 560
  horn of, 521, 560, 561
  lateral part, 401, 559
  lines of, transverse, 559
  process of, articular, superior, 386, 560
  promontory of, 319, 335
  ridges of, 559
  surface of, anterior, 559
    articular, 559–561
    pelvic, 559
    posterior, 560
    terminal, superior, 559
  tuberosity of, 560, 561
  vertebral column, part of, 544–546
scaphoid, 118, 120, 129, 132–134
  tuberosity of, 135
scapula, 6, 25–28, 32, 50, 52, 140, 157
  acromion of, 15, 21, 23, 26–31, 33–37, 51, 61,
    137, 140, 233, 257, 258, 524, 574, 576
  angle of, inferior, 26, 27, 34, 36, 258
    lateral, 26, 27
    superior, 21, 26, 27, 34, 36, 51, 258, 523
  border of, lateral, 26–28, 34, 36
    medial, 26, 27, 34, 36, 205
    superior, 26, 27
  cavity of, glenoid, 26–30, 34–36, 137
  foramen of, nutrient, 34
  fossa of, infraspinatus, 26, 34
    supraspinatus, 26, 34, 574
  labrum of, glenoid, 34
  neck of, 26, 27, 34
  of fetus, 398
  process of, coracoid, 6, 15, 16, 21, 22, 26–29,
    31, 32, 35, 36, 49, 53, 136, 137, 151, 257, 574
  spine of, 23, 24, 26, 30, 32–34, 36, 51, 61, 258,
    523
  surface of, dorsal, 26, 28, 34
    ventral, 27, 28
  tubercle of, infraglenoid, 6, 26, 28
  view of, posterior, 52
sesamoid, 118, 131, 132, 135, 503, 504
sphenoid, 601, 636, 645, 659, 661, 662, 667–669,
    675
  body of, 613, 636, 640, 662, 663, 684, 726
  lingula of, 645
  process of, pterygoid, 612, 613, 615, 631, 646,
    647, 663, 684
    lateral lamina of, 662
  section through, sagittal, 636
  sella turcica, 613, 636, 685, 691
  spine of, 735
  tuberosity of, pterygoid, 698, 700
  wing of, greater, 601, 614, 629, 646, 728
    lesser, 601, 635, 642, 645, 663
stapes, 781, 782, 785, 788, 793, 805
  base of, 797
  crus of, anterior, 795–797
    posterior, 784, 795–797
  head of, 789, 795, 796, 798
sternum, 141, 145, 157, 158, 177, 188, 208, 209,
    227, 243
  body of, 141, 142, 145, 214
  manubrium of, 141, 142, 144, 145, 147, 149,
    175, 188, 212, 587, 726
  notch of, clavicular, 141, 142
    costal, 141, 142
    jugular, 141
  ossification, centers of, 145
  process of, xiphoid, 141, 142, 145, 176, 186,
    188, 230, 255, 299, 399
  surface of, articular, 138
talus, 502, 504, 510, 512, 515
tarsal, 503
temporal, 601, 663, 694, 754, 779, 787, 789, 790,
    794, 800

Bone(s), temporal, *continued*
  border of, occipital, 777
    parietal, 777
    crest of, supramastoid, 787, 789
    notch of, mastoid, 777
    part of, petrous, 594, 629, 645, 647, 749, 777, 790, 801
      squamous, 629, 631, 645, 669, 777, 786
      tympanic, 774, 777, 790
        vaginal process of, 790
    process of, mastoid, 574, 594, 615, 623, 646, 748, 751, 754, 755, 774, 777–779, 788, 790
      styloid, 529, 574, 608, 610, 612, 613, 615, 646, 722, 737, 740, 744, 745, 748, 751, 753, 754, 774, 776, 778, 790
      vaginal, 790
      zygomatic, 612, 777, 789
    tubercle of, articular, 614, 646, 735, 777
  thoracic, anterior, 148. See also *Thorax*
  tibia, 444, 446–448, 451, 452, 457, 458, 462, 471, 477, 478, 480–483, 491, 508, 509, 512
    area of, intercondylar, anterior, 452, 457
      posterior, 452
    body of, 457
    condyle of, lateral, 442, 446, 452, 453, 457, 459, 481, 484
      medial, 442, 446, 448, 452, 453, 457, 459, 474, 478, 481, 484
    condyles of, showing menisci, and origins of cruciate ligaments, 453
    eminence of, intercondylar, 484
    end of, proximal, 452
    extremity of, distal, 484
    groove of, malleolar, 484
    line of, epiphysial, proximal, 459
    soleal, 448, 484
    margin of, anterior, 490
      interosseous, 484, 489
      medial, 484, 490
    of fetus, 400
    shaft of, 481
    surface of, articular, inferior, 481
      lateral, 490
      medial, 464, 466, 489, 490
      meniscotibial, 448, 459
      popliteal, 448
      posterior, 484, 490
    tubercle of, intercondylar, lateral, 446, 452, 457
      medial, 442, 446, 452, 457, 459
    tuberosity of, 442, 444, 446, 452, 464, 466, 467, 480, 481
  trapezium, 118, 132–135
  trapezoid, 118, 129, 132–135
  triquetral, 118, 120, 129, 132–135
  ulna, 77, 79, 91–93, 97, 99–101, 114, 118, 129–135
    circumference of, articular, 87
    crest of, interosseous, 87, 88
      supinator, 88
    diaphysis, 94, 95
    disc, articular, 132
    epicondyle, medial, 67
    extremity of, distal, 74
    foramen of, nutrient, 87
    head of, 50, 79, 87, 88, 118, 132, 134
    margin of, interosseous, 132
      posterior, 51, 99, 100
    notch of, trochlear, 87, 88, 93, 96, 133
    of fetus, 451
    olecranon, 96, 97
      styloid, 37, 87, 88, 114, 118, 129, 131–133, 135
    surface of, anterior, 87, 100
      lateral, 88
      medial, 100
      posterior, 87, 88, 100, 132
    tuberosity of, 87, 88
  vertebral, See *Atlas; Axis; Vertebra(e)*
  vomer, ala of, 726
  zygomatic, 601, 603, 612, 624, 625, 629, 651, 652, 661, 671
    surface of, orbital, 661
Brain, 633
  cerebellum, 639, 644
  convolutions of, markings of, 645
  cortex, cerebral, 633
  gyrus. See *Gyrus*
  hemisphere, cerebral, 669
  lobe of, frontal, 635
  mammillary body, 639
  medulla oblongata, 563, 566, 638, 639

Brain, *continued*
  of newborn, 563
  vessels of, 643, 644
  view of, ventral, 639
Brain stem, 565
Breast, female, lymphatic drainage of, 5. See also *Mammary gland*
Bronchial tree, diagram of, 169
  divisions of, bronchopulmonary and lobar, 169
Bronchopulmonary segments, of lung, 162, 163, 166, 167, 169
Bronchus (Bronchi), divisions of, segmental, 168
  eparterial, to upper lobe of right lung, 165
  hyparterial, to middle and lower lobes of right lung, 165
  lobar, left, 168
    right, 168, 220, 228, 229
  primary, 187, 216
    left, 164, 168, 185, 218, 220, 224, 258
    right, 165, 168, 184, 216–218, 224, 227, 228, 258
  view of, with larynx and trachea, anterior aspect, 168
Bulb, inferior, of internal jugular vein, 576, 586, 587, 754, 755, 782
  of duodenum (1st part), 269, 294, 331
  of penis, 343, 352, 359, 361
  olfactory, 639, 644, 690, 691
  vestibular, 368, 371, 372, 382, 388
Bulla ethmoidalis, 585
Bundle, atrioventricular, 191, 207, 210–213
Bursa(e), anserine, 489
  between pectoralis major and long tendon of biceps, 49
  bicipitoradial, 66, 99
  coccygeal, subcutaneous, 523
  deep to obturator internus muscle, 429
  iliopectineal, 420, 423, 431
  infrapatellar, 416, 445, 453, 455, 456, 458, 463
    deep, 446
  infraspinatus, 63
  intermuscular, 429
    beneath gluteus maximus muscle, 430
  ischial, 434
    beneath obturator internus tendon, 434
  of calcaneal tendon, 462, 463
  of gastrocnemius muscle, 477, 478
  of knee joint, cast of, 455
  of latissimus dorsi muscle, 53
  of olecranon, 82, 98
    subcutaneous, 48
  of popliteus, muscle, 448
  of semimembranosus muscle, 448, 477
    lining of, 448
  of tibial collateral ligament, deep to, 459
  of tibial tuberosity, 489
  of triceps muscle, 98
  omental, 262B, 264, 275, 277, 300, 305, 331, 332
    development of, stages in, 263
    recess of, inferior, 275
      splenic, 275, 300
      superior, 264, 275
    vestibule of, 275, 277
  pharyngeal, 726
  prepatellar, 416, 455, 458
    subcutaneous 444
  sacral, subcutaneous, 521, 523
  semimembranosus, 478
  subacromial, 13, 30, 31, 35
  subanserina, 423
  subcoracoid, 21, 34, 35, 49
  subdeltoid, 23, 49, 51, 59, 63
  subgastrocnemius, 474
  subhyoid, 741, 760, 769
  subsartorial, 423
  subscapular, 34, 35, 63
  subsemimembranosus, 448, 474, 477
    lining of, 448
  suprapatellar, 445, 455, 456, 458, 487
  synovial, subcutaneous, over posterior superior iliac spine, 430
    over sacrum, 430
  trochanteric, 427, 429, 430, 434, 523

Calcaneal region, 1
Calf, of leg, 520
Calvaria, viewed from above, 626
Calyx (Calyces), renal, 325, 327, 331, 332
  major, 327
  minor, 327
Canal(s), adductor, 386, 419, 421
  opening of, 440
    tendinous cover of, 419, 440

Canal(s), *continued*
  Alcock's, 314, 344, 345
  anal, inner surface of, 312
  carotid, 594, 646, 647, 778, 781, 791, 798
  carpal, 108
  cervical, of uterus, 377, 380
  cochlear, 640
  condyloid, 645–647
  facial, 778, 787, 788, 790, 793, 795, 796, 799
    hiatus of, 778
    prominence of, 778, 787, 789, 795, 799
    view of, lateral, 793
  gastric, 268
  hypoglossal, 536, 594, 613, 645, 646
  incisive, 683, 684
  infraorbital, 661, 663
  inguinal, 237, 245, 248, 253
    opened, 245
  mandibular, 709, 711, 720, 721
  mastoid, 646
  mental, 721
  musculotubal, 594
    septum of, 791
  obturator, 243, 386, 423, 439
  optic, 645, 662, 669, 670, 676
  palatine, greater, 663
  pterygoid, 663
  pudendal, 314, 344, 345, 387
  sacral, 355, 386, 438, 560
  Schlemm's, 678, 680
  semicircular, 789, 793, 800–805
    anterior, 640, 789, 793, 801–805
      crus of, common, 801
    lateral, 640, 778, 787, 789, 790, 792, 793, 795–798, 800–805
    posterior, 789, 801–805
    view of, lateral, 793
  vertebral, spinal cord within, dorsal view, 230, 565
Canaliculus (Canaliculi), alveolar, 720, 721
  cochlear, 805
  lacrimal, 656, 658, 660
    inferior, 656, 658
      ampulla of, 658, 660
    superior, 656, 658
Canine tooth, 699, 701, 705, 708–711, 713, 714, 717
Capitulum, of humerus, 84, 86, 94–97
Capsule, articular. See *Articular capsule*
  fibrous, of kidney, 322, 323, 325, 331, 332
    of penis, 348
    of spleen, 278
    of perirenal fat, 332
    of suprarenal gland, 300, 324
    of thyroid, 591
  Tenon's, 669, 677
Cardiac antrum, 216
Cardiac area, 153
Cardiac dullness, superficial, area of, 170
Cardiac notch, 153, 170
Carina, 768
Cartilage(s), alar, greater, of nose, 655–657, 682, 683, 690, 726
    lesser, of nose, 682
  annular, 726
  arytenoid, 759, 760, 762, 764, 768–770
    process of, muscular, 761, 765
      vocal, 761, 767, 770–772
  bronchial, 168
  corniculate, 759, 761, 764
    tubercle of, 726, 751, 753, 755, 765, 767–769
  costal, 144, 146–148, 158, 237, 238, 255
  cricoid, 136, 168, 257, 574, 583, 593, 726, 747, 757, 760–762, 764–766, 769, 770
    arch of, 726, 735, 761, 763
    origin of, 745
  cuneiform 753, 764, 765
  of acoustic meatus, external, 608, 787
  of auditory tube, 647, 690, 693, 746, 747, 753, 780
  of ear, external, 774
  of epiglottis, 726, 736, 769
  of larynx, 757, 759, 760
  of nose, accessory, 656
    at apex of, 722
    external, 682
    lateral, 655, 657, 682, 683, 722
    septal, 682, 683, 690, 726
  thyroid, 136, 152, 168, 228, 257, 583, 593, 726, 736, 744, 745, 747, 748, 756–760, 762–764, 769, 770
    border of, superior, 761
    horn of, inferior, 757–759, 763
      superior, 589, 751, 753, 757–761, 763

Cartilage(s), thyroid, *continued*
 lamina of, 217, 583, 652
  origin of, 745
  surface of, articular, 762, 765
  tubercle of, inferior, 735, 744, 745
 tracheal, 168, 217, 591, 744, 745, 748, 753, 757,
   759, 762, 763, 766, 769
 triteceal, 757, 759, 763
Caruncle, lacrimal, 648, 649, 655, 657, 658, 660, 677
 sublingual, 722, 726, 733, 734, 737, 738, 740, 746
Caruncula lacrimalis, 648, 649, 655, 657, 658, 660,
  677
Cauda equina, 340, 563, 567
Cavity, abdominal. See *Abdominal cavity*
 cranial, 635
 glenoid, 26–30, 34–36, 137
 nasal. See *Nasal cavity*
 oral, 740, 746, 747
 pericardial, 159, 215, 299
 peritoneal, 215, 262, 299, 300, 331, 332
 pharyngeal, 691, 726, 732, 751, 770
 pleural, 152, 157, 158, 299, 300, 331
 pulp, of tooth, 703, 720, 721
 tympanic. See *Tympanic cavity*
 uterine, 377, 380
Cavum conchae, 773
Cecum, 257, 258, 260, 261, 272, 297, 301, 302, 305,
  306, 310, 311, 374, 378
 of cupula, 805
 vestibular, 800, 805
Cells, air, ethmoid, 595, 669, 675, 686–688, 750
 mastoid, 595, 640, 695, 750, 751, 778, 779, 790,
   792, 793, 801, 802
 tympanic, 778
Cementum, 703
Cerebellum 639, 644
 of newborn, 563
Cerebral, convolutions, markings of, 645
Cerebral cortex, 633
Cerebral hemisphere, 669
 gyrus of, 639
  occipitotemporal, 639
  orbital, 639
  parahippocampal, 639
Cervix, of uterus, 379–381
Chiasma, optic, 639, 644, 668
Choana, 631, 646, 732, 751
Chorda tympani, 781
Chordae tendinae, 204, 206
Chorioid, 678–680
Chorion, 181
Chorion laeve, 181
Chorion villi, 181
Ciliary body, 680
 pigmented layer of, 680
Circulation of blood, 178, 181–183
 arterial, 182
 fetal, 181
 of newborn, 178
 schema of, 183
Cisterna chyli, 183, 318, 320, 341
Cleft, palpebral, 653
Clinoid process, anterior and posterior, of sphenoid
  bone, 645, 686
Clitoris, 367, 376
 crus of, 368, 372, 388
 frenulum of, 367, 368, 377, 388
 prepuce of, 244
Clivus, 613, 683, 747, 750, 751
Coat, longitudinal, of rectum, 312, 313
 muscular, of gall bladder, 284
  of stomach, 268, 270
 serous, of gall bladder, 284
  of spleen, 278
  of stomach, 268
Coccygeal horn, 561, 562
Cochlea, 640
 canaliculus of, 805
 coil of, basal, 800
 cupula of, 800, 805
 lamina of, osseous spiral, 640, 800
Cochlear window, 640, 799, 805
Cochleariform process, 778, 781, 789, 791, 796, 798
Colliculus, prostatic, 356, 361
Colon, ascending, 136, 257, 259–261, 272, 277, 295,
  298, 301, 304–306, 310, 311, 320, 328, 331,
  399
 descending, 256–258, 272, 302–304, 310, 311,
  328, 332, 399
 flexure of, splenic, 260, 311, 331
 sigmoid, 257–260, 272, 297, 298, 302–305, 310,
  317, 318, 340, 342, 344, 354, 374, 377

Colon, *continued*
 transverse, 136, 215, 257, 259–261, 273, 277,
  295–297, 301, 302, 305, 307, 310, 311, 332
 wall of, free of omentum, 305
Columns anal, 312, 342
 renal, 325, 327
Commissure, labial, anterior, 367
 posterior, 367, 388
 of aortic semilunar valve, 212
 palpebral, lateral, 648, 677
  medial, 677
Concha(e), nasal, 601, 751
 inferior, 601, 684, 685, 691–693, 732
 middle, 601, 684, 685, 688, 691–693, 732
 superior, 684, 685, 692, 693, 732
 of ear, 773
Conjunctiva, 648, 649, 665, 671, 680
 bulbar, 649, 657
 fold of, semilunar, 649, 658
 fornix of, inferior, 649, 657, 673
  superior, 673
 palpebral, 649, 653, 657
Conus arteriosus, 136, 176, 188, 190, 194, 204,
  208
Conus elasticus, 761, 762, 769
Conus medullaris, 563, 566, 567
Convolutions, cerebral, markings of, 645
Cord, of brachial plexus, lateral, 22, 54
 medial, 19, 54
 posterior, 19, 54
 oblique, 50, 80, 91, 93
 spermatic, 12, 231, 232, 236–239, 242, 246, 247,
  251, 341, 347, 354, 355, 416
 nerves of, 347
 vessels of, 347
 umbilical, 178, 255, 399
Cornea, 664, 665, 680
 epithelium of, anterior, 680
 membranes of, limiting, 680
 plexus of, marginal, 678
Corona, of glans penis, 246, 343, 349, 351, 352, 361
Coronary arterial system, 196, 197
Corpus albicans, 380
Corpus cavernosum penis, 248, 348, 352, 355, 363,
Corpus cavernosus, of clitoris, 368, 377, 388
Corpus luteum 380
Corpum spongiosum penis, 248, 343, 344, 352, 363
Cortex, adrenal, 324
 glomerulosa of, 324
 reticularis of, 324
 cerebral, 633
 renal, 325, 327, 331
Costal margin, 7, 61
Cranial cavity, 635
 base of, 638, 801
Crease, palmar, longitudinal, medial, 37
 radial, 37
 transverse, distal, 37
  proximal, 37
Crest, infratemporal, 646
 intertrochanteric, 400, 401
 lacrimal, anterior, 661, 662
  posterior, 661, 662
 occipital, internal, 645
 supraventricular, of right atrium, 204, 209
 tympanic, 735
Crista galli, 645, 668, 683, 684, 686–688
 ala of, 687
Crista terminalis, 201, 202, 208
Crista vestibuli, 640
Crus (Crura), anterior, of stapes, 795–797
 common, anterior and posterior, of semicircular
  canals, 801
 lateral, of greater alar cartilage, 682
  of superficial inguinal ring, 231, 235, 236, 244,
   245, 248, 253, 333
 long, of incus, 784, 785, 791, 792, 797
 medial, of greater alar cartilage, 682
  of superficial inguinal ring, 12, 231, 235, 236,
   239, 244–246, 248, 253
 of antihelix, 773
 of clitoris, 368, 372, 388
 of diaphragm, 215, 216, 221, 223, 230, 299, 329,
  333, 335
 of helix, 773
 of penis, 352, 354, 359, 361
 posterior, of stapes, 784, 795–797
 short, of incus, 780, 787, 791, 792, 797, 801
Crus membranaceum commune, 803
Crus membranaceum simplex, 803
Crypts tonsillar, 743
Cubital region, anterior, 1

Cupula, cecum of, 805
 of cochlea, 800, 805
 of diaphragm, 227
 of pleura, cervical, 153–155, 170, 215, 219, 227,
  258, 593
 of recess, epitympanic, 781
Cusp(s), of tooth, buccal, 704
 lingual, 704
 of valve, mitral, anterior, 206, 207, 212
  posterior, 201, 206, 212
  tricuspid, dorsal, 201–204, 208, 214
  septal, 201–204, 208, 214
  ventral, 202–204, 208, 214
Cutaneous nerve fields, in leg and foot, 409–411
 in the thigh, 408, 409
 of femoral nerve and its saphenous branch,
  409
 of peripheral nerves in the thigh, 408
 of peroneal nerve, 411
 of sural nerve, 410, 411
 of tibial nerve branches, 410
Cutaneous nerves, distribution of, in lower
  extremity, 405, 407
 in upper extremity, 38, 39
Cuticle, 125–128
Cymba conchae, 773

Dartos tunic, 248, 255, 354
Decidua basalis, 181
Decidua capsularis, 181
Decidua parietalis, 181
Decussation, of pyramids, 566, 639
Dens, fovea for, 530, 533, 537
 ligament of, apical, 538
 of axis, 532, 533, 538, 540, 543, 690
 surface of, articular, anterior, 533, 537
  posterior, 537
Dentin, 703
Dentition, at one year of age, 708
 deciduous, full, of 5-year old child, 709
 of 20-year old person, 711
Dermatomes, of head and neck, 609
 of lower extremity, anterior aspect, 404
  posterior aspect, 406
 of trunk, anterior, 2
  dorsal, 519
 of upper extremity, 45
Dermis, of scalp, 633
Diaphragm, 136, 148–150, 152, 170, 172, 175–177,
  184–186, 188, 200, 212, 214, 215, 218, 219,
  224, 229, 230, 243, 256, 257, 264, 265, 273,
  281, 285, 299, 300, 320, 331, 333–335, 338
 costal part of, 170, 219, 230, 242, 243, 317, 333,
  335
 crus of, 215, 216, 221, 223, 230, 299, 329, 333, 335
  left, 299
  right, 335
 cupula of, 227
 dome of, 136, 170, 227, 257, 258, 269
 fascia of, inferior, 299, 300
 liver, contact with bare area of, 316
 lumbar part, 170, 231, 300, 320, 331, 334
 pelvic, 354, 359, 365
 sternal part of, 230, 243, 299, 335
 tendon of, central, 184, 185, 215, 216, 230,
  333–335
 urogenital, 343, 354, 355, 359, 366, 371, 376, 382
  in female, 369, 388
 vena caval aperture in, 299
Diaphragma sellae, 636, 642
Digital sheath, fibrous annular part, 108
 cruciform part, 108
Digiti minimi, fibrous sheath of, 108
Disc, articular, 614
 of sternoclavicular joint, 144
 of wrist, 132, 134
 interpubic, 366, 369, 386, 438
 intervertebral, 214, 215, 219, 393, 535, 540, 550,
  551, 557, 572
 optic, 679, 680
Diverticulum, ileal (Meckel's), 308
Dorsum sellae, 613, 645, 683, 686, 750
Duct(s), aberrant, of epididymis, 363
 aberrant inferior, 250
 bile, common, 265, 268, 272, 283, 284, 286–293,
  300, 317, 331
  and cystic, union of and variations in, 283
  and pancreatic, union of and variations in,
   288–293
 bulbourethral, 354, 361, 366
 cochlear, 800, 802, 803, 805
  basal coil of, 800

Duct(s), *continued*
  cystic, 270, 272, 283, 285, 286, 300, 317
    and common bile, union of and variations in,
      283
  endolymphatic, 801–805
  ejaculatory, 352, 357, 363
  excretory of lacrimal gland, 651
  hepatic, 270, 272, 285, 286, 317
    common, 283, 284
  hepatopancreatic, 288–290, 293, 332
  lactiferous, 8, 9
  longitudinal, of epoophoron, 379, 380
  lymphatic, right, 223
  mesonephric, 363, 372
  Müllerian, 363, 372
  nasolacrimal, 658, 660, 685
    opening of, 685
  of epididymis, aberrant, 363
  of epoophoron, 379, 380
  of gland, bulbourethral, 363
    lacrimal, 653
    vestibular, greater, 388
  of Santorini, 293
  of vesicle, seminal, 352
  of Wirsung, 284, 288–293
  pancreatic, 268, 284, 287–293
    accessory, 268, 287, 293
    and common bile, union of and variations in,
      288–293
    orifice of, 284
  paramesonephric, 363, 372
    infundibulum of, 363
  parotid, 576, 603, 606, 608, 727, 730, 733, 748
    opening of, 746, 747
  prostatic, 361
  salivary, 733
  semicircular, anterior, 800, 802, 803, 805
    lateral, 796, 800, 802, 803, 805
    posterior, 802, 803, 805
  sublingual, greater, 733, 734, 737, 740, 746,
      747
    smaller, 733, 734, 740, 746
  submandibular, 625, 727, 733, 734, 739, 740, 746,
      747
  thoracic, 183, 185, 214, 218–221, 223, 229, 230,
      299, 300, 320, 331, 332, 573, 588, 592, 593
    origin and course of, 223
  transverse, of epoophoron, 379, 380
  utriculosaccular, 805
  vitelline, 261
  Wolffian, 363, 372
Ductule(s), efferent, of epididymis, 250
  mesonephric, 363
    caudal, 372
    cranial, 372
Ductus arteriosus, 176, 178, 181, 208, 209
  in neonatal, heart, 179
Ductus deferens, 243, 248, 250, 252, 255, 258, 305,
    317, 338, 340, 343, 347, 354
  beginning of, 250
Ductus reuniens, 800, 804, 805
Ductus venosus, 178, 181
Duodenal fold, circular, 284, 287, 302, 316
  inferior, 316
  longitudinal, 268, 284, 287
Duodenojejunal flexure, 258, 287, 294, 296, 303,
    305, 331, 332
Duodenojejunal junction, 302, 316
Duodenum, 136, 224, 258, 261, 272, 283, 285,
    288–294, 320, 331
  1st part (superior), 257, 268, 270, 273, 277, 286,
      294, 305, 316, 317, 330, 331
    ampulla of, 269, 294, 331
  2nd part (descending), 268–270, 285–287, 294,
      310, 316, 317, 331, 332
  3rd part (horizontal), 258, 268, 270, 285–287,
      294, 296, 301, 316, 317
  4th part (ascending), 258, 287, 294, 310, 316
  covered by peritoneum, 297
  pancreas and, 285
Dura mater, 219, 226, 320, 540, 565–567, 570–572,
    633–635, 638, 726, 744, 793, 805
  cranial, 638
  filum of, 565
  intracranial, 637
  lacuna of, lateral, 634, 635
  layer of, meningeal, 570, 571, 573
    periosteal, 571
  of cranial fossa, anterior, 668
  of vertebral canal, 722
  spinal ganglion ensheathed with, 573
  surface of, 634

Ear, 773–805
  concha of, 773
  external ear, cartilage, of, 774
    muscles of, 775, 776
  fossa of, triangular, 773
  helix of, 773–775
  lobule of, 773
  malleolar processes of, 780, 784, 786, 791, 797
  middle ear, muscles of, 792
    ossicles of, 792, 797
    wall of, lateral, 786, 787
  notch of, intertragic, 773
  of fetus, 400
Elbow, 520
  arteries of, lateral view, 72
    medial view, 71
  joint of, 91, 92
    roentgenogram of, 94–97
    section of, sagittal, 82
  line of, epiphyseal, 95
  nerves of, lateral view, 72
    medial view, 71
Eminence, arcuate, 787
  frontal, 629
  hypothenar, 37
  iliopubic, 386, 391, 401
  parietal, 626, 629–631
  pyramidal, 795, 796, 799
  thenar, 37
Enamel, 703
Endocardium, 206
Endometrium, 380
Epicardium, 158, 160, 202, 212
Epidermis, of scalp, 633
Epididymis, 242, 250, 319, 353, 363
  appendix of, 247, 249, 253
  body of, 250, 252
  head of, 247–249, 251, 253, 254, 343, 363
  ligament of, superior, 249
  section of, longitudinal, 251
  sinus of, 249, 252, 253
  tail of, 249–251, 254, 363
Epidural fat, 573
Epidural space, 343, 571, 726
Epiglottis, 685, 732, 743, 746, 751, 753, 755,
    757–760, 762, 764, 765
  cartilage of, 736, 766, 767, 771, 722
  stem of, 759, 760, 762
  vallecula of, 685, 736, 743, 758, 769
Epineurium, 571
Epiphysis, of humerus, 94
  of radius, 94
Epitympanic recess, 780–782, 786, 791, 801
Eponychium, 125–128. See also *Finger nail*
Epoophoron, 372
  duct of, longitudinal, 379, 380
    transverse, 379, 380
Esophageal-tracheal space, 591, 726, 769
Esophagus, 157–159, 184, 185, 214–220, 224,
    228–230, 258, 268–270, 294, 299, 335, 573,
    574, 588, 590, 591, 593, 723, 726, 735, 744,
    745, 748, 750, 753, 754
  beneath pericardium, 189
  hiatus of, 170, 214, 216, 230, 317, 321, 333, 335,
    338
  junction with pharynx, 735
  lower, at tracheal bifurcation and diaphragm, 216
  muscle deficient region, 590
  part of, abdominal, 214–216, 224, 299
    cervical, 217
    thoracic, 216, 217
  traversing esophageal hiatus, 335
Ethmoid air cells, 669, 675, 686–688
Expansion, extensor, 123, 124
Eye, 648
  angle of, lateral, 648, 653
    medial, 648, 649, 653
  chamber of, anterior, 680
    posterior, 680
    vitreous, 680
  margin of, infraorbital, 664, 671, 714
  muscles of, lateral, view, 664, 667
  orbit of, 653–657
  septum of, orbital, 650–652, 655–657, 673
  space of, intervaginal, 680
  tarsi of, 651, 652, 655–657, 673, 677
Eyeball, 638, 664, 665, 667, 668, 674, 678, 679
  diameter of, equatorial, 680
  muscle insertions of, behind, 666
    in front, 666
  pole of, anterior, 680
    posterior, 680

Eyeball, *continued*
  section of, horizontal, 680
  tunic of, inner neural, 680
    middle vascular, 680
    outer fibrous, 680
  view of, sagittal, 673
Eyebrow, 604, 648, 677
Eyelashes, 677
Eyelid, 648–650, 653, 658, 660, 664, 669
  innervation of, 650
  lower, 649, 650, 656, 658
  palpebral borders, 648, 649, 653
  palpebral cleft, 653
  surface of, inner, 653, 656
  upper, 650, 658

Face, nerves of, See *Nerve(s), facial*
  vessels of, deeper, 623
    superficial, 622
Facet(s), articular, of atlas, inferior, 531
    superior, 530
  of rib tubercle, 143
  of vertebra, 573
    for head of rib, 568
    for neck of rib, 573
  superior, of vertebra, 573
  calcaneal, anterior, with talus, 511
    middle, with talus, 511
    posterior, with talus, 511
  costal, inferior, 548
    superior, 558
      of 6th thoracic vertebra, 547, 548
    transverse, 558
      for ribs, 553
      of 6th thoracic vertebra, 547
      transverse process with, 548
  navicular, posterior, with talus, 511
Facial canal. See *Canal, facial*
Facial expression, muscles of, 603, 604
Falciform process, 394, 396
Falx, inguinal, 234, 239, 240, 243, 245
  opened, 245
Falx cerebelli, 637
Falx cerebri, 633, 637, 638, 722
Falx septi, 206, 208
Fascia(e), antebrachial, 51, 53, 55, 57, 59, 65, 74,
    77, 98–104
  axillary, 7, 12, 13, 47, 63
  brachial, 7, 12, 13, 21, 64, 575
  buccinator, 737
  Buck's, 348, 351
  bulbar, 653, 657, 673, 677
  cervical, 152, 155, 604, 722
    angular band of, 597, 727
    attachment to mandibular ramus, 733
    deep, 740, 766
      superficial investing layer of, 733
    middle, 571
    pretracheal layer of, 151, 583, 726
    prevertebral layer of, 726, 740
    submandibular, 597, 617
    superficial, 575, 591, 599, 603, 606, 727, 726
  clavipectoral, 13, 15
  cremasteric, 248, 249, 252, 343
  cribriform, 341
  crural, 444, 472, 473, 489–491
  cubital, 98, 99
  deep, of penis, 246, 351
    overlying antebrachial muscles, 47, 48
    overlying brachial muscles, 47, 48
    overlying external oblique muscle, 332
    overlying volar carpal ligament, 108, 114
  deltoid, 7, 48, 63, 523
  diaphragmatic, inferior, 299, 300
  dorsal, deep, of foot, 515, 516
    of hand, 121
  endothoracic, 227, 230, 299, 573
  femoral, 344
  gluteal, 344, 370, 424, 427, 430, 521, 523–525
    overlying gluteus medius muscle, 426
  iliac, 243, 317, 345
  inferior, of diaphragm, 299
    of pelvic diaphragm, 345
    of urogenital diaphragm, 344, 366, 368–370,
      387
  infraspinatus, 57, 61, 527
  intercostal, 184
    external, 526
  lumbar, anterior layer, 332, 522
    posterior layer, 522
  masseteric, 597, 733, 737
  mylohyoid, 739

Fascia(e), *continued*
 nuchal, deep, 548, 584
 obturator, 344, 345, 370
  in perineum, 345, 387
  overlying obturator internus muscle, 243, 365
 of arm, 47, 48
 of eyelid, superficial, 653
 of foot, 515, 516
 of hand, 121
 of inferior oblique muscle, 673
 of infraspinatus muscle, 523
 of penis, 246, 348, 351
 of psoas muscle, 522
 of rectum, 313
 of spermatic cord, 239
 of supinator muscle, 99
 of tensor tympani muscle, 791
 of teres major muscle, 523
 of thigh, anterior, 416
 over external oblique muscle, 13, 253, 332
 over latissimus dorsi muscle, 7
 over obturator internus muscle, 386
 over serratus anterior muscle, 13
 over triceps muscle, 7
 parotid, 575, 604, 737
 pectineal, 416
 pectoral, 7, 8, 35, 63, 575
  platysma muscle and, 575
 pelvic, 343
 pharyngeal, 737, 740, 770
 pharyngobasilar, 615, 625, 748, 750, 753, 755
 popliteal, 487
 prevertebral, 584, 591, 640, 746, 747
 pterygoid, 737
 renal, 331, 332
 rhomboid, 523
 spermatic, external, 239, 246, 248, 253, 255
  internal, 246–249, 252, 253, 255
 submandibular, 733
 subsartorial, 486, 487
 subserous, 240, 320
 superficial, of eyelid, 653
  of penis, 347, 348
  of rectum, 313
 superior, of pelvic diaphragm, 345
 temporal, 654
  adipose layer of, 606, 623
  deep layer of, 606
  superficial layer of, 606
 thoracolumbar, 230, 424, 521, 523
  anterior layer of, 219, 334
  lumbar part of, 523–526
  posterior layer of, 334
  thoracic part of, 524
 tonsillar, 737
 transversalis, 149, 240, 241, 243, 245, 253, 332,
  335, 522, 526
  overlying quadratus lumborum muscle, 526
 visceral, cervical, 584
Fascia bulbi, 669
Fascia lata, 244, 246, 416–420, 430, 486, 487
Fascia penis, 234
Fascia propria, subperitoneal, 320
Fascial planes, of neck, in newborn, cross section
 of, 584
Fasciculata, of adrenal cortex, 324
Fat, cardiac, 189, 194
 epidural, 573
 orbital, 652, 668, 669. Also see *Fat pad, orbital*
 pararenal, 331, 332
 perirenal, 300, 320, 321, 331, 332
 preperitoneal, 240
 subpleural, 185
Fat body, of breast, 8
Fat pad, axillary, 7, 15
 buccal, 576, 603, 604, 606, 729, 737, 740
 cervical, 740
 infrapatellar, 458
 infratemporal, 635
 laryngeal, 726, 757, 759, 765
 mediastinal, 227
 orbital, 652, 656, 657, 668–670, 673, 677
 pre-epiglottic, 769
Fauces, isthmus of, 729, 731
Fetus, 181, 319, 399, 400
 heart of, right atrium, 180
Fibers, intercrural, 12, 233, 235, 236, 244, 246
 zonular, 680
Fibrous sheaths, of digits, 108, 494
 of flexor hallucis longus tendon, 494
Fibular notch, 481
Filaments, dorsal root, 568, 570, 573

Filaments, *continued*
 ventral root, 568, 573
Filum terminale, 343, 566, 567
Fimbria(e), of uterine tube, 374, 377–380
 ovarian, 379, 380
Finger(s), arteries of, 112, 113
  index finger, 122
 articular capsule of, middle finger, 130
 bones of. See *Bone(s), phalanx (phalanges)*
 expansion of, dorsal digital, of middle finger,
  123, 124
  extensor, of middle finger, 123, 124
 joints of, 109, 114, 129, 131, 132, 134
  carpometacarpal, 134
  index finger, 132
  little finger, 134
  middle finger, 129
 ligaments of, 108, 129, 131, 132
  of middle finger, 129
 mesotendon, of middle finger, 123, 124
 nerves of. See *Nerve(s), digital, of hand*
 pad of, distal digital, of index finger, 37
 periosteum of, middle finger, 123, 124
 region of, palmar, 4th digit, 37
 section of, cross, middle finger, 123, 124
 tendon insertions, index finger, radial side, 109
 See also *Hand*
Finger nail, bed of, exposed, 126–128
 body of, 125, 126
 lunula of, 125, 127, 128
 margin of, free, 125, 126
  hidden, 128
  lateral, 128
 matrix of, 126
 root of, 126–128
 view of, dorsal, 125
Fissure, antitragohelicine, 773, 744
 cerebral, longitudinal, 639
 horizontal, 165, 170
  right lung, 136, 153, 161, 215, 257, 258
 median, anterior, of spinal cord, 566–568, 570,
  572
 oblique, 154, 160, 164, 170
  lung, left, 136, 153, 156, 160, 164, 258
  right, 136, 153, 161, 165, 215, 257, 258
 orbital, inferior, 601, 640, 646, 659, 661, 664, 667
  superior, 645, 661, 675, 686, 728
 palpebral, 652
 petrosquamosal, 645
 petrotympanic, 777, 790
 pterygomaxillary, 615, 720, 721, 735
 sphenopetrosal, 645
 tympanomastoid, 777, 790
Flexure, colic, left (splenic), 136, 257, 260, 261,
  269, 272, 297, 298, 302–305, 311, 331
  right (hepatic), 136, 257, 260, 272, 273, 275,
   296–298, 301, 305, 311
 duodenal, inferior, 286
  superior, 286
 duodenojejunal, 258, 287, 294, 296, 303, 305,
  331, 332
 perineal, 313, 354
 sacral, of rectum, 313, 354
Flocculus, cerebellar, 639
Fold(s), aryepiglottic, 746, 751, 753, 755, 764, 767,
  769, 771
 axillary, anterior, 37
  posterior, 37
 chorda tympani, 785
 conjunctival, 649, 658
 duodenal, circular, 284, 287, 302, 316
  inferior, 316
  longitudinal, 268, 284, 287
 gastric, 268, 295
 gastropancreatic, 274, 275, 277, 305, 316
  for left gastric vessels, 275
 glossoepiglottic, lateral, 732, 743, 769
  median, 743
 ileocecal, 260, 301, 305, 309, 316, 374
  inferior, 305, 309
  superior, 305, 309
 inferior vena caval, 305
 interarytenoid, 768
 interdigital, 37
 lacrimal, 685
 laryngeal, 766, 770
 malleolar, 781, 784–786, 792
  posterior, 791
 mucosal, of bladder, 356, 361
  of uterine tube, 380
 muscular, of palate, 685, 731
 of mucous membrane, of gall bladder, 284

Fold(s), *continued*
 of ovarian vessels, 316
 of ureter, left, 316
 of vas deferens, 359
 palatine, transverse, 701
 peritoneal, 277, 301, 305, 340
  over hepatic artery, 300
 petroclinoid, anterior, 801
  posterior, 801
 petrosphenoid, 642
 pharyngoepiglottic, 726, 746, 751, 753, 755
 pterygomandibular, 735
 rectal, transverse, 312, 343, 377
 rectouterine, 374, 377, 379, 382, 383
 salpingopalatine, 685, 726, 751
 salpingopharyngeal, 726, 732, 751, 755
 semilunar, 306, 307, 332
  between haustrae, 301
 spiral, of cystic duct, 284
 stapedial, 795
 sublingual, 733, 737–739
 triangular, 743
 umbilical, lateral, 256, 259, 321, 340, 359
  medial, 256, 259, 321, 340, 352, 359
  median, 243, 256, 320, 321, 340, 352, 359
 vestibular, 726, 766–769, 771, 772
 vocal, 726, 766–770
Follicle(s), lingual, 692, 743
 lymphoid, 268, 751
 ovarian, 380
Fontanelle, anterior, 629, 743
 anterolateral, 629
 posterior, 629–631
 posterolateral, 629, 631
Foot, dorsal, 1, 520
 arteries of, 471, 493, 496, 497
  deep, 471
 bones of, 501–503
  showing muscle attachments, 502
 cross sections of, 515, 516
 muscles and tendons of, 468–470
 nerves of, deep, 471
  superficial, 468
 veins of, superficial, 468
 cutaneous nerve fields of, 409–411
  peroneal neve, 411
  sural nerve, 410, 411
  tibial nerve, 410
 ligaments of, 508–510, 513, 514
  dorsolateral view, 508
  medial view, 509
 plantar aspect, bones of, 503
  showing muscle attachments, 504
 ligaments of, superficial, 513
 section of, cross section, 515, 516
  horizontal, 510
 sole of, 492–498, 520
  arteries of, 493, 496, 497
   superficial, 493
  muscles of, first layer, 494
   second layer, 495
   third layer, 498
  nerves of, 493, 496, 497
   superficial, 493
 surface anatomy of, 412, 413
Foramen (Foramina), apical, 703
 epiploic, 264, 273, 275, 305, 316
 ethmoid, anterior, 661, 662
  posterior, 661, 662
 for perineal vessels and nerves, 344
 for pudendal vessels and nerves, 344
 for superior laryngeal vessels and nerve, 757,
  759, 762, 763
 incisive, 646, 702
 inferior vena cava, 216
 infraorbital, 601, 671
 intervertebral, 546, 551, 572
 jugular, 638, 645–647, 754
 mandibular, 698–700, 728
 mastoid, 587, 645, 646
  of temporal bone, 777
 mental, 598, 601, 603, 610, 697, 699, 708, 709,
  711, 720
 nutrient, 484
  of clavicle, 138
  of femur, 434
  of humerus, 52, 84
  of radius, 89
  of scapula, 34
  of ulna, 87
 obturator, 388–390, 401
 optic, 661, 686

Foramen (Foramina), *continued*
palatine, greater, 646, 702
lesser, 702
parietal, 626, 628
pterygospinous, 613
sacral, dorsal, 560
pelvic, 393, 559
sciatic, greater, 386, 388, 389, 393, 394, 397, 429
lesser, 388, 389, 393, 394, 397, 429
sphenopalatine, 662, 684
stylomastoid, 646, 695, 750, 751, 788
supraorbital, 601
transverse, of atlas, 530, 531
of axis, 532, 533
of 5th cervical vertebra, 541
vena caval, 216, 229, 333–335
vertebral, 529, 532, 541, 554
of atlas, 530, 531
of 7th cervical vertebra, 542
of lumbar vertebra, 555
zygomaticofacial, 661
zygomatico-orbital, 659, 663
Foramen cecum, 645, 686, 732, 736, 743, 753
of tongue, 685, 726, 736
Foramen lacerum, 645–647
Foramen magnum, 631, 637, 645, 646, 735
Foramen ovale, 180, 181, 208, 645, 646, 686, 735
remainder of, 180
Foramen rotundum, 645, 662, 663, 686
Foramen spinosum, 645, 646, 735
Foramina venarum minimarum, 201, 203
Forearm, anterior, arteries of, 62, 67, 68, 70
muscles of, 37, 65, 66, 69, 70, 74
deep, 69
extensor, 37
flexor, 37
nerves of, 67, 68, 70
bones of, showing, muscle attachments, 80, 81
cross section of, 98–101
dermatomes of, 45
fascia of, deep, 47, 48
muscles of, 37, 61, 65, 66, 69, 70, 74–76, 79
lateral view of, 61, 75
nerves of, 38, 39, 41, 43, 67, 68, 70, 76, 78
cutaneous, 38, 39, 41, 43
posterior, arteries of, 43, 62, 76, 78
muscles of, 74–76, 79
nerves of, 43, 76, 78
surface anatomy of, 37
veins of, superficial, 41, 43, 44
Fornix, of conjunctiva, 649, 657, 673
of lacrimal sac, 658
of vagina, 373, 377
Fossa, acetabular, 401, 437
axillary, 1, 37, 231
coronoid, of humerus, 82, 84, 98
cranial, anterior, 645
middle, 645, 787
posterior, 645, 787, 789
cubital, 37
digastric, 583, 698, 700
for incus, 778, 791
for lacrimal gland, 689
glenoid, 34
hypophyseal, 645, 683, 686, 722, 802
iliac, 390
infraclavicular, 37, 575
infraspinatus, of scapula, 26, 34
infratemporal, 664
inguinal, lateral, 340, 359
medial, 340, 359
intercondylar, 433, 442, 448, 450, 457, 459
interpeduncular, 639
intersigmoid, 302
ischiorectal, 344, 346, 359, 370
jugular, 575, 594, 646, 792
mandibular, 614, 646, 735, 777
navicular, 343, 350, 361
of cochlear window, 778, 784, 785, 789, 798, 799
of vestibular window, 799
olecranon, 82, 83, 96, 97
petrosal, 646
popliteal, 413, 429, 440, 441, 472, 473, 487, 489, 520
pterygoid, 683
pterygopalatine, lateral, view, 662
medial view, 663
radial, of humerus, 84, 96
rectovesical, 359
retromandibular, 574
scaphoid, 773, 774
subarcuate, 665

Fossa, *continued*
submandibular, 574
subscapular, 27
supraclavicular, 574, 575
supraspinatus, of scapula, 26, 34, 574
supratonsillar, 729
supravesical, 340, 359
triangular, of ear, 773
uterovesical, 181
Fossa ovalis, 202, 203, 208
Fovea, for dens, 530, 533, 537
of head of femur, 401, 432, 433
sublingual, 700
submandibular, 700
Fovea centralis, 784, 785
Foveola, radial, 108
Frenulum, 306, 350, 351
of clitoris, 367, 368, 377, 388
of labia minora, 367, 368
of lips, 729, 738
of tongue, 733, 735, 737, 740
Frontal, crest, 645
Frontal notch, 661
Frontomaxillary suture, 682
Fundus, of bladder, 352
of gall bladder, 136, 284, 301, 305
of internal acoustic meatus, 801
of stomach, 136, 268–270, 273, 294
of uterus, 318, 378, 380, 381
Furrow, antebrachial, lateral, 37
medial, 37
bicipital, medial, 37, 47

Galea aponeurotica, 603, 604, 606, 608, 633, 635
Gall bladder, 136, 257, 259, 265, 272, 273, 275, 281–283, 296, 310, 331, 332, 399
biliary duct system and, 284
body of, 284
coat of, muscular, 284
serous, 284, 331
fundus of, 136, 284, 301, 305
mucosa of, 331
neck of, 284
Ganglion (Ganglia), abdominal autonomic, 338
aorticorenal, 318
cardiac, 185
celiac, 225, 226, 300, 318, 320, 331, 339
cervical, inferior, 220, 224, 225, 228, 588, 593, 754, 755
middle, 224–226, 228, 582, 593, 754, 755
superior, 225, 582, 640, 693, 694, 737, 754, 755
cervicothoracic, 220, 226
dorsal root, on thoracic nerve, 226
ciliary, 225, 640, 672, 674, 793
nasociliary branch to, 674
oculomotor branch to, 674
sympathetic branch to, 674
geniculate, 640, 695, 742, 788, 793, 801, 802
inferior, of glossopharyngeal nerve, 640, 695, 794
of vagus nerve, 694, 754, 755, 793
mesenteric, inferior, 225
superior, 225, 318, 332, 339
otic, 225, 318, 339, 793
rami to chorda tympani nerve, 793
pelvic, 225
pterygopalatine, 225, 611, 640, 693–695, 793
branches of, 640, 693
renal, 339
semilunar, 642, 670, 672, 694, 696, 788, 801
spinal, 10, 219, 220, 518, 563, 567, 568, 570, 571, 573
cervical, 563, 565
lumbar, 563, 565
sacral, 563
thoracic, 320
spiral, 372, 804
splanchnic, 219, 226
stellate, 220, 224–226, 591
submandibular, 225, 611, 625, 727, 740, 746, 747
superior, of vagus nerve, 640, 694, 754
sympathetic, 10, 218, 219, 224, 320, 518, 573
cervical, 793
lumbar, 320, 339, 670
sacral, 339, 364
thoracic, 184, 185, 224, 226–229, 339, 593, 755
sympathetic trunk, 10, 184, 219, 224, 226, 299, 793
trigeminal, 793, 801
vestibular, inferior, 804
superior, 804
Ganglion impar, 337, 339

Genitalia, female, 367–388
arterial supply of, 381
external, 367, 368, 388
internal, 378
male, 246–254, 347–363
Genitourinary system, female, 372
male, 363
Genu, of facial nerve, 795, 796
of internal carotid. artery, 640
Gingiva, 548, 703, 729, 735, 740
Gland(s), areolar, 4
buccal, 730, 737
bulbourethral, 344, 352, 354, 359, 361, 363, 366
bulge of, 366
labial, 722, 730, 737
lacrimal, 651–653, 656, 657, 659, 670–672, 674
innervation of, 659
orbital part of, 653, 656, 657
palpebral part of, 653, 656, 657
laryngeal, 769
lingual, anterior, 733
mammary. See *Mammary gland*
mucous, in bile ducts, 284
of mucous membrane, 751
of uvula, 731
palatine, 690, 701, 722, 731, 746, 747
parathyroid, 258, 590, 591, 750, 751, 753, 755, 766
left inferior, 588
parotid, 576, 577, 583, 585, 586, 597, 603, 606, 607, 622, 727, 733, 737, 740, 747, 751, 789
accessory, 733
parasympathetic innervation of, 607
pharyngeal, 750
pituitary, 636–639, 641, 642, 685
infundibulum of, 636
lobes of, anterior (adenohypophysis), 636
intermediate, 636
posterior (neurohypophysis), 636
sagittal section through, 636
prostate, 258, 343, 352–359, 362
colliculus of, 356, 361
lobe of, 362
salivary, 733. See also *Gland(s), parotid, sublingual, submandibular*
sebaceous, 633, 722
sublingual, 625, 722, 727, 733, 734, 737, 739, 740, 746, 747, 756
submandibular, 579–581, 583, 585, 597, 599, 600, 606, 624, 625, 727, 733, 734, 737, 739, 740, 746, 747, 750, 751
suprarenal, 258, 277, 285, 300, 316–320, 322–324
capsule of, 300, 324
left, 300
sweat, 7
tarsal, 649, 677
thymus, 152, 153, 175, 177, 184, 185, 256, 726
lobes of, 175
thyroid, 136, 152, 177, 178, 186, 214, 217, 257, 258, 576, 580, 581, 583, 586–592, 746, 750, 753–756, 758, 766, 769
capsule of, 591
isthmus of, 217, 574, 585, 589, 591, 592, 726, 756
lobe of, left, 588
pyramidal, 152, 588
tracheal, 591, 755, 759, 760
vestibular, greater, 368, 371, 373, 388
Glans clitoris, 244, 368, 370, 371, 388
Glans penis, 246, 343, 351, 352, 361, 363
corona of, 246, 343, 349, 351, 352, 361
Glenoid cavity, 26–30, 34–36, 137
Glenoid labrum, 29, 30, 34, 35
Glomerulosa, of adrenal cortex, 324
Gnathion, 574
Granulations, arachnoid, 633–635
Groove(s), costal, 143
deltopectoral, 37
for anterior intermuscular septum, 467
for aorta, 158
for flexor tendons, 131
for vertebral artery, 530, 543
mylohyoid, 613, 678, 700
obturator, 390
radial, 59, 83
Gubernaculum testis, 255, 363
Gum, 699, 703, 725, 729
Gyrus (Gyri), occipitotemporal, 639
orbital, 639
parahippocampal, 639

Hamulus, of hamate bone, 108, 118, 131, 133, 135
  pterygoid, 613, 615, 646, 647, 662, 663, 683, 684,
    721, 722, 731, 735, 746–748
Hand, 1, 37–39, 45, 61, 62, 102–107, 520
  arteries of, 62, 102, 104–107, 110–113
    dorsal, 102, 104, 105
    palmar, 62, 106, 107
  arteriogram of, 113
  bones of, 118–119
    showing muscle attachments, 119
    cross section of, at level of 1st carpal bones, 120
      through metacarpal bones, 121
  dorsal, arteries of, 102, 104, 105
    nerves and veins of, superficial, 102
  intertendinous connections of, 103
  joints of, dorsal view, 129, 132
    palmar view, 131
  ligaments of, 129–131
  muscles of, 37, 61, 107, 108, 114–117
  nerves of, 38, 39, 102, 104, 106, 107, 110–112
    cutaneous, 38, 39
  palm of, 1, 37–39, 62, 106, 107, 110–112, 114, 115
    arteries of, 62, 106, 110, 111
    creases of, 37
    eminence of, hypothenar, 37
      thenar, 37
    monticuli of, 37
    muscles of, 37, 107, 114, 115
    nerves of, 38, 39, 106, 110, 111
    tendons of, 107, 112
  tendons and synovial, sheaths of, 103, 104, 107,
    112
  veins of, 102
  x-ray of, 133, 135
  See also *Finger(s)*
Haustrum (Haustrae), 259, 301, 306, 307, 332
Head, nerves of, superficial, 609, 622, 623
  of fetus, 400
  vessels of, superficial, 622, 623
  viscera of, mid-sagittal, section, 726
Heart, 136, 170–174, 176, 186, 192, 194–199, 257
  aorta of. See *Aorta*
  apex of, 136, 188, 190, 192, 194, 195, 202, 204,
    208, 212, 257, 258
  arterial system of, 196–199
  arteriogram of, 200
  ascultation of, sites on chest wall for, 171
  atrium of. See *Atrium, of heart*
  auricle of. See *Auricle, of heart*
  cardiac dullness, area of superficial, 170
  dorsal half of, 201
  neonatal, 179
  of child, 176, 208, 209
  of fetus, right atrium of, 180
  position of, during full expiration, 174
    during full inspiration, 173
  projected onto anterior thoracic wall, 136, 170,
    172, 257
  section through, frontal, 201, 205
  valves of, 171, 180, 190
    superior view, 190
    Also see *Valve(s), aortic, atrioventricular*
  veins of, 180, 193, 215. Also see *Vein(s), cardiac,*
    coronary
  vena cava of, See *Vena cava*
  ventricle of. See *Ventricle(s), of heart*
  view of, anterior, 136, 170–174, 176, 186, 194,
    196–199, 257
    posterior, 192, 194, 195
Helix, 773–775
Hemisphere, cerebral, 669
Hemorrhoid, 312
Hiatus, adductor (tendineus), 420, 422, 423
  anal, 386
  aortic, 170, 214, 216, 285, 317, 320, 333–335
  esophageal, 170, 214, 216, 230, 317, 321, 333,
    335, 338
  for basilic vein, 47
  for cutaneous nerve, lateral antebrachial, 47
    posterior antebrachial, 47, 48
  for posterior interosseous vessels of forearm, 69
  maxillary, 684
  urogenital, 386
Hiatus semilunaris, 685
Hilum, of lung, 158, 188
  of spleen, 274, 277, 278
  renal, 323, 329, 332
Hydatid, 360
Hymen, 367, 368, 388
Hypoglossal canal, 594
Hypothalamus, infundibulum of, 639, 642
Hypotympanic recess, 782, 792

Ileocecal fold. See *Fold, ileocecal*
Ileocecal junction, 306
Ileum, 259–261, 272, 295–297, 301, 306, 308, 310,
  374
  terminal part, 301, 302, 305, 311
Iliotibial tract, 296, 416, 424, 430, 444, 463, 482,
  486, 487
Incisors, 699, 701, 705, 708–710, 712, 713, 716, 717,
  720
  permanent, lower, 709, 710, 716, 717, 720
    upper, 710, 712, 713, 720
Incisures, in cartilage of acoustic meatus, 774
  sacrococcygeal, 388
Infraglottic space, 766
Infraorbital margin, of eye, 664, 671, 714
Infratemporal crest, 646
Infundibulum of hypothalamus, 639, 642
  of paramesonephric duct, 363
  of pituitary gland, 636
  of uterine tube, 372, 377–379, 381, 382, 399
Inguinal canal, 237, 245, 248, 253
  opened, 245
Inguinal, falx, 234, 239, 240, 243, 245
Inguinal ring, deep, 242, 243, 253, 340, 364
  superficial 231, 232, 235, 236, 244, 248, 255, 347,
    388
  crus of, lateral, 231, 235, 236, 244, 245, 248, 253,
    333
    medial, 12, 231, 235, 236, 239, 244–246, 248,
    253
Insula, 644
Interarytenoid notch, 751, 755, 758, 767, 772
Interpleural area, inferior, 153
  superior, 153
Intersection, of ocular axis and visual axis, 680
  tendinous, 238, 242
Intertragic notch, 773
Intertrochanteric crest, 400, 401
Intestine, large, 257, 305, 311
  radiograph of, 311
  small, 215, 256–260, 399
    fetal, 400
Iridocorneal angle, 680
Iris, 648, 680
  arterial circle of, 678
  surface of, anterior, 680
Isthmus, of aorta, 176
  of fauces, 729, 731
  of thyroid gland, 217, 574, 585, 589, 591, 726, 756
  of uterine tube, 316, 318, 374, 375, 377–380, 383
  of uterus, 375, 379, 380

Jejunum, 260, 261, 269, 285, 295–297, 301, 332
Joint(s), acromioclavicular, 29, 31, 36
  ankle, 512
  atlantoaxial, 534, 536, 537, 594, 722, 726
  atlanto-occipital, 534, 536, 538
  calcaneocuboid, 510, 515
  carpometacarpal, 134
    of thumb, 131, 134
  costotransverse, 554
  costovertebral, 552, 554
  cricoarytenoid, 759, 770
  cricothyroid, 761, 763
  cuneonavicular, 510
  elbow, anterior, 91
    articular capsule of, 82, 91, 98
    posterolateral, 92
    roentgenogram of, 94–97
    sagittal section of, 82
  finger, 129, 132
  hip, anterior view, 282, 287, 435–439
    articular capsule of, 394–396, 437, 438
    socket of, 401, 437
  incudomalleolar, 787, 797, 801
  incudostapedial, 797
  interphalangeal, distal, 132
    proximal, 132
  intertarsal, 510
  intervertebral, capsule of, 526, 529
  knee, 444–459
    bursa of, 455, 456
    capsule of, articular, 447, 448, 459
    cavity of, 455, 456
    ligaments of, 448
    menisci of, 446, 448, 453
      arterial supply of, 454
    radiograph of, 457
    section of, frontal, 458, 459
      sagittal, 458
    vessels at, network of, 422
    view of, anterior, 444–446, 451, 457

Joint(s), knee, view of, *continued*
    posterior, 447, 448, 456
  mediocarpal, between two rows of carpal bones,
    134
  metacarpophalangeal, 109, 114, 129
    capsule of, 132
  metatarsophalangeal, 514
    of hand, 129, 131
  radiocarpal, 134
  radioulnar, 93, 101, 131, 133, 134
  sacrococcygeal, 343, 354
  sacroiliac, 386, 393, 401, 438
  shoulder, 31–36
    capsule of, articular, 24, 30, 32–35, 49–51
    section of, frontal, 30
    posterior, 34
  sternoclavicular, 13, 144, 151
  sternocostal, 144
  sternomanubrial, 144, 147
  subtalar, 510
  talocalcaneonavicular, 511, 515
    capsule of, 515
    viewed from above, 511
  talocrural, 512
  talonavicular, 510
  tarsometatarsal, 510
  temporomandibular, 612, 613, 616, 617
    capsule of, articular, 608, 612, 614, 647, 748
  tibiofibular, proximal, 480, 498
    superior, 448, 459
      capsule of, articular, 459
  wrist, 129, 131–134
Junction, between pharynx and esophagus, 735
  duodenojejunal, 302, 316
  ileocecal, 306
  of inferior mesenteric vein and splenic vein, 272
  of jugular and subclavian veins, 586
  of retromandibular and facial veins, 586

Kidney, 215, 258, 262, 273, 285, 300, 303, 305, 316,
  317, 319–323, 325–327, 329, 331, 332, 340,
  363, 372
  artery and vein of, 331
  border of, lateral, 326
    medial, 326
  calyx (calyces) of, 325, 327, 331, 332
  capsule of, fibrous, 322, 323, 325, 331, 332
  cortex of, 325, 327, 331
    lobules of, 323
  extremities of, 326, 327
  hilum of, 323, 329, 332
  left, 300, 320
    inferior pole of, 302, 316, 328
  lymph nodes of, 331
  of newborn, 563
  pelvis of, 271, 285, 304, 323, 325–328, 331, 332,
    363, 372
  pyramid (medulla) of, 331, 332
  right, 320
    superior pole of, 305
Knee joint. See *Joint(s), knee*
Knee region, anterior, 1, 444, 445, 520
Knots, false, 255

Labium majus, 245, 367, 376, 388
  skin of, 244
Labium minus, 367, 368, 370, 371, 376, 377, 388
  frenulum of, 367, 368
Labrum, acetabular, 437, 439
  glenoid, 29, 30, 34, 35
Labyrinth, ethmoidal, 687, 689
  membranous, 800, 803–805
Lacertus, of lateral rectus muscle, 675
Lacertus fibrosus, 49
Lacrimal canaliculus, 656, 658, 660
  ampulla of, 658
Lacrimal crest, anterior, 661, 662
  posterior, 661, 662
Lacrimal gland. See *Gland, lacrimal*
Lacrimal papilla, 649, 658, 677
Lacrimal sac, 652, 656–658, 660
  fornix of, 658
Lacuna(e), lateral, 634, 635
  urethral, 361
Lacus lacrimale, 649
Large intestine, 305
Laryngeal prominence, 575, 576, 585, 586, 626
Laryngopharynx, 746
Larynx, 151, 168, 257, 723, 756–759, 760, 762, 766
  aditus of, 758
  aperture of, superior, 736
  cartilages of, 757, 759, 760

Larynx, *continued*
  cavities of, 766
  entrance into, 685, 753
  external, lateral view, 744, 745, 763
  fat body of, 757
  folds of, 766, 770
  ligaments of, 757, 759
  section of, frontal, 766
  ventricle of, 685, 726, 736, 766, 769
Leg, 1, 462, 463, 489–491, 520
  compartment of, anterior, muscles of, 464
      nerves and arteries of, 465
    lateral, muscles of, 463, 467
      nerves and arteries of, 465
    posterior, muscles of, 473, 474, 477, 479
  cross sections of, 489–491
  cutaneous nerve fields of, femoral nerve, 409
    peroneal nerve, 411
    sural nerve, 410, 411
    tibial nerve, 410
  interosseous membrane of, 480
  lymphatic channels and nodes of, 466
  posterior, nerves of, 475, 476, 479
    vessels of, 475, 476
  surface anatomy of, anterior 412
    posterior, 413
  tibiofibular union of, 480
Lens, pole of, anterior, 680
  posterior, 680
Lenticular process, of incus, 785, 791
Ligament(s), acetabular, transverse, 387, 437
  acromioclavicular, 29–32, 34
  alar, 536, 538
  annular, of radius, 79, 91–93
    of trachea, 168, 726, 759, 760, 765, 766
  anococcygeal, 343, 344, 346, 354, 368, 370, 371, 376, 387
  anterior, of head of fibula, 446, 451, 463, 480
  apical, of dens, 538, 722, 726
  arcuate, of pubis, 245, 366, 369, 376, 387, 394–396, 438
    superior, 369, 395, 397, 419
    over quadratus lumborum muscle, 333, 334
  atlanto-occipital, 595
  bifurcate, 508
  broad, of uterus, 379, 380
  calcaneocuboid, 508, 509, 511, 513, 514
  calcaneofibular, 463, 508, 512, 513
  calcaneonavicular, 508, 511, 513
    plantar, 514
      long, 498, 508, 509, 513, 515
      superficial, 513
  carpal, radiate, 114, 120, 129, 131
  carpometacarpal, dorsal, 79, 129
  cervical, transverse, 385
  circular, of tooth, 703
  coccygeal, lateral, 393
  collateral, fibular, 431, 434, 445–448, 454–456, 459, 463
    of middle finger, 129, 130, 132
    radial, 79, 91, 92, 134
    tibial, 445–448, 454, 456, 459
    ulnar, 91, 134
  conoid, 29, 31, 35, 49, 151
  coracoacromial, 29, 31–35, 151
  coracoclavicular, 31, 34, 49, 53
  coracohumeral, 31, 32, 34, 35, 63
  corniculopharyngeal, 759, 760, 762
  coronary, of liver, 272, 274, 280–282, 299, 316, 318, 320, 331
    margin of, 300
  costoclavicular, 50, 51, 138, 144
  costotransverse, 227, 550, 552, 554
    lateral, 526, 551–554
    superior, 227, 526, 552
  costoxiphoid, 12, 151, 231
  cricoarytenoid, 761
  cricopharyngeal, 759, 760
  cricothyroid, 168, 589, 592, 593, 726, 735, 756, 757, 760, 762, 763, 765, 769
  cricotracheal, 744, 757, 759, 766
  cruciate, anterior, 336, 446, 448, 453, 454, 459
    occupying intercondylar fossa, 459
    origins of, 453
    posterior, 446, 448, 451, 453, 459
  cruciform, of atlas, 536, 726
  cuboideonavicular, 508, 513–515
  cuneocuboid, dorsal, 511
  cuneonavicular, 508, 511, 513
  deltoid, 462, 509, 512, 513
  denticulate, 226, 570–573
  duodenal suspensory, 285, 287

Ligament(s), *continued*
  duodenocolic, 277, 316
  falciform 243, 256, 259, 261, 262, 272, 273, 280, 281, 299, 300, 305, 316, 331, 332, 359
  fibular collateral, 431, 434, 445–448, 454–456, 459, 463
  fundiform, of penis, 12, 231–233, 236, 343
  gastrocolic, 259, 273, 305, 331, 332
  gastrohepatic, 262
  gastrolienal, 262
  gastrophrenic, 299, 316
  gastrosplenic, 273, 274, 277, 278, 300, 305, 331
  genicular, transverse, 451, 453
  genital, 363, 372
  glenohumeral, 31, 34, 63
  hamatometacarpal, 131
  hepatoduodenal, 270, 273, 275, 277, 283, 305, 316
  hepatogastric, 273, 275, 299, 300, 305
  hyoepiglottic, 726, 760, 765, 769
  iliofemoral, 333, 395, 397, 420, 435–437, 439
  iliolumbar, 321, 333, 393, 395–397, 526
  inferior, of epididymis, 249
  inguinal, 11, 231, 235–237, 239, 242–244, 253, 333, 335, 340, 352, 369, 393–395, 397, 399, 416–418
    reflected, 12, 233, 235, 245, 246, 253
  intercarpal, dorsal, 120, 129
  interclavicular, 144, 151, 576, 726
  intercuneiform, dorsal, 511
  interfoveolar, 239, 242, 243, 245, 340
  intermetatarsal, plantar, 514
  interosseous, between ulna and radius, 50
  interosseous metacarpal, 134
  interosseous metatarsal, 510
  interosseous sacroiliac, 386
  interosseous tarsal, 510
  interspinal, 214, 526
  intertransverse, 526, 552
  intra-articular, of spine, 551
  ischiofemoral, 430, 436, 439
  lacunar, 236, 243, 335, 369, 398
  lateral, of temporomandibular joint, 612, 647
  lienorenal, 277, 300, 331
  longitudinal, anterior, 214, 393, 395, 397, 535, 550, 573, 726
    posterior, 214, 557, 572, 573, 726
  lumbocostal, 331
  malleolar, lateral, 780, 781
    superior, 780, 781, 791, 801
  meniscofemoral, posterior, 448
  metacarpal, dorsal, 129, 131
    interosseous, 134
    palmar, 131
    transverse, deep, 108, 131, 132
      superficial, 106
  metatarsal, dorsal, 508
    interosseous, 510
    transverse, deep, 508, 514
      superficial, 513
  nuchal, 523–525
  of ankle and foot, 508, 509
  of femur, head of, 359, 437, 438
  of fibula, head of, 446, 448
  of foot, 513
  of hand and finger, dorsal, 129, 131
  of inferior vena cava, 280, 282
  of larynx, 757, 759
  of pelvis, 394, 395, 397, 398
  of rib, head and neck of, 299
  of umbilical artery, 321
  of umbilical vein, 243, 332
  of wrist, dorsal, 129, 131
  ovarian, 372, 374, 378–381, 399
  palpebral, lateral, 651, 652, 655, 656
    medial, 576, 603, 606, 651, 652, 654–656, 658, 660
  patellar, 412, 417–420, 424, 431, 444, 445, 453, 455, 458, 462–465, 467, 487, 489
  pectinate, at iridocorneal angle, 680
  pectineal, 335
  pelvic, female, 394
  perineal, transverse, 366, 369, 387
  petrospinous, 612, 642
  phrenicocolic, 273, 277, 305, 316
  pisometacarpal, 131
  popliteal, arcuate, 447, 474
    oblique, 447, 474, 477
  posterior, of head of fibula, 447, 448
    of incus, 780, 787, 791, 792, 801
  pterygospinous, 647, 747

Ligament(s), *continued*
  pubic, arcuate, 245, 366, 369, 376, 387, 394–396, 438
    superior, 369, 395, 397, 419
  pubofemoral, 435, 439
  puboprostatic, 354
  pubovesical, 343, 354, 385
  pulmonary, 159, 164, 165, 184, 220
  radiate, of head of ribs, 227, 550, 554
  radiocarpal, dorsal, 129
    palmar, 114, 131
  radioulnar, anterior, 93
  reflected inguinal, 12, 233, 235, 245, 246, 253
  round, of liver, 259, 265, 272, 273, 281, 282, 300, 305, 331, 359
    of uterus, 244, 245, 316, 318, 372, 374, 377, 378, 380, 381, 383, 385, 388, 399
      insertion of, 244
  sacrococcygeal, 334, 343, 376, 386, 393, 396, 397, 438, 521
    superficial dorsal, 394
  sacroiliac, 320, 395–397, 438
    interosseous, 386
    ventral, 386
  sacrospinous, 333, 346, 364, 383, 388, 393, 394, 419, 431, 438
  sacrotuberous, 333, 344, 346, 370, 386–388, 393, 394, 396, 427, 429, 430, 436, 438, 523, 526
  scapular, transverse, inferior, 21, 22, 24
    superior, 24, 31, 32, 34, 49, 53, 151
  scrotal, of testis, 253, 255
  sphenomandibular, 613, 722, 747, 750, 753
  splenorenal, 300
  sternoclavicular, anterior, 15, 144
  sternocostal, 144, 147
  stylohyoid, 598, 615, 647, 722, 735, 744, 745, 747, 748, 750
  stylomandibular, 612, 613, 647, 722, 737, 740, 747, 750, 751
  superior, of incus, 791
    of malleus, 780, 781, 791, 801
  supraspinal, 214, 219, 396, 552
  suspensory, duodenal, 285, 287
    of clitoris, 244, 368
    of ovary, 374, 377–379
    of penis, 12, 232, 234, 239, 246, 248, 347
  talocalcaneal, 508, 510–512
  talofibular, 508, 512
  talonavicular, 515
  tarsal, interosseous, 510
    plantar, 514
  tarsometatarsal, 508, 509, 511, 513, 514
  thyroepiglottic, 726, 746, 747, 760, 762, 769
  thyrohyoid, 760
    lateral, 757, 759, 763
    medial, 741, 757, 763
    median, 726, 745, 762
  tibial collateral, 445–448, 454, 456, 459
  tibiofibular, 480, 508, 512
  tracheal, annular, 168, 726, 759, 760, 765, 766
  transverse, of atlas, 537, 540, 722, 726
    of knee, 446
  trapezoid, 29, 31, 35, 49, 151
  Treitz's, 285, 287
  triangular, of liver, 272, 280, 281, 305
  ulnar collateral, 91, 134
  ulnocarpal, palmar, 131
  umbilical, lateral, 253, 256
    medial, 11, 240, 243, 253, 256, 321, 340, 355, 377
    median, 243, 256, 343, 353, 356, 358, 377, 378, 383
  uterosacral, 380, 385
  vestibular, 760, 766
  vocal, 760–762, 766, 770
Ligamentum arteriosum, 187, 188, 190, 194, 195, 212, 216, 217
Ligamentum flavum, 219, 552–554
Ligamentum patellae, 446
Ligamentum venosum, 282, 299
Limbus fossa ovalis, 201, 208, 214
Limen nasi, 685, 691, 732
Line, arcuate, 238, 242, 243, 255, 259, 340, 359, 393, 390
  condylopatellar, lateral, 446
    medial, 446
  gluteal, anterior, 389
    inferior, 389
    posterior, 389
  Hilton's, 312
  intercondylar, of femur, 433
  intermediate, of iliac crest, 390

Line, *continued*
  intertrochanteric, 432
  mylohyoid, 613, 615, 698, 700
  nuchal, inferior, 646
    superior, 646
  oblique, of larynx, 763
    of mandible, 697
  pectineal, 433
  Reid's base, 574
  soleal, of tibia, 448, 484
  temporal, inferior, of parietal bone, 626, 627, 777
    superior, of parietal bone, 626, 627
  tendinous, of levator ani muscle origin, 345
  trapezoid, 212
Linea alba, 12, 231, 233, 235–237, 240, 241, 242,
    245, 253, 255, 300, 332, 343, 377
  adminiculum of, 240, 242, 243
Linea aspera, of femur, 430, 433, 440, 448, 486
Linea semicircularis, 240
Linea semilunaris, of rectus abdominis, 238, 239,
    243
Linea terminalis, of pelvis, 333, 359, 376, 386, 397,
    399
Lingula, of lung (left), 152, 153, 156, 160, 164, 170
  of mandible, 613, 698, 700
  of sphenoid, 645
Lip(s), 730, 732, 736, 738
  aponeurosis of, 736
  mucosa of, 736
  upper, frenulum of, 729, 738
Liver, 139, 178, 215, 257, 258, 261, 273, 279, 296,
    299, 310, 331, 332
  bare area of, 264, 282, 299, 316, 321
    colic impression on, 282
  calyx of, 331
  capsule of, fibrous, 331
  impression of, colic, 282
    duodenal, 282
    esophageal, 282
    gastric, 282
    renal, 282
    suprarenal, 282
  ligament of, coronary, 272, 274, 280–282, 299,
      300, 316, 318, 320, 331
    falciform, 243, 256, 259, 261, 262, 272, 273,
        280, 281, 299, 300, 305, 316, 321, 332, 359
    round, 259, 265, 272, 273, 281, 282, 300, 305,
        331, 359
  lobe of, caudate, 265, 272, 273, 275, 277, 280,
      282, 299, 300, 305
    papillary process of, 305
    left, 256, 259, 265, 272, 273, 275, 280–282, 299,
        300, 305, 331
    quadrate, 272, 273, 275, 282, 300
    right, 256, 259, 265, 272, 273, 275, 279,
        280–282, 299, 301, 305, 331, 332, 399
  margin of, anterior, 299, 300
    inferior, 255, 258, 281, 301, 399
  surface of, anterior, with diaphragmatic
      attachment, 281
    diaphragmatic, 281, 282, 321
    posterior, 282
    visceral, 282, 283
  tuber omentale, 300
Lobe(s), frontal, 635
  mammary, 7, 8
  of liver. See *Liver, lobes of*
  of lung. See *Lung(s), lobes of*
  of prostate, 362
  of thymus, 175
  of thyroid, left, 588
    pyramidal, 152, 158
Lung(s), 136, 151–156, 160, 161, 164, 165, 170, 172,
    175–177, 186, 188, 189, 208, 209, 212, 215,
    228, 256–258, 299, 320, 388
  apex of, 136, 151, 156, 160, 161, 164, 165, 170,
      257, 258
  bronchopulmonary segments of, 162, 163, 166,
      167, 169
  cardiac notch of, 152, 153, 156, 160, 164, 170,
      257, 270, 399
  hilum of, 158, 188
  left, 136, 152, 160, 164, 170, 175, 177, 188, 189,
      208, 209, 212, 215, 257, 299, 588
    cardiac impression on, 164, 170
    interlobar fissure of, horizontal, 165, 170
      oblique, 136, 153, 154, 156, 160, 161, 164,
          165, 170, 215, 257, 258
    lobe of, lower, 152, 153, 156, 164, 170, 175,
        186, 256
      upper, 152, 153, 156, 170, 175, 186, 215, 256
    surface of, costal, 160

Lung(s), left, *continued*
    diaphragmatic, 164
    mediastinal, 164
  lingula of, 152, 153, 156, 160, 164, 170
  margin of, anterior, 136, 152, 160, 164, 170,
      175–177
    inferior, left lung, 136, 152, 160, 164, 170, 186,
        215, 219, 258, 299
    right lung, 136, 154, 161, 170, 219, 257, 258,
        299, 399
  projected onto thoracic wall, anterior view,
      153–156
  right, 152, 161, 165, 170, 172, 175, 178, 188, 189,
      208, 209, 212, 215, 228, 320
    base of, 161
    cardiac impression on, 165
    interlobar fissure of, horizontal, 136, 153, 161,
        215, 257, 258
      oblique, 136, 153, 161, 165, 215, 257, 258
    lobe of, lower, 152–155, 161, 165, 170, 175,
        186, 215, 220, 256
      middle, 152, 153, 155, 165, 170, 175, 186,
          215, 256
      upper, 152–155, 161, 165, 170, 175, 186,
          215, 256
    surface of, costal, 161
      diaphragmatic, 165
      mediastinal, 165
Lunula, of finger nail, 125, 127, 128
  of semilunar valve, 212
Lymph nodes, aortic, 331, 341, 384
  apical, 587
  auricular, posterior, 619
  axillary, 3, 5–7, 13–15, 63
    anterior, 5, 6
    central, 5
    scapular, 5
  bronchopulmonary, 164, 165, 185, 187, 215
  buccinator, 619
  cervical, 587, 619, 621
    deep, 5
  cubital, superficial, 3
  diaphragmatic, 177, 187
  duodenal, 284
  gastric, left, 279, 318, 341
    right, 279
  gastroepiploic, left, 279
    right, 279
  hepatic, 279, 300
  ileal, 296
  ileocecal, 296, 306
  ileocolic, 296
  iliac, 359
    external, 243, 340, 341, 383
    internal, 340, 341, 383
  infracardiac, 230
  infraclavicular, 5, 6
  inframammary, 5
  inguinal, 341, 359
    deep, 359, 384
    superficial, 244, 246, 341, 415
  intercostal, 227
  jejunal, 296
  jugular, 591
  lumbar, 318, 340, 341, 383, 384
  maxillary, 619
  mediastinal, 175, 177, 187, 188, 219, 220
    posterior, 299
  mesenteric, 295, 296, 332
  mesocolic, 296
  obturator, 340, 383
  occipital, 587, 619
  of face, head, and neck, 587, 621
    superficial, 587, 619
  of thorax, 3, 5, 6, 187
  pancreatic, 300, 331
  para-aortic, 332
  parasternal, 5
  paratracheal, 188, 592, 726
  parotid, 587
  pectoral, 5, 6
  pelvic, 341, 383
  popliteal, 487
  preaortic, 300
  preauricular, 587, 619
  pyloric, 279
  rectal, 312, 383
  renal, 331
  retroauricular, 587
  retropharyngeal, 747
  Rosenmüller's, 341
  sacral, 341, 383

Lymph nodes, *continued*
  splenic, 300, 331
  sternal, 11
  subauricular, 587
  subinguinal, deep, 341
  submandibular, 587, 597, 599, 619, 621, 727
  submental, 587, 599, 619, 621
  subpleural, 185
  subscapular, 6
  superficial, of head and neck, 587, 619
  supraclavicular, 5, 6, 587, 592, 619, 621
  supramandibular, 619
  suprarenal, 341
  tibial, anterior, 466
  tracheal, 187
  tracheobronchial, superior, 187, 220
  vertebral, 227
  Virchow's, 592
Lymph vessels, intercostal, 227
  of pancreas, 279
  of pelvis, female, 383
  of porta hepatis, 279
  of stomach, 279
  vertebral, 227
Lymphangiogram, of pectoral and axillary nodes, 6
Lymphatic drainage, of female breast, 5
Lymphatic ring, oro-naso-pharyngeal, 752
Lymphatics, of thorax, 3, 5, 6, 187

Malleolar processes, of ear, 780, 784, 786, 791, 797
  anterior, 791
Malleolus, lateral, 1, 412, 413, 463, 464, 466–468,
    470, 475, 476, 480, 485, 508, 512
  medial, 412, 413, 464, 468, 472, 474, 476, 477,
      480, 481, 512
Mammillary body, 639
Mammary gland, 3, 4, 7, 8, 257, 399
  areola of, 4, 257, 399
  fat body of, 8
  lobes of, 7, 8
  nipple of, 3, 4, 9, 399
Mandibular notch, 700
Manubrium, of malleus, 780, 781, 784–786, 789,
    791, 792, 797
  of sternum, 141, 142, 144, 145, 147, 149, 175, 188,
      212, 587, 726
Mastoid air cells, 640, 695, 751, 778, 779, 790, 792,
    793, 801, 802
Mastoid antrum, 778, 792, 795
Mastoid notch, 646, 777, 787
Mastoid process, of temporal bone, 574, 594, 615,
    623, 646, 748, 751, 754, 755, 774, 777–779,
    788, 790
Matrix, of finger nail, 126
Meatus, acoustic, external, 610, 612, 624, 646, 748,
    773, 776–778, 784, 785, 787
    cartilage of, 608, 787
    osseous part of, 787
    internal, 645
    fundus of, 801
  nasal, inferior, 684, 732
    middle, 684, 732
    superior, 684, 732
  nasopharyngeal, 726, 732
Mediastinum, 157–159, 168, 185, 186, 219
  anterior, 158, 159, 227
  posterior, 159, 219, 220
  superior, 157
Mediastinum testis, 251, 252, 343
Medulla, adrenal, 324
  renal, 325, 327
Medulla oblongata, 563, 566, 638, 639
  pyramid of, 566, 639
Membrane, arachnoid, 226
  atlanto-occipital, anterior, 535, 594, 722, 726
    posterior, 529, 534, 609
  intercostal, external, 151
    internal, 227, 526
  interosseous, of forearm, 78, 79, 80, 93, 105, 114,
      132
    of leg, 480, 489, 490
  mucous. See *Mucous membrane*
  obturator, 314, 333, 359, 395, 435, 438, 439
  periodontal, 703
  pharyngobasilar, 735, 746
  phrenicoesophageal, 299
  quadrangular, 766
  stapedial, 793, 795, 796
  synovial, 459
  tectorial, occipital, 425, 539, 540
  thyrohyoid, 217, 588, 592, 593, 722, 735, 744,
      745, 756, 757, 759, 760, 762, 763, 765, 766

Membrane, *continued*
  tympanic, 783, 784, 786, 787, 791, 795
    pars flaccida of, 766, 782, 786
    pars tensa of, 782, 784, 786
    secondary, 799
Membranous wall, tracheal, 591, 726, 759, 765
Meninges, 570, 571, 633
Meniscus, 453, 454
  lateral, 446, 448, 451, 453, 455, 456, 458, 459
    arterial supply of, 454
    femoral, surface of, 446, 459
  medial, 446, 448, 451, 453, 456, 459
    site of attachment on tibial plateau, 446
    tibial surface of, 459
Mental foramen, 598, 601, 603, 610, 697, 699, 708, 709, 711, 720
Mental protuberance, 598, 697
Mental tubercle, 574, 598, 697
Mesentery (Mesenteries), 264, 295, 302, 305, 308, 344
  developing, 261, 262
  dorsal, 261
  of small intestine, 296, 305, 332
  root of, 295, 301, 302, 310, 316
    of small intestine, 264
Mesoappendix, 301, 302, 305, 309, 316
Mesocardium, 195
Mesocolon, sigmoid, 264, 302, 305, 317, 318, 321, 341, 354
  root of, 316
  transverse, 260, 264, 273, 275, 277, 296, 297, 303, 305, 307, 331, 332
    root of, 301
Mesosalpinx, 278–280
Mesotendon of digit, 123, 124
Molar teeth, 699, 701, 704, 705, 708, 711, 715, 718, 719
  deciduous, 708, 709
  permanent, 708, 709, 715, 718, 719
  socket for, 598
Mons pubis, 370, 393
Mouth, vestibule of, 690, 729, 732, 736, 737
Mucosa, lingual, 736
  nasopharyngeal, 746
  of palate, 735, 747
  of stomach, 299
  oral, 603, 694, 699, 734, 737, 739, 744, 746
  tracheal, 591
Mucous membrane, esophageal, 769
  of bladder, 356
  of conus elasticus, 770
  of gall bladder, 284
  of hard palate, 747
  of nasal septum, 722, 726
  of stomach, 267, 268
  of tongue, 741, 758
  pharyngeal, 769, 770
Muscle(s), abdominal, anterior, 151, 238
  posterior, 333
  abductor digiti minimi, of foot, 413, 463, 494–498, 504, 515, 516
    of hand, 108, 111, 114, 119, 120, 121
  abductor hallucis, 413, 462, 494–498, 504, 507, 515, 516
  abductor pollicis brevis, 107, 108, 110–112, 114, 119, 120, 121
  abductor pollicis longus, 61, 65, 66, 74, 75, 77–79, 81, 100, 119, 120
  adductor brevis, 420, 422, 423, 430, 431, 434
  adductor hallucis, 497, 504
    oblique head of, 497, 498
    transverse head of, 495, 497, 498
  adductor longus, 412, 417–420, 422, 423, 431, 434, 486
  adductor magnus, 344, 413, 417, 420, 422, 423, 427–431, 434, 440, 486, 523
  adductor minimus, 423, 427, 429, 430
  adductor pollicis, 61, 105, 107, 108, 110–112, 114
    oblique head of, 108, 119, 121
    transverse head of, 108, 119
  anal sphincter, external, 312, 313, 343–346, 354, 368, 370, 371, 376, 387
    internal, 312, 343, 376
  anconeus, 51, 52, 58–61, 74–79, 81, 98
  antitragicus, 775
  arm, anterior, 55
  arrector pili, 633
  articularis cubiti, 50, 80, 81
  articularis genu, 431, 445, 487
  aryepiglottic, 753, 755, 764–766
  arytenoid, oblique, 753, 755, 758, 764, 765
    transverse, 726, 753, 755, 764, 765, 769

Muscle(s), *continued*
  auricular, anterior, 576
    oblique, 776
    posterior, 576, 604, 776
    superior, 776
    transverse, 776
  biceps brachii, 13–15, 23, 37, 47, 49, 50, 53–61, 64, 65, 67, 68, 71, 72, 75, 80, 82
    long head of, 21–23, 30, 31, 49, 50, 53–55, 63, 233
    short head of, 21, 22, 35, 49, 50, 53, 55, 56, 151, 233
  biceps femoris, 426–431, 434, 441, 443, 458, 467, 473–475, 477, 482, 487
    long head of, 413, 424, 427–430, 440, 463, 486
    short head of, 413, 424, 427–430, 440, 463, 486
  brachialis, 23, 49–53, 55–61, 64–71, 74, 75, 80, 82, 98
  brachioradialis, 47, 50–53, 56, 57, 59, 61, 65–69, 71, 72, 74–78, 80, 81, 98–100
  buccinator, 576, 603, 606, 608, 615, 622–625, 722, 729–731, 733, 737, 739, 740, 746–748
  bulbocavernosus, 371
  bulbospongiosus, 244, 245, 344, 346, 354, 368, 370
  calf, 473, 474
  chondroglossus, 741
  ciliary, 680
  coccygeus, 355, 364, 365, 376, 386, 387, 431
  coracobrachialis, 13, 14, 16, 21, 22, 35, 37, 49, 50, 53, 55, 56, 63, 64, 151, 233
  corrugator supercilii, 603, 606, 608, 654, 655
  cremaster, 12, 231–233, 237, 239, 246, 248, 249, 252, 253, 255, 343, 354
  cricoarytenoid, lateral, 765, 766
    posterior, 753, 755, 758, 764, 765, 770
  cricothyroid, 152, 217, 228, 589, 592, 735, 744–749, 756, 763, 765, 766
    oblique head of, 735
    straight head of, 735
  deltoid, 12–16, 20–24, 35, 37, 49–61, 63, 151, 231, 233, 523, 524, 527, 576, 579–583
  depressor anguli oris, 575, 576, 597, 603, 604, 606, 608, 622, 748
  depressor labii inferioris, 576, 603, 604, 606, 608, 730, 740
  depressor septi, 603
  depressor supercilii, 603, 604, 606, 608
  digastric, 529, 580, 581, 586, 623, 693, 722, 733, 735, 740
    anterior belly of, 151, 233, 576, 579, 583, 585, 587, 597–600, 606, 608, 615, 625, 647, 727, 734, 735, 739, 740, 748
    posterior belly of, 151, 233, 526, 576, 583, 587, 594, 598, 608, 623, 625, 640, 647, 727, 735, 748, 750, 751, 753–755, 788
  epicranius, 576
  erector spinae, 331, 332, 524, 525
  esophageal, circular, 755
    longitudinal, 755
  extensor carpi radialis brevis, 37, 47, 50–53, 57, 59, 61, 65, 74–81, 98–100, 120
  extensor carpi radialis, longus, 37, 47, 50–53, 57, 61, 65, 66, 69, 74–78, 80, 81, 98, 99, 120
  extensor carpi ulnaris, 37, 51, 52, 74–77, 81, 99, 100, 105
  extensor digiti minimi, 74, 75, 77, 81, 99, 100
  extensor digitorum, of forearm, 51, 52, 74–76, 78, 81, 99–101
  extensor digitorum brevis, 463–465, 467, 469–471, 502, 505, 515
  extensor digitorum longus, of leg, 431, 463–466, 469, 482, 489–491, 502, 505
  extensor hallucis brevis, 463, 464, 469, 470, 502, 505, 515
  extensor hallucis longus, 464, 465, 467, 469–471, 482, 490, 502, 505
  extensor indicis, 77, 79, 81, 100, 101
  extensor pollicis brevis, 61, 74–77, 79, 81, 100, 105, 120
  extensor pollicis longus, 75, 77–79, 81, 100, 120
  extensor retinaculum, 48, 112
  extensors, in forearm, 37
  external oblique, 7, 12, 14, 19, 20, 61, 151, 152, 219, 231–233, 235–242, 253, 255, 259, 320, 321, 332, 334, 359, 374, 376, 521–525
    aponeurosis of, 239, 240, 244
  extrinsic, of tongue, 741, 744, 745
  facial, superficial, 603, 604
  facial expression, muscles of, 603, 604
  flexor carpi radialis, 47, 49, 50, 61, 65–68, 99, 100, 119

Muscle(s), *continued*
  flexor carpi ulnaris, 37, 47, 50, 51, 58, 65–67, 69–71, 74, 75, 77, 79–81, 100, 101, 107, 110, 111, 119
  flexor digiti minimi brevis, of foot, 494, 495, 497, 498, 504, 516
    of hand, 108, 114, 119, 121
  flexor digitorum brevis, 494–496, 498, 504, 507, 515
  flexor digitorum longus, 434, 462, 474, 476–479, 483, 490, 504
  flexor digitorum profundus, 50, 69, 71, 81, 100, 119
  flexor digitorum superficialis, 50, 65–69, 80, 99–101, 119, 120
  flexor hallucis brevis, 494–498, 504, 516
  flexor hallucis longus, 462, 474, 476–479, 483, 490, 491, 504
  flexor pollicis brevis, 108, 110, 111, 114, 119, 121
  flexor pollicis longus, 61, 65, 66, 68–70, 80, 100, 120
  flexor retinaculum, 47
  flexors, in forearm, 37
    superficial, 47
  frontalis, 622, 623, 656, 657
  gastrocnemius, 426, 434, 441, 464, 467, 474, 475
    lateral head of, 413, 424, 427, 429, 441, 443, 447, 458, 463, 473–475, 489
    medial head of, 412, 413, 427–429, 440, 441, 443, 447, 462, 474, 475, 477, 478, 489
  gemellus, inferior, 427, 429, 430, 434, 523
    superior, 427, 429, 430, 434, 523
  genioglossus, 615, 647, 693, 694, 722, 726–728, 734–737, 739–741, 744–747, 756
  geniohyoid, 615, 647, 693, 694, 722, 726–728, 734–736, 739, 741, 744–747, 756
  gluteal, 424, 427, 523
  gluteus maximus, 344, 346, 354, 359, 370, 371, 413, 424, 426–430, 434, 523–526
  gluteus medius, 359, 419, 420, 423, 427–430, 434, 523
  gracilis, 344, 370, 417–421, 423, 426, 427, 429–431, 434, 440, 441, 462, 473, 482, 486, 487
  helicis major, 775
  helicis minor, 775
  hyoglossus, 151, 233, 576, 585–587, 615, 625, 722, 727, 735, 737, 739–741, 744, 745, 756
  iliacus, 243, 321, 333, 335, 339, 340, 345, 359, 376, 419, 431
  iliococcygeus, 365, 386
  iliocostalis cervicis, 525
  iliocostalis lumborum, 320, 525
  iliocostalis thoracis, 524, 525
  iliopsoas, 333, 335, 417–423, 431, 434
  infraspinatus, 23, 24, 33–35, 51, 52, 59, 63, 523, 524
  intercostal, 219, 230, 321
    external 16, 151, 218, 219, 227, 233, 237, 238, 299, 300, 525, 526, 573, 592
    innermost, 227
    internal, 16, 148, 151, 218, 227, 233, 237, 238, 299, 300, 526, 573, 592
  interfoveolar, 239, 243, 244, 340
  internal oblique, 151, 233, 237–239, 241, 242, 244, 245, 248, 255, 320, 321, 332, 359, 374, 376, 431, 434, 522–526
  interossei, dorsal, of foot, 469, 470, 500, 502, 516
    of hand, 61, 79, 103–105, 108, 109, 111, 112, 114, 116, 121
    palmar, 111, 114, 115, 121
    plantar, 494, 495, 498, 499, 504, 516
  interspinales, 526, 529
  intertransversarii, 219, 526, 529, 594
  ischiocavernosus 244–246, 344, 346, 354, 368, 370, 371
  latissimus dorsi, 7, 12, 14, 16, 19–22, 49–52, 57, 61, 151, 231–233, 237, 238, 332, 521–525, 527
  levator anguli oris, 576, 603, 606, 608, 614, 655–657, 748
  levator ani, 312–314, 339, 344–346, 354, 355, 359, 365, 370, 371, 376, 382, 383, 387, 434
    iliococcygeus part, 387
    pubococcygeus part, 387
  levator costae, 525
  levator labii superioris, 576, 603, 604, 606, 608, 654, 657, 730, 748
  levator labii superioris alaeque nasi, 576, 603, 604, 606, 608, 650, 654–657, 748
  levator palpebrae superioris, 638, 652, 655–657, 664, 667, 668, 670, 672–676

Muscle(s), *continued*
  levator scapulae, 23, 49, 51, 52, 61, 151, 233,
    523–525, 527, 575–577, 592, 594, 608
  levator veli palatini, 615, 647, 685, 690, 722, 735,
    746–748, 750, 751, 753, 780, 793
  levatores costarum, 525, 526
  lingual, transverse, 736
  longissimus, 525, 551
  longissimus capitis, 151, 525–529, 584, 594, 647
  longissimus cervicis, 525
  longissimus thoracis, 320, 524, 525
  longitudinal, of tongue, 737, 739, 741, 744, 745
    inferior, 735
    superior, 736
  longus capitis, 151, 233, 593, 640, 647, 722, 747
  longus colli, 151, 584, 591, 593, 594, 747
  lumbrical, of foot, 494, 495, 516
    of hand, 107–112, 114, 117, 121
  masseter, 524, 576, 597, 603, 606, 608, 615,
    622–624, 647, 727, 733, 737, 740
  mentalis, 576, 603, 604, 606, 608, 730, 748
  multifidus, 259, 320, 526, 528, 529
  mylohyoid, 151, 233, 576, 580, 581, 583,
    585–587, 597–600, 615, 625, 647, 693, 694,
    722, 726–728, 733–736, 739, 740, 746–748
  nasalis, 576, 603, 604, 608, 654, 748
  nuchal, 574
  oblique, external, 7, 12, 14, 19, 20, 61, 151, 152,
    219, 231–233, 235–242, 253, 255, 259, 320,
    321, 332, 334, 359, 374, 376, 521–525
    aponeurosis of, 239, 240, 244
    inferior, 14, 652, 656–658, 660, 664–667, 671,
      673, 676, 677
    internal, 151, 233, 237–239, 241, 242, 244, 245,
      248, 255, 320, 321, 332, 359, 374, 376, 431,
      434, 522–526
    superior, 656, 657, 667, 668, 670, 672, 674–676
  obliquus capitis, 526, 528, 529, 647
  obturator externus, 359, 423, 429–431, 434
  obturator internus, 243, 314, 345, 359, 364, 376,
    387, 417, 427–431, 434, 523
  occipitalis, 528, 606, 622, 635
  occipitofrontalis, 527, 528, 576, 577, 603, 604,
    606, 608, 654, 656, 657
    belly of frontalis, 656, 657
  ocular, 664–670, 672–677
  of ear, 775, 776, 792
  of larynx, 753, 764, 765
  of orbit, 654, 655
  of pharynx, 217, 228, 576, 582, 590, 597, 608, 741,
    744, 745, 748, 749, 753–755
  of soft palate, 753
  of tongue, 736, 740
  of uvula, 690, 731, 753
  omohyoid, 20–22, 49–53, 61, 524, 575, 581, 582,
    584–587, 592, 597, 608, 722, 735, 741, 748
    belly of, inferior, 151, 233, 576, 579, 580, 583,
      585
    superior, 151, 152, 233, 576, 579, 583, 599,
      600
  opponens digiti minimi, of foot, 463, 498, 516
    of hand, 107, 108, 114, 119, 121
  opponens pollicis, 107, 108, 111, 112, 114, 119, 121
  orbicularis oculi, 576, 603, 604, 606, 608, 650,
    654, 655, 657, 658, 660
  orbicularis oris, 576, 603, 604, 606, 608, 623, 690,
    722, 730, 735, 737, 740, 748
  orbitalis, 675
  palatoglossus, 615, 731, 735, 737, 740, 741,
    743–747
  palatopharyngeus, 615, 690, 731, 737, 740, 743,
    746, 747, 753, 755
  palmaris brevis, 106, 121
  palmaris longus, 50, 65–67, 99, 100, 120
  papillary, 202, 209, 211, 212
    anterior, 203, 204, 206, 207
    posterior, 201, 203, 206, 207
    septal, 201, 203
    small, 203, 204
  pectinate, 201–203
  pectineus, 412, 417–421, 423, 431, 434
  pectoralis major, 7, 12–16, 19–23, 35, 37, 49, 50,
    52–54, 56, 57, 61, 63, 151, 152, 186,
    231–233, 237–240, 576, 579–583, 585, 586,
    592
  pectoralis minor, 14–17, 20–22, 35, 49, 50, 53,
    151, 152, 186, 233, 580–582
  perineal, transverse, deep, 344, 354, 366,
    368–370, 387, 434
    superficial, 344, 366, 368–371, 387
  peroneus brevis, 463–465, 467, 474, 475, 478,
    479, 482, 483, 490, 491, 502, 505

Muscle(s), *continued*
  peroneus longus, 412, 431, 463–467, 474, 475,
    477, 479, 482, 483, 489, 490, 504–506
  peroneus tertius, 467, 469, 502, 505
  pharyngeal constrictor, inferior, 217, 228, 233,
    576, 582, 588, 590, 597, 608, 735, 741, 744,
    745, 748–750, 754, 756, 770
    middle, 590, 615, 735, 741, 744, 745, 747–750,
      754
    superior, 615, 690, 731, 735, 737, 740,
      744–747, 749, 750, 753–755
  pharyngoepiglottic, 747, 753, 755
  piriformis, 354, 355, 376, 417–420, 423,
    427–431, 434, 523
  plantaris, 424, 434, 440, 443, 463, 473, 474, 476,
    478, 489
  platysma, 12, 13, 575, 577, 581, 583, 591, 597,
    599, 603, 604, 608, 622, 727, 739, 748
  popliteus, 434, 443, 447, 448, 455, 456, 477–479,
    483, 489
  procerus, 603, 604, 606, 654, 655, 722, 748
  pronator quadratus, 65, 66, 69, 70, 80, 101, 108,
    111, 114, 119
  pronator teres, 49, 50, 56, 61, 66–71, 80, 81, 99, 100
  psoas major, 215, 230, 243, 285, 319–321, 328,
    331–333, 335, 338, 340, 359, 419, 431, 522
  psoas minor, 215, 333, 335
  pterygoid, lateral, 614, 615, 624, 625, 647, 722,
    750
    medial, 614, 615, 624, 625, 647, 693–695, 722,
      727, 734, 737, 740, 747, 750, 751, 753, 793
  pubococcygeus, 365, 386
  puborectalis, 386,
  pyloric sphincter, 268, 287, 331
  pyramidalis, 11, 237–240, 253, 255
  quadratus femoris, 417, 428–431, 434, 482, 523
  quadratus lumborum 219, 229, 230, 285, 321,
    331–333, 335, 338–340, 431, 522
  quadratus plantae, 495–498, 504, 515
  quadriceps femoris, 417, 419
  rectouterine, 379
  rectus, inferior, 657, 664–667, 673, 675–677
    lateral, 659, 664–670, 672, 675–677
    medial, 657, 665–669, 674–677, 680
    superior, 638, 657, 664–668, 670, 672–674,
      676, 677
  rectus abdominis, 11, 149, 151, 152, 230,
    237–241, 243, 253, 255, 259, 300, 321, 331,
    332, 335, 340, 354, 359, 374, 393
    insertion of, 240
  rectus capitis anterior, 151, 594, 647
  rectus capitis, lateralis, 151, 529, 594, 647
  rectus capitis posterior major, 526, 528, 529, 647
  rectus capitis posterior minor, 526, 529, 647
  rectus femoris, 412, 417–424, 431, 434, 647
  rhomboid major, 23, 49, 51, 52, 523, 524, 527,
    528
  rhomboid minor, 23, 49, 51, 52, 523, 524, 527,
    528
  risorius, 575, 603, 604, 606, 730
  rotatores, 526
  sacrococcygeus, 365, 376
    ventral, 386
  sacrospinalis, 522
  salpingopharyngeus, 615, 690, 746, 753, 755
  sartorius, 412, 417–424, 431, 434, 440, 462, 482,
    486, 487
  scalene, 583, 584
  scalenus anterior, 20, 61, 151, 152, 184, 186, 224,
    233, 576, 580, 582, 587, 591–594, 608
  scalenus medius, 61, 151, 233, 524, 529, 575, 576,
    587, 591–594, 608
  scalenus posterior, 61, 151, 233, 524–526, 529,
    587, 593, 594, 608
  semimembranosus, 413, 424, 426–431, 434, 440,
    441, 443, 462, 473–475, 483, 486, 487, 523
  semispinalis capitis, 233, 523–529, 576, 604, 608,
    647
  semispinalis cervicis, 525, 526, 528, 529
  semispinalis thoracis, 525, 526
  semitendinosus, 370, 426–428, 430, 431, 434,
    441, 443, 462, 473, 475, 482, 486
  serratus anterior, 7, 12, 14, 16, 19–21, 49–51, 61,
    151, 231–233, 237–240, 255, 524
  serratus posterior inferior, 332, 524, 525
  serratus posterior superior, 533–535
  soleus, 412, 434, 443, 462–464, 467, 473–479,
    483, 489, 490
  sphincter, pupillary, 680
    pyloric, 268, 287, 331
    urethral, 354, 366, 387
    vaginal, 387

Muscle(s), *continued*
  sphincter ani, external, 312, 313, 343–346, 354,
    368, 370, 371, 376, 387
    internal, 312, 343, 376
  spinalis capitis, 525, 526
  spinalis cervicis, 525
  spinalis thoracis, 524, 525
  splenius capitis, 61, 233, 523–529, 575, 576, 581,
    594, 604, 608, 647
  splenius cervicis, 523–525, 529
  stapedius, 640, 695, 789, 793, 798
  sternalis (variation), 151
  sternocleidomastoid, 12, 13, 15, 18, 20, 50, 52,
    61, 151, 152, 231, 233, 257, 523, 527,
    574–577, 579–581, 583–586, 588, 591, 594,
    603, 604, 606, 608, 622, 623, 722, 727
  sternohyoid, 52, 61, 148, 151, 152, 233, 576, 579,
    582–584, 586–588, 591, 592, 597, 599, 600,
    608, 647, 722, 727, 735, 741, 748
  sternothyroid, 148, 151, 152, 233, 576, 579,
    582–584, 587, 591, 592, 608, 735, 741, 766
  styloglossus, 587, 608, 625, 647, 722, 727, 735,
    737, 740, 741, 744–748, 750, 756
  stylohyoid, 151, 233, 576, 580, 583, 585, 587,
    597–600, 608, 615, 623, 625, 647, 722, 727,
    735, 740, 744, 745, 748, 750, 753, 788
  stylopharyngeus, 647, 722, 735, 737, 740, 744,
    745, 747–750, 753, 754, 770
  subclavius, 16, 21, 35, 50–53, 151, 152, 184–186,
    188, 227, 592
  subcostales, 333, 556
  sublingual, 735
  subscapularis, 16, 21, 22, 31, 35, 49, 50, 53, 55,
    63, 151, 233
  supinator, 50, 66–69, 72, 77–81, 99
  supraspinatus, 21, 23, 24, 33–35, 49–53, 57, 63,
    520, 524
  temporalis, 608, 615, 623–625, 635, 647, 669
  temporoparietalis, 576, 603, 604, 622, 623
  tensor fasciae latae, 412, 413, 416–419
  tensor tympani, 695, 780, 781, 791–793, 795, 796,
    798, 801
    semicanal for, 778, 796
  tensor veli palatini, 615, 647, 694, 735, 746–748,
    753, 755, 793
  teres major, 16, 19, 21–24, 34, 49–53, 56–61, 63,
    151, 233, 523, 524, 761
  teres minor, 23, 24, 33–35, 51, 52, 59–61, 63,
    523, 524
  thyroarytenoid, 765, 770
  thyrohyoid, 152, 233, 576, 583, 586–588, 592,
    597, 608, 722, 735, 741, 744, 745, 748, 766
  tibialis anterior, 412, 431, 462–467, 482, 489,
    490, 504, 506
  tibialis posterior, 434, 476–479, 483, 490, 504,
    506
  tragicus, 775
  transverse lingual, 736
  transverse perineal, deep, 344, 354, 366,
    368–370, 387, 434
    superficial, 344, 366, 368–371, 387
  transversospinal, 526
  transversus abdominis, 151, 238–243, 245, 253,
    255, 259, 321, 332, 333, 335, 338, 340, 359,
    376, 431, 522, 526
  transversus thoracis, 148, 149, 152, 299
  trapezius, 13, 21, 23, 50–52, 55, 61, 523, 524, 527,
    528, 575–577, 580, 583–585, 592, 604, 608,
    623
  triangularis, 576
  triceps, 7, 14, 37, 49, 51, 60, 61, 75, 76, 81, 82, 98,
    524
    lateral head, 23, 49, 51, 52, 57–61, 64, 75, 523
    long head, 21–24, 29, 31, 33–35, 49–53,
      55–61, 63, 64, 523
    medial head, 49, 51–53, 55–59, 61, 64–66, 74,
      75, 77, 81
  vastus intermedius, 420, 423, 431, 434, 486
  vastus lateralis, 412, 417–420, 423, 424, 426, 427,
    429, 431, 434, 440, 444, 446, 463, 467, 486,
    487
  vastus medialis, 412, 417–421, 423, 431, 434, 440,
    444–446, 462, 486, 487
  vocalis, 766, 770
  zygomaticus major, 576, 604, 606, 622, 623, 647,
    654–657, 730, 748
  zygomaticus minor, 576, 603, 604, 606, 654–657,
    748
Muscular coat, of stomach, 268, 270
Musculotubal canal, 594
Myocardium, 201, 202, 206, 208, 209
Myometrium, 380

Nail. See *Finger nail*
Nares, 602, 726, 732
Nasal cavity, 613, 669, 684, 685, 691, 692, 723
  lateral wall of, 684, 685, 691, 692, 723
  nerves of, 694
Nasal vestibule, 685, 690, 691, 732
Nasolacrimal duct, 658, 660
  opening of, 685
Nasopharynx, 746, 747
  mucosa of, 746
  muscles in, 746
  openings of, 685
Neck, 574–588, 591–594
  arteries of, 577–582, 586
  features of, external, 574
  lower, nerves and vessels in deep part of, 588
  muscles of, 523, 525–527, 583
  nerves of, 577–582
  root of, 83, 152, 592–594
    superficial structures at, 592
  triangles of, 576
  veins of, 585, 586
Nerve(s), abducens, 638–642, 644, 670, 672, 674, 676, 788, 801
  accessory, 18, 257, 528, 566, 577, 579–582, 638–640, 642, 644, 754, 755, 788, 801
    spinal and bulbar roots, 801
  alveolar, inferior, 623–625, 693, 694, 696, 724, 737, 739
    superior, 624, 625, 695, 696, 725
  ampullar, anterior, 800, 804
    posterior, 801
  anococcygeal, 336, 346, 371
  auricular, great, 517, 527, 575, 577, 622
    posterior, 577, 623, 787, 794
  auriculotemporal, 607, 611, 622–625
  axillary, 18, 19, 22, 24, 56, 60, 63, 517
  buccal, 611, 622, 624, 625, 724, 725, 737
    branches of, 740
  calcaneal, 493, 515
  cardiac, cervical, inferior, 226
    superior, 188, 219, 582, 591, 754
    sympathetic, 588
    middle, 219, 220, 228, 582, 593, 754
    sympathetic origin, 185, 593
    vagal origin, 185
  caroticotympanic, 695, 793, 794
  carotid, internal, 640, 695, 754
  cervical, 228, 528, 581, 592
    openings for, 722
    rami, ventral, 580, 593
    rootlets of, 540, 639
    view of, posterior, 755
  chorda tympani, 625, 640, 693–695, 742, 747, 781, 755–789, 791–795, 801
  ciliary, long, 674
    short, 674
  cluneal, inferior, 336, 346, 371, 407, 425, 426, 517
    medial, 517, 521
    middle, 407, 425, 426
    superior, 407, 425, 517, 521
  coccygeal, 339, 364, 567
  cochlear, 801–804
  cranial, 639
  cutaneous, antebrachial, lateral, 38–41, 47, 54, 56, 58, 60, 98–101, 106, 517
    hiatus for, 47
    medial, 14, 18, 22, 38–41, 54, 63, 64, 98–100, 330
      anterior branch, 38
      ulnar branch, 38
    posterior, 39, 40, 42, 43, 48, 58–60, 98–100, 102, 112, 517
    anterior, 10, 11, 13, 20
      hiatus for, 48
    brachial, anterior, 14
      lateral, axillary branch, 24, 38, 39, 42, 58, 64
      medial, 14, 22, 38–43, 54, 64, 517
      posterior, 38, 39, 43, 58, 60, 64, 517
    cervical, transverse, 577
    crural, medial, 460, 468
    distribution of, in lower extremity, 405, 407
      in upper extremity, 38, 39
    dorsal, intermediate, 461
      lateral, 10, 460, 468
      medial, 461, 527
    femoral, anterior, 11, 337, 405, 407, 409, 414, 486, 487
      lateral, 317, 318, 320, 321, 336–338, 340, 359, 405, 407, 408, 414, 418, 425, 517
      medial, 409

Nerve(s), cutaneous, *continued*
    posterior, 336, 346, 371, 407, 408, 425, 426, 428, 460, 486, 517
    iliohypogastric, anterior, 245, 336
      lateral, 336, 405, 407
    intercostal, anterior, 232, 239, 240, 585
      lateral, 232
    interosseous, anterior, 70
    lateral, 10, 11, 13, 14, 18–20
      mammary branches, 19
    obturator, 405, 407, 414, 421, 422, 486, 487
    of foot, dorsal, 515
    of forearm, 67, 68, 70–72
    of hand, 112
    peroneal, superficial, 515
    plantar, lateral, 493, 516
      medial, 493, 496, 516
    radial, posterior, 42
    saphenous, medial, 489
    subcostal, anterior, 232, 246, 521
      lateral, 339
    sural, 468
      lateral, 397, 405, 428, 441, 460, 487, 489, 490, 516, 517
      medial, 426, 428, 460, 487, 489
    ulnar, 43, 106
      dorsal, 70, 76, 78
      palmar, 106
  digital, of foot, 468, 471, 493, 496, 516
    of hand, 38, 39, 102, 106, 110–112, 122–124
      dorsal, branch, 39, 112
      palmar branch, common, 38
        proper, 38, 39, 112, 123, 124
  dorsal, of clitoris, 245, 369, 371
    of penis, 246, 346, 347, 366
  esophageal, 220, 573
  ethmoid, anterior, 674, 676, 692, 693
    posterior, 674, 676
  facial, 225, 577, 605, 609, 622–625, 638–640, 644, 694, 695, 787–789, 791, 793, 794, 796, 798, 799, 801, 802, 804
    auricular branch, posterior, 580, 605, 625, 787, 794
    buccal branch, 605, 622, 654, 655, 657
    cervical branch, 579, 597, 599, 605, 622
    digastric branch, 623, 625, 788
    genu of, 795, 796
    mandibular branch, 599, 605, 622
    stylohyoid branch, 788
    temporal branch, 605, 622, 650, 654, 656
    zygomatic branch, 605, 622, 654–657
  femoral, 243, 317, 336–338, 340, 341, 359, 418, 421, 422
    branch to iliopsoas muscle, 321, 336, 338
    cutaneous nerve fields of, in leg and thigh, 409
    muscular branch, 421, 422, 486
  frontal, 517, 611, 640, 670
  genicular, 475
  genitofemoral, 11, 239, 317, 318, 320, 321, 336–338, 340, 359, 364, 383, 405
    femoral, branch, 321, 336–338, 340, 405, 408, 414
    genital branch, 243–246, 321, 336–338, 340, 347, 364, 408
  glossopharyngeal, 225, 565, 609, 638, 639, 642, 644, 692, 724, 737, 740, 742, 746, 747, 754, 755, 758, 788, 794, 801
    hiatus for passage of, 735
    lingual branch, 692, 758
    pharyngeal branch, 754, 793
    tonsillar branch, 692, 758
    tympanic branch, 607
  gluteal, inferior, 336, 428, 430
    superior, 451, 430
  gluteus maximus, 523
  hypoglossal, 565, 566, 580–582, 585, 586, 597, 600, 608, 625, 638–640, 642, 644, 727, 737, 739, 740, 746, 747, 754–756, 801
  iliohypogastric, 11, 218, 232, 239, 240, 244–246, 317, 318, 321, 331, 332, 336–338, 340, 359, 405, 408, 414, 425, 517, 521
  ilioinguinal, 11, 232, 239, 240, 244–246, 248, 317, 318, 321, 336–338, 340, 341, 347, 359, 408, 414
  incisive, 690
  infraorbital, 608, 611, 622–625, 650, 655–657, 659, 675, 676, 694–696, 793
    labial branches, superior, 622, 725
    nasal branches, external, 622
    palpebral, branch, inferior, 623, 654, 655
  infratrochlear, 611, 622–625, 650, 654–657, 674, 676

Nerve(s), infratrochlear, *continued*
    nasal branch, 654
    palpebral branch, 655
      inferior, 654
  intercostal, 11, 184, 185, 218, 220, 224, 226–230, 239, 240, 255, 299, 321, 359, 521, 526, 563, 573
    meningeal branch, 226
    ramus of, anterior primary, 219, 518
      posterior primary, 219, 518
    thoracic branch, 226
  intercostobrachial, 14, 18–20, 40, 582
  intermedius, 638, 788
  interosseous, anterior, 100
    posterior, 78, 100, 105
  jugular, 754
  labial, anterior, 244, 245
    posterior, 371
  lacrimal, 611, 640, 659, 670, 672, 674
    branches of, 653
    palpebral branches, 650, 654–656
  laryngeal, inferior, 758
    internal, 588, 756
    recurrent 176, 177, 185–187, 218, 228, 582, 586, 588, 591–593, 699
      esophageal, branches, 588, 758
      left, 176, 188, 189, 218–220, 224, 586, 588, 591, 592, 755
      inferior cardiac branch, 186
      right, 186, 218–220, 224, 755
    superior, 581, 592, 597, 600, 640, 737, 740, 741, 744–746, 748, 751, 753–755, 758, 770, 793
      external branch, 593, 754
      internal branch, 217, 593, 754, 758
  lingual, 586, 611, 624, 625, 693, 694, 696, 724, 727, 731, 737, 739, 740, 742, 746, 747, 756
    branches of, 740, 746, 747
    to tongue, 740
  lumbar, 320, 332, 339, 354
  mandibular, 625, 638, 639, 670, 676, 694, 696, 740, 801
    branches of, 625
  masseteric, 623–625, 740
  maxillary, 638–642, 670, 672, 676, 694–696, 788, 801
  median, 7, 14, 18, 22, 38, 41, 51, 54, 56, 63, 64, 67, 68, 70–72, 98–101, 106, 108, 110, 120, 121
    lateral cord contribution to, 14
    palmar branch, 38, 67, 101
  meningeal, 638
  mental, 611, 622–624, 696, 724
    labial branches, 740
  musculocutaneous, 14, 18, 22, 54–56, 63, 64
  mylohyoid, 580–582, 599, 600, 624, 625, 693, 694, 737, 739, 740
  nasal, external, 611, 622–625, 654–657, 690, 692, 694
  nasal septal, 692
  nasociliary, 610, 670, 672, 779, 793
    branch of, 793
  nasopalatine, 690, 692–694, 725
  obturator, 243, 336–338, 359, 364, 376, 383, 405, 408, 421, 422, 517
  occipital, greater, 517, 527, 528, 577, 579, 582, 622, 623
    lesser, 517, 527, 577, 579, 582, 622, 623
  oculomotor, 225, 639–642, 644, 670, 672, 674, 676, 788, 793, 901
    inferior branch, 674–676
    superior branch, 672, 674
  of neck, 588
  of orbit, 654, 655
  of palate, 692, 723, 725
  of pancreas, 279
  of penis, 248, 347
  of porta hepatis, 279
  of pterygoid canal, 640, 693–695, 746, 794
  of spermatic cord, 347
  of stapedius muscle, 640
  of stomach, 279
  of upper extremity, cutaneous, 38, 39
  olfactory, 690, 692
    lateral, 691
    medial, 690, 691
  ophthalmic, 638–642, 670, 672, 674, 676, 694–696, 788, 801
    frontal branch, 793
    lacrimal branch, 793
  optic 636–642, 644, 659, 664, 666–670, 672–677, 679, 793
  palatine, 611, 640, 693

Nerve(s), palatine, *continued*
greater, 692–694, 725, 731, 747
lesser, 692, 725, 731, 747
posterior, 693
pectoral, 15, 18, 582
perineal, 346, 366, 371
peripheral nerves, cutaneous fields of, in thigh, 408
peroneal, common, 336, 346, 347, 405, 426, 428, 441, 463, 465, 486, 487, 489
cutaneous fields of, in leg and foot, 411
deep, 405, 411, 465, 468, 471, 490, 491
lateral cutaneous branch, 411
superficial, 405, 411, 461, 465, 468, 490, 491, 515
petrosal, deep, 640, 693, 695
greater, 638, 640, 642, 645, 693–695, 788, 793–796, 798, 801, 802
lesser, 607, 638, 642, 645, 694, 695, 793, 794, 801
pharyngeal, 747
phrenic, 20, 152, 175, 176, 184, 189, 220, 228, 229, 318, 573, 580–582, 586, 592, 593, 596
accessory, 592
left, 176, 177, 185–188, 208, 209, 218, 230
right, 18, 177, 184, 186–188, 208, 209, 230
plantar, lateral, 407, 410, 493, 496, 497, 515
medial, 407, 410, 493, 496, 497, 515
pterygoid, lateral, 625
medial, 694, 793
pterygopalatine, 640, 694, 695, 793
pudendal, 336, 339, 345, 346, 359, 364, 366, 371
radial, 18, 22, 38, 51, 54, 56, 58, 60, 63, 64, 67, 68, 70–72, 98, 112, 517
deep branch, 67, 68, 70, 72, 76, 78, 81, 99
superficial branch, 38, 39, 41, 43, 67, 68, 70, 72, 76, 78, 99–102, 112
rectal, inferior 336, 346, 364, 371
saccular, 800, 803, 804
sacral, 320, 339, 343, 364
saphenous, 374, 407, 409, 421, 422, 460, 468, 486, 487, 489–491, 517
infrapatellar branch, 407, 414, 460, 487
scapular, dorsal, 18, 527, 528, 592
sciatic, 336, 428, 430, 486, 523
scrotal, anterior, 246
posterior, 346
septal, 690
nasal branch, 692
spinal, 10, 518, 564, 568
cervical, 527, 565
lateral branch, 10, 518
lumbar, 565, 567
medial branch, 10, 518
meningeal branches, 10, 572, 573
ramus of, anterior, 10, 571, 572
anterior primary, 573
dorsal, 10
posterior, 10, 517
posterior primary, 518, 563, 571–573
ramus communicans, 10, 518
root of, dorsal, 10, 563
dorsal root, ganglion, 10
ventral, 10, 571, 573
sacral, 354, 565
thoracic, 320, 527, 563, 565
splanchnic, greater, 10, 184, 185, 218–220, 224, 226–230, 299, 300, 320, 331, 328, 573
root of, 10
lesser, 218, 219, 224, 226, 229, 230, 299, 300, 320, 338
lumbar, 318, 320, 332
stapedial, 789, 793
subclavian, 185
subcostal, 218–220, 224, 226, 239, 240, 244, 246, 255, 332, 337–339
sublingual, 740, 746, 747, 756
submandibular, 740
suboccipital, 528
subscapular, 22, 24
supraclavicular, 11, 13, 517, 577
posterior, 40, 42
supraorbital, 622–624, 650, 654–657
ramus of, lateral, 650, 656, 657, 670, 672
medial, 650, 656, 657, 670, 672
superior palpebral, 654, 655
suprascapular, 18, 22, 24 582
supratrochlear, 611, 622–625, 650, 654–657, 670, 672
sural, 405, 407, 410, 411, 460, 490, 491, 515, 517
cutaneous nerve fields, of, in leg and foot, 410, 411

Nerve(s), *continued*
temporal, deep, 624, 625
thoracic, 14, 226, 228, 300, 338, 339, 405, 517, 527
cutaneous branch of, lateral, 14
intercostal branch, 226
long, 14, 18–20, 582
rami of, posterior, 517, 527, 528
ventral root of T-5, T-6, T-7, T-8, T-10, 226
thoracodorsal, 18–20, 22, 582
thyrohyoid, 580, 597, 600
tibial, 336, 426, 428, 441, 475, 476, 479, 486, 487, 489–491
calcaneal branch, 410
cutaneous nerve fields of, in leg, 410
to coccygeus muscle, 336
to digastric muscle, 793
to gemelli muscles, 336
to levator ani muscle, 336
to levator scapulae muscle, 528
to nasalis muscle, 656
to obturator internus muscle, 336
to omohyoid muscle, 592
to pectineus muscle, 418
to pterygoid muscle, medial, 747, 793
to quadratus femoris muscle, 336
to subclavius muscle, 592
to tensor tympani muscle, 694, 793
to tensor veli palatini muscle, 694, 747, 793
to teres minor muscle, 24
trigeminal, 610, 637–639, 644, 670, 672, 674, 676, 693, 695, 696, 788, 801
alveolar branches, inferior, 611
superior, 611
mandibular branches, 611
root of, motor, 639, 642, 694, 695, 793, 801
sensory, 642, 694, 801
semilunar ganglion of, 639
trochlear, 638–642, 670, 672, 674, 801
tympanic, 640, 695, 793–796, 798, 799
ulnar, 14, 18, 22, 41, 51, 54, 56, 58, 60, 63, 64, 67, 68, 70, 71, 76, 78, 98–102, 106, 108, 110, 111, 120, 517
dorsal branch, 39, 67, 101
palmar branch, 38, 67
utricular, 800, 803
utriculoampullar, 803
vagus, 20, 184, 224, 225, 228, 565, 581, 582, 591, 593, 608, 609, 625, 638, 639, 642, 644, 695, 737, 740, 754, 755, 788, 794, 801
auricular branch, 622–625, 640, 787, 789, 793, 794
bronchial branches, 218, 220, 224, 228, 229
cardiac branches, 186, 188, 219, 220, 228, 582, 592, 593, 754, 755
inferior, 592
middle, 592
superior, 592
esophageal branches, 218, 220, 229, 230
left, 176, 177, 185–188, 208, 209, 218, 220, 224, 318, 573, 586, 588, 591, 592, 755
pharyngeal branch, 754, 793
recurrent laryngeal branch, 177, 184, 208, 219, 220, 593
right, 186, 187, 189, 218–220, 224, 228, 229, 573, 580, 582, 586, 592, 755
superior ganglion of, 755
tracheal branches, 228, 593
vertebral, sympathetic, 226, 593
vestibular, 801–804
vestibulocochlear, 638, 639, 642, 644, 694, 788, 800
zygomatic, 664, 659, 676, 695
zygomaticofacial, 622, 623, 654–657
cutaneous branch of, 650
zygomaticotemporal, 611, 622, 654
Nervus intermedius, 639, 695, 801
Network, arterial, calcaneal, 479, 496
dorsal carpal, 62, 105
genicular, 422, 465
malleolar, 465, 471
nasal septal, 690
patellar, 414
trochanteric, 428
venous, of dorsal foot, 460
of dorsal hand, 102
Nipple, 3, 4, 7–9, 19, 136, 172, 232, 399
Node, atrioventricular, 210, 213
sinoatrial, 213
Nodule of semilunar valve, 212
Nose, conchae of, 601, 684, 685, 688, 691–693, 732, 751
external, bones of, 682

Nose, external, *continued*
cartilages of, 655–657, 682, 683, 690, 726
septum of, 601, 669, 683, 690, 692, 726, 751, 753
vestibule of, 685, 690, 691, 732
Nostrils, 602, 726, 732
Notch, angular, of stomach, 269, 273
cardiac, 153, 170
interarytenoid, 751, 755, 758, 767, 772
intertragic, 773
jugular, 136, 257
mandibular, 700
mastoid, 646, 777, 787
of Rivinus, 786
sciatic, greater, 389, 390, 401
lesser, 389, 390
supraorbital, 652, 689
thyroid, superior, 136, 257, 757, 761, 763
trochlear, of ulna, 9, 87, 88, 93, 133
tympanic, 785, 786

Occipital condyle, 610, 646, 748
Occipital, crest, internal, 645
Occipital protuberance, external, 523, 528, 574, 646, 647
internal, 645
Odontoid process. See *Dens*
Olecranon, 43, 51, 57–59, 61, 71, 74, 75, 77, 78, 88, 92, 98
Olfactory bulb, 639, 644, 690, 691
Olfactory stria, 639
Olfactory tract, 639, 644, 690, 691
Olive, 639
Omentum, greater, 256, 259–261, 265, 266, 270, 273, 275, 277, 279, 296, 299–302, 305, 307, 310, 331, 332, 343, 399
lesser, 111, 261, 264, 273, 300
Opening(s). *See also Orifice*
adductor canal, opening of, 440
atrioventricular, 202, 204, 206, 212–215
bulbourethral gland, opening of, 361
coronary sinus, opening of, 180, 191–193, 203, 208, 213–215
ejaculatory duct, opening of, 356, 361
frontal sinus, opening into, 685, 686
lymphatic duct, right, opening of, 587
nasolacrimal duct, opening of, 685
nasopharynx, opening of, 685
pancreatic duct, opening of, 284
paranasal air sinuses, opening of, 685, 686
paraurethral ducts, opening of, 367
preputial, 343
prostatic ductule, opening of, 356
sphenoethmoidal sinus, opening of, 685
sublingual gland, opening of, 737
tympanic, for auditory tube, 778, 786, 791, 795, 798
ureter, opening of, 356, 357, 361, 377
urethral, external, 343, 351, 361, 367, 368, 370–372, 376, 377, 388
internal, 343, 356, 357, 361
uterine, 377, 380
vaginal, 367, 368, 370, 372, 388
vestibular gland, greater, opening of, 367, 368, 370
Optic canal, 645, 662, 669, 670, 676
Optic chiasma, 639, 644, 668
Optic disc, 679, 680
Ora serrata, 669, 680
Oral cavity, 694, 723–725, 729, 732, 737–740, 746, 747
mucosa of, 603, 694, 699, 734, 735, 737, 739, 744, 746, 747
musculature of, 735
vessels and nerves of, 740, 746, 747
Orbit, 653–657
apex of, 675
dissection of, anterior, 654–657
eyeball, exposure of, 657
muscles of, superficial, 654
vessels and nerves of, 654–656
superficial, 654
Orbital cavity, bony, 661–663
wall of, lateral, 663
medial, 662
Orbital septum 650–652, 655–657, 673
Orifice, cardiac, of stomach, 268, 299, 316
of appendix, 306
See also *Opening(s)*
Oro-naso-pharyngeal lymphatic ring, 752
Oropharynx, 732, 746, 747
muscles in, 746
Osseous spiral lamina, of cochlea, 800

Ossicles, of middle ear, 792, 797
Ovary (Ovaries), 310, 316, 318, 372, 374, 377–382, 399
  developing, 372
  stroma of, 360

Pad, distal digital, 37
Palate, 725
  arteries of, 692
  folds of, muscular, 685, 731
    transverse, 701
  glands of, 690, 701, 722, 731, 746, 747
  hard, 685, 690, 701, 702, 721, 722, 726, 729, 732, 747
  mucosa of, 735, 747
  nerves of, 692, 747
  soft, 685, 701, 726, 729, 732, 747, 751
  vessels of, 747
Palatine process, of maxilla, 631, 683, 684, 702
Palatine tonsil. See *Tonsil, palatine*
Palatoglossal arch, 729, 731, 732, 735, 737, 743
Palatopharyngeal arch, 726, 729, 731, 732, 735, 737, 751, 755
Palm, of hand, 1, 37–39, 106, 107, 520. See also *Hand*
  arteries of, 62, 106, 110, 111
    superficial, 106
  creases of, 37
  eminence of, hypothenar, 37
    thenar, 37
  monticuli of, 37
  muscles of, 37, 107, 114, 115
  nerves of, 38, 39, 106, 110, 111
    superficial, 106
  surface anatomy of, 37
  synovial sheaths of, 107
  tendons of, 107, 112
Palmar arch, deep, 62, 111, 113, 182
  superficial, 62, 110, 111, 113, 182, 183
Palpebra(e). See *Eyelid(s)*
Palpebral commissure, lateral, 648, 677
  medial, 677
Pancreas, 215, 261, 265, 266, 279, 285, 288–293, 300, 303, 316, 331, 332
  body of, 275, 277, 286, 302, 305
  duodenum and, 285
  head of, 25, 258, 272, 285, 296, 310, 316, 317, 332
  lymphatic vessels of, 279
  nerves of, 279
  tail of, 258, 272, 277, 285, 287, 305, 317, 331
  unciate process of, 286
Pancreatic duct. See *Duct, pancreatic*
Pancreatic duct system, 287
Papilla(e), conical, 743
  duodenal, 268, 283, 284, 287–293
    greater, 332
  filiform, 743
  foliate, 732, 743, 746
  fungiform, 743
  incisive, 701
  interdental, 740
  lacrimal, 649, 658, 677
    inferior, 658
  optic, 681
  renal, 325, 327, 328
  vallate, 692, 732, 743, 751, 753, 755, 758
Papillary process, of caudate lobe of liver, 305
Paradidymis, 363
Paroophoron, 372
Pars flaccida, of tympanic membrane, 766, 782, 786
Pars iridica retinae, 680
Pars optica retinae, 680
Pars tensa, of tympanic membrane, 782, 784, 786
Pecten, of pubis, 335, 389, 393, 417, 419, 420
Pedicles, of vertebrae, 553
  lumbar, 555
  thoracic, 547
  of vertebral arches, 557, 573
Peduncle, cerebral, 639
Pelvis, brim of, 359
  female, 316, 345, 377, 378, 385–388, 393, 396, 398
    ligaments of, 394
    outlet of, 394
    skeleton of, 388, 393
  lesser (female), 385
  lymph nodes and vessels of, 383
  male, 321, 343, 345, 359, 395, 397
  minor, 316, 321, 398
    diagrammatic section through, 385
  muscular floor of, 365, 386, 387
  nerves of, 340

Pelvis, *continued*
  radiograph of, 401
  renal, 285, 320, 323, 325–328, 331, 332, 363, 372
  section through, diagrammatic, 385
  skeleton of, 389–392
  vessels of, 340
Penis, 1, 12, 242, 348–351
  bulb of, 343, 352, 359, 361
  capsule of, fibrous, 348
  corpus cavernosum, 248, 348, 352, 355, 363
  corpus spongiosum, 248, 343, 344, 352, 363
  erectile bodies of, 352
  ligaments of, fundiform, 12, 231–233, 236, 343
    suspensory, 12, 232, 234, 239, 246, 248, 347
  nerves of, 347
  prepuce of, 246, 343, 349, 351, 361
  vessels of, 347
Pericardial cavity, 159, 215, 299
Pericardium, 170, 175, 176, 184–186, 188, 189, 191, 195, 208, 209, 212, 214, 215, 229, 256, 257, 399
  aortic recess of, 179, 188, 194, 214
  diaphragmatic, 170, 189, 214, 573
  over pulmonary surface of heart, 170
  parietal, 152, 159, 177, 189, 194, 204
  visceral, 159, 204
Perichorioidal space, 680
Perimetrium, 380
Perineum, central tendinous point of, 344, 367, 370, 376, 387
  female, 370
  male, 345, 346
Periorbita, 664, 667, 675
Periosteum, 606, 608, 664, 675
Peripheral nerves of thigh, cutaneous nerve fields of, 408
Perirenal fat, 332
Perithyroid space, 591
Peritoneal cavity, 215, 262, 299, 300, 331, 332
Peritoneal fold, over hepatic artery, 300
Peritoneal reflections, 264, 312, 353, 354, 373
Peritoneum, 255, 259, 268, 280, 316, 317, 331, 335, 340, 345, 352, 354, 379
  diaphragmatic, 321, 331
  inferior reflection of, over pelvic organs, 312, 353, 354
  parietal, 253, 259, 262A, 299, 300, 316, 321, 331, 332, 340, 359, 377
  rectouterine pouch, 181, 264, 305, 313, 316, 321, 343, 352–354, 373, 374, 377, 379, 383
  retovesical pouch, 305, 313, 321, 343, 352–354
  vesicouterine pouch, 264, 316, 373, 374, 378
  visceral, 299, 300, 331, 332
Pes anserinus, 420, 423, 444, 462, 489
Phalanx (Phalanges). See *Bone(s), phalanx (phalanges)*
Pharyngeal cavity, 691, 726, 732, 751, 770
Pharyngeal recess, 685, 691, 726, 732, 751
Pharyngoepiglottic fold, 726, 746, 751, 753, 755
Pharynx, 258, 692, 723, 729, 731, 740, 744–747, 750, 751, 760
  junction with esophagus, 735
  muscular wall of, 747
  vessels and nerves of, 747, 754
Pia mater, 571, 633
Piriform recess, 751, 753, 755, 758, 770
Pituitary gland, 636–639, 641, 642, 685
  infundibulum of, 636
  lobes of, anterior (adenohypophysis), 636
    intermediate, 636
    posterior (neurohypophysis), 636
  sagittal section through, 636
Placenta, 181, 399
  septum of, 181
  sinus of, marginal, 181
Plate(s), cribriform of ethmoid bone, 645, 683, 684, 686, 687, 689
  perpendicular, of ethmoid bone, 613, 683, 687–689
    of palatine bone, 684
  pterygoid, medial, hamulus of, 747
  tarsal, 651, 652, 656
Pleura, 136, 155, 156, 164, 165, 170, 219, 257, 300, 320
  cervical, 227, 592
  cupula of, 153–155, 170, 215, 219, 227, 258, 593
  costal, 154, 170, 175, 184, 185, 215, 219, 220, 227, 256, 299, 320, 331, 573, 593
  diaphragmatic, 152, 154, 175, 177, 185, 186, 188, 189, 208, 209, 212, 215, 220, 227, 256, 299, 331, 333, 573
  margin of, anterior, 170

Pleura, margin of, *continued*
  inferior, 170, 320
  mediastinal, 154, 170, 175–177, 184, 185, 188, 189, 212, 220, 227, 255, 256, 258
  parietal, 136, 152, 157, 158, 170, 227, 258, 300
  recess of, costodiaphragmatic, 150, 152, 154–156, 170, 175, 186, 215, 219, 220, 230, 257, 258, 273, 299, 300
    costomediastinal, 152, 153, 158, 170, 189, 299
    phrenicomediastinal, 300
  vertebral, 219
  visceral, 157, 159, 215, 299
Pleural, cavity, 152, 157, 158, 299, 300, 331
Plexus, abdominal aortic, 226
  aortic, 185, 219, 224, 229, 339, 573
    ramus to, 227
  basilar, 642
  brachial, 19–22, 184, 185, 187, 188, 227, 228, 576, 577, 579–583, 586, 588, 596, 608
  cardiac, 184–186, 188, 189, 208
  carotid, 152, 638, 640, 693, 754, 755, 793, 794
  celiac, 318, 339
  cervical, 577, 579
  choroid, 639, 644
  coccygeal, 336, 337
  dental, inferior, 696
  esophageal, 184, 185, 224
  gastric, 224, 318
  hypogastric, 318, 340
  iliac, 339
  lumbar, 320
  lumbosacral, 336, 337
  marginal, of cornea, 678
  mesenteric, 296, 318, 339
  parotid, 605
  pelvic, 225
  pharyngeal, 754
  pterygoid, 620, 793
  pudendal, 336, 339, 364
  pulmonary, 188, 219, 220, 229
  renal, 339
  sacral, 336, 337, 339, 364
  tympanic, 793, 794
    branches to cochlear and vestibular windows, 793
  venous, biliary, 331
    pampiniform 248, 254, 255, 347
    prostatic, 359
    thyroid, 152, 586, 591
    vaginal, 382
    vertebral, 227, 573
      internal, 226
    vesical, 240, 355, 382
Plica fimbriata, 735, 738, 741, 756
Pole(s), of brain, frontal, 635, 639
    orbital gyri, 639
    orbital sulci, 639
  occipital, 635, 639
  temporal, 635, 639
  of kidney, 302, 305, 316, 328
Pons, 566, 639
Porta hepatis, 262B, 316
  lymphatic vessels of, 279
  nerves of, 279
Pouch, of Douglas, 264, 373
  rectouterine, 181, 264, 305, 313, 316, 321, 343, 352–354, 373, 374, 377, 379, 383
  rectovesical, 305, 313, 321, 343, 352–354
  vesicouterine, 264, 316, 373, 374, 378
Premaxilla, 631
Premolar teeth, 699, 701, 705, 710, 711, 714, 715, 717, 718
Prepuce, of clitoris, 244, 367, 368, 370, 388
  of penis, 246, 343, 349, 351, 361
Processus vaginalis, 253, 255
Prominence, laryngeal, 574–576, 585, 586, 589, 599, 600
  of facial canal, 795, 798, 799
  of lateral semicircular canal, 792, 795
Promontory, sacral, 303, 319, 321, 335, 355, 393, 546
  of tympanic cavity, 778, 781, 784, 785, 789, 790, 795–799
  subiculum of, 778, 799
Prostate. See *Gland, prostate*
Protuberance, mental, 598, 610
  occipital, external, 523, 528, 574, 646, 647
    internal, 645
Pterygoid canal, 663
  nerve and artery of, 746
Pterygoid hamulus. See *Hamulus, pterygoid*
Pterygoid plate, 702, 722, 748

Pterygoid plate, *continued*
  hamulus of, 747
Pterygoid process, of sphenoid bone, 640, 646, 647, 684, 746
  lamina of, lateral, 735
    medial, 746, 747
      hamulus of, 746
Pubis, body of, 386, 391, 392
  pecten of, 335, 389, 393, 417, 419, 420
  ramus of, inferior, 242, 352, 369, 389–392, 401, 430
    superior, 242, 352, 369, 390–392, 401
  tubercle of, 244
Pulp, splenic, 278
Pulp cavity, of tooth, 703, 720, 721
Punctum lacrimale, 649, 653, 657, 658
  superior, 658
Pupil, 648, 665
Pyloric antrum, 268–270, 331
Pylorus, 136, 224, 257–259, 268, 270, 273, 277, 287, 305
Pyramid(s), of medulla oblongata, 566, 639
  decussation of, 566, 639
  renal, 325, 327, 331, 332
Pyramidal, eminence, tympanic, 778, 785, 795, 796, 799

Quadrangular space, 23, 51, 53, 60, 523

Radiograph of knee joint, 457
  of large intestine, 311
Ramus (Rami), of ischium, 366, 369, 389–392
  of mandible, 601, 608, 613, 697, 700, 722, 728, 737, 740, 754
  of pubis, inferior ramus, 242, 352, 369, 389–392, 401, 430
    superior ramus, 242, 352, 369, 390–392, 401
  of spinal nerve, anterior ramus, 10, 571, 572
    dorsal ramus, 10
    posterior ramus, 10, 517
    primary ramus, anterior, 573
      posterior, 518, 563, 571, 573
  of supraorbital nerve, lateral, palpebral ramus, 650, 656, 657, 670, 672
    medial palpebral ramus, 650, 656, 657, 670, 672
    superior palpebral ramus, 654, 655
  of thoracic nerve, posterior rami, 517, 527, 528
  of ulnar and median nerves, cutaneous ramus, 38
    to aortic plexus, 227
Rami communicantes, 10, 185, 219, 224, 227, 320, 339, 518, 571, 573, 593, 654
Raphé, mylohyoid, 583, 598, 600
  of deep transverse perineal muscles, 366
  of scrotum, 248, 252, 344
  palatine, 701, 729, 731
  pharyngeal, 590, 750
  pterygomandibular, 615, 722, 731, 735, 737, 740, 746–748
  tendinous, of gastrocnemius muscle, 472
Recess, costodiaphragmatic, 150, 152, 154–156, 170, 175, 186, 215, 219, 220, 230, 257, 258, 273, 299, 300
  costomediastinal, 152, 153, 158, 170, 189, 299
  duodenal, inferior, 302, 305, 316
    superior, 302, 305, 316
  epitympanic, 780–782, 786, 791, 801
  hypotympanic, 782, 792
  ileocecal, 301, 302
  intersigmoid, 316
  mediastinovertebral, 219, 227
  omental bursa, inferior, 275
    splenic, 275, 300, 316
    superior, 275, 316
  pericardial, of aorta, 170, 188, 194, 214
    of pulmonary trunk, 188, 194
  pharyngeal, 685, 691, 726, 732, 751
  phrenicomediastinal, 300
  piriform, 751, 753, 755, 758, 770
  retrocecal, 305
  sphenoethmoidal, 685
  subpopliteal, 678
  superior, of tympanic membrane, 781
  trigeminal, 778
Rectum, 257, 258, 264, 272, 303, 305, 311–314, 316, 317, 319, 335, 338, 339, 343, 345, 353, 354, 365, 373, 376, 378, 382, 383, 385
  ampulla of, 312, 314, 343, 377
  longitudinal coat of, 312, 313
Reflections, peritoneal, 264, 373
Region, acromial, 520
  anal, 520

Region, *continued*
  antebrachial, anterior, 1, 520
    lateral, 37
    medial, 37
    posterior, 1, 520
  atlanto-occipital, median section of, 539, 540
  auricular, 602
  axillary, 1, 37
  brachial, anterior, 1
    lateral, 37
    medial, 37
    posterior, 1, 520
  buccal, 520, 602
  calcaneal, 1, 520
  clavicular, 37
  crural, anterior, 1, 520
    posterior, 1, 520
  cubital, anterior, 1, 37
    lateral, 37
  deltoid, 1, 37, 520
  digital, palmar, 37
  elbow, 520
  epigastric, 1
  femoral, anterior, 1
    posterior, 520
  frontal, 1, 520, 602
  gluteal, 520
  hyoid, 520
  hypochondriac, 1, 520
  infraclavicular, 1, 37
  infraorbital, 602
  infrascapular, 520
  infratemporal, 624, 625
  inguinal, 1, 244–246
  interscapular, 520
  knee, anterior, 1, 444, 445
    posterior, 520
  laryngeal, 602
  lumbar, 520
    lateral, 520
  mental, 1, 602
  nasal, 1, 602
  neck, anterior, 1, 602
    lateral, 1, 602
    posterior, 520
  occipital, 520, 602
  of body, anterior, view, 1
    posterior view, 520
  oral, 1, 602
  orbital, 1, 520, 602
  parietal, 1, 520, 602
  parotidomasseteric, 520, 602
  pectoral, 1, 37, 520
  prevertebral, 594
  pubic, 1
  sacral, 520
  scapular, 520
  sternal, 1
  sternocleidomastoid, 1, 520, 602
  submental, 602
  suboccipital, 528
  suprascapular, 520, 602
  temporal, 1, 520, 602
  thoracic, lateral, 37
  trochanteric, 1
  umbilical, 1
  vertebral, 520
  zygomatic, 520, 602
Renal calyx, 325, 327, 331, 332
Renal cortex, 325, 327, 331
Renal fascia, 332
Renal hilum, 323, 329, 332
Renal pelvis, 271, 285, 304, 323, 325–328, 331, 332, 363, 372
Renal pyramid, 325, 327, 331, 332
Renal sinus, 332
Reticularis, of adrenal cortex, 324
Retina, 669
  ciliary part, 669, 680
  neural part, 669, 679
  pigmented layer of, 679, 680
  vessels of, 678, 679, 681
Retinaculum, extensor, of foot, 462–470, 505, 507
    of hand, 61, 65, 74–76, 78, 101, 103, 105, 120
  flexor, of foot, 462, 474–478, 491, 493, 496, 507
    of hand, 107, 108, 110, 111, 114, 120
  patellar, 431, 445, 462, 463
    lateral, 444, 446
    medial, 444, 446
  peroneal, inferior, 463, 467, 469, 505
    superior, 463, 467, 474–478, 491, 505, 513
Retroesophageal space, 726

Retromolar triangle, 700
Ridge(s), for insertion of pronator teres muscle, 90
  longitudinal of stomach, 268
  of nail matrix, 126–128
Rima glottidis, 766–768, 771, 772
Rima vestibuli, of larynx, 766
Ring, femoral, 383
  fibrocartilaginous, of tympanic membrane, 629, 631, 781, 784–787, 791
  inguinal, deep, 242, 243, 253, 340, 364
    superficial, 231, 232, 235, 236, 244, 248, 255, 347, 388
  lymphatic, oro-naso-pharyngeal, 752
  tendinous, common, of orbit, 640, 664, 668, 675
  umbilical, 181, 240, 243, 255, 256, 261
Roof, of tympanic cavity, 782
Root(s), dorsal, of spinal nerve, 10, 563
  motor, of trigeminal nerve, 639, 642, 694, 695, 793, 801
  of finger nail, 126–128
  of mesentery, 264, 295, 301, 302, 310, 316
  of mesocolon, sigmoid, 316
    transverse, 301, 302, 305, 316
  of tongue, 743, 745, 751, 753, 755, 769
  of tooth, 703, 720, 721
  of tympanic cavity, 787, 789
  sensory, of trigeminal nerve, 642, 694, 801
  ventral, of spinal nerve, 10, 571, 573
Root canal, 703, 721
Rugae, vaginal, 380

Sac, endolymphatic, 802, 805
  lacrimal, 652, 656–658, 660
    fornix of, 658
Sacculus, 800, 803, 805
Salivary glands, 733. See also *Gland, parotid; Gland, sublingual; Gland, submandibular*
Salpingopalatine fold, 685
Salpingopharyngeal fold, 726, 732, 751, 755
Scala tympani, 640, 800, 805
Scala vestibuli, 640, 800, 805
Scalp, 633, 635
  dermis of, 633
Sclera, 669, 679, 680
  cribriform area of, 679, 680
Scrotum, 242, 248, 252, 343, 344
  dartos layer of, 255, 343, 344, 354
  septum of, 248, 252
  skin of, 248, 252, 255
Sella turcica, 613, 636, 685, 691
Semicanal, for tensor tympani muscle, 778, 796
  of auditory tube, 796
Semicircular canal, common crus of, 801
Seminal vesicle, 258, 352–355, 357–360, 362, 363
Septum (Septa), dural, 801
  interalveolar, 720, 721
  interatrial, 180, 201, 202
  intermuscular, lower limb, 464, 474, 486, 487, 489, 490
    upper limb, 7, 47–49, 51–53, 55, 57–59, 61, 64–67, 69, 71, 74, 75, 77, 81, 98–101
  interventricular, 201, 202, 204, 206, 207, 209, 211, 212
    membranous part, 212
    muscular part, 212
  intra-alveolar, 720, 721
  nasal, 601, 669, 683, 690, 692, 726, 751, 753
    cartilaginous, 655–657, 682, 683, 690, 726
  of musculotubal canal, 778, 785, 791, 796, 798
  of penis, 348–350
    of glans penis, 350
  of testis, 250–252, 343
  of tongue, 736, 739, 741
  orbital, 650–652, 655–657, 673
  placental, 181
    primum, 180
    secundum, 180
  scrotal, 248, 252
Septum canalis, musculotubarii, 778, 785, 791, 796, 798
Sheath(s), carotid, 584
  dural, 793
  femoral, 337
    vascular components, of, 335
  of dura mater, for hypoglossal nerve roots, 726
    for spinal nerve roots, 726
  of rectus abdominis muscle, 61, 149, 300, 331, 332, 359
    anterior layer, 7, 12–14, 16, 151, 231, 237–241, 253, 255

Sheath(s), *continued*
    posterior layer, 151, 238–243, 255, 340
    optic nerve, 669, 673, 675, 676, 680
    synovial. See *Tendon sheath, (synovial)*
    tendon. See *Tendon sheath, (synovial)*
    vaginal, of styloid process, 646
Shoulder joint, See *Joint, shoulder*
Sinus(es), air, paranasal, openings of, 685, 686
    anal, 312, 343
    aortic, left, 207
    basilar, 638, 642
    carotid, 588
    cavernous, 587, 620, 638, 640–642, 801
    confluence of, 620, 637
    coronary, 180, 191–193, 213–215
        orifice of, 180, 191, 202, 203, 208
        valve of, 180, 191, 202, 203, 208, 214
    costomediastinal, 159
    dural, 637
    frontal, 635, 683, 685, 686, 690, 691, 722
        opening into, 685, 686
    intercavernous, 638, 642
    lactiferous, 8
    marginal, of placenta, 181
    maxillary, 660, 663, 664, 667, 695, 793
    occipital, 637
    of epididymis, 249, 252, 253
    of finger nail, 126
    pericardial, oblique, 189
        transverse, 189, 190, 214
    petrosal, 587, 620, 637, 638, 642
        superior, 801
    prostatic, 356
    renal, 327, 332
    sagittal, inferior, 620, 637, 638
        superior, 620, 633–638, 645
            at confluence of sinuses, 634
            opening of cerebral veins into, 634
    septum, 208
    sigmoid, 536, 587, 620, 637, 638, 640, 645,
        787–790, 801
    sphenoethmoidal, opening of, 685
    sphenoid, 613, 636, 641, 663, 669, 683–686, 690,
        691, 693, 722, 726, 732, 747, 793
    sphenoparietal, 637, 638
    straight, 620, 637, 638
    transverse, 587, 788
        of pharynx, 754
    tympanic, 778, 796, 799
Sinus septum, 208
Sinus venarum, 192, 195
Sinus venosus, of sclera, 678, 680
Skin, 9, 348, 518
    of anus, 312
    of labium majus, 244
    of scrotum, 252
Skull, 601, 610, 633
    at birth, 629–631
    base of, 645–647
    brachycephalic, 627
    dolichocephalic, 628
Small intestine, 302, 343
    mesentery of, root of, 264
Socket(s), for teeth, 598, 663, 697, 720, 721
    of hip joint, 401, 437
Sole, of foot, 492–498, 520, Also see *Foot, sole of*
    arteries of, 493, 496, 497
        muscles of, 494, 495, 498
        nerves of, 493, 496, 497
        plantar aponeurosis, 493
Soleal line, of tibia, 448, 484
Space(s), calcaneal subtendinous, 491
    cavernosus, of penis, 361
    epidural, 343, 571, 726
    esophagotracheal, 591, 726, 769
    infraglottic, 766, 769
    interfascial, dorsal, of foot, 516
    intervaginal, 673, 680
    parapharyngeal, 737
    perichorioidal, 680
    perithyroid, 591
    prevertebral, 591
    prevesical, 240, 343
    quadrangular, 23, 51, 53, 60, 523
    retroesophageal, 726
    retrogastric, 305
    retropharyngeal, 740, 747
    retropubic, 253, 255, 343, 353, 373, 385
    subarachnoid, 343, 571–573, 633
    subdural, 572, 573
    suprasternal, 214
    triangular, 21, 23, 51, 53, 523

Spermatic cord, 12, 231, 232, 236–239, 242, 246,
    247, 251, 341, 347, 354, 355, 416
    fascia of, 239
    nerves of, 347
    vessels of, 347
Sphincter, of Oddi, 288–293
    urethral, 376
Spinal column. See *Vertebral column*
Spinal cord, 219, 518, 563, 565, 566, 570, 573, 639, 644,
    cervical part, 563, 566
    fissure of, anterior median, 566, 567, 568, 570,
        572
    gray matter, 518
    lumbar part, 563, 566
    meninges of, 570, 571, 633
    sulcus of, anterolateral, 566, 568
        posterior median, 570
    thoracic part, 563, 566
    with nerve roots, 568
    within vertebral, canal, 230, 565
Spine(s), genioglossal, 698, 700, 728
    iliac, anterior inferior, 387, 389, 390, 393, 401
        anterior superior, 12, 233, 235–237, 253, 257,
            387, 389, 390, 392, 393, 395, 398, 401, 412,
            417, 401
        posterior inferior, 258, 389, 390, 401
        posterior superior, 258, 387, 389, 390, 394,
            523, 526
    ischial, 258, 314, 389–391, 393, 401
        anterior inferior, 387
    mental, 698, 700
    nasal, anterior, 601, 610, 683, 684
        posterior, 646, 702
    of helix, 774
    of scapula, 23, 24, 26, 30, 32, 33, 36, 51, 61, 258,
        523
    of sphenoid bone, 613, 646
    palatine, 702
    supramesal, of temporal bone, 777
    tympanic, greater, 785, 786
        lesser, 785, 786
Spleen, 136, 257, 258, 261, 265, 272, 273, 275, 277,
    278, 299, 300, 310, 331
    extremity of, anterior, 256, 274, 276, 300, 316
        posterior, 274, 276, 300
    fibrous capsule of, 278
    hilum of, 274, 277, 278
    impression on, gastric, 274, 278, 305, 316
        renal, 274, 278
    margin of, inferior, 274, 276
        superior, 274, 276, 305, 316
    serous coat of, 278
    surface of, diaphragmatic, 276, 278
        visceral, 274
Squama, of frontal bone, 610
    of occipital bone, 630
    of temporal bone, 631
Stomach, 136, 215, 224, 257, 258, 261, 265, 269,
    270, 272, 273, 279, 294, 299, 310, 330, 332
    angular notch of, 269, 273
    bed of, structures of, 277
    body of, 259, 268–270, 273, 275
    cardiac orifice of, 268, 299, 316
    cardiac part, 136, 257, 258, 268, 270, 273, 305,
        316, 317, 321, 338
    coat of, muscular, 268, 270
    curvature of, greater, 111, 256, 259, 268, 269,
        273, 275, 294
        lesser, 111, 257, 268, 269, 273, 275, 294
    fundus of, 136, 268–270, 273, 294
    interior, 268
    lymphatic vessels of, 279
    mucosa of, 299, 332
    nerves of, 279
    pylorus of, 136, 224, 257–259
    serous layer of, 215, 268
    wall of, 300
        layers of, 215, 268, 299, 331, 332
Stria, olfactory, 639
Styloid process, of temporal bone, 735, 740, 790
Subarachnoid space, 343, 571–573, 633
Subdural space, 572, 573
Subiculum, promontory, of temporal bone, 778,
    799
Substance, perforated, anterior, 639
Sulcus (Sulci), bicipital, medial, 49
    carotid, 645
    cerebral, 635
    coronary, 188, 192, 195
    cubital, 73
    cuboid, 503
    esophageal, on lung, 164

Sulcus (Sulci), *continued*
    for corpus spongiosum penis, 352
    for flexor hallucis longus tendon, 513
    for peroneus longus endon, 513, 514
    for petrosal nerve, greater, 645
        lesser, 645
    for petrosal sinus, inferior, 645
        superior, 645
    for popliteus muscle, 448
    for sigmoid sinus, 536, 645
    for splenic artery, on pancreas, 286
    for sagittal sinus, superior, 645
    for temporal artery, middle, 777
    for transverse sinus, 645
    for trigeminal ganglion, 642
    for vertebral artery, 534
    genitofemoral, 388, 393
    gluteal, 388, 413
    infraorbital, 661, 662
    inguinal, 393
    intertubercular, of humerus, 84, 85
    interventricular, anterior, 176, 188, 208
        posterior, 192, 195
    lingual, median, 743
    of aortic arch, on lung, 164
    of azygos vein, on lung, 165
    of spinal cord, anterolateral, 566, 568
        posterior median, 570
        posterolateral, 570
    of splenic artery, on pancreas, 286
    of subclavian artery, on 1st, rib, 143, 164, 165
    of subclavian vein, on 1st rib, 143
    of superior vena cava, on lung, 165
    olfactory, 639
    orbital, of frontal pole, 639
    palatine, 702
    palpebral, superior, 603, 648
    paracolic, 260, 301, 302, 305
    paraglenoid, 390
    promontory, of temporal bone, 778, 799
    pubic, 393
    temporal, inferior, 639
    tympanic, 778, 781, 784
Sulcus terminalis, of right atrium, 188, 192, 195
    of tongue, 743, 753
    of ulnar nerve, on humerus, 83
Supraorbital margin, 601, 667
Supraorbital notch, 652, 689
Supraventricular crest, of right atrium, 204, 209
Sustentaculum tali, 503, 509, 513
Suture, coronal, 601, 610, 626, 628–630, 635
    frontal, 630
    frontoethmoid, 645
    frontolacrimal 601
    frontomaxillary, 601, 661, 682
    frontonasal, 601, 682, 683
    frontozygomatic, 610
    incisive, 646, 702
    infraorbital, 661
    internasal, 601
    lacrimoethmoidal, 662
    lacrimomaxillary, 610
    lambdoidal, 610, 626, 628, 629, 635, 646
    nasofrontal, 682
    nasomaxillary, 601, 610, 682
    occipital, transverse, 629, 631
    occipitomastoid, 610, 645, 646
    palatine, median, 646, 702
        transverse, 646, 683, 702
    parietomastoid, 610
    sagittal, 626, 628, 630, 632, 633
    sphenofrontal, 601, 610, 635, 645, 663
    sphenoparietal, 601
    sphenosquamosal, 610, 645, 735
    sphenozygomatic, 601, 610, 659
    squamosal, 610
    vomeromaxillary, 683
    zygomaticomaxillary, 601, 661
    zygomaticotemporal, 610
Sympathetic trunk ganglia, 10, 184, 219, 224, 226,
    299, 793
Symphysis pubis, 235, 240, 242, 253, 311, 333, 342,
    343, 353, 364–366, 373, 387, 388, 393, 395,
    396, 399, 401, 439
Synchondrosis, petro-occipital, 647, 750, 751, 753
    spheno-occipital, 645
    sternocostal, 147
    sternomanubrial, 147
Syndesmosis, arycorniculate, 764
    tibiofibular, distal, 480, 491
Synovial, tendon sheath(s). See *Tendon sheaths
    (synovial)*

Taenia coli, 259, 260
Taenia libera, 260, 277, 296, 301, 302, 306, 307, 332
Taenia, mesocolica, 277, 307, 332
Taenia omentalis, 259, 273, 277, 301, 305, 307, 332
Talus, head of, 501, 503
    process of, lateral, (malleolar), 501
    trochlea of, 501
Tarsal plates, 651, 652, 656
Tarsus, inferior, of eyelid, 651, 652, 673, 677
    superior, of eyelid, 651, 652, 655–657, 673
Taste pathways, 742
Tegmen tympani, 782, 787, 789, 792, 802
Temoral line, inferior, of parietal bone, 626, 627,
        777
    superior, of parietal bone, 626, 627
Tendinous arc, for origin of levator ani muscle, 365,
        376, 386
Tendinous intersections of rectus abdominis
        muscle, 151, 231
Tendon(s), Achilles, 473, 505, 507
    calcaneal, 413, 462, 463, 467, 472–479, 491, 502,
        505, 507, 509
    central, of diaphragm, 184, 185, 215, 216, 230,
        333–335
    conjoint, 242
    cricoesophageal, 753
    extensor, of dorsal, wrist, 103
    flexor, common, of forearm, 50, 80
    of abductor hallucis muscle, 507
    of abductor pollicis longus muscle, 61, 65, 75, 76,
        79, 101, 105, 107, 108, 112
    of adductor magnus muscle, 423, 440, 447, 487
    of ankle region, 505, 506
    of biceps brachii muscle, 21, 23, 29–31, 34, 35,
        49, 53, 55, 59, 63, 66, 67, 69, 70, 91, 98, 99,
        151
    of biceps femoris muscle, 426, 430, 440, 441, 467,
        472, 478
    of brachialis muscle, 55, 66, 99
    of brachioradialis muscle, 47, 65–70, 75, 101, 114
    of digastric muscle, intermediate, 598–600
    of extensor carpi radialis brevis muscle, 74, 75,
        77, 79, 101, 112
    of extensor carpi radialis longus muscle, 74, 75,
        77, 79, 100, 101, 112
    of extensor carpi ulnaris muscle, 74, 76–79, 101,
        120
    of extensor digiti minimi muscle, 76, 77, 101, 120,
        121
    of extensor digitorum brevis muscle, 470
    of extensor digitorum longus muscle, 462–464,
        467, 469, 505, 515, 516
    of extensor digitorum muscle, 61, 77, 79, 103,
        109, 112, 116, 120, 121
    of extensor hallucis brevis muscle, 467, 469, 471,
        516
    of extensor hallucis longus muscle, 462–464, 469,
        471, 491, 515, 516
    of extensor indicis muscle, 79, 120, 121
    of extensor pollicis brevis muscle, 61, 66, 75,
        77–79, 101, 121
    of extensor pollicis longus muscle, 61, 77–79,
        101, 105, 112, 121
    of flexor carpi radialis, muscle, 37, 65, 66, 68–70,
        101, 108, 110, 111, 120
    of flexor carpi ulnaris muscle, 65, 66, 68, 70, 108,
        114, 120
    of flexor, digitorum brevis, muscle, 495, 496, 498,
        516
    of flexor digitorum longus, muscle, 462, 477, 478,
        483, 491, 495, 498, 515, 516,
    of flexor digitorum profundus, muscle, 69, 70,
        101, 108, 109, 114, 117, 120–124
    of flexor digitorum superficialis, muscle, 69, 70,
        101, 108, 109, 114, 117, 120, 121, 123
    of flexor hallucis longus muscle, 462, 477–479,
        483, 515, 516
    of flexor pollicis longus muscle, 69, 101, 111,
        114, 121
    of foot, dorsal, 469. See also names of specific
        muscles
    of gastrocnemius muscle, 462, 474, 490
    of gracilis muscle, 423, 462, 489
    of hand, 112. See also names of specific muscles
    of iliopsoas muscle, 429, 430
    of latissimus dorsi muscle, 21, 49, 53, 55, 63, 625
    of lumbrical, muscles, of foot, 498
        of hand, 116
    of oblique muscle, inferior, 671
        superior, 652, 665–668, 671, 674, 676, 677
    of obturator internus, 387, 429
    of palm, 107. See also names of specific muscles

Tendon(s), *continued*
    of palmar, interossei muscles, 116
    of palmaris longus muscle, 37, 65, 66, 68–70, 101,
        108
    of pectoralis major muscle, 23, 59
    of peroneus brevis muscle, 467, 469, 470, 483,
        505, 508, 511, 514, 515
    of peroneus longus muscle, 467, 483, 491, 495,
        498, 506, 514, 515
    of peroneus tertius muscle, 463–465, 467, 469,
        470, 505, 516
    of piriformis muscle, 359
    of plantaris muscle, 473–475, 479
    of popliteus muscle, 448, 454
    of pronator teres, muscle, 77, 79
    of psoas minor muscle, 317, 335, 340
    of quadriceps femoris muscle, 444, 445, 455, 458
    of rectus femoris muscle, inferior, 673
        lateral, 669–671
        medial, 669, 671
        superior, 671
    of rectus abdominis muscle, 151, 239
    of rectus femoris muscle, 417, 419, 435–437, 439,
        446, 463
    of sartorius muscle, 420, 423, 489
    of semimembranosus muscle, 427, 429, 430, 434,
        440, 447, 448, 462, 473, 477, 489
    of semitendinosus muscle, 423, 427, 429, 430,
        440, 462, 473, 487, 489
    of stapedius muscle, 792, 795, 796
    of sternocleidomastoid muscle, 583, 647
    of subscapularis muscle, 34, 49, 63, 151
    of supraspinatus muscle, 51, 151
    of temporalis muscle, 737, 740
    of tensor tympani muscle, 781, 785, 791, 793, 795,
        796, 801
    of tensor veli palatini muscle, 722, 731, 753
    of teres major muscle, 49, 55
    of tibialis anterior muscle, 462, 464, 466, 467,
        469–471, 491, 506, 509, 514, 515
    of tibialis posterior muscle, 462, 474–479, 483,
        491, 498, 509, 514, 515
    of trapezius muscle, 51, 647
    of triceps brachii muscle, 51, 57, 59, 74, 75, 77, 82
    of vastus intermedius muscle, 446
    of wrist, 103, 107. Also see names of specific
        muscles
Tendon sheath(s) (synovial), of abductor pollicis
        longus muscle, 112, 114
    of digital tendon, of hand, 123, 124
    of extensor carpi radialis brevis muscle, 112
    of extensor carpi radialis longus muscle, 112
    of extensor digitorum muscle, 112
    of extensor digitorum longus muscle, 462, 463,
        505, 515
    of extensor hallucis longus muscle, 462, 507
    of extensor indicis muscle, 112
    of extensor pollicis brevis muscle, 112, 121
    of extensor pollicis longus muscle, 112, 121
    of flexor carpi radialis muscle, 37, 108, 114
    of flexor digitorum longus muscle, 462, 507
    of flexor hallucis longus muscle, 462, 492, 507
    of flexor pollicis longus muscle, 107, 108, 114
    of foot, 462, 463, 497, 505, 507, 515. See also
        names of specific muscles
    of hand, 103, 107–109, 114, 121, 123, 124. See
        also names of specific muscles
        of digital tendons, 123, 124
    of long biceps tendon, 31, 49, 55, 151
    of peroneus brevis muscle, 463, 505
    of peroneus longus muscle, 463, 495, 505, 515
    of tibialis anterior muscle, 462, 463, 507
    of tibialis posterior muscle, 462, 507
    of wrist, 103, 107, 108, 112, 114
Tenon's capsule, 669, 677
Tentorium cerebelli, 637, 638, 685, 722
Testis, 242, 247–253, 319, 353, 363
    appendix of, 247–249, 253, 363
    developing, 363
    ligament of, scrotal, 253, 255
    lobules of, 250–252, 343
    septa of, 250–252, 343
Thigh, anterior, 1, 337, 407, 414–424
    muscles of, 417–420, 423, 424
    cross section of, 486, 487
    fascia of, 416
    nerve fields of, cutaneous, 408, 409
        peripheral, 408
    posterior, 425–429, 520
        muscles of, 426–429
    surface anatomy of, 412, 413
Thoracic inlet, 592

Thoracic wall, anterior, 148, 149, 151, 231, 232, 257
    posterior, 218, 221, 226, 227, 258
        nerves of, 226, 227
        sympathetic trunks of, 226, 227
        vessels of, 226, 227
Thorax, area of superficial cardiac dullness in, 170
    aspect of, lateral, 14
    lymphatics of, 3, 5, 6, 187
    position of heart within, 170
    radiograph of, 150
    section of, cross, 157–159
        frontal, 215
        sagittal, 214
    sites for ascultation of heart, 171
    skeleton of, 137, 140, 153–156, 172
        natural contour of, 146
    vessels of, great, 586
    viscera of, 152, 257
Thymus gland, 152, 153, 175, 177, 184, 185, 256,
        726
    left lobe, 175
    right lobe, 175
Thyroid ansa, 226
Thyroid cartilage. See *Cartilage, thyroid*
Thyroid gland, See *Gland(s), thyroid*
Thyroid notch, superior, 136, 257, 757, 761, 763
Toe(s), 425–437
    phalanges, 501, 503
    See also *Bone(s), phalanx (phalanges); Foot*
Tongue, 621, 625, 724, 732, 737–739, 743, 746, 756
    apex of, 741, 743, 744
    artery and vein of, 740
    dorsum of, 692, 729, 731, 732, 740, 743, 753, 758
    foramen cecum of, 685, 726, 736
    frenulum of, 733, 735, 737, 740
    lymphatic drainage of, 621
    membrane of, mucous, 741, 758
    muscles of, extrinsic, 741, 744, 745
        intrinsic, 736
        longitudinal, inferior, 735, 740
            superior, 736, 740
    root of, 743, 745, 751, 753, 755, 769
    septum of, 736, 739, 741
    surface of, inferior, 738
    vessels and nerves at base of tongue, 746
Tonsil(s), cerebellar, 639
    lingual, 732, 736, 743, 753
    palatine, 692, 726, 729, 731, 732, 735, 737,
        743–746, 751–573, 755, 758
    pharyngeal, 685, 690, 691, 722, 726, 732, 746,
        751–753, 755
Tooth (Teeth), 692–722, 729–731, 734
    bicuspid, 699
    canine, 699, 701, 705, 708–711, 713, 714, 717
    crown of, 703, 720, 721
    cusp of, 704
    deciduous, 707–710
    incisor, 699, 701, 705, 708–710, 712, 713, 716,
        717, 720
        permanent, lower, 709, 710, 716, 717, 720
            upper, 710, 712, 713, 720
    molar, 699, 701, 704, 705, 708, 709, 711, 715, 718,
        719
    neck of, 703
    nerves of, 696
    permanent, 705, 706, 709, 710, 712, 713, 716,
        717, 720
    premolar, 699, 701, 705, 710, 711, 714, 715, 717,
        718
    pulp cavity of, 703, 720, 721
    roots of, 703, 720, 721
    section of, longitudinal, 703
    sockets for, 598, 663, 697, 720, 721
    surfaces of, 705
Torus, of levator veli palatini muscle, 726, 751
Torus tubarius, 685, 722, 726, 732, 751, 755
Trabecula(e), of corpus cavernosum penis, 361
    septomarginal (moderator band), 202–204, 209
    splenic, 278
Trabeculae carnae, 201, 206, 211, 212
Trachea, 136, 151, 168, 177, 186, 188, 189, 214, 216,
        219, 224, 257, 258, 582, 588–590, 592, 726,
        744, 750, 755, 756, 758, 760, 766, 768, 769
    bifurcation of, 157, 168, 214–216, 768
    glands of, 591
    muscosa of, 591
    wall of, membranous, 591, 726, 759, 765
Tract, iliotibial, 296, 416, 424, 430, 444, 463, 482,
        486, 487
    olfactory, 639, 644, 690, 691
Tractus solitarius, nucleus of, 742
Tragus, 773, 774

Triangle(s), carotid, 574, 602
  deltopectoral, 1, 12, 15, 231, 575, 583
  femoral, 1, 418
  lumbar, 320, 521–524
  of neck, 576, 579
  retromolar, 700
  sternocostal, 175
  submandibular, 520, 597, 602, 727
  suboccipital, 528, 529
Trigone, fibrous, of heart, 191
  of bladder, 356, 357, 361
  inferior, without pleura, of heart, 170
  retromolar, of mandible, 737, 740
  superior, without pleura, of heart, 170
Trochanter, greater, 333, 394–396, 401, 427,
    429–433, 435, 436
  lesser, 333, 401, 423, 429–433, 435, 436, 439
Trochlea, of humerus, 82–84, 86, 96–98
  of orbit, 656, 657
  of superior oblique muscle, 667, 676
  of talus, 501
Trochlear notch, of ulna, 9, 87, 88, 93, 133
Trunk, brachiocephalic, 182, 188, 208, 214, 219,
    593, 594, 726, 755
  celiac, 181, 182, 216, 218, 226, 265, 266, 271, 272,
    285, 317, 318, 321, 335, 338, 339, 341
  costocervical, 218, 226, 569, 596
  lumbosacral nerve, 336–339, 364
  lymphatic, bronchomediastinal, 219, 220
    anterior, 592
    femoral, 384
    iliac, 384
    intestinal, 223, 296, 318, 320, 332, 341
    jugular, 223, 587, 592, 593
    lumbar, 223, 318, 320, 340, 341, 384
    mammary, 593
    preaortic, 384
    subclavian, 223, 587, 592, 593
  of body, dermatomes of, 2, 519
    superficial vessels and nerves of, 11, 232
  pulmonary, 136, 150, 172, 176, 181, 188,
    190–192, 194, 204, 208, 209, 212
  sympathetic, 10, 185, 218–220, 224, 226, 229,
    230, 299, 300, 320, 332, 338–340, 573, 593,
    740, 754, 755
    in posterior thoracic wall, 226, 227
    lumbar, 332, 338
  thyrocervical, 17, 20, 182, 569, 581, 582, 592, 596,
    755
    spinal branches of, 569
  vagus nerve, 229
Tube, auditory, 615, 694, 695, 779, 780, 791–793,
    795, 798, 801
    cartilage of, 647, 690, 693, 746, 747, 753, 780
    mucosa of, 793
    openings of, 685, 691, 726, 732, 746, 751–753,
      778
    semicanal of, 796
    tympanic opening for, 778, 786, 791, 795, 798
    view of, lateral, 793
  uterine, 372, 379, 380, 382, 399
    ampulla of, 310, 316, 318, 374, 375, 377–380
    developing, 372
    fimbria of, 374, 377–380
    infundibulum of, 372, 377–379, 381, 382, 399
    isthmus of, 316, 318, 374, 375, 377–380, 383
    openings of, 375, 377, 380
Tuber cinereum, 639
Tuber omentale, 275, 277, 300
Tubercle, accessory, of upper 1st molar
    (Carabelli's), 704
  adductor, 457
  anterior, of atlas, 530, 531, 594
    of cervical vertebrae, 541
  articular, of temporal bone, 614, 646, 735, 777
  auricular, of Darwin, 773
  carotid, 151, 574, 593, 594
  conoid, 138
  corniculate, 726, 751, 753, 755, 765, 767–769
  cuneiform 726, 751, 755, 765, 767, 769
  epiglottic, 764, 767, 772
  greater, of humerus, 30, 32, 36, 83–85
  infraglenoid, 6, 26, 28
  intercondylar, of tibia, 442, 444, 446, 452, 457,
    459, 464, 466, 467, 480, 481
  intervenous, of atrium, 202
  jugular, 645
  lesser, of humerus, 84
  mental, 574, 598, 697
  obturator, anterior, 389
    posterior, 389, 390
  of rectus muscle, lateral, origin of, 663

Tubercle, continued
  of rib, 143, 551, 554
  pharyngeal, of occipital bone, 646, 751
  posterior, of atlas, 523, 526, 530, 531, 540
    of cervical vertebrae, 541
  pubic, 244, 333, 369, 386–389, 393, 397, 398, 417
  scalene, of 1st rib, 143
  serratus anterior, of 2nd rib, 143
  supraglenoid, 28
  thyroid, inferior, 735, 744, 745
Tuberculum sellae, 645
Tuberosity, calcaneal, 413, 467, 473, 474, 477, 492,
    494, 495, 503, 509, 511, 513, 514
  deltoid, of humerus, 84
  gluteal, 436
  ischial, 25, 258, 333, 344, 369, 370, 387–391, 393,
    394, 401, 427, 523
  maxillary, 720
  muscular, of inferior angle of scapula, 26
  of distal phalanx, 118, 132
  of 1st metatarsal bone, 503
  of 5th metatarsal bone, 501, 503, 510, 511, 513
  of ilium, 390
  of navicular bone, 513
  of radius, 89, 96, 97
  of scaphoid, 135
  of tibia, 442, 444, 452, 464, 466, 467, 480, 481
  of ulna, 87, 88
  pterygoid, of mandible, 614, 730
    of sphenoid bone, 698, 700
  sacral, 560, 561
Tunica albuginea, of testis, 250, 251
Tunica vaginalis testis, 247, 248
  cavity of, 253, 343, 353
  parietal layer, 247–249, 252, 253, 255, 353
  visceral layer, 248, 252, 253, 255, 343, 353
Tympanic air cells, 778
Tympanic antrum, 801
Tympanic cavity, 695, 778, 779, 781, 782, 785, 790,
    791, 793, 795, 796, 798, 800–802
  roof of, 695, 782, 792
  wall of, lateral, 791
    medial, 787, 789, 790, 793, 795, 796, 798
  window of, cochlear, 799
    vestibular, 799
Tympanic crest, 735
Tympanic membrane, 783, 784, 786, 787, 791, 795
  secondary, 799
Tympanic notch, 785, 786
Tympanic plexus, 793, 794
Tympanic sinus, 778, 796, 799

Umbilical cord, 178, 255, 399
Umbilical fold, lateral, 256, 259, 321, 340, 359
  medial, 256, 259, 321, 340, 352, 359
  median, 243, 256, 320, 321, 340, 352, 359
Umbilicus, 12, 231, 232, 240, 242, 255, 257, 368,
    393, 399
Umbo, 781, 784, 787, 789
Uncus, 639
Unguis, 125
Urachus, 240, 243, 255, 256, 261, 319, 321, 352, 356,
    358, 363, 372, 377, 399
Ureter, 178, 243, 301, 319, 320, 325–328, 338, 363,
    372
  left, 258, 271, 285, 302, 316–318, 320, 321, 332,
    340, 341, 352, 354, 363, 376, 379, 382, 383
  orifices of, 343, 356, 357, 361
  right, 258, 271, 285, 304, 305, 317, 318, 321, 322,
    340, 352, 355, 358, 359, 363, 374, 377–379,
    382, 383
Urethra, 248, 349, 362, 369, 372
  female, 368, 369, 371, 372, 376, 377
  male, 343, 348–353, 355–357, 361–363, 366
    crest of, 356, 361
    navicular fossa of, 343, 350, 361
    penile, 343, 348, 361
    prostatic, 356, 357, 361
    membranous, 352, 357, 361, 365, 366
    opening of, 343, 351, 361, 367, 368, 370–372,
      376, 377, 388
Urinary bladder. See *Bladder, urinary*
Uterine cavity, 377, 380
Uterine tube. See *Tube, uterine*
Uterus, 178, 264, 310, 342, 372–375, 378–380, 382,
    383, 385, 399
  body of, 316, 318, 379–381, 399
  cervical canal of, 377, 380
  external os of, 181
  fundus of, 318, 378, 380, 381
  isthmus of, 375, 379, 380
  supravaginal part, 379

Uterus, continued
  surface of, anterior (vesical), 378
    intestinal, 379
Utricle, prostatic, 343, 356, 361, 363
Utriculus, of inner ear, 800, 803, 805
Uvula, of bladder, 356, 361
  of soft palate, 615, 690, 692, 693, 729, 731, 732,
    751, 753, 755

Vagina, 181, 369, 372, 380–382
  fornix of, 373, 377
  surface of, posterior, 379
  vestibule of, 367, 368, 388
Vallate papillae, 751, 753, 755
Vallecula, of epiglottis, 685, 736, 743, 758, 769
Valve(s), aortic, 171, 172, 191, 207, 212
  left semilunar cusp, 191, 207, 212
    posterior semilunar cusp, 191, 207, 212
    right semilunar cusp, 191, 207, 212
    nodule of, 212
  atrioventricular, 171, 172, 191, 201
    left (bicuspid, mitral), 171, 172, 191, 201, 211,
      212, 215
      anterior cusp, 191, 212
      posterior cusp, 191, 201, 212
    right (tricuspid), 171, 172, 180, 191, 201–205,
      208, 214
      dorsal cusp, 191, 201–205, 208, 214
  septal cusp, 191, 201–204, 208, 214
    ventral cusp, 191, 202–205, 208, 214
  bicuspid. See *Valve(s), atrioventricular, left*
  cross section of valve, in vein, 46
  ileocecal, 306
  mitral. See *Valve(s), atrioventricular, left*
  of coronary sinus, 180, 191, 202, 203, 208, 214
  of foramen ovale, 206, 208
  of Houston, 312
  of inferior vena cava, 180, 202, 208, 214
  of navicular fossa, 361
  pulmonary, 171, 172, 204
    anterior semilunar cusp, 191, 204, 209
    left semilunar cusp, 191, 204, 209
    right semilunar cusp, 191, 204, 209
  tricuspid. See *Valve(s), atrioventricular, right*
Vas deferens, 352, 357–360, 362, 363
  ampulla of, 340, 352, 357–359, 362
Vasa recti, 332
Vein(s), alveolar, inferior, 740
  angular, 587, 620, 654–657
  antebrachial, median, 40, 41, 100
  appendicular, 272
  auricular, posterior, 527, 528, 577, 579, 587, 787
  axillary, 14, 19, 20, 63, 185, 187, 188, 227, 581,
    582, 585
  azygos, 158, 159, 184, 188, 195, 214, 215,
    218–221, 226, 229, 230, 299, 331, 573
    arch of, 184
  basilic, 3, 14, 40, 41, 43, 47, 54, 63, 64, 98–100,
    102
    hiatus for, 47
  basisvertebral, 214, 572
  brachial, 19, 21, 22, 54, 98
  brachiocephalic, left, 20, 152, 172, 175, 177, 178,
    185, 186, 188, 189, 193, 214, 223, 580–582,
    586, 588, 592–594, 726, 755
    right, 152, 172, 175, 177, 178, 184, 186, 188,
      189, 195, 208, 223, 586, 587, 592, 755
  bronchial, 184, 188
  cardiac, anterior, 190
    great, 190, 191, 193–195, 204
    middle, 191–193, 195
    small, 191
  cecal, anterior, 296
  cephalic, 3, 7, 11–14, 20, 40–43, 47, 54, 63, 64,
    98–102, 231, 576, 579–582, 585, 586
  cerebral, 634
    great, 637, 638
    inferior, 637
    middle, 793
    superior, 637
  cervical, deep, 528, 593, 620
    median, 587
    superficial, 11, 585–587, 592
    transverse, 585–587
  circumflex, humeral, anterior, 54
    posterior, 19, 42
    iliac, deep, 239, 245, 317, 338, 376
      superficial, 11, 232, 239, 246, 416
    scapular, 14, 19
    dorsal, 527
  colic, 320
    left, 272, 297, 303

Vein(s), colic, *continued*
 middle, 272, 277, 285, 296, 297
 right, 272, 285, 297
collateral, ulnar, inferior, 54
conjunctival, 678
coronary (of stomach), 285
 left (of heart), 190
cremasteric, 239, 246, 347
cross section of, with valves shown, 46
cubital, median, 40, 41, 82, 98, 99
cystic, 265, 272
digital, dorsal, of foot, 468, 516
diploic, 632, 633
 frontal, 620, 633
 occipital, 620, 632
 temporal, anterior, 620, 632
  posterior, 620, 632
dorsalis pedis, 515
emissary, 620, 633
epigastric, inferior, 11, 149, 239, 243, 245, 256,
  297, 317, 318, 321, 338, 340, 352, 376, 383
 superficial, 232, 239, 245, 246, 414
 superior, 11, 255
esophageal, 220, 573
facial, 574, 579, 580, 585–587, 597, 599, 600, 620,
  622, 623, 727, 737
 deep, 623
 transverse, 574
femoral, 335, 414, 416, 418, 421, 422, 486
 anterior, 414
 deep, 422
gastric, left, 265, 270, 272, 273, 277, 300, 317
 right, 270, 272
 short, 270, 272
gastroduodenal, 285
gastroepiploic, 273
 left, 265, 272
 right, 266, 270, 272, 296, 316, 332
genicular, 460
hemiazygos, 219, 300, 573
 accessory, 185, 219
hepatic, 183, 215, 230, 280, 299, 300,
  316–318, 321, 340, 573
humeral circumflex. See *Vein(s), circumflex,
  humeral*
hypoglossal, 586, 587, 600, 620, 727, 737, 739
ileal, 272
ileocolic, 272, 296
iliac, common, 316, 317, 321, 338, 341, 355, 364,
  376, 382
 external, 243, 317, 338, 352, 354, 359, 376, 377,
  383, 418
 internal, 321, 354, 355, 382
iliac circumflex. See *Vein(s), circumflex iliac*
iliolumbar, 320, 321, 338
intercapitular, 102
intercostal, 184, 185, 218, 227, 229, 230, 239, 255,
  299, 359, 526, 573
 spinal branches, 226, 572
 superior, left, 176, 185, 188, 208
jejunal, 272, 297
jugular, anterior, 575, 585–587, 591
 external, 527, 575, 579–582, 585–587, 592,
  597, 620, 727
 internal, 152, 172, 178, 186, 576, 579–588,
  591–593, 608, 620, 621, 640, 740, 754, 755, 793
  bulb of, 576, 586, 754, 782
labial, anterior, of vagina, 244, 245
 inferior, of face, 620
 posterior, of vagina, 244, 245
 superior, of face, 620
lacrimal, 638
laryngeal, superior, 587, 741, 744, 748, 755, 770
lingual, 756
 deep, 737, 756
lumbar, 317, 321, 354
 ascending, 218–221, 338, 340
mammary, external, 11
marginal, lateral, of foot, 468
 right, of heart, 190
masseteric, 740
maxillary, 620
meningeal, middle, 620, 635
 frontal branch, 635
 orbital branch, 635
 parietal branch, 635
mesenteric, inferior, 272, 285, 296, 303, 316, 317,
  320, 331, 332, 340
 superior, 266, 272, 285, 286, 296, 297, 303, 316,
  317, 331, 332
metatarsal, dorsal, 516
 plantar, 516

Vein(s), *continued*
 nasofrontal, 587, 620, 638
 oblique, of left atrium, 195
 obturator, 340, 359, 376, 383
 occipital, 527, 528, 577, 579, 585, 586, 620
  mastoid branch, 528
 of clitoris, dorsal, 245, 369, 376
  superficial, 244
 of glans penis, 351
 of neck, 585
 of penile bulb, 366
 of penis, dorsal, 248, 343, 347, 348, 351, 355, 366
  superficial, 246, 343, 347
 of tongue, apex of, 740
 of vertebral column, 573
 of vestibular bulb, 371
 ophthalmic, 620, 638
 ovarian, 326
  left, 318, 323
  right, 285, 318, 383
 pancreaticoduodenal, 272
 paraumbilical, 11, 240, 243
 perforating, 486
 pericardiophrenic, 175, 177, 187, 573
 pharyngeal, 620, 754
 phrenic, inferior, 243, 321, 341
  superior, 230
 plantar, lateral, 515
  medial, 515
 popliteal, 426, 428, 441, 475, 476, 487, 489
 portal, 178, 181, 183, 265, 266, 270, 272, 285, 286,
  299, 300, 317
  branches of, 299
  right, 300
  formation of, 266
 prepyloric, 265, 272
 pudendal, external, 245, 246, 414, 416
  internal, 346, 428
  superficial, 244
 pulmonary, 184, 188, 213, 228
  left, 158, 159, 185, 187, 189, 192, 195, 215, 220
  right, 158, 165, 187, 189, 192, 195, 220, 227, 229
 rectal, inferior, 312
  middle, 383
  superior, 272, 303, 382, 383
 renal, 285, 318, 323, 325, 326, 331
  left, 178, 272, 321, 331
  right, 321, 322, 331, 332
 retromandibular, 579–581, 585–587, 620, 622,
  623, 727, 737, 740
 sacral, lateral, 354
  middle, 317, 321, 338, 383
 saphenous, accessory, 486
  great, 11, 232, 341, 412, 414, 416, 418, 422,
  425, 460, 461, 468, 486, 487, 489–491, 515
  small, 425, 426, 428, 441, 460, 468, 472, 475,
  487, 489–491, 515, 516
 scapular circumflex. See *Vein(s), circumflex,
  scapular*
 sigmoid, 272, 303, 317
 small intestinal, 285
 spermatic, 285
 spinal, anterior, 226, 573
 splenic, 266, 272, 274, 278, 285, 286, 300, 303,
  317, 331
 subclavian, 177, 184, 580, 587, 592, 593
  left, 172, 223, 586, 588, 755
  right, 18, 172, 186, 223, 586, 594, 755
 subcostal, 218
 sublingual, 586, 727, 747, 756
 submental, 580, 585, 587, 599, 600, 620, 623, 727
 subscapular, 19
 superficial, of arm, 40
  of foot, dorsal, 468
  of forearm, 41
  of hand, dorsal, 102
  of gluteal region, 425
  of leg, posterior, 460
  of limb, upper, 42, 43
  of thigh, posterior, 425
  of trunk, ventral, 11
 suprarenal, 300, 318, 321–324, 326
  central, 300, 324
  left, 321
  right, 322
 suprascapular, 587, 592
 supratrochlear, 620
 temporal, middle, 623
  superficial, 587, 604, 620
 testicular, 243, 254, 320, 326, 338, 340
  left, 317, 321, 323, 332
  right, 317

Vein(s), *continued*
 thoracic, internal, 11, 20, 149, 152, 175, 177,
  187–189, 243, 585, 586, 593, 594
  perforating branches of, 13
  lateral, 3, 19, 20
  superficial, 232
 thoracoacromial, 15, 42, 585
 thoracodorsal, 19, 20
 thoracoepigastric, 3, 7, 11, 13, 14, 19, 20, 232, 582
 thymic, 175, 188, 189, 586
  superior, 592
 thyroid, inferior, 152, 188, 582, 585, 586, 592, 593
  middle, 586, 592
  superior, 152, 580, 582, 585, 586, 588, 592, 594,
   597, 600, 620, 726, 766
 thyroid ima, 175, 187, 189, 588, 726
 tibial, anterior, 466, 490, 491
  posterior, 475, 490, 491
 ulnar, 108
 ulnar collateral. See *Vein(s), collateral, ulnar*
 umbilical, 178, 181, 232, 255, 256, 261, 262
 uterine, 181, 383
 valves in, cross section of, 46
 ventricular, posterior (of heart), 192, 193, 195
 vertebral, 194, 528, 582, 591–593
  internal, 226
 vesical, inferior, 243, 355
  superior, 255, 340, 355
 vorticose, 638, 678
 zygomatico-orbital, 656
Vena cava, inferior, 150, 178, 180, 181, 189, 192,
  195, 202, 215, 220, 221, 229, 230, 258, 262,
  265, 266, 272, 277, 280, 282, 285, 299, 300,
  305, 316–321, 331, 332, 338, 340, 341, 573
  superior, 136, 150, 157, 172, 176–178, 180, 181,
   184, 186, 188–190, 192, 194, 195, 202, 208,
   209, 212, 213, 219, 223, 228, 257, 586, 755
Vena caval aperture, in diaphragm, 299
Vena caval foramen, 229, 333–335
Venous mesocardium, 195
Venous network, of dorsal foot, 460
 of dorsal hand, 102
Ventricle, of heart, left, 136, 150, 158, 159, 188,
  192, 194, 195, 206, 207, 215, 257
 right, 136, 158, 159, 188, 192, 194, 195,
  201–204, 214, 257
 of larynx, 685, 726, 736, 766, 769
Vermis, cerebellar, 639
Vertebra(e), body of, 157, 215, 228, 230, 298, 518,
  522, 532, 533, 535, 536, 538, 540–543, 551,
  554–556, 573
 cross section of, containing spinal cord, 262,
  518, 571, 572
 sagittal section of, showing costovertebral
  articulations, 551
 cervical, 25, 137, 530–536, 539–546, 571
  foramen of, transverse, 532, 541
   vertebral, 532, 541, 542
  process of, articular, 541, 542
   spinous, 219, 523, 541, 542
   transverse, 258, 529, 542
  1st. See *Atlas.*
  2nd. See *Axis.*
  3rd, 540, 543
  4th, 543
  5th, 541, 543
  6th, 137, 140, 543
  7th, 25, 523, 542, 543, 565, 591
 coccygeal, 258, 388, 544–546, 561, 562
  horn of, 561, 562
  process of, transverse, 562
 lumbar, 137, 223, 311, 335, 342, 393, 395, 397,
  544–546, 555, 556, 558
  body of, 230, 522, 555–558
  cross section of, 522
  foramen of, vertebral, 555
  lamina of, 555
  pedicle of, 555
  process of, accessory, 555, 558
   articular, inferior, 331, 556, 558
    superior, 331, 555, 556
   costal, 331, 555, 556
   mammillary, 555, 558
   spinous, 219, 230, 331, 332, 393, 522, 523,
    555
   transverse, 219, 332, 333, 393, 401, 555, 556,
    558
  surface of, articular inferior, 556
  1st, 25, 137, 140, 230, 331, 334, 523, 558, 565
  2nd, 558
  4th, 311
  5th, 417, 523, 565

Vertebra(e), *continued*
  sacral, 354, 393, 544–546, 557, 559–561
  thoracic, 159, 215, 544–549, 552–554, 558, 572,
    573, 594
    body, 547–549, 554, 558
      section of, transverse, 554
    facet of, articular, 573
      costal, 547, 548, 558
    foramen of, vertebral, 547, 554
    lamina of, 219, 300, 549
    pedicle of, 547, 553
    process of, accessory, 558
      articular, 547–549, 558
      spinous, 214, 320, 518, 547–549, 554, 558
      transverse, 219, 547–549, 554, 594
    6th, 547, 548
    10th, 549, 558
    11th, 558
    12th, 558
Vertebra prominens, 523, 543, 546, 574
Vertebral column, 214, 228, 543–546, 551, 573
Vertex, corneal, 680
Vesicle, seminal, 258, 352–355, 357–360, 362, 363
Vesicouterine pouch, 264
Vessels. See also *Artery (Arteries); Vein(s)*
  abdominal, anterior, 239
    posterior, 338
  brachial, 21
  central, of retina, 676, 678, 679, 681
  circumflex, iliac, deep, 355
    superficial, 414
  colic, left, 316, 320
    middle, 301, 302
  coronary, 190, 191
  duodenal, 332
  epigastric, inferior, 149, 240, 355, 377
    superior, 149, 240
  femoral, 419, 421
  gastric, short, 305, 316
  gastroepiploic, left, 266, 270
    right, 265, 270
  great, of thorax, 194, 195, 586
  iliac, common, 374
    external, 382
    internal, 376
  iliac circumflex. See *Vein(s), circumflex, iliac*
  infratrochlear, 657
  inguinal, superficial, 244
  intercostal, 240, 299
    anterior, 149
  jejunal, 303

Vessels, *continued*
  labial, 244
  laryngeal, superior, 597, 751, 753, 784
  lymphatic, of pancreas, 279
    of porta hepatis, 279
    of stomach, 279
  meningeal, middle, 635, 637
  mesenteric, inferior, 303
    superior, 297
  musculophrenic, 149
  obturator, right, 355
  of abdominal wall, anterior, 239, 240, 243, 244, 246
  of abdomen, inferior, 340
  of arm, 54, 62
  of axilla, 20
  of back, upper, 528
  of cranial cavity, base of, 638, 643, 644
  of elbow, 73
  of eyeball, 678
  of face, deep, 623
    superficial, 622
  of forearm, 62, 73
  of gluteal region, 428
  of head, superficial, 623
  of leg, posterior, 476
  of neck, 588
  of orbit, 654, 655
  of pelvis, 340
  of penis, 246, 347
  of popliteal fossal, 441
  of spermatic cord, 347
  of suboccipital region, 528
  of thigh,. posterior, 428
  of thoracic wall, posterior, 226, 227
  of upper extremity, 62
  of ureter, 340
  ovarian, 316, 377–380, 382
  palatine, greater, 747
    lesser, 692, 747
  pericardiacophrenic, 185, 186, 189
  perineal, 366
  pharyngeal, 747, 754
  phrenic, inferior, 318
  plantar, 497
  pudendal, external, 347
    internal, 345, 355, 359, 366, 371, 376, 382
  rectal, inferior, 355, 382
    middle, 355, 382
    superior, 355
  renal, 320, 338
  scrotal, 246

Vessels, *continued*
  splenic, 266, 277, 278, 300, 316
  sublingual, 740
  submental, 599
  sural, 475
  testicular, 250, 252, 253, 320
  thoracic, internal, 152, 585
    lateral, 582
  thoracoacromial, 580
  thyroid, inferior, 751
  tibial, posterior, 474, 475
  tympanic, 799
  uterine, left, 382
Vestibular bulb, 368, 371, 372, 382, 388
Vestibular cecum, 800
Vestibular window, 778, 790, 799, 805
Vestibule, of ear, 640
  of larynx, 767, 769
  of mouth, 690, 729, 732, 736, 737
  of nose, 685, 690, 691, 732
  of omental bursa, 151, 275, 305
  of vagina, 367, 368, 388
Vibrissae, 722
Vinculum, 108, 109
Vocal fold, 726, 766–770
Vocal process, of arytenoid cartilage, 768, 770–772
Vomer, 601, 613, 631, 646, 683, 751

Window, cochlear, 640, 799, 805
  branches of tympanic plexus to, 793
  vestibular, 790, 799, 805
    branches of tympanic plexus to, 793
Wing(s), of crista galli, 645
  of sphenoid bone, 601, 614, 629, 635, 642, 645,
    646, 663, 728
Wrist, arteries of, 105
  bones of, 118, 119, 132, 133
  joints of, 129, 131–134
  ligaments of, 129, 131
  roentenogram of, 133
  synovial sheaths, of, 107
  tendons of, 103, 107

Xiphoid process, of sternum, 141, 142, 145, 176,
  186, 188, 230, 255, 299, 399

Zona orbicularis, of hip, 438
Zygomatic arch, 606, 608, 614, 615, 624, 625, 635,
  646, 678
Zygomatic process, of frontal bone, 671, 689
  of temporal bone, 612, 777, 789